The GENTLEMAN

By EDISON MARSHALL

FARRAR, STRAUS AND CUDAHY

NEW YORK

Library of Congress catalog card number 56-5753

First printing, 1956

Published simultaneously in
Canada by Ambassador Books, Ltd., Toronto.
Manufactured in the U.S.A. by
American Book–Stratford Press, Inc., New York

To John Farrar and Roger W. Straus, Jr.
in appreciation of ten years of
pleasant concert

Contents

BOOK ONE
    I. The Dream   1
    II. Captain of the Deck   26
    III. Creatures of the Night   43

BOOK TWO
    IV. The Secret   73
    V. The Ball   90
    VI. The Slaver   116
    VII. High Play   135

BOOK THREE
    VIII. Partial Payment   157
    IX. Young Moon Setting   172

BOOK FOUR
    X. The Raider   203
    XI. The Rider   211
    XII. The Discovery   231

xiii. The Stalk   244
xiv. I Did It All Alone   263
xv. River's End   275

BOOK FIVE
xvi. The Hunters   287
xvii. Hunt's End   303
xviii. The Park of the Three Lions   322

BOOK SIX
xix. The Challenge   331
xx. Sea Meeting   348
xxi. The Shawl   360
xxii. The Verdict   375
Aftermath   396

THE GENTLEMAN

BOOK ONE

CHAPTER I

The Dream

THIS TALE of a Charlestonian and his dream can well begin on a late fall afternoon on a street in my native city.

The street was not an alley, such as I lived in, off Marsh, in Upper East Bay: nor a cool, shady avenue of stately houses. It was a lane of once respectable but now shabby lodginghouses in a kind of no-man's land between. The year was 1841. I, Edward Stono, had recently passed my tenth birthday. The leaves of the neglected shrubbery and dying trees in the yards had the subdued but lovely colors of the Low Country autumn. The central figures of the scene were a group of boys, in their teens or younger, playing toss-at-a-crack for quarters. Not only the amount risked, but the clothes and appearance of the players showed they were foreign to this neighborhood. I knew them for youths from up about the Battery, some being bona fide Charleston aristocrats, others the sons of rich merchants, who had wandered here in unconscious quest of adventure.

Some neighbor boys and I stood back at a respectful distance, watching. Since I was more neatly dressed and better scrubbed than they, I did not want the resplendent boys to count me among them and had drawn off alone. The doings of their

1

betters, especially when making such a display of wealth, never ceased to fascinate poor whites. A boy of about fifteen, Butler Mims, a Johnny-come-lately but a natural leader whose shrill laughter discomforted even his best-born companions, excited them by winning all the stakes.

His opponents fell away as their pockets emptied. Presently only two were left, and they soon drew back, shaking their heads. "You've got your rabbit's foot with you today, Butt," one of them said.

Butler jingled a big handful of quarters, squinted at the sky, then turned with a mocking grin to the cluster of ragamuffins.

"Any of you fellows want to try a toss? I'd just as soon take money from sow's ears as from silk purses."

I had heard a similar saying once before—mouthed by a customer of my seamstress mother. She had said, speaking of a new-rich man trying in vain to get invited to the Saint Cecilia Ball, that "you can't make a silk purse out of a sow's ear." The woman had assumed that we were sow's ears too, an inference we could not miss. Yet Mamma had not spoken, her mouth full of pins, then her eyes had filled with tears; and the gross insult rankled in my heart.

As Butler Mims used this expression now, a strange thing happened to me. It was some effect of fury I had never felt before. It was an explosion that did not change me outwardly, and which left me cold and capable.

"I'll toss with you, Butler," I said.

"To you, I'm Mr. Mims, but that won't stop me taking your money. Let's see the color of it."

I brought four quarters from my pocket. Running an errand for my mother, I had collected them, along with a dollar bill, only half an hour before. I had not the least hesitancy over risking the money, in spite of our need. Truly I felt no sense of risk.

"They look all right," the crude youth went on. "I reckon they're not tin."

He slapped a coin on the back of his hand.

"Heads or tails for first toss."

"Tails."

"I win."

He tossed then, and the coin slid in the dust within eight inches of the line. I tossed with a concentration of mind, a power of aim, that I have never since been able to explain. The coin fell and lay still exactly on the line.

That was the first of eighteen throws. Not one of mine missed the line by more than six inches, or failed to beat his throw by at least half that distance. It would seem that the boys gathering about, boys who had never noticed me before, would ruffle me and break the run of deadly accurate pitches; but it did not. The game went on with the cold monotony of machinery; I did not invoke Chance because I did not need her, I played with a chill fury and won by some sudden endowment of coordination between hand and eye.

After the eighteenth throw, Butler turned his pockets inside out. Flushed and hot-eyed, he scraped the toe of his shoe in the dust, contemplating what he might do to recoup. Only the presence of his friends and companions, before whom he must not forsake all show of sportsmanship, saved me from his violence.

"You were just off your game, Butler," said one of the younger boys, toadying to him.

"No, that was old Lady Luck, paying me off good and proper for playing with white trash," he answered.

It was a very effective answer. He could have studied all day without doing better. It caused his companions to spit, look at trees, avoid one another's eyes in embarrassment that they did not quite understand, whistle and grunt, and then suddenly collect in a compact band and hurry down the street. The ragamuffins who had watched me win, perhaps with glowing hearts, dared not speak to me, again not knowing why, and straggled away.

I was left alone. My noble fury passed. Over me fell a long

shadow from the march of coming event. My face twisted, and I cried.

2

Christmas of that year had come to the Carolina Low Country, bringing raw, windy weather. It was being celebrated on the great plantations and in the mansions by the High Battery with a merriment, an easy grandeur, and a tradition worthy of the noble houses in England. If anyone had asked me, Edward Stono, I could have given a glowing and quite full account of the festivities there, despite the brevity of my years and my never having entered a plantation gate or crossed a mansion's threshold. But I had listened with ears that felt as though they were standing up and out like the ears of a skittish mule to the boasting of Negro coach and carriage drivers, white overseers and bailiffs, and, occasionally, the gossip of harlots.

There would be dinners and balls and eggnog parties, and, if weather permitted, oyster bakes on the riverbanks. For the gay, lithe, handsome, outdoor-loving men, there would be duck shooting on the flooded rice fields, fox hunting on horseback, and deer and turkey shoots in the hills. For youths and maidens only a little older than I, there would be picnics, square dances, and kissing games. Although I could kiss, if I pleased, the raggedy but pert and pretty daughters of our neighbors, it would be in no way the same. There was a wall higher than St. Michael's steeple between the alleys of Upper East Bay and the Battery. Still I need not fear its long, cold shadow for someday I would climb it.

Christmas was not so fine in our damp, mouse-ridden hovel, yet it had a saving grace, and that was love. In token of it my mother gave me a new coat, of a cut above my station, bought with silver earned by her tired fingers, and on one of them I slipped a ring, gold-plated with an imitation diamond, that Faro Jack had given me for running a delicate errand. I heard love in her soft voice whenever she spoke to me. I saw love in her face at every glance. It was once a beautiful face, I thought, with an olive skin, flashing dark eyes, and a wide warm mouth. A gentleman such as Charles Stono, my father, taking a tour through the West Indies, could think it was the most beautiful face he had ever seen. Although now it looked older than her years, love lighted it still.

She had got herself something, too—a double quantity of cheap West Indian rum such as she bought every Saturday. She had begun on one of the bottles on the morning of Christmas Eve; late on Christmas Day she had opened the second.

"Look out, Mamma, or you'll get tipsy," I warned her.

"Just a leetle—on Christmas."

When she had swallowed the inch of pale liquor in a chipped teacup she caught a glimpse of herself in the cracked mirror hanging over the kitchen table. Then she picked up the candle and stared. When she spoke, it was as though she had read my mind.

"I'd not want him to see me now."

"How could he see you, when he's been dead—nine years?"

"Is it nine? Let me sink. My head swim." She waved the candle in a circle.

"Put down the candle, Mamma, and sit down."

"Yess, I had better. I am a liddle dizzy." She smiled into my eyes and became less dizzy. Some strength I had seen before was taking hold of her.

"Tell me again about my father. You have hardly spoken of him since last Christmas."

"Oh, he was as fine a gentleman as ever wore a gold ring!"

"And he came from Charleston?"

"From nearby. Is there not an island, no a river—a beeg creek—named for his folk? Oh, they had great plantation zair, in ze old days. Ze house, it was fine as Brickhouse, on nearby Edisto. Now she is burn down."

"But the family must own some land there, yet. You told me the ten dollars Mr. Whitlow brings every month is rental from the land."

"No, Edward. I tell you not so. If I did, I was not zinking

what I say. Ze money, it come from a little land my fat'er family still own in Guadeloupe."

"Still, it's queer I've never heard of any other Stonos."

"Zair is a family of great folk named Stony. Why, I sew las' year—I mak a brocade gown—for ze beautiful daughter. I sink it the same name, wis a little change."

I would be proud to be a distant kinsman of the highborn, wealthy Stonys. But I could not rest with that.

"But your family too were great folk, on Guadeloupe Island."

"Yess, yess, on Grand Terre. My fat'er own a fleet of sponge boat and he was lost in the hurrican of '25. Oh, she blow down ze whole town of Basse-Terre. Ze island is beautiful beyond compare!"

She began to speak in rapid French which I understand as well or better than English.

"I wish you could see the great mountain, La Soufrière! The forest is green as emerald and the clouds on its summit are pearl. Then there are the twin mountains that we call the Breasts. It is a good name, except that they give forth smoke instead of milk. And to speak of breasts makes me remember the *métisses* in their first bloom. I am a true Creole—all four of my grandparents came from Chalon on the Saône—but the good God never shaped more beautiful faces and forms than those He gave the métisses of Guadeloupe!"

"Didn't some of the métisses work as maidservants in the villa where you were born?"

"Well, I remember! There was Louisa—and Jacqueline—and young Teresa—and old Cecile. There were black slaves too. They kept the chambers spotless—and the great silver service on the sideboard—I could see my face in it as in a mirror. The silver was made by François Germain in Paris, and my grandfather brought it to Guadeloupe when he settled there. My name is only Marie Aubry, but he was Viscount Edouard Aubry du Monsole before he fled the Terror. You were named for him, Edward. It is a great heritage."

Then she sat dreaming, and I must wake her from her dreams.

"How did my father look? You told me, but I want to hear it again."

"Oh, he wass tall and fine." My mother lapsed for causes unknown into her dialectal English. "He wass brunette, like so many of the noblesse of Huguenot blood, and his eyes wass like yours, and his nose wass beeg—as my boy's nose is growing!"

She laughed a deep throaty laugh, but only half of it was love of me and the other half was rum.

"But he died so young!" I reproved her.

"*Oui*, he die of ze plague when he wass marry only two year."

"Mamma, tell me the truth, and don't lie for my sake or for any sake. Was he a gentleman?"

"I swear 'fore ze Good God your fat'er wass fine gentleman as any in Charleston."

"Then I am going to be one, too!"

"So, so."

"Nothing can stop me! Do you hear? This can't stop me." I swept away the mean room with a wave of my hand. "Being called white trash won't stop me."

"Oh, they dare not call you that!"

"One of them might. A big boy, fifteen or so, like Butler Mims. And if he did I couldn't fight him now. He'd get me down and tear all my clothes. But I'll fight him someday, I swear before God. Maybe I'll meet him a duel. Both of us would have our seconds, and we'd keep shooting till one was hit, and I'd die a gentleman, rather than bow down."

"Oh, be still!"

The strange cry shook me out of the frenzy of my dream.

"What is it, Mamma? Surely you don't doubt—"

"Drink a little rum, my boy. It won't hurt you, and 'twill quiet you."

She rose and mixed a small tot with water and handed me the cup. I drained it in quick gulps.

"It's good," I said in the long silence that followed.

"It will brace you for what I'm about to tell you, and that's the truth."

For a moment I could not speak. A dread was upon me, and a choke in my throat.

"The truth about—what?"

Then my mother could not speak. She could only sit, pale in the face, and stare at her worn hands.

"Go on!" I cried, running to her. "Tell me! You've got to."

Her eyes changed in a curious way and she stole a quick glance into my face. "Oh, well, you might as well know it, first as last. It may be I haven't much longer to live."

"Mamma, don't say that."

"Old Dr. Sams from Beaufort told me so. He came into Charleston and Mr. Whitlow brought him to see me. And it didn't cost me a penny, Edward. Mr. Whitlow paid him himself, more the wonder."

"What did he say? Tell me the truth."

"There's a weakness in my—chest. If it gets worse, I'll die soon—and then what will happen to my little gentleman? But the doctor says that sometimes it stays the same, year after year, or even goes away. So I may live till my hair is white as snow."

Now it was raven black, fit for a young girl to wear—a high-born daughter of the plantation of Huguenot name and ancestral fame.

"You will, Mamma! You must. I'll make you."

She smiled and kissed me and nodded, and I believed the nod and went peacefully back to my dreams. Mamma sipped at her cup. And now there was only one little cloud in this blue and radiant sky. Somehow I was not sure what Mamma had told me was the truth she had meant to tell.

3

On every Sunday morning in fair weather, I bathed and dressed with great care and walked in the Battery. It would be almost deserted at my arrival, but later would come mammies caring for highborn children, and old gentlemen of renown taking the air, and, when church was out, whole fashionable families enjoying the sunlight before they went to the two o'clock feast in their mansions. I knew the names of almost all, where their houses stood, and the lordly appellations of their great plantations. Once in a while, someone would notice me walking alone, or even ask his companion who I was.

No one ever spoke to me, and I was not sure that I wished for such a happening. It might lead to questions to which I had no proud answer; and if I lied, I would be found out, and all gentlemen knew that gentlemen did not lie. In a few years, the difficulty would be removed: this was the faith as staunch as my heart's beat, and which only rarely fluttered as did my heart. Meanwhile I was content to see the fine folk, take note of their dress, watch their ways with eyes as sharp as the jaybird's in the trees, imitate their accents, and dream great dreams.

I know now that loneliness is a pitiful state except for the very old, or the very wise, or the very brave; but great dreams substitute for those high situations, so I felt no need of pity for my solitude, and probably deserved none. I was pursuing a real and exciting ambition. My heart told me that I was making headway.

There came a morning of great gain. It was a cool, moist Sunday, with greenery bursting everywhere, not long after my eleventh birthday. Seated on a park bench, apparently in deep thought, was a middle-aged man in a black broadcloth coat, long tight trousers, silken cravat, and tall hat; and although I had seen him only a few times, I recognized him presently as Mr. Mason Hudson. He lived in one of the finest houses on the promenade. He owned an immense plantation twelve miles up the river known as Hudson Barony. He was a thin man with a high forehead and long, gaunt hands. As I came nigh, he rose and walked on, absently swinging his stick. I noticed that he had left a book on the bench.

I picked it up and ran after him. He turned to me with a smile.

"What is it, younker?" he asked in a kind voice.

"Why, sir, you forgot your book!"

"So I did, indeed! It's one that I treasure, too—not that particular volume, since 'tis a common edition, and worn besides, but I love the tale. Let's see." He took it in his hands. "You've read it, I suppose."

"No, sir. I've never read a book."

"What's your name, lad?"

"Edward Stono, sir."

"Do I know your father?"

"No, sir. He's been dead many years. He came from about Stono Creek."

"Is your mother living?"

"Yes, sir. She's a French lady from the West Indies."

I thought that his next question would be where and how we lived, and I would choke on the answer. But he took a different tack.

"Lad, can you read?"

"Oh, yes, sir. I go to the free school."

"Then take this book and keep it. Read it carefully and soak in every word—especially the part where Robin is on the island. The going will be hard at first, then you'll revel in it."

"Thank 'ee kindly."

"Do you come often to the Battery?"

"About every Sunday morning, it's so green and pretty."

I saw doubt come into his eyes but it faded out and he gave me a smile.

"Say in two weeks—about this time of morning—meet me here again. If you've liked Robin, I'll have another book for you—maybe two or three. No boy's mind can develop properly unless he reads, and it is one of the greatest joys our world affords."

He walked on and left me staring at the printed pages, my heart leaping.

4

When I told my mother of the meeting, her eyes shone, and she had me recite every detail.

"But it is no wonder that the grand gentleman was attracted to you," she told me in happy lilting French. "He could see you are a gentleman's son. And maybe he has no son of his own!"

I gladly accepted the latter guess as a fact. Certainly no boy of this name had crossed my path. However, some of the loftiest of the old Charleston elite lived very quietly, raising their children mainly on their plantations, educating them under private tutors; and of these I had little knowledge. Only at our third meeting, when he came with a notably graceful boy about two years older than I, must I face the truth.

"This is my younger son, Mason Hudson, Junior," Mr. Hudson told me in unmistakable pride.

I was instantly attacked by disappointment and jealousy. At the age of eleven boys may dream without shame of their own credulity—there is no cage of reason to confine their dreams— and I had pictured the rich planter adopting me, and making me his heir. Although I had dreamed, now my eyes were quick and keen. They told me that this boy was the most aristocratic looking I had ever seen. I could not say that he was especially handsome, although I know now there was something of real beauty in the structure of his facial bones, the shape of his body and especially of his head and hands, and in his dark luminous eyes.

Rather lightly built, still he would excel at games—but he would not play rough enough. There was a kind of gentleness in his movements and expressions and voice that might bring him to defeat.

"I'm glad to meet you, Mason," I told him, bowing my head a little.

"I'm glad to meet you, Edward, and if you like you may call me Mate," he answered. "That's what all my friends call me."

"I'd be mighty pleased to call you Mate."

"Have you any brothers or sisters?" he asked me presently—that question newly acquainted boys and girls so commonly ask each other.

"Not one." And in my eagerness to make bond with him I had come close to saying "Not ary one," the speech of my playmates of Upper East Bay.

"I have two. One is named Arnold Hudson; he is five years older than me. Then there is Clay Hudson, fifteen years older, but he's only my half-brother. He was borned by Papa's first wife, who died a long time ago. Clay has been gone so long I wouldn't know him if I saw him."

There came back to me some talk I had heard of a young man of this name, the son of a great aristocrat, who had left Charleston about eight years before and had never returned. He had got in some trouble, which I had heard related at a later time and which I could almost—not quite—recall. I noticed that Mr. Mason's face fell and turned gray. It looked like a face just then struck by a heavy fist.

Mate did not see it. He did not watch faces as I did, and his eyes were not as sharp. He began to tell me about the book he had brought to me, containing pictures of most of the animals in the world. I could keep it always. But I did not pay much attention to what he was saying, being so surprised and pleased to find myself no longer jealous of him, and instead being drawn to him . . . Mate Hudson. He was a kind of mate to me. When he and his father went on their way it seemed that I had nearly—barely missed it, somehow—made a friend.

Yet I did not see the boy again for nearly a year, and our rare future meetings did not bring us as close together as we had come at first. Perhaps he had found out where I lived and that my mother was a seamstress, but I did not quite believe in this. I had a feeling that he needed friends, yet could make none. Sometimes, I saw wistfulness in his dark eyes.

By the time I was fifteen I had forty books—occupying more space than our ramshackle house could readily spare—and read a hundred others. Almost all had been given or lent to me by Mason Hudson, and always in a careless way that saved me from accepting charity or incurring obligation. As for bringing them himself instead of having them sent by a Negro slave—he confessed a certain pleasure in discussing them with me, since I was of another generation.

I came to read quite well—even to be well-read for a youth of my years—because I had ample time. My mother had not been willing for me to accept an apprenticeship in some trade; and when I finished the free school, she made dresses for the wife of the schoolmaster in exchange for his assigning me more advanced studies in mathematics, the natural sciences, and law. In the first of these I shone. The good master was half-sorry he could not show me off before the ladies and gentlemen of Charleston. I did well enough in the second, but found the third tedious and hard to grasp. Even so, I kept at it, perceiving that of all my reading this alone held out any hope of material advantage.

My progress was snail-slow; so why did I not insist on going to work, to lessen my mother's burden of supporting me and instead lend a hand to her support? I stood five feet nine, weighed a hundred and forty-five pounds, and was patently able-bodied. No doubt I could obtain a minor clerkship to some merchant or professional man. I did not because of the power of a dream.

My mother fought for its survival as stubbornly as I did. She preached it when she was sober and pleaded for it when half-drunk. Nor was either of us content for me to be a "Nature's gentleman." The kind I must be owned a great plantation worked by gangs of singing, well-cared-for slaves, he dressed and lived with elegance, he went to the Saint Cecilia Ball, no man could scorn him, none thrust him aside.

But the time for some benison from the skies to fall was getting short. Still my mother turned aside my questions as to our monthly revenue. When, without her permission, I politely asked Matthew Whitlow for some accounting, he threatened to drop the business altogether. He frightened me, because we needed those few dollars more than ever before. Instead of growing fat, as so many West Indian women do, my mother thinned with the years, the olive skin of her face drawn tight over the bone; and this slow loss of flesh reflected a slow diminishing of her strength. And with our deeper need Whitlow became increasingly careless about delivering the sum on time.

Sure that he was a rascal, I could do nothing but submit. He was too powerful and I was too young. A rather portly man, probably in his late forties, with expressive brown eyes, round cheeks, a coarse nose, and, rather curiously, a small, prim mouth, he had a bluff air about him that people took—or mistook—for candor. His plain dark clothes, setting him apart from our richly and rather gaily dressed aristocrats, no doubt brought him clients; and his resonant voice, somewhat like a preacher's at the poor-white churches, won him many cases. Even so, I knew I must come to some kind of grips with him before very long.

April of the year 1847 had half-passed, with me approaching my sixteenth birthday, without Whitlow's carriage stopping at our door. Mustering my nerve and dressed as neatly as possible, I went to seek him in his office; and, not finding him there, made bold to follow him to the courthouse. Directed to an anteroom, I found him seated with a client whom I had known ever since I had begun to roam the holes and corners of Charleston.

"Good morning, Faro Jack," I called to him.

"Mornin' to you, Edward Stono," he answered.

Matthew Whitlow seemed a little surprised that the gambler knew my name—but I was not surprised. I had stood for hours watching Faro play, and when he bought drinks for the house he had always ordered me a beer. He dealt faro only a small part of the time. When the customers were mainly countrymen from the back country he soon switched to blackjack, bluff, or craps, which were faster, higher, and handsomer as he put it, and, although the poor fools knew it not, caused a swifter parting between them and their money. He was a big ruddy-colored man with a gruff voice and broad, quick hands. One of those hands was presently bandaged—I thought it had to do with his business in court.

"What in the Devil do you want?" Matthew Whitlow demanded.

"Sir, the ten dollars my father provided for us every month was due a fortnight gone."

"You don't belong to come bothering me about it here," he said in his poor-white dialect. "Besides, I doubt if that property makes ten dollars a month since the price of indigo went down. That's six per cent a year on two thousand dollars." Matthew could do such sums instantly in his head.

"I've got one friend who'll look into it for us, if you haven't the time."

No doubt I was thinking of Mason Hudson, although I would hardly be able to bring myself to turn his attention to such a trifling matter.

"Well, I haven't the change with me. But wait a minute. There's Sheriff Matson, going past the door, and he'll give it to me."

Matthew Whitlow rose nimbly and hurried after the sheriff. At once Faro Jack spoke from under his bandaged hand.

"Wait in the yard for me."

Mr. Whitlow returned with a handful of bills. When he had counted me out ten ones I bowed to him—not as deep as the bow I had learned to imitate from watching the 'ristocrats, but fine enough to bring a sparkle to Faro Jack's cold gray eyes. In a little over an hour I saw the gambler come out of the courthouse. His gaze did not overlook me, sitting on the coping, and he gave me a guarded gesture. I followed him until I was close to his rooms, then went down an alley, and tapped on his back door.

It opened instantly. At once he poured a flagon of ale for me, and a glass of "shine" for himself.

"What's this about Lawyer Whitlow giving your mother ten dollars every month?" he asked.

I told him, and of Whitlow's neglect.

"What friend were you going to ask to look into it for you, or was it a bluff?" he went on.

"It was a bluff. But Mr. Mason Hudson might do it, if I had the nerve to ask him. Mr. Hudson gives me books to read."

"Mr. Hudson is one of Mr. Whitlow's clients. He'd believe anything Whitlow told him, and more besides. Anyway, I reckon Whitlow don't take more than a reasonable commission —he's very careful to stay inside the law. Anyway, it's chicken-feed, while what I have in mind— But deal me a hand of stud."

He handed me a deck of cards. I shuffled them carefully and dealt. He showed an ace, a pair of tens, and a four, I a pair of eights, an ace, and a six. My hidden card was likewise a six, giving me two pairs.

He bet half a dollar. I raised by a dollar, and he by another dollar. When I met this and raised again by a like amount— my total bet being three and a half dollars, a substantial portion of my mother's remittance—Faro threw in his hand. His back card proved to be a useless king.

I did not have to show him mine, but I did so.

"That's what I know," he told me, "but when I kept raising, why didn't you figure I had you beat?"

"If your card-in-the-hole was an ace, a ten, or a four, you would have," I answered. "But I didn't think it was an ace, since I had one, and that would have put three of the four aces in less than one-fifth of the deck, and that's against chance."

This was according to Faro's own book as I had read it over his shoulder a hundred times. So was the rest of my play.

"Well, that might be. I grant it. But cards are like the Charleston aristocrats—they're a law to themselves."

"I didn't think your back card was a ten, giving you three of a kind, partly because I had a ten and that would put all four tens in one-fifth of the deck."

"There was nothing to stop it being a four, giving me two pairs that beat yours."

"I figured it was a face card."

"Why?"

"In the first place, none of the twelve face cards had showed up in the nine cards I could see, 'way below percentage. In the second place, I think—I'm not sure—I saw your king. At least I felt sure it was a face card and believed it was a king."

Faro looked at me in an odd, startled way. "Edward, I don't deny you saw my king, or else you had a hunch," he told me earnestly. "I've played too long to deny hunches, but they're a weak staff in time of trouble, such as a sucker gets in when he plays with a sharper. But seeing the card is something else again. A hawk isn't in it, when it comes to seeing, with a born gambler. It's a gift that can be quickened by play and practice, but a gambler who don't start with it never gets it. The best card-reader I ever played agin was only seventeen years old."

"I've got quick eyes, Mr. Jack, and quick fingers."

"I saw them fingers. They go with quick eyes. And it happens I can't deal no more. My right hand was stepped on in a fight—such things happen, sometimes, even in such high-class joints as Faro Jack's gaming rooms—and my fingers are broken past mending. Could you use a job?"

"Yes, sir, I could."

" 'Twould be in Augusta, not Charleston—a hundred and thirty miles up the line. I've sold out my rooms here—the climate's got unhealthy for me—and have opened up there. They'll be the finest this side of New Orleans, more like a bank than a joint. There'd be nothing but straight play with a rake-off for the house, tables for customers, roulette, and a few dice games—until you learn to deal."

"How much could I earn?"

"Not much, at first—say ten a week guaranteed. The hours would be long—four in the afternoon until four in the morning. A lot of that time you'd spend in practice—the same old thing, over and over, to drive you crazy. But in five years—unless I miss my guess—you could be one of the best this side of the Mississippi."

I sat and thought a moment.

"I want to be a gentleman. My mother says my father was a gentleman."

"I don't deny it. You've got some of the earmarks. It's a fine thing to be a gentleman—but I'll tell you first and last, a gentleman without money is a carriage without a horse. You can't ride in it. You can't strut in it. Take the finest 'ristocrats in Charleston, take away their rice plantations and their money, and what have you got? One generation hanging on. They'll be asked to Saint Cecilia—they'll get together old togs and be seen at the routs—a few callers, patting themselves on the back for their charity, will go to see 'em. But in the second generation they're freaks and drunks and crazy people. They can only look back to the glory that was. Take my advice, Edward. Get the money first. Then you can be a gentleman, and welcome. Maybe not in Charleston. They're different here than anywhere I know —more haughty and high than in Richmond or even New Orleans. But you can go to Columbia and marry an heiress. You could make a go at Vicksburg, that brags she's another Charleston, although she ain't, or at Memphis, or old Mobile. Your sons and daughters could marry the best in the land. Some men couldn't fetch it no matter how fat their wallets— they're too crude—and I'm one of the crudest. But you've got an air about you."

"I thank you." And I could hardly keep tears out of my eyes, heaven knows why.

"Do you remember what Iago said? Get money. Get money. Get money."

"I remember it well."

"You've got something, Edward, that takes my eye. It's your eyes, with light in 'em—eyes without light mark a stupid man, a man who can't see—and your mouth with strength in it—a mouth that can be cruel as a wolf's in your need—and your quick, light hands. Stay with me for five years. By then, I'll have enough to buy me a cabin on a little pond, a yellow wench, and a good boat, and then I'll gamble with bass and bream for the rest of my days, and maybe my soul will be saved. By then I'll give you a college education. You'll be able to skin the pants off the suckers, and take the shirts from the slickers on the river boats. What do you say? You're sixteen or so, and 'tis time you knew your own mind. Will you work for me and get rich, or be a would-be gentleman with empty pockets all your days? Speak out!"

"Sir, I've got to ask you a question."

"Ask it."

"A gentleman can't cheat. It's against the code. Would you want me to cheat?" But he had told me that already.

"That depends on what you mean by cheating. If you mean taking a sucker, then the answer's yes. If he comes here at all, you know he's a fool who's born to feather somebody's nest, and it might as well be ours. I've played for more than thirty years. I still don't know what brings these jackasses through the door. Ask the grog-seller what brings the dolts who drink themselves broke and crazy, and if he's an honest man he'll tell you he don't know, no more than I. The men who play in this house can add two and two, and yet they can't add—or they won't add—what a five per cent drag for the house will do to their stake when the game's o'er. It's rare that I deal a card from the bottom of the deck—it's too damn boring. It's boring enough to let 'em throw away their money on a so-called honest game. Don't you know that a trained dealer can read a sucker's face? His effort to look glum when he's a hand of aces, or to look happy when he's a pair of deuces. What do they take us for, boys in school? With other professionals sometimes the game's worth playing! But with the run and ruck—among 'em these fine gents you want to copy—why, it's child's play."

Still I thought of Mate Hudson and I could not speak.

"I'll tell you what," Faro Jack went on. "I'm going up the Coast for a month's vacation—I'll visit my brother who's a light-house keeper off Hatteras—and watch the big seas and the gulls and the petrels for the good of my soul. Here's ten dollars.

Spruce yourself up a little, to see how you like prosperity. But when I come back I want my answer, without any fiddling."

"I'll have it for you, sir," I promised.

5

After a fortnight of foggy, misty weather, my sixteenth birthday fell on a bright Sunday in mid-May. In thinking over the big seas and the gulls and petrels, none of whose doings would be safe bets for Faro Jack, I took a yearning to see wide waters and windswept beaches, and skimmers and oyster-catchers and little sandpipers, and perhaps swim a little, and maybe make a friend, for one is still hopeful of making friends when only sixteen. So, dressed in my best, I took the ferry to Sullivan's Island, about two miles from the city.

The ferry proved to be crowded, mostly with people of my own class. But on the beach, separated from hoi polloi by an invisible wall, were several families of gentry; and one of these, as I had half-expected, half-foreseen, showed at a good distance to be the Mason Hudsons. Invisible in the crowd, I drew nearer. Mr. Hudson sat under a palm tree, reading. His wife, a tall, gray-haired woman as different from my mother as a cool gladiola from a faded poinsettia, sat beside him, plying a needle on a little white cloth. Occasionally he would lower his book to speak to her of something, or to read her a passage. Sometimes she called him from it by a remark. I sensed a wonderful closeness between them that I could hardly believe I could ever have with any other soul.

Their older son Arnold and his beautiful young wife played in the surf. Arnold was a rather priggish man whom others called a snob; I did not, with a curious shunning of the word, perhaps because its use implies that one has been, or can be, snubbed. The fact remained that I shunned him too, walked wide of him in fact, and his presence seemed to wither any hope of my talking to Mr. Hudson or of making a good impression on his wife.

Mason Hudson, Junior, the younger son, about eighteen now, was strolling the beach with a tall girl whose clothes and hairdress indicated she was about fourteen.

I had been told I could call him Mate. All his blue-blooded friends did so. But I did not. I was afraid he had forgotten and his face would change. Still I might talk to him, if I wanted to enough. He had never rebuffed me, only remained alone and apart as though he could not help it. I would have to run the risk of a silent refusal to present me to his young-lady companion. Upper-crust Charleston men often stooped to casual association with underlings, male and female, but they closely guarded their ladyfolk from any such contact.

As I watched them they stopped to complete an earnest conversation, then Mate turned back to join his family while the girl continued on up the beach. It was she, not that splendid but forlorn young man, who now gripped my attention.

After a little thought I knew who she was—a niece of the first Mrs. Hudson, lately come from an old manor on Edisto Island. It struck me forcibly that she was an orphan, her mother dying young, her father recently drowned in a boating accident. She had a very odd name, which for a moment I could not call to mind. Then it returned to me with a pleasant start—Salley Sass. Although both the first and last names stood for Low Country families of historic place, still a girl bearing it might not be so haughty as most plantation daughters of fourteen; it might serve to humanize her. When I saw her stroll off down a stretch of beach, forsaken by the bathers because of shallows and potholes and poisonous jellyfish, I fetched a big, quick loop so I could meet her.

It might be she would not know who I was. It might be that, even if she did, she would talk to me.

When she saw me coming to meet her in the little walking space between the grass and the waters, she started to turn back. But either because it did not matter to her, or else—a hundredth chance, it seemed to me, she thought it might interest her—she continued on.

The nearer I drew, the more I hated her. Hate was not the right word, I knew, for my resentment at her being so nearly in my reach and yet so distant; and it was all the greater for the grace with which she walked, and the little smile upon her face that was not for me. She was not even thinking of me. She could meet a dozen youths from town strolling the beach, but none could interfere with her privacy, which was with herself. She was looking at the water and the seabirds and the little bright shells left by the falling tide.

At sixteen I was more of a man than most youths of my age—especially those to whom circumstance was not always shouting, "Grow up, grow up"—but she was likewise more of a young woman. Dress her hair a little differently, array her in a low-cut gown at one of her uncle's parties, and you would think she was eighteen. All who came could see her in that low dress. Seeing her, dancing with her perhaps, they could have a claim upon her—some day to go riding with her, some night to be her escort at dinners and plays.

The well-born bucks who came to her uncle's Charleston mansion or were guests at Hudson Barony would not woo her openly for two years more, but they were bucks as surely as the horned deer of the woods, and they would not overlook the young doe pretty as a picture; and every jest they made to her, every romping with her that her youth permitted, caused a warm little cloud to cross their brains. I knew that cloud already. I knew those bucks. I hated every one . . . .

She was not very pretty, I told myself. The skin of her face was too tight over its bones. But she was beautiful, and I might as well deny my own mother, full of West Indian savagery and half-full of West Indian rum, as to deny that. The trouble with me was, I knew beauty when I saw it. I would be better off not to know it, dwelling among the hovels of an Upper East Bay alley where it showed so rarely—and when we did see it, we could never have it. I would be better off if I mistook common prettiness for beauty, for now and then that would fall into my hands.

Yet as we passed, it was as though I had swigged courage out of one of Mamma's bottles, for I spoke to her.

"Good day, miss."

"Good day, sir."

She paused very slightly before she started to walk on, so I spoke again.

"I saw a porpoise just now. He gave his big sigh and went under."

"I wish he'd come up again. I love to see porpoises."

"There aren't many birds today. I guess the crowd has frightened them away. The last time I came to Sullivan's Island, there were dozens of flocks of pelicans." This happened to be true.

"Do you come here often?"

"This is the first time this year."

"It's the first time for me, too." She had fully stopped now, and was looking at me closely. "Do you live in Charleston?"

"Yes."

"What's your name? I haven't been there very long and have met only a few of the young people."

"Edward Stono."

"When we lived at Edisto, we went often to Stono Creek. But I didn't know that Stono was a family name."

"I guess they've about died out."

As I listened to her voice, warm and lilting, my eyes were drinking in her face. Her coloring was rather dark. The deep-green gloom of Edisto had worked upon her, I thought—cypress forest, shadow-filled ponds, dark rivers slowly winding. Her lips were dark red, her eyes were pale brown, her skin was olive.

"Will you tell me your name, please, ma'am?" I asked.

"Yes, it's Salley Sass."

"Are you going to live in Charleston?"

"There, and at Hudson Barony."

"I've seen it. It's a wonderful place."

"My uncle's very kind to me. He's no blood kin to me—his first wife was my father's sister, yet he treats me like a daughter. I don't know what I'd do—" She stopped, and the distance between us did not seem quite as great as before. "Perhaps you heard I lost my father—"

"I lost mine many years ago."

"That puts us in the same boat, doesn't it?"

No, it didn't. It never could. Still I must speak.

"I wish I could see you again sometime."

"Are you occupied for this coming Friday night?" she asked.

"No—"

"Well, my aunt is giving a party for me. It's for nine o'clock and we'll have square dances. The invitations are already out, but that doesn't matter. There will be plenty of room for one more, if you'd like to come."

"I'd love to come."

"I'll see you then. So goodbye, Edward."

"Goodbye, Salley."

She went on up the beach. I avoided everyone the rest of the day, holding communion only with the ever-changing waters, the tide that mysteriously fell then started to rise again, the boldly winging cormorants, the great rapacious pelicans, the silver terns air-dancing over a school of menhaden ere they careened, the long-billed curlews flying in ordered flocks, and even the little sandpipers forever lighting and taking off along the sand. I saw a porpoise that came up and uttered his long, sad sigh, and since I had lied about him, I thought his appearance brought me luck. I moved lightly as in a dream.

Sometimes a cold chill frost-nipped all my dreams. But a rush of hope, and it seemed more than that, soon restored my faith. My father had been a gentleman. My mother would not lie to me on that score. My mother was a West Indian girl, but none of the 'ristocrats had ever seen her as sometimes I had seen her. It was only a young people's party. We would bake oysters and boil shrimp or do square dances, and even if her uncle and aunt did not place Edward Stono as the well-spoken boy who borrowed books, they would let it go this time. And I would do nothing at the party to attract undue attention. I would linger in the background until Salley let me know that I could join the lucky group about her. No boy there would be better read, or have nicer manners. . . .

And the next time the Hudsons gave a party my name would be one of the first to be written down. . . .

All the next day I walked on air. The old, trite saying seemed literally true. And on the following morning, my heart missed only a beat or two when the old postman stopped at our door. Often the ladies who were my mother's customers sent their orders by mail. . . .

But the envelope was addressed to me. My hand was steady— fit for dealing blackjack—as I tore it open. The paper was very fine and heavy, bearing the engraving Hudson Barony. The handwriting was precise:

Dear Mr. Stono:

To my regret, my niece Miss Salley Sass made a mistake when she invited you to a picnic supper this coming Friday night. She did not know that the invitation list had already been filled.

My husband hopes you will continue to make use of his library.

With every good wish for your success.

Sincerely,
Mildred (Mrs. Mason) Hudson

I had opened the letter in the presence of my mother, partly because I had been ashamed to do so in secret, partly in bitter pride. Now she heard me laugh aloud.

"What is it, Edward?" she asked, groping for her spectacles.

"It's an offer of a job. It will begin in a week, but I won't tell you what it is—I'll let it be a surprise. And you needn't have the least fear that I won't make good."

My voice had a resonant ring. Knowing my mother could read only French, not English, I dropped the letter carelessly on the table. With a shaking hand she poured herself a tot of rum.

"I feared 'twould be bad news, your face was so white," she said. "Let it be a surprise."

CHAPTER II

Captain of the Deck

IT WAS A hard chore to tell my mother that the job would begin in Augusta. I came out with it in as casual a voice as possible, then, before she could grasp what I had said, I made haste to soften the blow.

"It's only one day's ride by train or two by packet steamer. I can come home every fortnight—at least every month. It's a healthy city—very little malaria and no yellow fever—and growing fast with lots of chances to make money and get ahead. Cotton is king there."

For a long space she did not speak, and I could not read the deep trouble in her face and became frightened. Then she smiled very dimly and spoke softly.

"Maybe it is a good thing, Edward, for you to go away."

"It means a whole lot of loneliness for both of us."

"We are used to it, aren't we, Edward?" She spoke in a proud tone, and with that she always employed French. "You have never been other than lonely except for little intervals, little hours. They were like sunny islands that you touched on a long, lonely journey. Do you think I did not know? When you went to the park on Sunday mornings and the gentleman gave you

26

the books—that was a happy isle—and the happiest of all was one you found the day you went to the beach. I do not know what happened but I saw your face when you returned, and heard your voice, and watched your quick step. I thought then maybe the long, lone journey was almost over. But I was wrong."

"Yes, Mamma, you were wrong."

"Except for you, I've been alone—for how many years? And some of the deepest lonelinesses were when you were in the room. It is not your fault, Edward. God knows it is not mine. But that is why—partly—it is best for you to go."

I could not answer the awful charge, because I knew it was true. I could only ask, "What's the rest of it?"

"This city. This Charleston. Here there is no mercy on the dead. They are not allowed to die, always they must haunt the living, whether a bright reflection in which the living walk proudly, or an obliterating shadow. It is by the past that we are measured, not the future. Edward, it is terribly wrong. In Castile, in Savoy, in Tuscany it is less wrong. These are old kingdoms, and the crowns are old, and the castles, and the ways of thinking and believing, and those who are called lowborn have never been told that the very word is blasphemous beyond measure. The noble is a noble, and the peasant a peasant, world without end. But this is America, the new land, the land of hope. All who look upward may read the writing, written in fire in the sky, of men born equal before God. Is it a lie, Edward? In Charleston there is a philosophy, a cult, almost a religion, that makes it out a lie. And that is why—"

She paused, staring into my face. Knowing I must speak, I spoke too loud.

"Charleston is the most wonderful city in the world."

My mother's eyes slowly filled with tears. She rose then, and went about collecting my clothes for packing.

"No need of that, yet," I told her. "Maybe Mr. Fargo has changed his mind—I won't know till I see him tonight." Only a few in the city knew Faro Jack by this name.

"I think not."

"Anyway I won't leave for two or three days."

My mother stopped what she was doing and, with an effort of will, spoke with her eyes on mine.

"Edward, it is better that you go. Come back for short visits, but not every fortnight or every month—if I can see you every six months I'll be more than content. And don't come to stay until you feel sure you can win."

"Don't you mean, until I have won?"

"No, I feel you can never win except in Charleston—the kind of winning you crave. The gains won elsewhere will fall short until you have won here. That is a sad thing, yet I hold it true. But you can prepare yourself for winning here. Maybe you can earn a sword and a shield. They may be gold, but better yet they may be of steel."

Only once or twice had my mother talked in this strange way, and then the bottle on the table had been half-empty. Now it remained unopened, and I tried not to understand.

2

The railroad from Charleston to Hamburg—the latter town lying across the Savannah River from Augusta—was the pride of the state. At its completion twenty years before, it had been the longest in the world—one hundred and thirty-five miles—and the first laid to carry passengers behind locomotives. Faro Jack and I rode in comfortable, covered, upholstered cars; and watching through the windows we saw the beautiful Carolina countryside hurtle by at a dizzy pace. My great venture was well begun!

Through the lovely, brooding low country, beside little ponds half-hidden by moss-draped oaks, into pine or cypress forest, we slowly gained the uplands rich with cotton and corn. True, the country looked newer and rougher, the plantation houses not nearly so grand, but towns and roads and bridges were a-build-

ing everywhere, the smell of money was on the breeze; and I
meant to fill my pockets from the overflow.

Augusta was a mixture of the rough and the smooth. Rather
lately it had become one of the great cotton markets of the
earth; countless wagon trains and mule carts brought in the
snowy stuff, and in season they rumbled all day and night in
the chuckholes of Broad Street; Eli Whitney's gin, endlessly
multiplied, seeded it and packed it into bales; most of these and
thousands of their like brought in from the hinterlands were
shipped by flatboat or flatcar to Savannah or Charleston and
from hence beyond the seas; and the remainder were changed
into cloth by the new mills on the new, broad, deep canal.
Rivermen ate and slept and brawled with railroad and mill-
builders in the river-front inns. Demimonde that you would
almost mistake for ladyfolk had pretty nests on Jones Street;
their coarse-voiced, hard-swearing but sometimes softer-hearted
sisters plied their trade at the low-grade taverns and mughouses; and along mud roads stood rows and clusters of shacks,
some of them housing poor whites or free Negroes, and some
beautiful mulatto and quadroon slave girls, visited by their
owners in the dark of night.

But in handsome offices on Cotton Row sat many gentlemen
with gold chains, readers of good books, and connoisseurs of
wines. On Green and Broad and Telfair streets, above and
below the markets, stood high, narrow houses, many of them
brick, furnished—I was told—as elegantly as the mansions of
Savannah. On the hill to the west, only an hour's drive from
the city's center, rose the larger and finer houses of Summerville, already giving itself airs over the sprawling town below,
and to the east, across the river, lay the old settlement of Beach
Island, that sometimes thought itself a very Edisto Island when
it came to rank. By and large, however, Augusta was not
Charleston by a hundred and thirty-five miles of farm and piney
wood. It was a hundred years younger, very much smaller and
only a fraction as proud. There was a gentry here, but no aristocracy. Storekeepers and cotton dealers, let alone doctors and

lawyers, sat often at table with slave owning planters, and the latter did not walk, talk, act, think, or feel like the owners of the baronies of the South Carolina Low Country. Although some of them managed to dress much the same, still they did not look the same. I could not quite tell why. Perhaps holding themselves so high had stamped the grandees' faces. Perhaps Augusta was part of the United States while Charleston had become the island of a dream.

If so, it was the dream I meant to follow to the end.

3

I doubted if Faro Jack's new gaming rooms were the most elegant this side of New Orleans. Yet, occupying the ground floor of one of the more imposing houses on Washington Street, they were certainly the finest in the city, putting in the shade the more gaudy but tawdry resort of his only formidable rival, known as Memphis. The parlor was the grandest I had ever set foot in, with horsehair sofas and chairs, a crystal chandelier, and a marble fireplace. My bedroom was on the third floor, small and well back; Faro Jack occupied one of the front chambers, and five other rooms were made available for renters for one night—often for only an hour—at prices higher than current in the lodginghouses of the town. The renters were almost always couples, the lady veiled and the gentleman with his head bowed and his hat pulled low over his eyes, tiptoeing up the back stairs.

Within three months, I had made good as Faro Jack's assistant. The work itself was not difficult—selling and cashing chips, supplying cards and dice, collecting the house's share of the stakes on various play, acting as croupier to our roulette tables, and even dealing faro, the fairest to the player of all our games. I had no trouble with customers—Faro Jack called them patrons or suckers according to the degree of his misanthropy— and in fact I got along with them astonishingly well, considering my youth. Faro Jack soon learned he could leave me in charge of the rooms, with never, so far, my having to call on Hans, a burly, stupid, but loyal and completely honest German who was told to stroll about, his simian arms swinging in front of his huge chest, when a fight looked to be brewing. Faro Jack set much store on this development. He attributed it to the quiet of my voice, coolness in excitement, and good manners.

I could have told him that I had been a dedicated student of these things since I first began to imitate our great Charleston aristocrats. Instinct or experience told me that courtesy warms a customer, frightens an enemy, and very subtly suggests reserve strength. You would think my stylish dress would encourage a river-front ruffian to try to break me in two. I believe that actually it tended to discourage the venture, if only through fear of the unknown.

To become Faro Jack's understudy was a far harder task. Happily he was a good teacher and I a tireless student. Hardly a day did I miss a two-hour lesson; on slack days or in slack seasons I often played or practiced the clock around. In two years I could stack decks and palm dice or deal an edged card as well as he and could empty his pockets at three-card monte. Still I had not put this prowess into play against our customers. The house did well on its share of straight games. To be caught cheating would have closed us up and caused Faro Jack and me too to lose face throughout the ghostly half-lit mirthless world of gamblers, even if it did not end his life or mine in a blaze of pistol fire.

In my fourth year I turned a little corner and came out on the road that led to great play. I could truly be called a "sharp," which in our gambling parlance was a little different from a "sharper," the former indicating a dependence on high prowess at straight play, the latter a master of trickery. The development was strangely sudden. Always good at calculating "percentage"—meaning the approximate value of my hand according to the laws of chance—I learned all at once to do it like lightning. Also I could see through almost every attempt at deception by my fellow players, as betrayed by remarks, voice, gestures and facial expressions.

When our play was slack, Faro Jack took to sending me where it was high and handsome. On these trips I did not play with suckers but with professionals who had already taken the suckers' money. The end of the fowling season might find me in Baltimore; the gathering of the shrimpers at Savannah might bring me there; the building of a new railroad or a river levee or a canal could fetch me up in Columbia, young raw Atlanta, Chattanooga, Nashville; or in the Blue Grass in the racing season, or as far afield as Mobile, when the planters from the fabulous black belt came to town with their purses stuffed. Wherever money jingled free I was one of a cold-eyed band that gathered like buzzards to a hog-killing. The only difference between me and most of them was that I was one of the kings.

Even so, I still operated on—and risked—Faro Jack's money. To him I made scrupulous account; and he paid me enough to eat and dress well, to keep my mother well supplied with rum and a few added comforts, and to save a little against a run of low cards. More than this, since he was my teacher, I did not ask.

None of this served to make me a gentleman. Indeed I had only to turn another corner to abandon all hope of becoming one, not of dismissing but of casting out my dream, as I fancied a Puritan father casting out a beautiful, beloved, but wayward daughter. Then, dealing or playing against all comers, I might make a fortune with my name renowned among all us gentry of the gaming tables, from here to new-found Frisco. I would not be honored anywhere but widely feared. Still I flinched from making the break with my childhood faith. It would mean a transformation, a kind of reverse transfiguration of my whole personality. So I clung on.

Meanwhile I had practiced in a few arts and crafts useful to gentlemen. My reading of books had been greatly curtailed since I took to reading pips, but several hundred I had read before had worked upon my mind, and hence I could talk of many things, and persuade gentlemen whom I met on my travels that I belonged to their caste. Traveling about the country called for much riding, and I cannot say I was a bad horseman considering that I was not raised on horseback as were the plantation children. It was partly a matter of my hands being strong from being quick—quickness cannot arise from weak, slack muscles. Besides, one cannot be a successful gambler without a certain deadliness, which even a dumb brute may feel.

In the summer of 1851, I made one of my flying, far-between visits to Charleston. I was twenty that year, but no one could guess it; I looked twenty-five and was often taken for a still older man of young appearance. Not quite six feet tall, finely made as a well-bred English hunter, I had almost every trick and mannerism of a Charleston aristocrat—these I had learned by imitation—and a certain physical grace I could not readily account for. Perhaps I had inherited it from my father, Charles Stono. Perhaps it had worked into my body from the extraordinary fluence and lightness of my hands.

I was somewhat more swarthy than most Charlestonians of Huguenot stock, although I had the big, aquiline beak characteristic of the breed. Dressed in the latest Charleston fashion, I wore a large, flashy, although flawed diamond on my right hand —it often served to catch the eye of an opposing player at three-card monte—and a fine gold watch, pawned cheap by a gentleman planter in temporary embarrassment—on a gold chain.

When my mother saw me in the door, she must dab her eyes. I took her in my arms, and so I hid the spasm that came and quickly passed across my visage. I wiped my eyes on her dark hair.

"You look better than you have for years," I told her. And this was partly true.

"I don't work so hard, now that you send me so much money." She spoke gaily, in French. "Sometimes when ladies send for me to come to their houses to sew, I do not go unless they provide a buggy, and sometimes when they bring cloth to my door, and speak too haughtily to me, I tell them I am too,

too busy to do the work. Oh, you should hear me, Edward. One of them whom I refused told me I was getting too big for my—what is *culotte?*"

"Breeches."

"The very word!"

"Who was it? Surely not one of the great ladies—"

"She did not use to be, but lately she had moved with her rich son into one of the fine houses by the High Battery. It is Mistress Mims. Her son is Butler Mims, gentleman of the finest." A note of irony crept into my mother's voice.

I wanted to say something that took courage—and although I flinched, I said it anyway.

"When he was a boy, he called me white trash."

"I knew someone did. He knew it was not true."

"Not then, but it is now. Perhaps that's the reason I can tell it. If a gambler isn't white trash, who is? But I won't always be. I'll make my stake and buy a plantation as fine as Hudson Barony."

"Why do you name that one? Aren't there many finer—or some less fine that would content you?"

"I reckon it's my ideal."

"A fine plantation must have a fine-haired mistress."

"I'll wed and bed me one. The daughter of a great Charlestonian, poor as a churchmouse. Money makes the mare go."

My mother made no comment. Her eyes brightened, but that might be caused by a mist of tears.

"Have you heard any report that I'm a gambler?" I persisted.

"Mistress Mims knew it. She didn't fail to bring it up."

"Butler Mims was a very knowing boy—and I guess he's grown up to be a knowing man."

Since Butler was a close acquaintance of Mate Hudson, Mason Hudson had no doubt heard of my occupation. I decided to write him a note of "confession." When an opponent suspected my tactics at draw poker I had often rigged it for him to catch a glimpse of my cards for several hands, meanwhile playing them in another fashion. In that way I could decoy him to the kill.

But Mason Hudson was not an opponent—he was a friend. I had never used subterfuge against a friend before; and it came to me with a mild pang of dying conscience, a little like that of a dying tooth, that he would not use it even against a foe. No doubt I had never envied the aristocrats' rigid honor as much as their clothes, manners, equipage, and riches, yet it had appealed to my sense of romance. Truly, I had taken a devious way to become a gentleman!

The writing was too easy:

Dear Sir:

    I am in Charleston for a few days, and I thought if you still walked in the Battery on Sunday mornings, I might have the pleasure of a word with you.

    But I am afraid that you will feel you have given and lent me books in vain, for I have come to live not by my best mind but by my wits. I can only tell you that I deal fairly against fair players, and I hope to find another livelihood before very long.

Sincerely,
Edward Stono

I dispatched the note, and that night I sat late with my mother over a bottle of Santiago rum. I had never done so before; it seemed I was trying to tell her something, if only that I was not ashamed of her or at least did not blame her for her deep draughts daily; but since John Barleycorn—in this case it was Juan Melote—had almost no part in my daily life, since I eschewed him, despite a certain yearning for his warm haze, solely to keep razor-sharp those wits by which I lived, tonight I could not bring myself to do more than sip at the glass; and my mother felt my sobriety as a wall between us, and all her bottle bubbles burst and all her boozy exultations fell to earth and cracked, and all I had showed her was that she was a sot.

4

In the morning I dressed and groomed myself with peculiar care. The weather was not quite hot but very warm and humid; greenery grew rampant; fever was starting to breed in the deep swamps, and it stood to reason that Mason Hudson's family had come in from Hudson Barony to their town house and that he had received my message. If he did not come, it was probably a sign he was done with me. But he would not like to fail me. He would still help me if he could.

My hopes declined rather swiftly; he would come early or not at all. And then, suddenly, a curious and powerful thrill, not altogether pleasant, frightening almost, passed over me. I had felt something the same, although not as strong, as cards were being dealt for a critical hand. I saw a tall girl walking toward me fully a hundred yards away. That was too far for me to identify her, yet I knew, better than I knew my name, who she would prove to be.

She came closer and closer, and then four years crammed with little events vanished from my cognizance like a dream of the night, and I walked again the beach at Sullivan's Island, upon the yellow sand that glittered here and there with bits of shell, between the green of the shore, and the snowy, murmuring, curling, ebbing and flowing surf; and when I spoke to a tall girl whom I met there, she made reply.

She had changed very little. I had to look hard, to see where she had changed at all. She had been fourteen; now she was eighteen; her form had been mature, light with an upward leap; she held her head the same way; her black hair had the same elegance although it was differently dressed; her open throat showed its touching hollow and the delicate collarbones; her lips were dark red and her eyes pale brown and her skin a deep olive, as though the intense shade of the Edisto forests with their dark creeks and moss-hung ponds had worked upon her, and the skin was too tightly drawn over the small, delicate, lovely bones of her face for her to be pretty. But she was beautiful, with a beauty I could not dream of being in my reach. I would have denied it if I had not been so proud. It was beauty saved for a highborn son of the old order, and it was greater than before, and that was the only change in her since I had seen her last, and I did not know what caused it. I knew only that I hated her for that beauty unsharable with me—that I could only see, and long for, and lose. Even its touch of sadness, a sense of something lonely and forlorn, like the heart of a wood nymph forsaken by her fellows, could not balm that hate.

Her name—why, her name was Salley Sass! It was a plain name, what we Southerners called homey, and it had deceived me once. Instead you could not find a prouder name in all the Low Country.

She stopped in the path, her face still, so I could look at her. I thought to pass on—I wished I could be that hard and relentless—but my hate turned inward, and I could not.

"Salley?"

"Yes, Edward."

"Are you bringing a message from your uncle?"

"Yes, but I asked to bring it."

"There's a bench. Have you time to sit down?"

"I have plenty of time."

She took her seat and made a little inviting motion with her hand. For a brief space she watched a game that squirrels were playing in the tree boughs; I sat beside her in the silence. My feelings were caught up in me in a curiously intense way.

"My uncle's message was that he would have been happy to meet you here, but he was feeling poorly and could not come," Salley said presently.

"I thank him for the thought."

"I asked to deliver the message because—I had something to say to you. It doesn't amount to much, perhaps. It is only to say how sorry I was that the invitation I gave you four years ago—to a beach party—had to be cancelled. But perhaps you'd forgotten?"

"Would you think what you said last to be very likely?"

She glanced into my eyes. "No."

"You know then that I remember only too well."

"Yes. I beg your pardon."

"You needn't. You mean it kindly. You were giving me a chance to pretend it didn't matter to me—that it didn't sting or at least leave a scar—and in that way save my pride. The truth is, I'm too proud to deny the truth. I think that's the only true pride I have—not to try to bluff myself. As you may know, bluff is the old name for draw poker."

"I want to say this too. Aunt Mildred—Uncle Mason's wife—is a kindly, gracious woman. She wrote that note to you with deep regret and quite a few misgivings. I grant that was only human. But whether you understand why she felt she had to write it—well, that's asking a good deal of you, still it seems to me possible that you do."

Her voice was low and very young, and glimmering as are often the voices of rich-toned Negresses.

"Let me see if I can tell you," I answered. "If only the family and maybe a cousin or two and the sons and daughters of a few old friends were to be present, your aunt could have let the invitation stand. But, as it happened, that beach party was the first party given for you, and the young people invited were the pick of the Low Country—each one standing for a great name and tradition. It was a gathering of the younger generation of the *haut noblesse*. I did not belong there. Everyone present would know it—if not at first, before the party was over, for the biggest difference between old snobs and young snobs is that the young ones are more cruel; and the youth of the Charleston noblesse aren't so noble that they wouldn't get off together and talk. Their parents would know it later. They would feel that your aunt and uncle had not stood up for their own—that they had let down the bars that must be kept raised at all times, especially since Charleston is located on nominally American soil, where the mob is ever-threatening to get out of hand. Mind you, I don't blame them, and only envy them. How I would have loved to be one of those youths you entertained that night —who doesn't have to explain who he is, because all who matter know already, secure in his birthright, assured of his seat among the elite; and in spite of his graciousness and generosity and gaiety, always ready and duty-bound to put an upstart in his place. Let me be fair. Your aunt thought of what was best for me, too. I wouldn't have had a good time, I would have had a most painful time. You would have been nice to me, some of the others would, but I would know I was being singled out for special treatment. I would also get many rebuffs, worse than kicks in the face. And after that, I'd have to go back where I started. I would be given a glimpse of high life, only to make me more discontented with low life. And pardon me for going into the matter to such length."

Her eyes had grown big and she made a curious comment. "Edward, you seem much older than any young man I know."

"I'm old already."

"And you've expressed it very well. Much better than I could."

"I've had plenty of time to think about it, lying awake at night."

"Did it hurt that much? I'm so sorry."

"I'm sorry I told you. It was a weak thing to say. Think of the poor devils lying awake at night from cold or hunger, not merely blows to their egos. Besides that, I have my ambition to stand by, and which stands by me. You needn't ever pity a young man with a devouring ambition until he either wins or is kicked in the face so much that he's groggy. God may pity him, because He knows the upshot, but his fellow humans can envy him—at least he lives ten lives in one—and perhaps they had better fear him."

"Edward, do you think you can win?"

"I don't think about it. I don't question it. You see, I'm bound to win."

"But you've taken a strange road!"

"I thought it was the shortest and the most sure."

"To money, perhaps, but not to position."

"I had no position to lose, and plenty to gain."

"Suppose I was giving another beach party, and supposing my aunt did not know anything about you—mistook you for a gentleman. Still I wouldn't do what I did before."

"You mean—invite me."

"I wouldn't invite you, Edward. I wouldn't foist a gambler on my friends."

"You spoke of your aunt but didn't mention your uncle. In regard to your other party, would you care to tell me whether he too favored sending me the note of cancellation?"

"Since you ask—and it isn't a fair question—I don't think a gentleman would ask it about someone who had lent and given him books—Uncle Mason said to let you come. But he didn't stand up for it. He was greatly troubled, and when Aunt Mildred made the hard decision, he—he seemed someway relieved."

"How about your cousin, Mate? It's another ill-mannered question, but I don't fool you anyway—"

"Mate Hudson is not my cousin." Salley spoke quickly and somewhat emphatically. "I am of no blood kin to any Hudson except Clay—a son by Uncle Mason's first wife. And I'm glad to tell you that Mate was very much against canceling the invitation. And when it was done anyway, he wouldn't go to the party."

I felt a warm prickling across the back of my neck and along my temples.

"Your face has flushed," Salley said.

"I can't help it. I'm—astounded."

"It's quite like him, really. And I suppose it's quite like your fellow gamblers to try to take everything he's got."

After a few seconds of sitting very still, my thoughts flying, I asked:

"Does Mate play?"

"Yes, and I can't keep him from it."

"Well, he's free, white, and twenty-one, as the saying goes."

"In this case it's a heartless thing to say about someone who stood up for you."

"I think I was trying to stand up for myself—but that's no use."

"Well, I've told you all that I have to tell, so I may as well—"

"I have something to tell you. You may not value it but I'll tell you anyway. You were beautiful when I saw you and you have waxed in beauty. And, believe me, as a card sharp I have sharp eyes."

"Thanks, Edward." But her eyes said something else. They grew and shone more than I could possibly expect. It must be she needed reassurance of her beauty, since it was her main fort and fortune. Perhaps it was going to be put to a severe test in some project she had in mind.

"I wish to ask another question," I said. "You were only four-teen when you gave the party and most of the guests not much older. If you care to tell me—did you play kissing games?"

"Quite late—when the grownups had left us—and the servants were all gone—we played kiss-in-the-ring."

"So if I had gone to the party, I would have gotten a kiss from you."

"Probably."

"Don't you think it would be fair to let me have it now?"

She gave me a long glance.

"Would you prize it?" she asked in low tones.

"Very much."

"Would it tend to remove a little of what you called the sting—efface a little of the scar—of that rebuff?"

"I told you I didn't want anyone feeling sorry—"

"This has nothing to do with that. I'll put it this way—if we kissed, would you remember me more kindly and—if the chance came—be more kind? For you said something else, a few minutes ago, that was quite true, and which I won't forget. You said that people shouldn't feel sorry for a man with such vaulting and ruthless ambition as you have, and perhaps should fear him instead."

"If ever you need kindness from me—which is hard to believe and yet, under certain circumstances possible—you can buy it from me—now—with a kiss."

She glanced quickly about. There was no one in sight except an old gentleman walking in the opposite direction.

"Lean toward me," she murmured.

I did so and her lips met mine in an unstinted kiss. Within and without everything became a little changed; and the stiff little park, with its summery foliage, became a scene to visit in many dreams. It was my greatest victory. It was my sharpest moment and closest link with beauty. Before I could begin to divine or to grasp its newborn force, she had risen and walked away.

CHAPTER III

Creatures of the Night

Two years passed by with small varying events. In this same period I made two brief visits to Charleston, on the first of these finding my mother not quite so well, and on the second somewhat better, and I felt no inkling of a new haunting when, returning from booming Salem on an autumn evening, Faro Jack handed me an envelope of heavy, faintly scented paper such as was used by Augusta ladies of quality. It had been brought the day before, he said, by a liveried servant.

It read:

Dear Edward:

    I am staying with my cousin, Miss Abigail Cumming, at her father's house, Pine Lodge, in Summerville, and I wish to talk to you on what is to me an important matter. Since I cannot come to your gaming rooms, would you be so kind as to call on me here at four on the first afternoon following your return to town?

    From a former acquaintance,

Salley Sass

Next day of three o'clock I was dressed and groomed with care. Instead of following the somewhat more democratic

Augusta style, I got myself up, to the last bootlace, as a Charleston gentleman of fashion, an insolence I thought that Salley would not miss. A hired carriage with a Negro driver waited at the door.

When I had knocked on the handsome iron-grilled door of big, rambling Pine Lodge, and asked for Miss Sass, the footman told me I would find her in the summerhouse, gained by a little path through the Cape jasmine. This structure proved nothing more than latticed arbor under an ancient scuppernong, but it might be nearly as important in the history of the mansion as the splendid parlor, for there the daughters of the house and their suitors could sit and make conversation, while here, hidden from all except amorous birds and butterflies, they could sit and make love. The South was full of such retreats, built by wise forefathers within walled yards, or by Mother Nature in woody patches by the road. Thus spring and summer and early fall are the wooing seasons in the South, and so the land has brought forth a warm and passionate race.

Salley stood in the vine-girded doorway, and I saw her in relation to the autumn. It had set in—the slow fading of the summer ere its lingering death, the summer that we love, that is our mother, the brooding spirit of the South, its intrinsic element and meaning, whose departure we watch with sorrow ere the alien, inimical winter besieges our soft land. Our gay lascivious greens had faded and darkened, and there was much brown in the vines and trees and herbage, but it was a warm brown still, and it matched her eyes and her skin, and brought out the native elegance of her black hair. By the same token there was an obscure brooding sorrow in the scene, and in her lovely face.

"Thank you, Edward, for coming," she told me.

"You're quite welcome, Miss Sass."

"Why do you call me that?"

"You signed your letter as a former acquaintance. I was not sure such a relationship entitled me to a more familiar address."

"Please don't speak so formally, and be the same to me as before. On the beach—and in the Battery. This is another informal meeting place. I chose it especially. Isn't it beautiful?"

"It becomes you very well."

"I'd talk some small talk, if I could—I mean before I get down to business," she said when we took the rustic seats. "It would seem better manners. But it's too urgent—and I don't know how."

"You can go ahead and deal from a cold deck." For I was quite sure her errand concerned my trade and this might put her at ease.

Why did I want to put her at ease? She was a lady of Charleston, a child of the proudest island of all the proud sea islands of our shore, a daughter of the Low Country aristocracy that was, perhaps more by attitude of mind than exalted ancestry, the most real, the most high of any in America, including far-richer Boston's merchant aristocracy and New York's dying patroon aristocracy and rising money aristocracy, and Philadelphia's industrial aristocracy. I stopped and reviewed the thought. The ancient, powerful families of the great cities would deny its truth, but the bloods of England would not nor would the high noblesse of France. Here they would recognize a branch of their own order. The aristocratic concept in the North had been weakened by democratic ideas. Stately Virginia stood too close to down-to-earth Pennsylvania.

Salley was a real one. She needed only to be herself, without a thought of herself, for the high or the low to know it. She was a highborn daughter of the plantation worked by slaves. It was in her face and form and voice and manner, and all of these were lit by beauty, and what the connection was I did not know. And for once I, Edward Stono, this particular person whom I knew so well and so often held in high contempt, had her at a disadvantage. I knew it by the look in her face and the tension in her tone. I had been booted from her door but at last she had had to come to me, as God's children sometimes have to come to the Devil for their soft hearts' sake. Why should I, of all people, try to put her at her ease?

It was a tribute to loveliness that I owed and could not help but pay.

"You look well, Edward."

"The nocturnal life agrees with me, as it must with foxes, owls—bats—and other creatures of the night. Today I came in from a raid, but ordinarily at this time of the day I'd be just beginning to feel wide awake. You are more beautiful than ever. I didn't think it possible when you were eighteen, but behold—at twenty it is an established fact. You dress with great art—I could almost think with great cunning. Your attire is not a mere adornment to you; instead it becomes you in both meanings of the word—becoming to you and becoming part of you."

Today she wore orange to call attention to her pale-brown eyes, olive skin, black hair and in subtle regard for the browns of autumn. And there was no doubt that as she had looked into the tall, gold-framed mirrors in a spacious chamber in Pine Lodge she had thought mainly of its effect on me.

"You talk fluently," she remarked. "I thought gamblers were noted for their silence."

"On the contrary, I often talk a blue streak, to confuse an opponent. But I'm not trying to confuse you."

"I've made quite a study of clothes, if that's what you meant. I have to make a little money go a long way. In fact, like the milkmaid, my face—meaning my whole appearance—is my fortune."

"I think you will marry well in spite of it."

"I'm afraid I won't. I'm afraid I'll make a marriage that I and everyone else knows would be a terrible mistake. I'll get down to business—although it isn't business, it's a petition. Edward, did you know that Mate Hudson is in Augusta?"

To maintain something—I did not know what—I replied with a calm no.

"He came here about two weeks ago," Salley went on. "He

fell in with a girl—her name is Clara Day—and I think she's a confederate, maybe the mistress of a gambler called Memphis. She's got him—maybe he would have done it anyway—to play at Memphis' rooms. The money he's spending is some that he borrowed against his share of the plantation and has in a bank in Charleston—and he's drawn heavily on it already. If it keeps up much longer, he'll be bankrupt."

The words caused a curious ringing in my ears. I knew Clara Day and I knew Memphis. As for Mate Hudson and Salley, it seemed to me suddenly that I did not know them at all, and perhaps could never know them, they being of a different breed, but both were in my life to stay, and that would put me to great trial and perhaps bring me to great sorrow. For God's sake, why? What had they done for me? I knew the count of it perfectly well—such little caring in contrast with my great caring. Yet Fate seemed to be closing around me like a stone wall. I could not climb it—I knew no aperture of escape.

"Clara Day is one of the most skillful and attractive of our demimonde," I said. I did not say that she was also one of the most predatory. "I've danced with her several times, and she is a beautiful dancer. She is Memphis' shill but not his mistress. Memphis takes no interest whatever in women except as far as they help him to make money; he's cold as a stingray. For that matter, Clara is no one's mistress, nor does she take money from her occasional lovers; she hires out only to Memphis who pays her well. She came from a good Alabama family and Mate is not the first gentleman to fall into her hands. Her favors are hard to win and are greatly prized."

"I want to ask what you may feel is an improper question—but you'll see its importance later. Have you ever stayed with her?"

"It's not only an improper question. It's an unfair question—both to her and to me. But since you ask it—I never have."

"Could you, if you wished?"

"I have no idea."

"I'd hoped you would take her away from Mate, and then he'd come home."

"I think that's a very strange proposal, coming from a lady."

"Why? You said her favors were restricted and greatly prized. You see, I heard that too. So I wasn't suggesting anything unpleasant. As for the moral side of it, I don't think I need consider that, in dealing with a gambler. Do I?"

"The facts—and common sense—appear to uphold your argument."

"You've had plenty of other girls—" She paused slightly.

"I'll not answer that."

"Mate hasn't. He's never had one until now. That's more common among young men of his class than you can readily believe; I know more of the seamy side of life than he does—remember my father was a rakehell if there ever was one. He's no doubt infatuated with Clara. And I beg you to break it up and get him out of Memphis' clutches and send him home."

"That's a rather large order."

"It's not an order. I used the word 'beg.' "

"Coming from a woman as high and proud as you—"

"Women stop being high and proud when someone they love is in danger. All that goes by the boards."

"You must love Mate a very great deal."

"He makes my heart glow—or faint—or ache—or tremble all the time. If that's not love, I don't know what it is. Also I love Uncle Mason. He's taken me in and treated me like a daughter and I can't bear for this to happen to him. Will you save them, Edward? By saving Mate, you save them both; believe me, that's true. Promise me you'll try."

She spoke quietly and her eyes looked deep and strange. But I hardened my heart and asked:

"Why should I?"

"I can't give any good reason. There is one, I know, if I could find it. One reason is, there's no one else I can call on. Arnold Hudson is mean and selfish—I don't know how that happens, when both of his parents are so fine. Clay Hudson is worse than that—so bad I can't tell you—and I understand that perfectly well from what I've heard of his mother, my father's sister—and anyway he's skipped the country for good. The young men I know in Charleston, my friends and suitors, wouldn't know how to start. Some of them visit the underworld and get girls, but they know nothing about it. They could as well go into the African jungle. But you're a jungle dweller. You can come out with the prize."

"Your prize, not mine."

"Remember he stood up for you. Remember Uncle Mason brought you books to read and helped to make you the culti- vated man you are. Remember I kissed you in return for a future kindness."

"I'll be impolite and say it's something more than kind- ness, for me to come to grips with Memphis, one of the dead- liest sharpers that ever stacked a deck. You understand there's a sort of truce between gamblers operating in the same terri- tory. It's a case of live and let live; otherwise we'd be at each other's throats and the suckers would get away. Mate is Mem- phis' sucker. He's got him hooked—through Clara, of course— and he'll play him for his last shirt stud, and then he'll let him go. It would be dangerous for me to interfere; Memphis could well lay for me and have my hands crushed past mending, for the jungle you speak of is quite real. Moreover"—and I smiled into her eyes—"it's a breach of professional ethics."

"Don't be sarcastic, Edward. It's cheap."

"I'm not a very expensive article, Salley. People like me come cheap."

"You won't do what I ask?"

"I didn't say that. But speaking of cheap and expensive, where will I get the capital for this venture?"

She looked at me in deep dismay.

"Oh, does it take money?"

"Money is the ammunition. I supposed you knew that. I

can't risk Faro Jack's money on a venture of this sort. How much has Mate got left?"

"He drew a thousand a week ago. It must have reached him about five days ago."

"Then he probably has about five hundred left. Memphis' policy is to take about a hundred a night from suckers with moderate rolls—if he took more it might scare them off. Well, I've got six hundred of my own. If I agree to undertake Mate's rescue, I'll risk half of it—about the same as Mason Hudson risked in the value of the books he used to lend to me."

Mason Hudson had also given me his time, his attention, his interest. By speaking only of material values, I had laid myself open to a charge of vulgar ingratitude. But Salley did not make the charge. She dropped her eyes and her lovely hands lay forlornly in her lap and the beautiful olive skin turned pale.

"Before I give you my answer, I want to point out another reason for refusing," I went on. "Mason Hudson represented an ideal—but so, in another sense, do you. When I've made my pile—it won't take long—I expect to marry—I won't be vulgar and say buy—a daughter of the Charleston aristocracy who happens to be very beautiful and very poor. For her sake I'll be decently treated by the bloods, and find what in time will be a great house. I'd picked you. You would be the perfect choice. There are many things in the way, and one of them is Mate. It would serve my campaign to let Mate go to the dogs. You see, I have a feeling that if you can save him, you intend to marry him. In fact, you've said so."

"In any case, Edward, I'd not marry you. I'd rather marry a poor cracker than a rich gambler. But as for the three hundred dollars—if you lose them, I'll pay you back. I don't know how or when, but I promise I will."

"No, you needn't. You'll recall I still owe you for the kiss. It was worth three hundred dollars, considering who you are, and who I am. But I must remind you again of the danger. That's the greatest risk I'm running, not the loss of the money. So if I undertake the venture, what will be my reward?"

She mused a little while, and I thought again of her walking the sunlit beach with its jewel-like inlay of broken shell between the greenery of the land and the white surf of the sea, in a lovely solitude; and behind that I thought of her in scenes I had imagined, scenes of her under the spreading live oaks, against the forest with its gloom of moss, and beside the dark rivers of Edisto. Under the olive skin of her face was a wonderful delicacy of bone. No mere choosing by her highborn ancestors of beautiful or distinguished mates had cast her in this mold; besides her birthright, beauty had wrought upon her in a strange and powerful way, and I thought it was the beauty of her own scenes, thoughts, and dreams.

"Edward, don't you know?" she said at last, replying to my question.

"No."

"I thought you might, judging from what you said the last time we met."

"No, I don't know."

"Your reward will be to feel—for a little while, and perhaps for the last time—like a gentleman."

My heart gave a great leap. I met her gaze with a great, proud glance.

"I think you are right. Under these circumstances—for that reward—I'll undertake the venture."

2

Salley said almost nothing more but a lonely and lovely half-smile was on her lips and a mist of tears in her pale-brown eyes. She gave me her promise to return at once to Charleston and walked with me to the gate, her hand in mine. It confided something to me—a sympathy perhaps, and a pledge not to forget. It need not matter to me so very much, yet it did matter. Her hand was not small and fragile but long and strong, and beautiful and warm.

She stood in the gateway until I got in my hired carriage and started down the hill, then disappeared among the subdued colors of our autumn herbage.

Back in our rooms I asked Faro Jack for the evening off.

"You can have it," he said, "but I'm a little worried about how you'll spend it."

"How is that?"

"I can add two and two. One of the figgers is that a young Charleston blood named Hudson, the son of Mason Hudson who lent you the books, has been hooked by Clara Day and is being fed in pieces to Memphis. The other is, your dressing up today in your best tucker and driving up to Summerville, where gamblers are usually as welcome as the smallpox. I think you've had a message from Mason Hudson, maybe a meeting with him. I think you intend to try to send the boy home. I wouldn't blame you—the debts we make when we're real young, before we find out that most of the cards are stacked, and to hell with it anyhow, well, those debts won't let us be. Memphis plays his cards well. He has only one weakness that I know of—in trying to recoup losses, he takes reckless chances. He's a bad enemy, so if you win for God's sake do it politely. And Clara—well, she knifed a man in Mobile, and she's not from a good family like she makes out when she's drunk but up out of the piney woods, and she's hellish proud."

"Thanks for the tips, boss."

I knocked on Memphis' door—he had flashy rooms on McIntyre Street—about nine o'clock. A Negro named Julius, who had a long memory for faces, and whose deft hands when removing cloaks were peculiarly talented at locating concealed weapons, peered at me through a small glass, grew wide-eyed, and admitted me with a handsome bow.

"Mister Memphis, he will sho' be glad to see you, suh," Julius informed me.

"I've come to pay my respects to an old acquaintance from Charleston, Mr. Mate Hudson. Is he playing?"

"Him and Miss Clara, they just playin' casino for quarters."

Only now, with my meeting with Mate only a few seconds

away, did I realize the large insufficiency of my own plans. My vague idea of taking all his ready money quickly and neatly, to return it later to a sadder, wiser man, had left out human equations. But the pulse of panic, chill in my veins, did not last long. As I charged myself, such an ambitious and calculating man, with failure to plot the game beforehand at once I perceived its impossibility. There were too many factors that I did not know. My play would have to depend upon the deal.

My confidence was instantly restored. I felt the same feeling that had crept through me, alerting all my nerves, before previous big games; I called it excitement, but it was cold instead of warm. It could not be called pleasurable. It was lonely and somehow desolate. I wondered if booze hounds felt something the same as they looked at and toyed with the first glass ere they started their strange journey to their special hell-on-earth. All the great vices are allied with Death. I did not know how, but the old gamblers and drunkards and whoremasters perceived the fact; and someday I might find the answer.

I almost lost heart again as I paused in the doorway of the card room. I saw Mate long and plain without his noticing my entrance, and I wished to God it was somebody else who had to stand this gaff. I remembered that he was two years older than I: he looked five years younger. I had seen the same boyish freshness of complexion in a country cracker, then watched him lose his meager month's pay without much remorse. On the other hand, Mate was the arch type of the Charleston aristocrat—his body at once strong and graceful, his face of fine molding. There was no lack of maleness in either. Then why in hell, I asked myself, didn't he grow up?

He saw me, leaped to his feet, and almost ran to meet me. He held out his hand and his face lighted up.

"Why, Edward! I was hoping to see you! And how damned grand you are—"

"I came here to see you, Mate."

"Did you indeed! I'm so pleased. We must have a drink. But, first, you must meet my lovely companion. Clara, my sweet, may I present a boyhood friend, Edward Stono? Edward, this is Miss Clara Day."

It is bad manners in the underworld for two of its inmates to reveal their acquaintance when being introduced by a "mark"—in Jack's rougher language, a sucker. Either might be playing a little game that the revelation might ruin. Clara's eyes only glimmered a little as she gave me a bow fit for a Legare Street parlor, for she remembered we had often danced to the playing of mughouse musicians and once came close to dancing to another piper. Those who knew Clara's ways would expect her to be cold-eyed and hard-mouthed; instead she had big, soft eyes and a tender-looking mouth with a shy smile. Her form was fine, slender and tall. She hardly missed being a beauty. She dressed modestly. . . . But there is an ancient law, the poor man's *noblesse oblige,* that the pot must not call the kettle black. . . .

"Isn't she wonderful, Edward?" Mate asked with glowing eyes. "Clara, you must tell him the story you told me—of how you came to be here. He'll treat it in the strictest confidence, and he's one who'll understand."

"I'll tell him some time, perhaps, but not now," Clara replied hastily.

There came to me the stunning thought that Mate was being swindled far worse than I had perceived. By great cunning, Clara had chosen for her act that of an unstained rose blooming among brambles, had made Mate believe it, and he was paying the piper without even getting to dance. If so, she had gone too far. My immoral indignation grew and grew until it turned to an anger almost fine. I could play now. My brain felt whetted; I saw more clearly, as though in a wonderful glass; my hands felt light and free.

I needed them this way, for Memphis had not taken kindly to my coming. He did not waste a thought that I might have come in peace. He approached with his light, silent step, a thin-looking man, with sky-blue eyes, a short nose and a long jaw and a fine flow of ashen hair. He had no eyebrows that I could see, and no eyelashes, and he had been a great power on the Memphis waterfront, until the son of an old friend of the Blount family drowned himself for his losses in the blond man's rooms, and he had had to flee the state. He had never recovered that eminence, but he was still deadly.

"Well, Stono, this is the first time you've honored us with a visit," he remarked.

"I dropped in to see an old friend," I answered.

"I told you, Memphis, that when I took a notion to try my luck, I intended to play with Edward," Mate said, with his natural courtesy. "My only reluctance was that, if the cards went against me, he might throw some good ones my way. He was out of town—so I came here—and have had a good run for my money—winning many pots and failing to win a whole lot more by just a pip or two. Wasn't it remarkable, Memphis, how many times you beat me by a nose?"

"The cards have been running high as the Mississippi in June," Memphis said, turning to me. "Mr. Mate's hands were not quite up to mine, by and large, but the way he played 'em—man, I had my work cut out for me."

"Coming from Memphis, that's a great compliment, Mate," I said.

"I know it is. And I still expect to win back all I've lost and a bit more. That is, of course, with a little help from my Lady Luck." He turned to grin at Clara.

"Mr. Stono, what can I offer you in the way of entertainment?" Memphis said handsomely as though business was done. "I'm sure you and your old friend would enjoy a drink together—"

"That, and a few hands of cards in your good company," I answered.

At most expecting me to try to inveigle Mate to Faro Jack's rooms—and this kind of piracy was greatly disparaged in the gambler's world—he could hardly believe that I meant to meet him head on in his own joint. True, this would be almost certain protection against physical attack. Bloodshed here would close him out and bring him before the unbribable and severe judge of the Richmond court. But by what conceit did I imagine I could win?

I was counted a good player, but too young a hand to match that of seasoned, cunning, clever Memphis. Faro Jack and I had purposely encouraged this report, to draw trade away from him. Memphis believed it utterly. So he solved the mystery by the gambler's way of thinking—either that I was enjoying a run of luck, or getting too big for my breeches. He believed he knew the right medicine for both.

"A social game, I suppose," he remarked blandly.

"I thought we might put out two hundred each, and declare a reasonable sum." The latter would represent the most any player could draw upon, and hence, plus table stakes, the most he could lose.

"Why, that would make a nice game. There'll be no crowd tonight—the middle of the week and almost the end of the month—and we wouldn't be interrupted. What do you say, Mr. Mate?"

"Clara, do you think I can win tonight?" Mate asked.

"I think your luck has hit the bottom and tonight will turn back."

"Then I'd enjoy it very much."

"What game would you choose, Mr. Mate?" Memphis asked.

"I'll leave that to Edward."

"Then I'll say twenty-one. Then both luck and skill will tell. And I'll declare two hundred above table stakes of the same sum." And Memphis made the same declaration.

"I'm with you, but if I lose you boys will have to stake me to bed and board until I can draw on my long-suffering banker," Mate said with his wistful smile. Then he turned to Clara and took both her hands.

"Memphis, do you agree to a head-to-head game?" I asked in an undertone. Clara was talking so gaily there was no danger of my being overheard.

"I wouldn't sink to any other kind, tonight," he answered,

his placid blue eyes on mine. And I could take that any way I liked.

In a minute or two we were seated at a cloth-covered table, Memphis and I opposite each other, Clara perched on a low stool beside Mate. The table stakes were stacked in bills in front of each player. Whiskey and glasses stood in easy reach.

The play began—and I became aware of an old haunting. I wondered if anyone enjoyed gambling—taking real pleasure in it—and at my choosing it as a road to fortune. At best it was a most melancholy road. It was more lonesome than the path the mountain men took in the Far West to gain their pelf in pelts. The mountain man climbed mountains. He saw scenes of grandeur, forests and waterfalls and deer drinking and the herds of buffaloes, firelight at night instead of the monotonous lamps and the strained mirthless faces of his opponents and cards shuffling and falling. The cards were time-eaters. In most games, for most players, that was all they were good for. They did not make for human sociability as did the long silences of chess, but for withdrawal from one's kind. There remained a strange, unpleasant passion, a kind of lust, that could not brook the least delay in the fall of the cards. The dealer must pick them up quickly and get on with the game. The winner must play fast, while his luck was in him. The loser must play fast, for his luck to change.

No luck was running in this game tonight, except Mate's bad luck in contesting such players as Memphis and I. The deck was cold, and the cards fell about as the laws of chance would decree, when Chance herself had turned her back on the play. Such hands as Memphis and I drew we played with caution. Our stakes of bills grew slowly, fed from Mate's dwindling stacks, but one was hardly higher than the other. Actually neither Memphis nor I was gaming in the true sense of the word. We were playing expertly but with no brilliance; perhaps we were both waiting for the coast to clear.

That would not be long. Midway our second hour of play,

Mate lost the last bill of his table stakes and drew upon the sum he had declared.

"My luck doesn't seem to be getting any better," he said with a weary smile.

"It will now," Clara mouthed. "You mark my words. Memphis could tell you how many times he's seen it turn when a player has to dig down."

But she did not look at him as she talked nor did she bother to throw any false conviction into her voice. He was hooked for what else he had; and her jaybird-sharp attention had become fixed on the play between Memphis and me. A thought had struck her that she could not credit but which brought a flush of excitement to her cheeks and a fascinating sheen on her eyes. Memphis and I were playing about even. Neither of us was crowding the other or burning up the deck, but she had thought to see Memphis far ahead by now. And so far, as no one knew better than she, we had played head-to-head. Was it possible he had met his match?

I grinned to myself and thought, "Has he met a sharper worthy of his steal?"

But I did not tarry long over the bad pun, nor with Clara's foxy mind and carnivorous nature. I was arrested by Mate's somewhat delayed reply to her hollow words of encouragement. Evidently he had considered them well and they had thrown a kind of shadow on the wall.

"No, my lovely little girl," he said quietly. "My luck's not going to change tonight and I doubt if it will ever change. I'm one of those fellows. You've seen some of us before. Fairies come to our borning. They bring us every gift man could desire. Fortune—rank—love—beauty in many forms. But we want none of them. We throw them all away. There's only one thing that we want. Do you know what it is?"

"A drink, I reckon," Clara answered pertly.

Mate paid no heed to the dreadful insolence. He never looked for anything like that or recognized it when it came. My hand quivered to slap her and refrained, not from the amount of gentlemanly training I had managed to absorb but because the end would be tragicomedy beyond bearing.

"Do you know, Edward?" Mate answered.

"Yes, sir, I think I do."

"Well, we get it sooner or later, every damned one of us." Falling silent, he looked at the two cards Memphis had dealt him, one of them a face card and the other, I thought, a seven, judging from my last glimpse of the shuffle. "Memphis, hit me again."

3

Almost all high-ranking card sharps can predict, roughly or with amazing exactitude, the run of the cards as they deal. It is a matter of keeping track of them during the shuffle, recognizing many of them, predicting the position of many more. A highly expert gambler may appear to look you straight in the eyes as he shuffles, let you cut, and still know most of the cards he deals you. However, it requires intense concentration and an amount of mental labor which most gamblers cannot force themselves to exert, except during high and exciting play.

In an odd way it was comparable to rifle and pistol shooting, at which many of the Low Country aristocrats surpassed. Good enough shooting, even fine shooting can be pleasurable; but to achieve a great shot—holding with immeasurable closeness and touching off in the right thousandth part of a second—demands an expenditure of nervous energy and puts a strain on body and brain that few riflemen can endure.

A few gamblers can keep track of the cards while an opponent shuffles. The feat is far more difficult and rare, requiring vision and what seems an almost psychic interpretation of things seen. Often such players know where cards are without awareness of having seen them, either through a kind of unconscious vision or some mental process even more mysterious. I had demonstrated some such gift on my last visit to Faro Jack's rooms in Charleston. Since then it had undergone cultivation and enhancement. Sometimes, usually late at night, when my nerves were alive and tingling like those of a hunting wolf, I knew the positions of the fifty-two cards in a shuffled deck almost as well as a pianist knows the eighty-eight keys on his board.

Tonight I had proposed that we play twenty-one because it would employ only a small part of the deck and hence lend itself to the uses of this special skill. About two o'clock in the morning, when Mate lost the last of his declared money and withdrew from the game, the iron was almost hot enough for me to strike. Memphis' ordinarily pale face had darkened from smoldering anger that he had not downed me yet; his eyes had a sullen look and his voice had coarsened. At my next deal he raised his bet from ten to twenty dollars. I took that hand, he the next two, I the fourth, having won by blackjack. As it was again my turn to deal, he laid down a crisp fifty-dollar note. The air in the ugly garish room seemed to swirl from some unknown force. Mate sat brooding, hardly watching. But on Clara's face was a flush of excitement as red as her lips.

Luck gave me an easy victory with two face cards. But as I picked up the cards to deal again I had a feeling they were not right—perhaps a hunch, as a gambler would say—and I employed a little trick—actually nothing more than a free-hand lighting of a cheroot—that suggested confidence in a run of luck. Taking the strange bait, Memphis bet only ten. My hunch, or whatever it was, proved true; the first two cards I dealt him were a ten and a jack.

It was now again Memphis' turn to deal, and his fury at his puny winning brought out his old weakness, and I knew by his eyes that he had turned reckless. I laid down a hundred dollars which he matched with a quick, pugnacious gesture. I watched his deal with all the eyes in my head and did not cut. He dealt me an eight and a three. The next card—I knew it past all doubting—was a six, but close to it, perhaps adjacent, were a face card and, I thought, a seven or a nine. Also there was an ace somewhere near the top. Yet I felt fairly certain there was a red four between. I asked to be hit, got the six, and then was faced with one of the hardest problems I had ever met with in the dens.

Eight and three and six made seventeen. Another four—if it were really there—would make twenty-one. If Memphis got it, then was hit with a face card and a seven, he would have twenty-one. If the supposed seven proved to be a nine, he would break his hand. If the four was not there—if my vision failed me—his first two cards would give him a count of seventeen or nineteen, tying or beating me. Then if he were in the mood to deal himself another card, I thought it would be an ace.

My confidence grew that the top card was the four of diamonds. If Memphis knew it, he dared not palm or shift it, for my eye was on him. More likely he thought I had seen the ace, the most quickly visible of all cards, which he knew was on or near the top. So I let him sweat a few seconds more. I could have sixteen, more likely seventeen or eighteen, he thought. Call on sixteen, stand on seventeen—that rule-of-thumb was ancient as the game itself. The beads came out on his big bald brow and his pale wicked smile was a cheat. And he had settled it with himself—except for one cold little draft blowing on his heart—that I would stand when, replying to his smile, I asked to be hit again.

He had no choice but to deal me the card and there it lay, face up on the table. When he saw it was not an ace and instead a four, his eyes bulged and Clara uttered a stifled shriek.

The last play of the hand was bound to be anticlimactic, but I enjoyed it, sitting there with an unbeatable score of twenty-one. Memphis dealt himself two cards, which I felt sure were a black face card and neither a nine nor a seven, but a ten. Now only an ace would improve his score; any other would break his hand, yet he feared to the depths of what served him for a soul that I had twenty-one. But I might have twenty, to tie him, or, fishing for the ace, I might have broken my hand.

He decided to stand—perfectly good twenty-one in any safe and sane play—and to his great bitterness and chagrin lost his last chance. This changed to wormwood, unspittable from his mouth, when he stole a look at the next card—the one he would have drawn if he had not stood—and it was an ace.

Memphis wondered if luck were running against him, for he still would not believe that I could outplay him. He bet only twenty dollars on the next hand, which I lost, but I placed forty on the following hand and won it by sheer luck on blackjack. Now he was growing rabid and restless, as was his wont when cards ran against him, but I did not expect him to break his given word, for that is the gambler's pride. There is honor among thieves and this, besides his skill, is his only pride, for his diamonds and fine dress are mockery before God and man, as he knows full well in his heart. But Memphis did break it. As he picked up the cards to hand to me, he palmed the ace. When, having shuffled, I let him cut, he slid it to the top of the deck.

It was a wonderfully deft maneuver—I had never given Memphis his full due as a sharper, but he was the least bit afraid I had seen him. Perhaps he was becoming suspicious of the sharpness of my eyes or that Luck, that fickle goddess of the dens, had turned her back on him. But his confidence was instantly restored as he looked at his second card. Color came back to his face and triumph to his soul. Even if I had not placed it for him, I would have known that it was a face card, giving him twenty-one.

Dealing myself a face card and an eight, I stood on them and lost. And now I was facing an entirely different opponent. He could take me, his hunch told him, any time he liked. What he had thought might have been card-reading was a piece of folly shot full of luck. To strengthen his illusions, I cut my next bet from forty to ten dollars, which I won on blackjack.

"I'll play you only one more hand," I told him. "You began the deal, and I'll end it. I intend it to be the *coup de grâce.*"

"What does that mean?" he asked contemptuously.

"It's a French term. My mother is of French descent. It might be said to mean the satisfactory end of a conflict."

Then Mate, who knew perfectly well the meaning of *coup de grâce*, started up out of his lonely reverie and stared at me.

"So you're an educated fellow!" Memphis mocked in polite tones. "Why, I'm glad to know it. And if this is to be our last hand, with you dealing, I'd like your opinion as to suitable stakes. My own idea would be to make it worth while." For Memphis felt the power and the luck within him, and did not remember that the same feeling had set many a man on a course to ruin and despair.

"Thanks. Suppose you lay your bet, giving me the privilege of halving it or doubling it."

"Then I say two hundred dollars."

He smiled his strange, foxy smile into my eyes.

"Well, it's late—and I'm playing a good part with Mate's money, so I'll double it."

He stared, but remembered I was a fool and took heart. When I shuffled, I let him cut. That did not stop me from dealing him eighteen points; I was too vengeful to let him off with an easy defeat. I wanted it to sting. I planned to have it rankle many a night. I had only to look at Mate's drawn face to be encouraged in this resolve.

As I dealt him the second card, I gave him a peek at the next, and it was a three.

"Hit me again," he said.

As I did so, my hand moved a little, too quickly for him to see, and the top card that fell was a five. I dealt myself a ten and a seven, stood on them, and won. I did not flatter myself that the grim game was over. There might or might not be an aftermath of the duel with Memphis. I had taken him for more than four hundred dollars, about two hundred of which he had won from Mate, and that left a festering wound; but, like most gamblers, he knew a good beating when it came to him, he could read cards however they fell, and wharf rats avoid the company of other wharf rats whose fangs they fear. For the nonce he controlled his temper and even attempted a heartiness that must have hurt him like working a rheumatic arm. Only his high color and hot, dry eyes betrayed his fury.

The next hand, if it were played, would be the most crucial of the night. I had not thought of proposing it until close to the end of my game with Memphis; when I was drunk on cold excitement, when the brilliant interplay of hand and eye with the most powerful working of my mind had demanded too-long concentration, at the fringes of which lay half-madness as from a potent drug. Certainly the idea was wild in the extreme. I could not have entertained it in a sane moment. It might prove the *coup de main,* for in it was a genius of great gambling, or a stunning disaster. The fact remained that Mate was not yet free of Memphis' and Clara's toils, he was only shocked and devaluated and left to lie awhile; and since I had undertaken the half-mad mission, I must not shrink from half-mad measures if they bid fare to win.

The time was now. The excitement in the air had not yet died away. Memphis was too badly beaten to act swiftly and boldly; Mate was deeply depressed and amenable to being led; and Clara, hardly believing what she had seen, felt cold and lost and ugly. Her eyes followed my winnings from the table to my hand to my wallet. The hunger in them was forlorn instead of fierce, like a child's whose belly aches in vain, for there seemed nothing for her tonight except an unearned cursing from Memphis and a dreary rewooing of Mate, the gains from which, if any, lay in a dismal future. The money made me, however, the central figure of her present world.

"I'd like to play one more hand, with Mate alone," I told Memphis.

"What for?" And this was a sensible question for a gambler to ask.

"That's the point. He's lost his money. Still, I think I should give him a chance for a consolation pot." I turned to him, and spoke in a voice as casual and commonplace as I could make it, for this was the most dangerous instant of the undertaking.

"Suppose I put up a hundred against—well, let's say Clara's favor for the rest of the night."

At first he was not sure he had heard me correctly. By the time he had reviewed the statement, a chill doubt of everything he held by slaked his fire. He got to his feet, but not in one angry bound, nor did his eyes blaze. He was disoriented and estranged by tonight's events and quite possibly he had made a great mistake. . . .

"What do you mean by that, Edward?" he asked, in a low, shaking voice. "As far as I know, Clara is a lady. If you've insulted her, you'll have to answer for it."

"Oh, sit down, dearie," Clara broke in before I could speak. "I'm not in the least insulted—Edward and I are old friends—and if he needs his face slapped, I'll tend to it myself. Anyway, you can use that hundred, and I feel in my bones you'll win it."

Clara spoke quietly, as she had carefully learned to do, but she could not keep a blitheness from out of her tone, and I did not think she tried. She had been suddenly revitalized. Her big soft eyes glowed quite beautifully and her breast was high and she seemed to stand on tiptoe. Mate looked from her to me, and there was sorrow in his eyes, but behind the darkness was a glimmer that I thought might be hope. . . . Hope of what? Perhaps he himself did not know.

"I won't play such a hand," he said, as he resumed his seat. "I wouldn't think of it."

"Then I'll play it for you, pard. Put out your hundred, Edward." And when I had done so she asked with a faked cunning, "Will you let me deal?"

"Surely."

"I'll deal honestly, but you might as well kiss those bills goodbye."

One of them, a ten, took its departure in Memphis' resolute hand before the play began. Half of it represented the house's rake-off when patrons play among themselves. This the old sharper was never known to forget or to forgive, and I thought that he found a little satisfaction, a small sop to his injured

vanity, in the present strict attention to his business. The other
five dollars was presumably room rent, soon to be owed by the
victor. I wondered if Mate presumed the same, and whether
his now numbed face could feel the smack.

In her countless hours of loafing about Memphis' rooms,
Clara had learned cascade shuffling. It was considered a pretty
thing to see, but Mate took no joy in the sight, for it evidenced
that his stainless rose growing among brambles had been in
blossom a good while. Her next maneuver was not so pretty.
I saw it perfectly plain, Memphis could have seen it had he
not drawn off by himself to mope; and since it was unadroit,
I was not sure that Mate did not see it. At least he might suspect it from her rapid talk as she played the trick, and that
could be the dregs of his bitter cup.

As she toyed with the cards, she managed to pick four and
place them on top the deck. In descending order they were an
ace, a jack, a ten, and a nine.

"You don't want to cut, do you?" she asked me gaily. "I
know you trust me."

Perhaps for my soul's sake, more likely to palliate a turning
stomach, I started to answer, "I'll cut for luck." I started to let
Fate decide the sorry game. But if I did, the luck might be bad;
and Clara, supposedly playing for Mate, might win. I could
not imagine a more lame and impotent conclusion. I myself
had intended to cheat if it were necessary to win, to fulfill some
kind of a tacit pledge made to Salley and myself. Why should
I blame Clara when the rich smell of money was in her nostrils?

Still I could not trust my mind or hardly my heart, and I
turned to Mate.

"Will you cut, sir?"

"I wouldn't consider it, sir," he answered, his eyes on mine.

That was the real end of the game. The fall of the cards—
the ace and the jack to me, the ten and the nine to her. We
went through the motions of standing, and then showing our
cards. Mate would not glance at them, I said nothing; and a
look, perhaps of fear, perhaps of remorse, crept into Clara's

face. Whatever it was, its stay was not long. I saw her pull herself together and turn with faked earnestness to Mate.

"Edward won, dearie. And he won fair, 'cause I dealt the cards myself. When the luck's with a fellow, it seems like he can't lose."

"Very well, and I'll be on my way."

"I hope I'll see you again before long."

"I'll see you in hell, I expect."

"Why, that's no way to talk—"

"Be still, Clara, and go on up," I ordered. "I'll join you in a moment."

She started to protest, but the cheapness went out of her face, God knew where, and she rose and walked with irrefutable grace to the stairs. These were white and broad and beautifully curved and had a mahogany banister, and belles had descended and brides had ascended in years gone by, when this house was a home instead of a pit of heartbreak. No bride ever mounted with a more queenly air. And the Devil was in Mate, too, for he stood in a kind of attendance upon her departure, and did not move until she vanished from sight.

"Mate, I don't expect you to speak to me," I said. "But will you wait in your hotel room for a communication from me? I'll dispatch it in a few minutes."

He nodded and went out the door. I had Julius bring me pen and ink and sealing wax, and going into an anteroom I wrote rapidly and briefly:

Dear Mate:

Once you stayed away from a party for my sake. I came to this one tonight for yours. I am returning the four hundred dollars that you lost. I most earnestly request that you keep the sum and return to Charleston; and you will deprive me of a great satisfaction if you refuse.

Edward

Putting four one-hundred dollar bills with the letter, I sealed and addressed the envelope and, going into the street, put it into the trusty black hands of a cabdriver I knew well. He promised to deliver it personally to Mas' Hudson at the Planter's Hotel within twenty minutes. Then I returned to the rooms to the desolate duty of winding up the game.

When I had climbed the stairs, a door opened in the hall. I entered it to find Clara ensconced in an easy chair, a drink at her elbow. Her eyes were alight and she could not wait to tell me something.

"It wasn't fair to Mate," she said, "but I stacked that deck."

"It's no news to me," I answered.

"Was I that clumsy? I hope Mate didn't see, because it would hurt his feelings, and I'd hate to do that." She paused and looked at me sharply. "You don't seem very grateful."

"I am, though. It saved me from rigging a deck against an old acquaintance. Now he's left the joint and you are free to go."

She echoed the last word—"go"—without emphasis. Then her breast rose and I thought she was going to burst out with something; instead she let go her breath slowly and in silence. She turned a little so I couldn't get a full view of her face. And suddenly I felt no longer vengeful for Mate's wrongs and only a desolate emptiness was in me and I was alone as on a desert island, and yet somehow Clara was with me there, and we had both arrived there in the same boat. It was like a bleak dream from which I yearned to waken.

"Let me get this straight," Clara went on, after a long pause. "You said I was free to go."

"Yes."

"I'm always free to go, or free to come. That's the one thing I get out of it—the life, I mean—perhaps I should say the only thing I've kept. I was born free and I'll die free. But what I want to know is—and pardon my curiosity—do you want me to go? It doesn't seem quite in keeping with the job you put up on Mate."

"I put it up on you too. I had to. I was paying off a debt. At first I didn't mind jobbing you—Mate would have gotten kinder treatment from a bitch jackal—but now I'm sorry it was necessary. You're not to blame for what you are. The fact remains I never intended to collect that bet, it would be a physical impossibility, and if you'll take twenty dollars and get the hell out, I'll be greatly relieved."

She walked aimlessly about the room. She was pale except for a high flush on her cheekbones and her prettiness was so marked that it would be mistaken for beauty. After a moment she stopped and looked at me.

"You're not to blame for what you are, either."

"I don't know about that."

"Do you know what you are? A tin-horn aristocrat. A card sharp trying to be a gentleman. Well, you'll never make it as long as you live."

"Well, if Mate goes home—and I think he will—and you'd better not do anything to keep him, and I mean that, Clara—"

"What would you do, kill me? I think you might kill me. I'd about as soon have you do it as what you did."

"Will you leave him alone?"

"Yes, I'll leave him alone. I'm truly afraid not to. Now what did you say would happen when he goes home?"

"I'll feel like a gentleman—for a little while."

"You never can. That's the joke of it. If you can feel like one, you are one, but you never can. The white and the black sheep are separated before they shed their milk teeth, and all the king's horses—and all the king's men—"

"Do you want me to go down first, or will you?"

"I will, but will you do a gentlemanly thing for me before we go?"

"If I can."

"There's a book on the table. Somebody left it here. Will you read it awhile? I won't disturb you."

My head swam and I did not catch her meaning.

"You fool," she said in bitter scorn of my amazement. "Do you think I want Memphis to know you've kicked me out? He'd cut my percentage tomorrow."

"I'll be glad to read the book a little while."

The book was a slender volume of tales by a little known Virginian named Poe, and I soon lost myself in it. Before long, Clara rose and spoke.

"I'm going now," she said distinctly, "and I want the twenty dollars you promised."

"Here it is." I handed her the bill.

"You poor bastard." And with that, with her graceful carriage, she walked out of the room.

4

The walk home from Memphis' rooms was of only a few blocks, with lampposts at the corners. There was no sound but my own footfall, weirdly loud in the silent night, and although I watched for wayfarers who might have grim business with me, I saw no living being but a homeless dog who gave thought to taking up with me, but after a tired wag of his tail abandoned the notion. The tall, locked-fast houses with their dark windows and sleeping inmates lent an uncanny effect to the solitude. It seemed to me deeper and more infiltrating than in any swamp of gray water and moss-hung trees.

My own lamps had never burned so dimly. I tried in vain to wish for something, to feel again the old and powerful sense of being and projection that had vitalized my boyhood, but I could get no farther than a lame wanting, a sick hope, for the night's affair to be over. I knew better than to believe it when, coming in sight of our resort, I made out a cab waiting at the curb, no doubt the same I had sent to the Planter's Hotel hardly an hour before. Its old black driver, Bruno, was not so quick in identifying me. I was almost to our gate before he climbed down from his high seat and removed his hat.

"Mas' Edwood, suh!"

"All right, Bruno."

"De gentaman, Mas' Hudson, he had me wait, and after he'd

done opened de envelope, he seal it up agin and sent it back to you."

"Why, that's fine." But I was not saving face in front of Bruno's black, manly, nigh to noble face. It was in the nature of a joke.

"He say to tell you he took somethin' out of it, so he could go back to Charleston tomorrow, and he thank you for 'at, and for wantin' to help him, but he was returning de rest, which he couldn't noways 'cept, and you and he was square now, and he reques' you don't pay no more mind to him or his business."

"All right, but I'll pay some to yours. Who's your master?"

"Mas' Stephen Jones, who own de stable."

"You're not a free Negro?"

"No, suh, I'm a slave."

"How much would he take to 'mancipate you?" I pronounced the word according to Bruno's understanding.

"I don't think more'n three hundred dollar, I being so old."

"Would you like to be 'mancipated? Mr. Jones is a gentleman, and he'd care for you till you die if you remain his slave. But if you were set free, you'd have to look out for yourself."

"Mas' Edwood, you ask me, suh, and I'll tell you. I was born a slave, which I couldn't help, nor my mammy neither, but I've prayed to God in Heabin I could die free."

I opened the envelope and looked in it.

"There's over three hundred dollars here," I said. "If you had it, could you deal with Mr. Jones yourself?"

"Yes, sah, I can!"

"Well, then, here it is. It's money that doesn't belong to anybody that I know of, now that Mr. Hudson refused it, and you are as good a one to have it as anybody I can think of. Don't thank me, if you please. Don't say anything, and get in your cab and drive off."

"Yes, suh."

He did exactly as I ordered him. As I turned through our gate I heard the cloppity-clop of hoofs on the cobblestones.

For the next few days I was a little anxious over every call of the postman at our door. But there was no other communication in the handwriting of the note I had received from Pine Lodge and no mail from Charleston of any kind, and I was greatly relieved that neither Salley Sass nor Mate had felt the need of penning a difficult letter. It would have taken away a little of the feeling that Salley had promised me as a reward.

BOOK TWO

CHAPTER IV

The Secret

ONLY A FEW years before, copper wires had been strung on poles along the whole length of the railroad between Charleston and Hamburg. By the brain of Samuel Morse, assisted by many other brains, electrical impulses were sent through these wires, whereby signals could be passed in the twinkling of an eye. Thus the explosion of a cannon in Fort Sumter might be known in Augusta before word of it had leaked to Upper East Bay.

On a bleak, biting, windy day in mid-January, when we sun-loving folk had already sickened of cold weather and longed for the spring, a boy from the telegraph office came riding wildly to our gate. The message borne as by a lightning bolt along the wires was for me. I opened it and read:

> Your mother stricken. Come at once.
> Dr. Sams

I held it out to Faro Jack. It was my pride, but an evil pride—maybe one the Devil recognized as his own—that the paper did not shake. He took it and read it. For a few brief seconds a mask dropped from his face and he looked like an entirely different man. Then it came back and he looked at his watch and spoke in his usual rather gruff tone.

"Well, you've got an hour and a half to catch the train."

"I could do it in half an hour."

"Yes, you could. We fly-by-nights learn to move fast, and sometimes it stands us in good stead. How are you fixed for money?"

"Over five hundred."

"If you need more, telegraph me."

"I don't think I will."

"Don't hesitate, even if you know you're not coming back."

"I have no intention of not coming back."

"Yes, but you may not. It may be you'll lose the anchor that holds you in these parts. I had a sister whom I loved. Like so many gamblers, I had no care for sweethearts, but I loved her without end. Until she died, I never got far from Natchez. After that there was nothing to hold me there, so I roved and roamed."

"I'll call on you, sir, if I need you."

"Meanwhile don't try to stand too straight. Bend a little with the gale. When a man's mother dies, he's buffeted by a mighty gale. It's as though the roots of his life have been torn out."

I went to my room, dressed finely, packed my bag, and in due course caught the ferry across the river. Then I watched the countryside come rushing up and pass, and thought upon the great trees that never roved or roamed, yet attained great beauty and venerability, I would almost think a wisdom, and who extended Christian shelter to busy squirrels menaced by weather, hawks, and men, and to pretty blithe birds with fast, tremulous hearts; and I considered the rivers deep and wide, and the rains that lashed them and their freshets that tore their banks; and I looked across the fields, chill and lonely-looking with their dried stalks, dead grass, and frostbit stubble, but as surely as spring would come they would be green again, buoyant, and vivacious.

At the station in Charleston I did not run with the drummers, rice buyers, and sea-cotton factors to the line of cabs and hacks to hire, but walked at my leisure, like a gentleman, to his own carriage. A Negro cabdriver, scenting a big tip, waved away the early-comers to save the seat for me.

But his expectations took a great fall when I named a street and number. "And I want to get there as fast as your horse can go."

The houses dwindled in size and drew in upon one another, until they were rows of shacks. The cobblestones gave way to half-frozen mud. Even the air changed, that free air of heaven of which the preachers ranted; and was fit only to give to the poor. But I made a handsome gift to the cabdriver when he stopped. Maybe I had a yellow girl, worth fourteen hundred dollars while he would not bring eight, stowed away here, and that would account for my haste. So he drove away with his nose a little pinched, but still held high.

But I had not come here to light a bright flame of life but to walk into the shadow of Death. And I knew that, as well as I had often known a certain card, greatly desired or deeply dreaded, would fall to my hand.

Quietly I opened the front door. Within I heard a man's voice through the thin walls of my mother's bedroom. I had expected to hear Dr. Sams's voice, which I barely knew; thus the familiarity of this voice blocked my mind. It spoke on—only half-hushed, in the speaker's harsh attempt to make someone hear—then my brain cleared, and I knew it for the voice of Matthew Whitlow.

"He's coming now, but don't you tell him," the shyster lawyer was saying. "You hear me, Marie? You'll hurt him, and not help him. I tell you not to tell him!"

There fell a brief silence, and then a voice, already quiet in a strange way, came through the wall as clearly as a rat's scratch in the deep night.

"I will tell him! I wish I had told him eleven years ago, when once I started to."

I had stopped in the doorway, unable to stir, then walked

with swift, light steps. Matthew Whitlow stepped out of my way and did not dare speak as I made for my mother's bedside. In a moment my arms were about her and her head was on my breast and I was hiding my face in her hair.

When the spasm had passed I turned, sat down on the edge of the bed, and spoke quietly to Matthew Whitlow.

"Where's the doctor?"

"He can't do any more for her, and has gone back to Beaufort."

"No doctor can do anysing for me now, Edward," my mother told me softly.

"In that case, sir, would you kindly get the hell out?"

"Will you remember what I told you, Marie?"

"I'll remember, but do as I please, and please get ze hell out, as Edward tell you."

"Edward, whatever she tells you—don't do anything rash. You'll be sorry if you do. You're not a gentleman. You wouldn't have a chance in the courts."

"Thank you. Excuse us, now."

He left with a certain dignity. I looked again at Mamma, and a little color had come back into her wasted cheeks, but the skin was drawn too tight over the bones of her face.

"I'm going to call another doctor," I told her.

"No, Edward." She began to speak in her beautifully accented French. "It has been a long time coming, but, at last, it has arrived. There are clots of blood in the little veins of my heart. These cause it to run fast, or slow, or miss its beat. Eight—nine hours ago there came a great attack, and I fell down, and the postman found me when I did not answer the door, and I had him send for Dr. Sams. The next attack—very soon, he thinks—it will be the last. It is an easy end for me, Edward. I will hardly know what hit me."

"Should you be sitting up?"

"I feel better to sit up. There is only a little pain in my chest and arm."

"Is there any medicine—?"

"Of course there is! See, the bottle on the table, almost full. Pour me what you call two fingers, and fill half the glass with water. I can breathe better, and talk with less effort, and feel less pain."

I did as she bade me and sat down at her side again.

"Do you want to tell me now?"

"The sooner the better."

"Are you sure you want to tell me—that you would die happier if you did? Otherwise keep the secret."

"I will die happier, Edward. You can live a lie only so long, then it turns inward and gnaws at the heart."

"What is the lie that you have lived?"

"There never was a Charles Stono."

Strangely, my only reply was a long sigh.

"There was no great house in Guadeloupe, with old retainers, no silver on the sideboard, no horses in the stables, or carriages in the shed. There were no boats lost at sea. I was the daughter of a poor schoolmaster, brought from France to tutor a sugar planter's children. He had married a governess, likewise brought from France. When my father died, there was no money, but his old friend brought me on a boat to Charleston, where perhaps I could marry a prosperous tradesman, or a foreman, or even the owner of a little farm. Meanwhile I went to sew for a lady here, for I was clever with my fingers. And—you can guess the rest."

"It wasn't Matthew Whitlow, was it, for the love of God?"

"No, the lady was the mistress of a great plantation, but her husband was tempted by a young and pretty girl—and I had grown up in the sun—"

"Who was it, if you want to tell me? I'll tell you again, you don't have to tell me. Maybe I'd be better off not to know—yet I want to know."

"I thought you would know without my telling. It was Mason Hudson."

"Mason Hudson," I echoed, hardly knowing what I was saying.

"But I can hardly believe it. That he should be the one to meet me in the park—"

"He planned that meeting."

"Then it was he who sent the—the—ten dollars."

"Don't look that way, Edward. That way lies evil. That way lies death for both of us—death of the soul."

2

I would let that go a little while, I thought. I would not look at this mean room where my mother had worked and slept for twenty years, whose ugliness and dirt and squalor she had so often charmed away with loving lies; and I would not see in fancy a mansion on the promenade where prism-hung lamps shone on warm carpets and glossy deep-red wood and curtains of damask, nor of a barony beside the river, with its league-wide sweep of rice fields, and its hall reached by horsemen and by coaches and carriages stately moving up the driveway lined by ancient oaks. My mother, who feared not Death, looked at me with frightened eyes. I would allay that fright.

"Are you ready for another tot?" I asked.

"If you please, Edward."

"What would Dr. Sams say?"

"He told me they might bring on the attack, or delay it."

I brought the glass and held it to her lips. She drank greedily.

"How many know about you—and him—and me?"

"No one, I think, but Dr. Sams and Mr. Whitlow."

"Not even Mistress Hudson?"

"No, she never suspected. She loves him greatly—and trusts him. They are a happy couple."

I knew that, it seemed, from my view of them on the beach.

"Did he fall in love—for a little while—with you?"

"I don't think so."

"Did you with him?"

"I tried not to, but couldn't altogether succeed."

"How long did—the affair—last?"

"One month."

"Did he ever come to see you here?"

"No. Perhaps he would have, if he had not feared discovery."

"Well, he's coming here now—tonight." My voice had changed subtly.

"No, Edward."

"I'm going now and get him. I want him to see the mother of his bastard son for the last time—"

"I tell you no. It's for me to say, not you. What I gave him was a free gift. I've never called on him for anything and I never will."

"His free gift was a ten-spot every month, sent by a shyster lawyer—"

"Drink a little of the rum, Edward, and compose yourself."

Hardly knowing what I was doing, I obeyed her. When I returned, she took my hand between both of hers.

"Listen. I will try to tell you something. How great was the wrong we did, that autumn month I stayed at the Barony, only the good God knows. The priests do not know, the judges would not know, he and you and I can never know. But since then I have done a wrong that I can hardly bear to go away and leave unrighted."

"Whatever it is, I take it on my head."

"No, because you are its victim. To make up for this"—her eyes moved about the wretched room—"I gave you a dream. It was a rainbow without a pot of gold. It was a bubble without substance. It may be that all your life you will chase it in vain."

I marveled at my mother's clear thought and good language, her tone low but distinct. I did not at once grasp the import of her words. Their full meaning went home to me slowly but with great power.

"I won't admit the possibility," I told her. "If I did, I'd be beaten now—and what could I do then? The dreams that men follow are hatched in their boyhood; they can't switch to some more probable dream as they grow up. Mason Hudson is a great gentleman—that was the basis of the myth—its solid foundation of fact. I think it eased your conscience in inventing the rest. Well, I've got to go far, even farther than I thought. I've got to climb high, up what ladder I don't know. What you have told me has heightened my ambition, not humbled it. Do you see that?"

I think she saw it, for her eyes filled with tears.

"Do you want me to speak of it?" I asked.

She nodded. "Who should you speak to, if not to your mother? Who has a better right to hear?"

"Was my father present at my birth?"

"No."

"But I presume he sent his old friend, Dr. Sams, to attend you."

"Yes."

"Did he care enough to look into my face?"

"He cared enough, perhaps, but he dared not do it until you were of an age to run outside and play. Then sometimes he came by in his carriage."

"I should thank him for muddying the wheels of his fine tack in the alleys of Marsh Street."

"Don't talk like that. Remember, he brought you books."

"Three hundred dollars' worth of books in all, I guess. I'll remember that, at the settlement. Did Dr. Sams tell him you were stricken with heart failure?"

"No, I asked him not to."

"Was it pride, or hate, or what?"

"It wasn't hate. How could I hate the father of my son? He had not taken advantage of me; I fell in love with him—he was drawn to me—and the rest—" She stopped, her eyes slowly growing round.

"What is it, Mamma?"

She looked at me in the silence of great surprise. Drops of sweat came out on her white forehead. Her mouth twisted in pain.

I thought to break it and run for a doctor but it seemed that she guessed the impulse and, amidst her pain, she shook her head.

It was great pain that I prayed would quickly pass. I had seen the death throes of a cat knocked down with a club, and a dog run over by a wagon, and a rabbit dropped by a hawk, and their pain was of the same order, for all that they were dumb creatures, beneath the dignity of man; and I was as helpless now as then, and the only help that could come to her was by the hand of Death. He was reaching out now. He came into the room, this mean and squalid room not fit for one so august, and at last he stretched out his hand. It was as though it lay lightly for a moment on Mamma's forehead. The flexed muscles of her twisted body slowly eased. But there was still light in her eyes as they sought mine.

"Goodbye, Edward, my little gentleman, my son," she whispered.

"I'll be true to you, Mamma. Goodbye."

She lay shuddering for a long minute, while the light in her eyes dimmed. Finally it died, and her hand grew limp in mine, and she lay still. Then as I saw her lying there so quietly, this little remnant, the gale that Faro Jack had told me would break upon me broke with great force. It was as though the roots of my life had been torn out. But I bent to it, as he had bade me, and did not try to stand erect, and so I endured it unwrecked, as had countless millions of my fellow men before me, as would countless millions to come.

For a moment I gave thought to my fellow men, and it was as though a lamp had been lighted in a dark room, it seemed that I was on the verge of a great discovery, but the vision dimmed as I remembered the tasks before me.

I closed my mother's open eyes. I drew the covering of the bed about her shoulders. Then I went to the door and waited for a passer-by.

3

Hailing from Chalon, near the Swiss border, my mother's parents had been French Protestants. Happily there was a small Protestant church in our neighborhood, known as the House of Eli's Children, and the Children themselves were poor whites settling here from the Upper Piedmont, from the mountings as they put it, blond, blue-eyed, illiterate people, fanatical in their faith. I went to their minister, known as Preacher Gale, and asked if he would conduct a simple funeral service for my mother, since our house was not fit for it. Although never a member, she had gone to a few of the night meetings, seeking I knew not what.

Preacher Gale was quick to assent. Moreover, since the word had got around Upper East Bay that Madame Stono had died, about fifty of its poor dwellers gathered to pay their last respects. They cried Amen to the fervent prayers and the roof rang with their shouting songs, strangely like Negro music. But they did not understand why I would not raise the coffin lid to give them a last glimpse of the dead. I feared they would weep and wail—not at this particular loss, for they barely knew my mother, but at the travail of life they knew full well, and at the positive way it ended. But it was what they expected at funerals, an old and universal custom, and I wondered if I, being what I was, had the right to omit it. Perhaps instead of protecting some cold clay that had housed a being I had loved, I had guarded only my own vanity.

Matthew Whitlow did not come to the funeral, and for this I thanked Heaven. But a tall, thin man, gray-haired and plainly dressed, stood for a few seconds in the door, and then sat down on one of the empty benches in the rear of the church. He stayed only a little while, and I think he prayed, and I could not dream what his prayer might be. He rose and left quietly before the service ended.

Only Preacher Gale, an undertaker, and six Negro pallbearers who acted also as sextons accompanied me and my dead to the burial ground. When the grave was filled and the mound shaped, and the others had gone away, I stayed and mused awhile, wrapped in my greatcoat against the piercing east wind. Then I was grateful for one thing that Mason Hudson had done, which was not giving me life but giving me books. In them I had found Gray's "Elegy" and, a far lesser but still great poem, Bryant's "Thanatopsis," both pertaining to this occasion. In them too I had found Poe's eerily beautiful visions of the Unseen. These wrought upon me, as I kept vigil over the grave; and turned aside some of my remorse.

In the darkness I returned to our strangely silent, empty house, and there, when the streets were empty, came a caller. It was no one I did not expect before very long; it was only Matthew Whitlow. He came in, his blunt nose blue with the cold, and his small, somewhat porcine eyes shifty with some anxiety. He gave me stock condolences in a haranguing tone, then he sat down and sprawled his legs.

"I'm a fellow to get to business right away," he told me, half-defiantly, half-complacently.

"I'm sure of it."

"I take it, you heard me advising your mother not to tell you something, 'cause 'twould do no good, but maybe harm, still like enough she told you anyway."

"She might have," I said, wondering if this would be a kind of game of poker.

"I'll ask you this. Did someone—a prominent person—a personage, I should say, according to Low Country counting—come to the funeral?"

"He appeared there."

"I wish I knew when you are in earnest, and when you're being sarcastic. I'm a blunt, plain-spoken man; I don't put on any airs. It can't be proven, there's no money for you, and if you tell it around—you'll make a lot of trouble and give a lot of heartache to a certain lady, and maybe break up a happy home. You wouldn't want to do that, would you?"

"I wouldn't likely set out to do it on purpose."

Suddenly he grinned. Mainly bluff, devoted to sharp practice, still the shyster was not without charm.

"You'd make a good lawyer, Edward," he remarked.

"Maybe I will, someday."

The grin died. "Well, see here. I don't want to hurt your feelings, but I want to remind you that both parties were free, white, and of legal age when it all happened. The same thing has happened to countless millions of people, high, low, and middling, some of the couples of the same station, some of 'em mixed as in this case; and usually nothing ever came of it or nobody heard about it; this is different only because a child was born. The gentleman didn't have to admit he was the father, but he believed he was, and he did what he thought was fair. He didn't have to do anything, mark you; he was a great somebody and the other party a nobody, as far as standing in Charleston went. If he'd wanted to be nasty about it, he would have tipped off the sheriff, and the other party wouldn't have dared to say a word and would have had to leave town."

I listened carefully. Far from his intention, he had waked in me a cold, cruel elation. It all stemmed from the fact that the "other party" was, indeed, as sure as hell, my mother. That changed everything. That knocked all of Whitlow's facts helter-skelter and his cynical logic sky-high. I need not attempt to justify what I was going to do. I would do it naturally, as a wolf kills, a snake bites. It was useless to try to measure the wrong; only God could do that. But I had seen my mother's struggles in my behalf, I had seen her take to drink and I had seen her miserably die; and now, taking a wicked pleasure in it, I could move powerfully in malice and in pride.

"For twenty-five years—" Then Whitlow stopped and stared. "No, it's twenty-three. I can't get it through my head you're only twenty-two. But twenty-two times a hundred and twenty dollars a year is two thousand six hundred and forty dollars."

"Quite a high price to pay a month's amour," I answered.

"There you go. Being sarcastic. Well, it *is* a high price. I don't

say your mother wasn't innocent when she went there to sew—
maybe she was, maybe she wasn't. But when the gentleman did
wrong, she did wrong with him. Right behind the back of the
woman who'd hired her. Edward, do you know the root of the
word bastard?"

An interesting question had occurred to me—whether or not
Mason Hudson had sent him on this mission. Presently I arrived at a negative opinion. Such an action would not be like
my ever-gentlemanly parent. Still I could not penetrate Whitlow's motive. . . .

It did not matter very much. I wished he would go, so I could
sit by the fire alone. Yet to bait him an ace—to liven up the
game a little—I asked him a leading question.

"Well, what do you want me to do? Bow and back off?"

"I don't say that. You and your ma haven't been treated exactly right. But it's the class, not the man himself, who's to
blame. They have their own way of looking at things—they're
a law to themselves. His wife, now—she was a Ravenal. He
couldn't confess to her that he'd slipped—there wouldn't be just
a big fuss, and kiss and make up like plain folks—she might
have gone home to her mother—at least there'd been a wall between 'em ever since. These Charleston aristocrats treat their
women like they were queens—although that don't always
stop 'em from sneaking down at night to some little cabin in
the Quarter—and I reckon the Missus would have come closer
to forgiving that than his staying with her sewing woman in
her own house. He did what he could for you without attract-
ing attention. Just remember he was mighty scared."

Whitlow paused a brief instant. I got the impression that he
had said more, or had been about to say more, than his better
judgment allowed. He went on in a haranguing voice.

"Edward, why don't you take a little toll? At least it would
balm your feelings, and line your pockets. Rent a room at the
Bay Hotel, and start a little game. I'll see that the management
won't bother you for a day or two, and I'll pass the word around,
and you needn't worry but what you'll have customers, and

with the biggest names and bank accounts in the Low Country.
The rice money's in, and you could take one thousand easy,
two thousand maybe, before anyone thinks about bringing a
horsewhip. Then clear out and call the whole thing square."

"That's a very sound idea. I'll think it over."

4

The lawyer moved as though to rise; I waited politely. But he
thought of the cold night and my low, warm fire, and the Devil
—or Destiny—prompted him to speak again.

"And think kindly as you can of the old gentleman," he
added in a somewhat sentimental tone which no doubt he often
used in trying to clinch a jury. The fact was, Mason Hudson
had hardly passed sixty.

"That's right." This was a Negro saying.

"I guess you've read the papers about the ball he and his wife
are giving Friday night, at Hudson Barony."

I had not read of it, my heart leaped once, then began to beat
slowly and with great force.

"No, sir."

"Well, you will. It's for their adopted niece, Miss Sass. And,
by an odd trick of Fate, your mother was making a new gown
for the girl when she was stricken—Mistress Hudson often sent
work to her, she being so expert, never dreaming of the truth.
I wouldn't wonder but the girl's engagement is going to be announced—"

"To whom?" I asked.

My tone was low and you would almost think idle. I had been
stunned and was not yet wide-awake. Yet I had long expected
this very news. It must be that I had never, in my heart, accepted it; for the pang that followed the first shock went straight
to my heart.

"I can't say for certain, but I have a good idea," Whitlow replied.

Evidently I turned white, for he looked at me in a startled,

puzzled way. For a moment I did not care; everything had gone
wrong. If Salley had told me herself in her warm voice, her
eyes fixed on mine, her head tilted back a little in a mannerism
I knew, I would have been saved this dreary sense of the cheapness of life and the crassness of Fate. Instead it had been
dropped by this shyster lawyer, who was puzzled by my pallor
because he simply could not imagine Edward Stono, Marie
Aubry's bastard, daring or even bothering to look up to Salley
Sass.

A moment passed; then the dreadful devouring instinct to
fight back, my dominant instinct, began to resurge.

"Well, what is your idea, unless it's a secret?" I asked, with
no feeling apparent in my voice other than the lively curiosity
Whitlow would expect.

I thought he was going to say Butler Mims. My thoughts
lighted on him because he was the most dominant young man
acceptable to the Charleston aristocracy, the one I hated and
feared the most. Instead he said, "To Mate Hudson, I reckon.
They've been mighty thick. And she's no blood kin, you
know, to either parent, though she calls Mistress Hudson Aunt
Mildred."

She was no blood kin to Mason Hudson, but I was. Whitlow
spoke on.

"Well, I started to say it's going to be one of the most elegant
affairs of the year. The beauty and chivalry of Charleston—and
I guess you know Byron's poems—"

"Yes, but I didn't think you did."

"You can never tell about me. Anyway, you may think it's
heartless of Mr. Hudson to go on with it, with the mother of
his son hardly cold in her grave—"

"His bastard son, remember. As you pointed out, that
changes everything." My heart was beating slowly now, and with
great force, and my nerves had begun to tingle.

"But what can he do but go ahead? The invitations are out.
What excuse could he use for calling it off? Who would be benefited? He takes no part in those affairs anyway. He'll probably

greet the guests, then go into his library to read or maybe sit with a crony or two over a glass."

Perhaps a little itch had made him speak of the glass, or speaking of it had wakened it. When he looked thirstily about the room, I went to look in the kitchen cupboard and returned with a half-filled bottle of rum. He braced himself against the raw and bitter weather, and took his leave. His manner was that of a man not quite sure of the success of his mission, but hopeful of it. Oddly enough, I still did not guess its motive.

At once I went into my mother's bedroom, and, without gazing too long at the now unwrinkled quilt and undented pillow, I looked in a closet near a window where she kept her sewing. Salley's gown was finished except for taking out basting threads, and being of scarlet velvet, as lovely a color as a scarlet tanager, it would set off her brunette beauty. Its bodice was cut rather low, I thought. That was only fair to the goddess who had endowed her with glossed and shapely shoulders and beautifully swelling breast; I knew of them and had dreamed of them without ever seeing them unbared. Charleston bucks were to have seen them, the disclosure in perfect taste, under the chandelier.

About two yards of the rich cloth had been left over—a narrow strip not much more than a foot wide, but when beautifully stitched to other strips the effect was more beautiful than broadcloth could attain. Pinned to it was a bill of sale from Charleston's most prominent importer. The bolt had been eighteen yards, and the price, to my amazement, two hundred and sixteen dollars. This had not been paid but had been charged to Mistress Mason Hudson about three weeks before. Likewise, in all probability, my mother had not been paid for the work as yet, since she had never accepted wages until the dresses she made were fashioned, fitted, and praised. The reason that Salley had not called for the beautiful gown on which she had set such store was, plain as day, my mother's sudden attack. The Hudsons and their ward had heard of it and they could not be so crass and calloused as to make inquiries about a party gown at the door in which Death had set his foot. No doubt Salley was reconciled to wearing some other dress, letting this matter wait a more suitable time.

I held up the beautiful garment and admired it. I looked at the stitching of my mother's aching but still clever fingers. Since it was fitted for a tall, slender girl, designed for a brunette, did I know anyone else who could wear it with beauty and grace?

Putting on my greatcoat, I went out into the chill, windy night. After a short walk, I hailed a cab; after a brief ride, I got down at the telegraph office. My eyes felt small and withdrawn, but very sharp, as I asked the operator for paper and pencil; and my lips were smiling in spite of myself as I wrote the message to Faro Jack.

You remember the lady who was escort to my friend Mate in recent affair. Please give her private invitation to come to Bay Hotel, Charleston, by train at once, advancing her enough for her ticket. Tell her I need her help in an elegant enterprise here and she will be well rewarded.

Edward Stono

The operator counted the words and charged me the proper toll. His key was clicking away, dispatching the message at lightning's pace over the wires, as I went out again into the howling wind.

CHAPTER V

The Ball

I HAD no fear that Clara Day would not come in good equipage for the enterprise. In our circles and better ones than ours she was known to dress well and in ladylike fashion. However, I had not expected her to bring a maid. Moreover, the latter was no young high-yellow, too pretty not to catch the roving eye, but to all appearances a very mammy of the old school, fairly fat, black of skin and snowy of hair, suggesting the impeccable respectability of her mistress and herself. She was called Aunt Nelly, and I recognized her as the long-time dishwasher of one of Augusta's most notorious waterfront resorts.

She received me openly and properly in the hotel parlor—safe from servants' eyes. In her own eyes was a glitter of challenge.

"You sent for me," she began. "I took it in good faith, and came. I hope it's not a sell."

"God forbid," I answered, for the thrust was sharper than she knew.

"You were against me the last time we played," she remarked. "You sold me down the river—one of your own world—for the sake of a Charleston aristocrat who wouldn't sit down with you at table and, back of him, most likely, a girl who might let you kiss her on the forehead but wouldn't be caught riding in the same carriage with you. But I guess that this time we'll be on the same side."

"That's an excellent analysis."

"What is the layout?"

"You're just to be my partner at a very elegant affair, and you'll have no duties other than acting as a perfect lady."

"Will Mate be there?"

"Yes, I think his engagement to a belle of the Low Country is going to be announced."

"You want me to try to block it?"

"That's ridiculous." Then, watching her intently, "What makes you think you could? I mean—still acting like a perfect lady."

"I couldn't if I didn't. Do you understand that? I couldn't fool you but I can fool him and a lot of other people. Mate doesn't blame me for what happened that night—he wrote me and told me so. Fine men like him make up stories to tell themselves about girls like me. They are beautiful stories—about beautiful, greatly gifted, sometimes even highborn girls against whom—note the good grammer—the cards were stacked. They think they've found a treasure in the city dump. Usually they won't marry us—they stick at letting us wear their proud names, showing they still may harbor a doubt or two—but they'll spend their money on us, and get all excited about us, and sometimes break up with their sweethearts at home on account of us. Even dumb girls can put it over, if they'll look sweet and keep their mouths shut. Smart ones like me can do wonders. Well, why don't we then? Why do we have to be gamblers' shills and so on, when we could be living on easy street? You don't know, do you?"

"No, Clara, I don't."

"Because an adventuress can't be happy unless she's adventuring. Because the other game is so easy that it's boring. Because some double-crossing cur like you comes along, who promises more excitement, and we let our easy fish get away to go upstairs with you. Sometimes even the smart ones figure it wrong. I thought you were jealous of Memphis getting all of Mate's money when he was from your own brier patch—maybe he'd snubbed you a couple of times or you had some other old score to pay—and, fool that I was, I thought you'd taken a quick fancy to me. Of course I wanted to keep close to that money, too—that's instinct in a girl who used to have to fight for a piece of a hoecake—so I played right into your hands. Well, you know what happened. You don't know—you couldn't—what happened inside of me. And I tell you you're taking a mighty big chance in asking me to shill for you. It may be the chance I was waiting for to get even."

"No, the game isn't big enough for that."

"What kind of a game is it?"

"I want to escort you to a ball. You are to look your loveliest and dance your best—although maybe the only one who asks you will be me. You don't have to play any tricks. You're not to try to steal Mate, although you're to dance with him if he asks you. Don't drink too much champagne, because it may raise the Devil in you. We won't stay very long. You might say we're just making an 'appearance.'"

"Uninvited?"

"Of course."

"What's the rake-off? In general, what's the idea? If you feel like telling me."

"I don't. But I'll promise you a glimpse of Charleston society, all your expenses paid, and a present worth two hundred and fifty dollars."

"If it isn't spite, it's hate. Love turned to hate—I read a book called that."

"Neither one, precisely."

"Then it's malice, the worst of the lot." Then her look changed, her eyes became soft, I felt the humanness of this predatory being, and when she spoke the mockery had gone out of her voice. "Edward, when Faro Jack sneaked me your message, he told me that your mother had been stricken. Did she die?"

"Yes."

"My mother came out of the piney woods of Alabama. I barely remember her, but I feel—I believed—she loved me, and it's saying a lot for anybody to love anybody in a cabin like ours. You ought to have seen my pa—and seen my brothers—and all my sisters but one. Well, you won't tell me, and I won't ask you, but I'll make the guess that your dead ma is holding a hand in this game. I mean you're playing it for her, probably all wrong. Where did you get that name Stono?"

"From Stono Creek."

"What's the name of the aristocrats giving the party?"

"Hudson."

"Well, I've got to have a little time to decide. I haven't got a dress that's really—"

"Put on your hat and come with me."

I escorted her to a cab and gave the driver directions. These neither astonished nor dismayed him; and in fact he drove cheerfully, confident of his tip. A neighbor woman peered out a window and shook her fist as I brought this lovely-looking girl, her cheeks flushed by the cold, to the door so lately hung with black. My purpose weakened; but when the door creaked on its hinges and scraped the boards, and Clara looked about her at the wretched room, it grew strong again.

"Oh, my God," she burst out, "was this your home?"

"Yes."

"Where your mother died?"

"Where she and I lived and where part of both of us died."

"Raised in this hovel, you can still succeed in passing yourself off as a gentleman?"

"Don't you sometimes succeed in passing yourself off as a lady?"

"Sometimes. Still, I don't think I want any of your elegant pay-off games. They're a good deal deeper than I want to go. If my guess is right, I don't blame you—"

"Come with me to the next room."

I brought from my mother's sewing closet the scarlet velvet gown. Clara uttered a little cry, and a quite wonderful change came over her. Her cheeks that had been painted by the wind had turned sallow in this dank house; now they flushed again. Her eyes, sullen and sunken-looking, began to shine. She held up the dress with a child's unbelieving joy in her face.

"I am to wear this?" she asked.

"Yes, and to have it to keep when I've paid for it."

"Who did your mother make it for?"

"Whom. She made it for Miss Salley Sass."

"The girl Mate's engaged—"

"Yes."

"Do you hate her that much?"

"In a way of speaking, although she's never harmed me."

"It's people that don't harm us that we guttersnipes hate the most."

"Speak for yourself, please, Clara."

"What did you say I had to do? Just walk around on your arm—and dance if someone asks me—and stay cold sober—and act like a lady?"

"That's all, and no more. I don't want any more. You understand that."

"You have a way of making yourself understood. Let me try it on."

Before me, smiling a little, Clara took off her own dress. Since it was a street dress, she removed a chemisette and a petticoat and slipped down and pinned the shoulder straps of her shift to accommodate the low-cut bodice. These actions she flaunted in front of me; and, as she expected, they tantalized me greatly. Still she was not the least vexed by my restraint; something that she desired more, just now, than a lover's arms was about to embrace her; her maiden-like body thrilled to its touch; she could believe in her beauty for a little while, without one wretched doubt, and what lover could give her that?

She raised it up and it was like a sheet of flame in the chill, weakly lighted room. She pulled it on over her head and worked it down over her lithe hips and her hands glided over it in love and her fingers flew at the scores of tiny fasteners. Then she stood before a tall mirror that a customer had given my mother many years ago, gilt-rimmed, finely beveled, and utterly out of keeping with the house except for an ugly crack close to the floor. Many of my mother's customers had seen their reflections there. Only one that I knew of could have been so lovely as this in the glass now, and it had failed to appear. What was not lovely in Clara, visible to my inward eyes, did not pass over. In the glass she was as she might have been, holding better cards.

She turned to me, her eyes gleaming with excitement.

"Is this to be my present?"

"That's my intention."

"What could stop it? The girl wouldn't take it, now that it's been on me."

"I never can be sure what they will do. I think I can handle it all right. If I can't, I'll give you its worth in money."

"I don't want the money. All I'd do is to live it up one way or another. I want this dress. I want to keep it always. I'll never wear it except for someone like—Mate."

"I wouldn't expect you to wear it for someone like—me."

"I started to say you, you fool. You're not a gentleman, but at least you know a pretty dress when you see one—and you wouldn't spill booze on it."

Her face twisted and she turned away. I attended to other business, including pouring drinks for us both. When she looked at me again she was herself once more, and you would never know she was at bay against the world.

"I'll follow your instructions to the letter," she told me gravely.

2

Quite a number of the guests who had plantations facing the river would come to the ball in their own slave-rowed barges.

Almost all who came out from Charleston owned carriages; the few up-in-name but down-at-heels would be given rides by their old friends. Hence there was no rush for hacks, and I was able to hire the fastest two-horse phaeton in the city. Clara and I covered the twelve miles of well-packed graveled road in just over an hour.

The trees lining the driveway were live oaks nearly a century old, to whom God must have given dominion over common white and black oaks, for these remained green and blessed and beautiful while those let fall their leaves, and let their limbs go naked in the winter winds. It came to me that no living thing could ever pass the bounds God had set down, that we could never change His giving or His withholding; that if we threw away what seemed precious gifts, He had withheld from us good taste, sense, and gratitude; that if we pulled ourselves up by our bootstraps, it was because He had given us strong arms. It was a dark view for a man as ambitious as I. And I imagined the live oaks, planted to beautify and glorify the approach to the mansion, looking down at Clara and me, and looking down on us for the interlopers that we were.

Many lighted windows glowed in the dark. A great bonfire blazed on the riverbank a little back from the sloping lawns, around which two hundred or more Negro carriage drivers and boatmen assembled—laughing and talking and boasting, I thought, though, at this distance they seemed eerily silent—and the firelight flung out over the broad flood, and showed a dozen or more barges, brightly painted, with awnings or snug cabins, moored at the landing. The footman accompanying our driver helped us down in front of the veranda steps. I bade him remain alert for my call, since our stay might be short, and my voice had the easy, pleasant drawl, with a touch of Gullah, of the well-bred Charlestonian.

I entered the hall with Clara on my arm. Bowing black servants directed her to the ladies' dressing room, me to the gentlemen's cloakroom. Divested of my greatcoat, in a dress suit of black broadcloth with a frilled white shirt, I waited for her at the foot of the broad stairs. In time with the languishing music flooding the stairway, we ascended to the wide bright door of the ballroom. My quick eyes told me much about it and its inmates in one deep-searching glance. It was about sixty feet long and forty feet wide, with big roaring fireplaces at each end. No more than forty couples danced on its dark-red floor of warm, polished heart pine; and most of these were young, no doubt the generation of Charleston aristocracy that had grown up with Mate or with Salley, the same I would have seen if I had gone to a beach party six years before. Instead of Negro fiddlers that played for most plantation dancing, the musicians were whites of practiced harmony brought out from the city. Negro servants attended huge silver punch bowls at opposite sides of the room, one of which would contain eggnog and the other champagne punch if the refreshments ran true to form. In chairs along the wall sat about twenty of the parental generation, including chaperones.

It came to me that Belgium's capital, or London, or Paris, or Vienna, let alone New York or Boston or Philadelphia, could not have gathered within this number beauty and chivalry surpassing these. The Carolina Low Country had produced an aristocracy worthy of the name. If it were not, I would have been long ago set free.

All the guests expected had already assembled. Their welcomers no longer stood in a beaming row, and now were dancing or had taken chairs. Our entrance was noticed first by the sitters; instantly their attention fastened on us, as we stood as though in complete ease, gazing pleasantly at the dancers. But I did not fail to mark the start of a thin, tall, gray man, with a high forehead and gaunt hands, as he recognized me. In that company he might have been the only one who did; but a gray-haired, distinguished-looking woman, chatelaine of the plantation, looked from me to her husband with mounting concern.

It must be that a wave of weakness passed over my father, Mason Hudson, on first recognizing his outcast son who had passed his door at last. After his first visible start, he sat utterly

still for a space of three or four seconds. Then terror drove him
to action. Leaping up, he hurried toward us. His frightened eyes
and pale face did not wake my pity and instead hardened my
heart.

"Edward!" he burst out. "Edward Stono!"

"Sir, I perceive you've not forgotten the name that I'm called
by," I answered.

"I didn't expect you here. I knew you were in Charleston but
on a sad errand. You've brought a charming lady, but it can't
be you expected to dance, so soon after—" He stopped with an
anxious look toward the row of sitters, but none had moved to
interrupt us yet.

"My mother wouldn't want me to sit at home, grieving for
her. Once she was a gay French Creole girl who enjoyed dancing
herself. And my coming here is different than going to some
stranger's house. Why, I feel as though I've come home!"

He passed his hand once across his eyes.

"I see, now," he said.

"It took me a long time to see."

He stepped closer and spoke in an almost inaudible tone.

"What are you going to do? Ruin me?"

"Not tonight. I'm going to—I read the poem in one of the
books you gave me—tread but one measure, drink one cup of
wine—or at least only two or three of each. The reception that
I and Miss Day receive, for that little while, I leave to you."

"Oh, my God! Then I'll tell the children and my wife that I
met you on the street, and condoled with you, and said something about—like—well, that if seeing people would comfort you,
to come out and call on me. No, that won't do. You're both in
evening dress. Say I invited you to the ball, leaving it to you if—
so soon—"

"Why not tell them we're intruders from the street?"

"That's a heartless thing to say. You might as well—"

"Look out. Here come Salley and Mate."

The tall handsome couple had seen us, had stopped dancing,
and were moving quickly toward us. There was no animosity on

Mate's beautifully cast countenance; I think welcome would have been there, if he had not been made aware of Salley's profound dismay.

She walked gracefully, her head lifted, her brunette beauty startling even in this galaxy of beauties, but her eyes were more round and brilliant than their wont, and her beautiful young mouth was a little drawn. Pretending not to observe her approach, yet I saw that her gown was of a rich brown brocaded in gold. She wore a comb of ancient yellow ivory in her black hair; around her neck were pearls.

I spoke grandly to the gray and trembling man. "Why, I haven't presented you to my partner of the evening. Clara, this is my benefactor, Mr. Mason Hudson of Hudson Barony. Sir, Miss Clara Day, of Augusta."

Salley and Mate joined us then, and my father, the man I still thought of as Mr. Hudson, rallied in quite a praiseworthy way. I had not realized he possessed this inward strength. In Mate's case, I thought that a certain boyish relish in the situation dulled his mature misgivings. When the music stopped, leaving all of us somehow exposed, Mate was the first to speak.

"Edward, I'll greet you in a minute. Clara, what in the world brought you to these parts?"

"I'm here for a short visit," Clara answered, in good voice. "It's nice to see you again."

"Is this Miss Clara Day?" Salley asked. She had caught her breath at last.

"I didn't expect you to have heard of me, Miss Sass."

"And that dress—it becomes you very well."

"Thank you."

"It was one my mother was making for a customer when she was stricken," I said in the intense silence. "Clara finished and, at my insistence, wore it."

"Salley, you'll want to dance with Edward, and I with Clara," Mate broke in.

"Will you dance with me, Salley, the dance after the next, provided Mate is free to dance with Clara?"

"With pleasure."

"Clara, may I have the dance after the next?" Mate asked.

"I'll be delighted."

"She's a lovely dancer, Salley, as you'll see. Now you two go and have some punch or some nog—I recommend the latter after a cold ride—and we'll meet you presently."

As we strolled, Clara's arm in mine, across the ballroom, we met with many a curious glance and a few admiring ones. We cut good enough figures, I being carefully and correctly dressed, and Clara's gorgeous gown casting a certain effulgence over us both. If any of these bucks had visited Memphis' gaming rooms, they did not recognize her as his pretty shill; it would have taken a bold leap of their imagination. I knew the faces of most of the young men and quite a few of the young ladies; but that did not mean that they knew mine; I had marked them of yore and could expect to see them here, while they had had little cause to notice or remember me. I did not see Butler Mims, who would not be misled, or Mate's older and somewhat arrogant brother, Arnold Hudson.

We emptied our cups, and when the orchestra began to play a romantic waltz came forth to dance. There came a sharp lift to my spirits. The cruel game I had played had so far given me a hot, dark pleasure, curiously like lust's, but I had found no gain but that, and to have it turn suddenly thrilling startled me greatly. Partly, of course, it was the joy of rhymed movement with Clara, one of the best waltzers in a good dancer's land. Couple-dancing, as practiced in western Europe and America, as separate from ritual dancing, is a subdued form of sexual intercourse, its only uncovert form except kissing games, and calling into play every natural beauty of the dancers, and sustaining in them a subtle excitement above and beyond their pleasure in melodic motion and in social intercourse; hence those backward peoples who wish to keep women in purdah, whether Indian rajahs or religious fanatics, do well to ban it. This form was enough to satisfy me, as far as Clara was concerned; I desired her beauty to this degree only. However, we had both entered into the dance with all our hearts, not muffing or skimping it.

Beyond that, I had a consciousness of power. It was not now, particularly, a power to hurt those who cast me forth from their lofty company, but rather a power to help myself in most adverse situations. I had never before played so boldly for the pure pleasure of winning.

My exultant mood did not wilt when two impressive-looking men, my seniors by only a few years, as I well remembered, but with the carriage of the great, came through a door. They were Butler Mims and Arnold Mason, and I guessed they had been to a buffet serving stronger drinks than these offered the young ladies. Arnold's darkly handsome face was slightly flushed. Butler looked somewhat pale as ever I remembered him, but this had never suggested weakness. They stood talking a moment; then Butler caught sight of me. He stared incredulously and spoke in an undertone to his companion. Both glanced at us and looked away. Both stood differently now, giving the illusion of increased size. That I would hear from them both before very long, I had no doubt.

3

The dance ended. I led Clara to an empty corner of the room, where conversations between us and any accosters would not be heard. At once the two men came walking toward us. As they approached I was aware once more of Butler's natural force, as well as his strong features and big powerfully built body; and I held all in instant respect; but at least I felt steady and cool.

Arnold spoke first. He attempted a tone of cold politeness that throbbed with menace. With a kind of undisturbed amazement, I remembered that he, the same as Mate, was my half-brother.

But the latter seemed of the blood, and this only of the bedroom; and just now I had no time to weigh the difference.

"Do I know you, sir?" he asked.

"I'm doubtful if you do, but of course I recognize you."

"My friend Mr. Butler Mims thinks he knows you—"

"I do know him, Arnold," Butler broke in with a strangely happy smile, evil perhaps but by no means forced. "That is, I recognize him. There's no doubt now."

"In that case, I wish to talk to you on a rather delicate but serious matter," Arnold went on. "The young woman whom you've escorted here may find it distasteful. If she wishes to retire to a chair—"

"I should have introduced you," I said. "Clara, may I present Mr. Mason and Mr. Mims. Gentlemen—Miss Clara Day. And I'm sure she is as interested in what you have to say as I am."

Clara gave them a fine bow.

"That's her name as I remember it, Arnold. I think you can go ahead now, without fear of hurting a lady's feelings."

"Well, then, I'll not mince words. The names of neither of you were on the invitation list. I want to know what in the Devil —I see no need to apologize for my language—you two are doing here."

"Let us see first if you have the right to put the question. May I ask who's giving this ball?"

"My father and mother, Mr. and Mrs. Mason Hudson."

"And who is it for?"

"Miss Salley Sass. And if you think—"

"Suppose, before you put any more ill-mannered questions to us, you ask permission of Mr. Hudson or Miss Sass."

These were high cards. The two thought about them and did not know how to respond.

"You've always had good nerve, Stono," Butler remarked. "I'll grant you that much. But I think you've overplayed it."

"In any case, will you excuse us now? Clara has the next dance with Mate—"

"Rot!" Arnold broke in, flushed with fury. "Mate is with Miss Sass—"

"Salley has promised it to me."

"I don't believe it—"

But Butler plucked at his sleeve. Coming toward us, hand in

hand, were Salley and Mate. As they crossed the floor, Mate waved to the musicians. Instantly they began to play a minuet.

"My pleasure, miss," Mate said, bowing to Clara. "You chaps will have to excuse us."

"And Miss Sass and me also—if you please, Salley."

"That was the agreement," she answered gravely, holding out her hand.

I had acquitted myself so well with the belligerent pair only because their guns were presently spiked. I had no reason to believe that the tide of battle would not turn, for now my own guns seemed silenced. Salley would not sell anything she greatly prized in order to buy safety. She knew insolence when she saw it. She had learned to penetrate trickery, and would not bow to blackmail. Still I did not feel on wholly untenable ground, and one little stroke of luck amused my inner man. This dance was a minuet, for which I had a peculiar fondness and a marked skill as well. This was natural enough, since it was the most stately of dances popular in the South, the one that had most appealed to my sense of romance, the grandest and most aristocratic.

Tonight the orchestra played it as it should be played, slowly and gravely, with great dignity; tonight too I had a superb partner. Without trying—indeed she would have had to try not to do so—Salley danced it as it should be danced, eloquent of the prides and graces of her high order.

Her steps, curtsies, turns, and even smiles and glances were at once enchanting and highly formalized; hence in the pauses, when flirtatious conversation was in order, her blunt speech startled me half out of my wits.

"I danced with you for two reasons. Otherwise I'd seen you in hell first. That last is my father's argot, but barely adequate to the occasion."

"Whatever the reasons, I'm grateful for such an accomplished partner."

"One of them is, what you did for Mate."

"I didn't do it for Mate. I don't go around rescuing fools for their own foolish sake. Ordinarily I line my pockets with fools' money."

"What did you do it for?" she asked, completing her turn.

"Partly for that kiss you gave me. The price of it, you remember, was a future kindness. Partly for the promise you held out to me—that it would make me feel like a gentleman."

"Did it?"

"It's difficult for me to know how a gentleman feels, but it was a rather pleasant feeling."

"I said—if you remember—for the last time."

"I presume it's the last time, for I've taken another course. I've another ambition, in fact. Perhaps I should say some important business has come up that I must attend to—before I can go mooning around any more after gentlemanliness."

She curtsied and I bowed at the stanza end; then she came into my arms for the soaring sweet refrain, danced as a waltz.

"You haven't asked my other reason," she remarked in the next pause.

"Curiosity killed the cat."

"I'll tell you anyway. I have a request to make—before the dance is over."

"A request won't do it. I must have a fee."

"Rascal though you are, you dance quite well."

"The two are not in opposition," I replied. "I have very quick, light hands, useful in my profession. Quick, light feet go with them, of course."

"And you've had plenty of practice with Clara. She's a beautiful dancer—as well as beautifully dressed."

"Excuse me. I forgot an important business matter. I found where the cloth of that dress was charged to Mistress Hudson. The amount was two hundred and sixteen dollars, which I have put in an envelope. Since I sold the unfinished dress to Clara, I wish to hand the envelope to you at the conclusion of our dance."

I made the long speech at the close of another stanza, when her ear was close to my lips. My fears as to its outcome—a sudden flame of fury, of which this high-breasted maiden, slender and graceful and almost as brown as a doe in the woods, would be perfectly capable—came to naught.

"I'm glad you took it off our hands. I tried to keep Aunt Mildred from ordering it—but she can't learn things are not as they used to be."

I was silent for a measure, and the dance flowed on, lovely and bright and almost as majestic as the Santee River, then I smiled and said, "I think things will be even more different in the future."

She heard me plainly and waited before she spoke.

"Because of you?" she asked.

"Yes."

"Is it a declaration of war?"

"It's only an announcement of an intention. I'll couple it with a suggestion, more for Mate's good than yours, that you don't announce your engagement tonight. If you couldn't afford that dress—which I gather—I don't see how you can afford to marry Mate. You have no dower and I think he has lost most of his inheritance. You may see the need of marrying a *nouveau-riche* such as Butler Mims. Mate had better woo an heiress. The great rice fields of Hudson Barony won't be pouring treasure into your coffers for many more years. You'll get what money they'll bring above the amount of the debts—"

"That won't be much—"

"But the good lands, the great rich plantation, Hudson Barony and the mansion by the sea wall will belong to me."

Her hand lay lightly in mine. "I wish I could be sure you are mad."

"I'm sure of it, but that won't help you any."

"Well, I won't start wooing Butler yet. I've the next dance with him, but I'll cut it—if you'll come into the library. I'd like to finish this conversation before I either break my engagement to Mate—or ask Butler and Arnold to chuck you out for the imposter, card sharp, charlatan you are."

"I'm a card sharp, neither of the others as far as I know. And

I'll come with you gladly into the library. I've been wanting to visit it for a long time."

4

Three sides of the library presented shelf after shelf of books all in fine leather bindings, their different tints and colors pleasing to the eye in the soft lamplight and the glow of a low, red fire on the fourth side. Salley dropped into a chair beside the library table, her chin in her hands, her expression pensive and strange; I walked about and admired the rare and costly volumes.

"I don't see where any are gone," I remarked in the stillness, barely and sweetly changed in mood rather than broken by distant strains of music.

"Perhaps those he gave you have been replaced by new editions," Salley answered.

"I don't think so. I think all of these editions are quite old. And the binding of those he gave me indicate that they never came from here in the first place. They were cloth and not leather —they'd been picked up for vacation or travel reading—they weren't meant to be kept in a gentleman's library. They didn't rank with the aristocrats. They were by good authors, but they'd been got on a pack saddle."

"I don't understand that last."

"It means, that among books they were bastards."

She started to speak—paused—then spoke clearly. "And they went to the right person?"

"The right heir."

"How many people know that?"

"None except a lawyer, a doctor, my father, my author, let us say, and you. And I didn't intend to tell you."

"You didn't tell me. My father told me."

"What?"

"My father was politely called a rakehell. He had some of his own, although he maintained that all were colored. His theory was, he was improving the Negro race. He was greatly amused that a Creole dressmaker from the West Indies had borne Mason

Hudson—the soul of rectitude in Charlestonian opinion—a son on the so-called wrong side of the blanket. I don't know how he found it out. And since he didn't tell me her name—or the boy's name—I never dreamed that you were he, when I met you on the beach that day."

"When did it dawn on you?"

"I thought of it when Aunt Mildred said you were a dress-maker's son of unknown antecedents. She said your mother was a wonderful dressmaker, but that didn't entitle you to associate with the Hudsons, the Ravenals, the Rutledges, the Sasses, and their like."

"You're putting it up pretty straight."

"That's the way you want it, isn't it, Edward? You yourself are not exactly subtle."

"Right."

"Then his being so disturbed over my inviting you—and I finding out he'd lent you books—and remembering your preten-sions to being a gentleman—well, I jumped to the conclusion.

"So you knew I was Mate's half-brother when you sent me to rescue him from Clara?"

"Otherwise, I would have hardly found the courage."

"Well, I didn't know it."

"Edward, that's not true."

"Didn't you say we were to deal straight?"

"But I can't believe it. Your mother would have told you long before that. Why should you have tried so hard to be a gentle-man—"

"My mother didn't tell me until on her deathbed. In fact she taught me I was one. So 'pretensions' wasn't quite the right word."

"No, it wasn't. I beg your pardon."

"Still, by asking me to save Mate, you assumed that I owed the family an obligation that the family didn't owe me."

"I suppose I did."

"Naturally enough, when I was in cloth binding and they

were in gilt leather. I had been blessed enough by this infusion of high blood. I ought to be grateful."

"I'm afraid that's the aristocratic viewpoint. You see, nobody sets such store on aristocracy as the aristocrats themselves, and their seeming so nice and simple about it—plain as an old shoe, they boast—is the last word in posing."

"How did your father treat his natural children, if I may ask?"

"He thought he'd done enough for them in giving them bright skins. But I thought he was a little more reluctant to sell them than the others, when the shoe pinched. And he took care to get them good masters."

"He should have a star in his crown for that!"

The sarcasm stung her.

"I told you he was a rakehell. Also he'd inherited some bad blood from his mother's side—one of the highest lineages in the Low Country—although his sister, who went after and married Uncle Mason, got the lion's share. Luckily, she died. Uncle Mason was set free, except for the son, Clay Hudson, that she bore him. He too is your half-brother."

"I'm beginning to believe my aristocrat relations didn't pan out very well."

"Uncle Mason is essentially good. My father wasn't, and that's why I love goodness—you may not believe that—and probably partly why I love Mate."

"My father sent my mother the handsome sum of ten dollars every month."

"Was that all? I supposed it was more—at least the first few years. Later the money melted away. And that reminds me—give me that envelope before you forget it."

I took it from my inner coat pocket and handed it to her. She put it in a drawer of a beautiful secretary, locked it up, and slipped the key into a little pleated square of her skirt.

"I suppose I shouldn't mention it," she went on. "It will only anger you more—but we said we were to deal straight. Uncle Mason always urged Aunt Mildred to send her sewing to your mother, even these last few years, after she raised her prices."

"Knowing at last the aristocratic viewpoint, it doesn't anger me at all."

"And do believe me about the money. The family's lived on a certain scale and couldn't cut it down—everything they bought seemed a necessity. Everyone's borrowed and borrowed—even Arnold who thinks he's smart—and in trying to recoup, Uncle Mason's lost a good deal in bad investments. Now, though, he's laid a second mortgage on the Barony and put the money in some fine cotton lands in Alabama, at a fourth of their value. He's going to make a real big haul, and pay off all our debts, and then everything will be as it used to be. And that's why I think a gambler with a grievance—even if he's as ruthless as a rattlesnake—can hurt us very much."

She looked up at me with a half-defiant, half-hopeful glance, yet so touching that I must steel myself to answer.

"It sounds foolish on the face of it, but I know Lady Luck—and how to woo her—and I still advise you not to marry Mate."

"One poor little bastard, against the power and the glory of the Hudsons. If I don't announce it tonight, it will be because Mate is not quite over his affair with Clara. I love him dearly—I think I always have—but I get a little tired of his derelictions."

"You may commit some yourself, but hide them better."

"I've got to go now, back to my equals. Do you like to have me talk that way? I rather think you do. But let me tell you, Edward, you're all wrong. I don't know why—but you are."

"Wrong or right, I'm going ahead. I'll own Hudson Barony. I'll appear, and the Hudson family will disappear."

"Through card-sharping?"

"No, through my wooing of Lady Luck and challenge of Fate."

"There's only one way you can hurt us, that I know of. In that way you can hurt us mighty bad. That brings me to my second request. I make it humbly. I ask that you grant it, in the name of the—noble?—yes, I'll say noble—blood that flows in your veins."

"Ask it."

"No breath of this has ever reached Aunt Mildred. She could

not possibly believe such a thing of Uncle Mason. She has very many limitations, but she wasn't to blame—Charleston was, her teaching was—for sending the note canceling the invitation to the party. She's been as kind to your mother as she knew how to be. I ask that you guard the secret from her if you possibly can."

"I promise that I will."

"For that I'll give you something to remember me by. You were entitled to it at the close of the minuet, according to the way it was danced in France. I want you to remember me as pleasantly as you can; I may have need of it yet."

She rose and bent over my chair and kissed me on the mouth, again a lovely, unstinted kiss, then she hurried out of the room.

5

When I went back to the ballroom, Clara was dancing a lively polka with Jeff Legare, the best if not all that Mate had in the way of a friend. A shy and oddly awkward man, he was suddenly exhibiting impetuosity, self-confidence, and something very like grace. I knew that Jeff would revert to type after Clara had gone, but I thought he would never forget her brief unlatching of his gates against the world, and it would do him a little good in the silences of the night, and that Clara had paid her passage.

When the dance ended I caught her eye and nodded. She joined me at once; all but concealed in the happy, laughing, moving throng we vanished from the ballroom. She went for her wraps; I went into a chamber used as a cloakroom. But now it appeared my movements had been watched. As a Negro footman was helping me on with my greatcoat, Butler Mims appeared in the door. The wan tint of his pale face seemed to accentuate the present frosty glitter of his blue eyes.

"Stono, would you step here a moment?" he said. "I've something to tell you that I don't want the attendants to hear."

"Certainly," I answered.

When I came close, I watched his eyes that would signal any sudden action of his hands. This proved needless now.

"I know why you came here, and brought the woman," he went on. "That is, your excuse for doing so. I'm one of the very few persons in the world that knows about you—I found out about it by accident, years ago—and I've never mentioned it to anyone through my friendship with this family. Your actions tonight show you've never properly gauged the difference between the two sides of the blanket."

"Do you know them?" I asked, politely.

"As a lawyer, I do, and I know them as a gentleman."

"Another lawyer tried to explain them to me not very long ago, but it may be I didn't fully grasp the point."

"That must have been Matthew Whitlow. He didn't speak bluntly enough—but I will. A bastard son has no more relationship to a legitimate son than a mistress has to a wife. His standing in good society is precisely nil. Yet you forced your way in here tonight, and by frightening a great gentleman who once amused himself with your mother you have escaped punishment. But it's coming yet."

"Would you tell me when and where, and by what means?"

"You hired Bailey's fast team of bays to come out here. Back of the stables there is a small paddock, walled in by some outbuildings. Ask Mr. Bailey to show you where it is, and meet me there at ten o'clock tomorrow morning. I'll have some medicine for you of just the right kind. If you don't come—if you try to run out of Charleston tonight—you'll regret it all your life."

"You'll be alone there?"

"Of course. What help would I need in doctoring you?"

"I'll be there." And then I thought—but I did not say it aloud, for my cunning warned against it, "It's the opportunity I've been waiting for ever since a game of toss-at-a-crack when we were both boys."

Clara was quiet and big-eyed when we started home, and before we had gone far she leaned her head on my shoulder and fell asleep. I could not account for it even by the great strain—perhaps far greater than I knew—that she had been under, for she too was a creature of the night, and I would expect her to be as wide-awake as a ferret. I was also somewhat touched by the action, she seemed so very young.

When we parted for the night I did not tell her of my engagement with Butler Mims. I had feared I would think about it a great deal and that when I went to bed it might easily keep me awake; but neither of these things happened; and the main reason was the fact that I had come close to telling him. I anticipated the meeting. I felt well equipped for it, physically and especially mentally. Many the time I had felt the same confidence when I sat down to cards.

When I had risen, I dressed carefully and had a leisurely breakfast. Exactly at ten I was at Bailey's livery stable; the back of my neck prickled but otherwise I felt a curious inner coldness, often experienced before games for high stakes. Mr. Bailey hurried to meet me and his face was white.

"You were my customer last night, and a good one," he said. "As for that other fellow, he's never spent a cent here. If you say the word, I'll call the police and stop this thing one way or another."

"Mr. Mims is waiting for me?" I asked.

"Yes, in the old paddock."

"Will you show me the way there? It's an appointment I feel duty-bound to keep, although I thank you for your consideration."

"Good God Almighty. All right. Just as you say."

Mr. Bailey showed me the little gate. I went through, closed it carefully, and walked between two sheds to the old paddock. For the use Butler wanted of it, it was almost ideal. It was enclosed by windowless outbuildings, once part of the stable, and an eight-foot board fence; and it was far enough back from the street that only very loud sounds would carry there. The ground was still as hard and free from vegetation as though horses had exercised and rolled only the day before.

Butler was waiting by the fence, a buggy whip in his hands.

Alone with me, on this closed ground, he loomed large—tall and powerfully made. I weighed a hundred and sixty, he about

two hundred and ten. No wonder he thought he could do what
he pleased with me.

"On time, I see," he remarked.

"Just about."

"I'll give you credit for that, and for not trying to sneak off—
it showed you were ready to take your medicine. But I guess you
knew you couldn't get out of it anyway."

"What medicine do you mean?"

"You know as well as I do. What do you think I've got this
buggy whip for? I intended to give you twenty lashes, but on
account of what I said before I'll give you just twelve. That will
teach you to come to gentlemen's houses where you're not invited and to bring a woman of ill-repute. Take off your coat."

"I'll leave it on, if you don't mind."

"I don't know what shape it will be in when I'm through."

"I'll take a chance on that."

"Well, let's get it over with. Turn your back."

"I can't do that either. Whatever's coming to me, I take in
the front."

"Well, if you prefer it that way—"

He advanced toward me, the whip held upright. I did not
move. As he drew in reach of me an expression of extreme cruelty
came into his face and he raised the whip above and behind his
shoulder to deal a hard blow. I still did not move, but I felt a
preternatural quickness in my hands and the perfect vision of
my eyes.

As the whip came down my hand shot out fast and true as a
snake's strike and caught its end. With all the strength of my
arm I jerked it back, and so strong was Butler's grasp of it that he
could not release it in time and stumbled forward. I was there
to meet him. Before he could begin to recover, I caught him with
my left fist on the side of the jaw.

Such power was in the blow that he seemed to raise off the
ground. But he tumbled soon enough, with me on top of him.
Now I intended to give him such a beating as I had seen, but
never shared in, on the river front in Augusta; and for a second

or two I could not understand what had tied my hands. Then I knew, and almost laughed. He was an inert mass. But even before then he had been a fool, to think I would stand and take a whipping from any man. That thought had been born of stupid, inordinate conceit. Such a man could not be my great adversary. If such a one existed, I had not met him yet; meanwhile I had greatly overestimated Butler Mims. He was not worth hating. Hatred is like love; its giving must be deserved, or it sickens the giver.

So I struck him, full force, only twice more. One blow fell under the eye, to give him something to look at in the mirror for the next week, and to waken the ribald mirth of his associates. The other was to the opposite side of his jaw, to double the shock to his brain and thus make sure he would sleep a good while. No surer soporific could be found; I had seen enough of human mauling to know that. Then I brushed my clothes—they were disarranged and dusty but unharmed—and, taking the buggy whip, broke it in about four pieces. After grinning at the sprawled, snoring, cut-down giant, I went back through the little gate I had entered hardly ten minutes before.

Mr. Bailey looked at me with bulging eyes.

"Good God Almighty, what happened?" he asked.

"Nothing to me. Quite a lot happened to Mr. Mims, and I'd like to ask one question about him. Is he politically powerful?"

"I reckon I'd say he was."

"Did he give you any instructions about disturbing us?"

"He told me not to disturb him, no matter what sounds I heard."

"Will you please obey those instructions for just about an hour? It might prove of great convenience to me."

"I'll be only too glad to, and the same with my boys."

"Could I reward you in any way?"

"No, sir. If what happened, what I think happened—what I can't hardly believe—you've rewarded me enough."

Again I gave thought to my fellow men, as in that strange moment after Mamma's death, and thought how many were bullied and browbeaten by the Butler Mimses; and I rejoiced that I had cut one of them down to size. Still I felt no great triumph, only sober satisfaction.

I would not let it dull my play. I remembered that I had so far to go.

CHAPTER VI

The Slaver

CLARA HAD been very quiet throughout the homeward journey, pensive but not petulant; and on the whole an agreeable companion. The last hour, as the train came in by Kathwood Springs and Beach Island, she told me a little more of her childhood in the piney woods of Alabama; and, looking at her soft eyes and tender mouth, the tale was hair-raising. As we neared Hamburg, she started to make her farewells.

"When we get on the ferry, we'll pretend we don't know each other," she said.

"If you think best."

"I don't want any of Memphis' bunco-steerers to see me with you. I've got to make my living, and while he never raised any brabble about our act that night—he's a gambler and he thought it was your winning—he'll never forgive you for showing him a three of diamonds that turned out a five. As for what you did that night to me—in plain words kicked me out—I'm going to consider that square. The reason is, your treating me like a lady in Charleston and buying me that dress."

"I'm mighty glad it's square."

"Did I pull off the Charleston job to suit you?"

"You did wonderfully well."

"If you need me again, call me, will you?"

"Thank you, ma'am. I certainly will."

My thought told me I never would, yet a little gambler's hunch said that I might.

We parted, and that night I sat late with Faro Jack in observance of soon farewell. I revealed to him as much as I knew of my own situation and aims. One of the latter was the winning of a fortune—something more than a "big stake" in gambler's parlance, as soon as possible.

"Have you thought how to go about it?" he asked.

"Not much, but there are new gold fields found every year or so where a good player might clean up. There are pearls in the South Seas and in the Gulf of Honduras, diamonds in Brazil, ivory in Africa. There is also what's called black ivory. Fortunes can still be made in the trade, although it's more dangerous than ever."

"That's dirty business, Edward."

"I agree with you, although I believe in slavery." And that was like saying no more than I breathed the air of the South, instead of Northern air.

"I couldn't deal in slaves—and I've never even aspired to be a gentleman."

"My aspirations have taken a fall. Maybe they're all dead. Anyway they're put away for an indefinite period. Still, I don't believe I could do it either."

"I think you'll find some better means to make your stake. To try for it, I mean. They may be on the wrong side of the law, but they won't stink up your hands too bad. You may not win, but you'll have a good run for your money. That's a gambler's hunch."

"What's behind it, Jack?"

"Well, I'll tell you. You're not afraid to take risks, certainly to your skin—I don't know about your soul. I believe in the human soul. More than that, you understand gambling. You can figure a percentage and about how the cat's going to jump

and what you can do with your head and your hands. I doubt if
you'll mess with cards, much more. That's tin-horn gambling,
at the best. I think you'll want more scope."

"There's a lot of scope when the deck's hot."

"It may be a good tool for you, in times of stress—and there'll
be plenty of those. But you've got a different look in your face
since you made that trip to Charleston—a different air—and I'm
good at noticing such things. The catch in it is—you may not
live very long. The good don't die young, and many of the great
players do."

"I won't have much to lose, Faro, except you. Mamma's gone—
I have no real friends, although, oddly enough, Mate likes me
fairly well—I have no family—no sweetheart—no fortune—no
name. My birth was an accident—there was no legal provision
for it—it was not within the care and the jurisdiction of either
the church or the law—as Butler Mims crudely put it, I have no
more relationship to a legitimate son than a mistress has to a
wife. It leaves me without protection—without the strongholds
that most men have—but also without the responsibilities. What
you see in my face may be this. I feel strangely free."

"Edward, I believe that you do."

"I'm going to act on that freedom, as long as it lasts."

"It will be mighty lonesome, I'll tell you that."

"My mother remarked once that neither she nor I had ever
been anything but lonesome."

"You had each other then. You had me. You had hopes—
although you didn't believe them—of getting that beautiful girl,
Salley—and I saw her in Charleston when she wore pigtails. I
knew her rake of a pa. Now you've got nothing but a dream.
Even that dream has changed—it never did make much sense—
now it makes even less. You know what made Cain a wanderer
on the face of the earth? He only had one brother—and he killed
him."

"I don't understand that, very well."

"I don't either. I'm saying just what comes to my mind. Well,
do you want me to put some money in your venture?"

"I wasn't going to ask you to."

"Didn't I know it! But I might as well. Easy come, easy go, as the saying is. I've got quite a little more piled up than I ever told you. I can lose several thousand, and still have enough to buy that yellow wench, a small whiskey still, and a little place on some lake where I can gamble with bass and bream. Moreover, you've kept faith with me for more than six years. That's a hell of a long time for a man to keep faith, although it's a common enough thing among women. How much have you got of your own?"

"About five hundred dollars."

"Suppose I'd put two thousand with it?"

"I could very well lose it, in one play."

"That's what I'd be giving it for, for you to lose in one play— or maybe to win. If you do win, you can pay me back. If you lose, I doubt if you'll be around here any more. That's my hunch, and you know I believe in hunches."

"Two thousand is quite a roll. You'll want some papers—"

"No, only your word, keepable if you live. And I want to say this, which has nothing to do with the money. Edward, I've been lonely too. I guess there's no class of men more lonely than gamblers, but you've eased it for six years. Do you want the notes in dollars, pounds, francs, or Spanish pesos?"

"In pesos, if you please. I'm going to start in Panama."

"How are you going to carry 'em?"

"In a money belt."

"Quite an interesting outcome to that little bit of spooning that a Charleston aristocrat and a West Indian girl started twenty-three years ago. Well, this isn't the outcome yet. God knows what it will be. Edward, I know a lot about cards—I know a lot about human nature—but what I don't know anything about—and I'll tell you straight—is Fate."

2

For nine months I roved and roamed with no gain save experience.

The first of my ventures as a rolling stone was the pursuit of pearls in the Bay of Panama. Catching the fever from an earnest, honest, but wildly visionary red-haired Scotchman, I put my capital in a bevy of oyster boats, hired Indian crews, and repaired to what my partner believed were virgin beds immoderately rich. There we put divers overside in forty feet of water, each with his basket and a signal cord weighted with a stone. The periods that they remained submerged astonished and frightened me— these were always shorter than they seemed, yet they often passed two minutes—and the amount of oysters brought to the deck was imposing; but instead of one oyster in a hundred containing a pearl, the proportion was more like one in two thousand. Worse luck, the season had not been favorable to pearl growing. A few were round and luminous, with the perfect "skin" and the glimmering "orient" of which the Scotchman ranted; but the most were scrawny, ill-shaped, and dingy.

Of my two thousand balboas invested—each was equivalent of a dollar—I retrieved five hundred. This sum I swelled to a thousand in card play against some sharpers gathered here to skin the gangs of gandydancers building a railroad between Panama and Colon; and I might have done better if my nerves were stronger. As it was, almost all of them were Forty-niners—at least they had gained the Golden Gate in the halcyon days of the Rush—and, regarding themselves as pioneers and me as a tenderfoot, they did not take kindly to my gains, and were quite equal to wiping out their losses in an abrupt, Western style.

A promising tobacco-smuggling operation from Havana to New York fetched me up with less than a hundred pesos in my poke. Then I made a quick thousand at the cockpits of Santiago de Cuba, not because I knew one bird from another, but because the faces of their breeders—"feeders" they were curiously called —reflected their ill-hidden hope, fear, discouragement, or boundless confidence in exactly the same way as the faces around a poker table. And while visiting this ancient, populous, and beautiful city, living richly at Casa Majested, I might have heard, had I listened well, some thunder rolling far off.

The great adventure awaiting me, still in the womb of time, had an oddly commonplace beginning. I had fallen to wondering whether the running of a shipload of Santiago rum, the best I had ever tasted, into the New England coasts where flowed the much more costly Medford rum, would be a profitable venture; and if so, whether I could induce some wealthy *destilador* to back me. With that thought in mind, I had scraped an acquaintance with the mate of an English vessel, presently in port. I had encountered him at one of the better mughouses on the waterfront.

It turned out that he had very little to tell me about rum-running. But in his youth he had sailed before the mast on a Bristol slaver, and the rum in his belly invoked sentimental memories of the Middle Passage. When I brought him another glass, he came forth with a piece of odd information.

"You're rolling in money, ain't you?" he asked.

"I could use a little more," I told him, grinning.

"You're from one of them rich Southern families, but you want more excitement than you'd find growing cotton. Well, I could tell you where to find it, and a big haul, too."

"That sounds interesting."

"It's no good any more, fetching black cargo from Africa," he went on. "The British gunboats are too fast, and too many good stinkin' vessels are caught or have to put their goods overside. But there's big and quick fortunes to be made in a trade yet, and not too many miles from where we sit."

"I'd like to hear about it."

"Well, I'll tell you. Then if you need a real blue-water sailor, who's weather wise, to command one of the ships you've chartered, you'll know where to find him. As you know, there's no legal slavery in Haiti, but there are more slaves there for sale than anywhere on the Guinea Coast. This is the way it happens. A third of the people—maybe a half—are just as uncivilized—heathen, I call 'em—as when they were first brought over. Of course they can't read or write. A few can speak a little French—most of them still speak an African lingo. They're not Chris-

tians—you don't have to worry about that—they worship a conjure god they call Agoon. Well, the country's overrun by bandit
gangs. You can call 'em bandits, but what they really are, are
slave catchers. The judges are hand in glove with them, and
so are the officials. If a man gets in debt—if he violates a law—
if he just ain't lucky, in no time at all those catchers have
got him and shut him up in a barracoon on the seacoast. Then
a ship comes in at night. Some are English, some Spanish and
French, but plenty are Yankee. They load with as many as
five hundred black cattle and make the little trip across the
windward passage to a port on these shores. There are two or
three ports where they're welcome, no questions asked, everything fine as silk, only the Don to take care of, but there's one
in particular that's the favorite with the shipping. The captain
of the port, the medical inspector, and the customs officer are
all the same toff. I call him that, 'cause he is a toff, as you can
see with half an eye. He came from one of them old English
families of Jamaica. He wants five dollars a head, handed to
him neat and proper, no more no less. He's going to get it, or
no business done. Then the runner—sometimes a charterer,
often the captain of the ship—can keep all the rest he can
make."

"How much is that?"

"That depends on how much he pays in Haiti. Often it's no
more than ten dollars a head, but say twenty on the average.
The sugar growers here will take the whole lot at a hundred
dollars a head. Four trips, and the bully boy can wash his
hands, wash his ship, and settle down to a pew in a Boston
church. It may not last much longer though; I'll tell you that.
'Cept for the toff I spoke of, 'twould be pretty well stoved by
now. Lately the Governor of Jamaica has sent gunboats to try
to catch the runners. That raises the risk and cuts down the
profits."

The abduction and the return to slavery of free Negroes in
Haiti seemed to me the ugliest phase of the slave trade ever of
my hearing. My flesh crawled a little at this ship's officer's eager

description, I had not the slightest temptation to seek its rich rewards, and I was mildly curious about the "toff" from Jamaica, the big gun of the trade, who would dirty—stink up, in Faro Jack's language—his gentleman's hands.

"Now there's a rum thing," the mate broke forth, his mouth slightly rounded.

"What is?"

"You didn't come from Jamaica, did you?"

"No, sir."

"Well, that toff—Captain Walker, he calls himself, but I've heard that ain't his real name—he talks a lot like you."

"In what way?"

"His accent, I mean. He says 'hoose' for house. And you know what?"

"No."

"He looks a lot like you, too. He's handsomer, I admit, but with the same coloring, and cast of feature, and something else I can't exactly name. I'll be damned if he don't look enough like you to be your brother."

I remembered then that I had a half-brother somewhere removed from Charleston. His name was Clay Hudson.

3

My seafaring friend gave the name of the slavers' port as Puerto Miramar—meaning to look at the sea. Actually it was not much more than a well-sheltered cove about fifty miles eastward of the city. The sponge boat I had boarded at Smith Key put out on the beautiful, landlocked bay and sailed up the narrow rockbound passage into the Caribbean; and the wide blue water, the white of the distant surf, the golden yellow of the sands, and the tempestuous green of the foliage, all blessed and beamed upon by the ardent sun, seemed to me like auspices of happy fortune. I did not ask much in the way of it, today. My request was a small one, easy, it seemed, for any Luck to grant. It was only that El Capitán, his English name assumed to be Sidney Walker, might bear that or any other name as long as it was not Clay Hudson. But my soul or my stomach, I could not tell which, could not rest until I knew for certain.

Surely the odds were immensely in my favor. Hereditary dwellers along the eastern seaboard from Brunswick to Baltimore said "hoose," for "house"—perhaps because of the salt air in our throats—and the same might be very marked in Jamaica. The only danger seemed to lie—and surely it was slight—in a half-tipsy English mate having deep, sure, penetrative vision. Such vision was extremely rare, as well I know. I would readily bet ten to one against my goblins.

We spanked into Puerto Miramar, and the cove with its swift-rising shores proved almost unbelievably picturesque, indeed one of the loveliest spots I had ever seen. But all was not well with the little port—I felt it, then I saw it, and at last could almost smell it. The small custom house, once ornate in the Spanish style, was falling into ruins. Probably it had not done ten thousand pesos' worth of legitimate business in the last ten years. About a half-mile back from the beach, at the edge of the verdant forest, stood an abandoned warehouse with nailed-up windows and oddly heavy doors, and, seeing it through the captain's glass, I had not much doubt of its use. Once in a while I thought the sweet fresh winds blowing along the shore were strangely tainted, as though they had brushed against something rotten.

Dressed in my best, I went at once to pay a call on El Capitán. As I waited in the entry, I was breathing slowly and deeply, a familiar sign of trying to steady myself before a crisis. In a few minutes a Cuban lackey showed me into his office. As he rose from his desk to greet me, I thought—I believed—I could almost, not quite, be sure I had made a wild-goose chase to a happy ending. As far as I could tell at first sight, Captain Sidney Walker, so-called, did not resemble closely any Hudson I had ever seen, including a disqualified one I saw in the mirror. What resemblance there was, it seemed to me, lay in his having the marks of ancient lineage.

It was no wonder that the ship's officer had called him a toff. He was delicately made, soft-voiced, courteous in the extreme, even with the air of diffidence. True, there was something in the bony structure of his face that haunted me. Long ago I had seen one of similar composition, which an artist would find beautiful to paint, but I could not think who it was, and forced it from my mind. His nose was rather large in the Huguenot style, but more Roman, more aristocratic-looking, than any Hudson's. His eyes were dark and I confessed them to be set somewhat like Mate's, but instead of a deep glow they had a brilliant sheen. His lips were perfectly molded and rather sensuous. His hair was as elegantly black and fine as that which grew on the small proud head of Salley Sass.

This last gave me a little jar. I remembered—I knew it by heart—that Mason Hudson's first wife had been the sister of Salley's father. If, against my judgment, and hope so deep I did not try to rationalize it, this renegade was indeed Clay Hudson, he was Salley's first cousin.

We spoke of the weather, the brilliance of the vegetation, the wonderful blue of the sea. It could be Charleston that I heard in his accents, but also it could be the old English aristocracy of Jamaica. Accepting me as a gentleman, he served me a tot of well-aged Santiago rum. He raised his glass with a little toss that worried me. Englishmen whom I knew did not do so. It was a drinking mannerism of the Low Country.

"How may I serve you, Señor Stono?" he asked presently. For I presented myself under my own name—all I had in the way of a name—quite certain that it would mean nothing to Captain Sidney Walker, whoever he might be.

"I have available some capital which I wish to invest for a quick turnover at a good profit," I answered.

He lighted a cheroot with a hand as fine and delicate and almost as small as a lady's.

"I won't say you've come to the wrong place," he replied.

"Is there anyone in hearing?"

"Shut that door, and there won't be." And when I had done

so, "Please speak frankly, sir, and to the point, as I'm somewhat pressed for time."

"I realize that a much greater return could be made if I began my operations in Haiti," I went on, "but also the risk would be much greater and, frankly, I wouldn't feel competent to back an entire venture from its beginning to its end. I thought, though, that since the next captain who moves in here may be eager to dispose of his cargo and set sail, I still might do quite well."

"You are an American," he suggested.

"Yes, sir."

"From somewhere about Charleston, to judge from your accent."

"I was raised in Charleston."

"There is a creek near Charleston in which I have run a few times, when I was in—shall I say?—the more active side of the business. It is called Stono Creek."

"My name derives from that part of the world."

"You are quite right that the big hauls are to be made by backing a venture from its beginning in Haiti to its end in a deal with sugar planters on this island. However, as you suggest, often the captains have no backers, use their own capital which is usually limited, and are glad to sell their cargoes at less than fifty per cent of their worth and beat a swift retreat. Even at that, they do quite well."

"Their cargoes are delivered safe and sound on shore?"

"The usual practice is for the buyer to pay earnest money, say about ten per cent, to the owners, the balance is to be paid when the livestock is locked in the barracoon. Also, at the time of settlement, he pays an import tax of five dollars a head directly to me."

"Isn't the cargo subject to confiscation by the Cuban government as long as it's on shipboard?"

"Nominally, yes, but it never happens. The cane that furnishes Cuba's sugar and rum, her only exports of importance, can't be grown without steady importation of black cargo. The dons know this—and look the other way. Because there is a good deal of fever in and about the fields and the mortality rate is quite high, the demand is always greater than the supply."

The trouble with slaving was—so I thought in some gray corner of my mind—that while you could use such terms as live-stock, black cattle, and black cargo, every once in a while you had to use words that plainly referred to human beings, such as mortality.

"I don't question that; nevertheless I couldn't make any payments until the goods are safe on shore."

"If there are several buyers present, you might lose out. If not, the owners would no doubt bow to your wishes."

"What I took for the barracoon is at the edge of the tropical forest. If some would break away, they would be hard to catch."

"Not merely hard. Almost impossible. Away in the forest dwell what are called the maroons—runaway slaves who live like their forebears in Africa—and they are always ready to help other fugitives. But the windows and doors are solid and strongly bolted. Also there are six guardsmen employed by each buyer in turn to keep watch with loaded rifles. Not one has ever escaped from the barracoon itself. The five that we lost some years ago broke away while being marched in from the ship; they had chewed their neck ropes in two. The guard who was supposed to be watching that part of the line had dropped back to make advances to a beautiful quadroon. I could only have him whipped, not hanged, but I assure you the job was well done."

He spoke more softly, toward the end, and there would have been charm in his voice if I could ignore the words.

"I'd consider that a very good record," I remarked.

"Our perfect record was smirched," he answered coldly.

For some reason I could not quite trace I was frightened, and becoming more frightened as the conversation continued.

"The present danger to the traffic lies at the other end," Captain Sidney Walker went on. "Ultimately it may prove quite serious. Already the Governor of Jamaica has had two gunboats put at his disposal to intercept the ships in the windward passage."

A remarkable expression came into the beautifully molded face.

"I judge you don't take kindly to that, Captain Walker," I remarked boldly.

"If you had been present—as I was—at the slave insurrection in Jamaica in 1831, you would not take kindly to it either. That was twenty-three years ago. I beg your pardon—it was not, strictly speaking, an insurrection—the events were caused by a false report that the slaves had been emancipated by royal decree. Bands of them started immediately to kill, rape, and burn. Among the people murdered were my father, my mother, my elder brother, and my elder sister—I, being sixteen, and in charge of my little sister of eight, watched the butchery through a crack in a cabinet door. Perhaps I have not been quite a normal person since. Certainly I have not gathered near as much pelf as I might have—as the opportunities offered—as the risks justified—simply because I have taken such joy in the work itself. I am not interested in the importation of African savages. Those I wish to see wearing chains are the blacks who have been emancipated—a beautiful word—who have tasted the joys of freedom—and now go back where they belong. I am glad to report that more than one shipload has come from Jamaica itself, right from under the noses of their emancipators from Great Britain; and of course I haven't forgotten the tales of the slaughter of the whites occurring in Haiti in 1804. In other words, Mr. Stono, my activities here—I can proudly say I have been the central figure in the importation and return to slavery of something over ten thousand emancipated Negroes— are only a small part motivated by my financial requirements. Almost altogether the labor is one of love."

He meant that it was one of hate. It seemed I had come face to face at last with human hate, without mitigation or forgiveness. Such hate was well accounted for by the story; I could understand how, under these circumstances, a scion of one of the aristocratic Jamaica families could become a slave dealer of the most repulsive sort.

But there was one thing wrong with the story, a serious thing. It was a lie from the first to the last.

I remembered whose face it was that I had seen, long ago, with this same beauty of bone structure. It was Mate Hudson's face, the first time I had met him in the Battery.

A cold wind blew upon my soul, for at last I knew.

<h1 style="text-align:center">4</h1>

What I did not know or could hardly guess was the next play. One choice I did not have was to pass. I could think of no reason. I longed to say polite farewell, go out the door, leave the port, and get out of Cuba. This game was going to get worse. I could feel it in my bones. The bad cards were on top of the deck, ready to fall.

Instead I kept my countenance with an aroused will, kept secret-telling tensions out of my body and especially out of my hands, and continued the conversation on an oblique course.

"It would give me great pleasure if you would dine with me tonight," he told me, when I rose to leave.

"I accept with many thanks," I answered.

He did not bother to tell me how to find his house. Evidently any dweller of the port could direct me there. It proved to be a *casa* of considerable sumptuousness, perched on a windy hill. Happily I had dressed formally, for I found him so. We dined at a table of San Domingo mahogany that must have been seeded close to Columbus' time; on a patio before a cool fern bed watered by a copious spring. The Spanish wines and the fricassee of wild guinea hen were beyond praise. The servants were all Cubans, some showing a dash of Indian blood but none a trace of African. The cloths were of ancient lace the color of ivory.

Meanwhile there was no sign that he knew or suspected our

strange brotherhood. Clay Hudson was about seventeen years older than me, and had left Charleston only two or three years after I was born. Nor did it cross his mind—unless I was badly fooled—that I had connected Captain Sidney Walker with the renegade son of a great Charleston house, named Clay Hudson, whom I had never seen.

After dinner he took me through the drawing room on the way to a cool veranda. On one wall hung the reproduction of a coat-of-arms, beautifully worked in silk, framed in gold, and under glass. Without appearing to glance at it, I perceived it in every detail. The name appearing there was not Mason nor was it Sass, his mother's maiden name, but Ashley, the maiden name of his maternal grandmother.

"Mr. Stono, are you of a mind to pursue the business you mentioned at my office this morning?" he asked, over our liqueurs and cheroots served on the breezy veranda.

"I would like to look into it, sir," I answered.

"The reason I ask, tomorrow a schooner is due to arrive from the Bay des Gonaïves, in East Haiti. I intend to go out and meet her in my gig—my usual custom when a ship hoves in—to see she has no plague aboard, and no contraband. If you would like to take the jaunt with me, you'll be welcome—and comfortable. If you care to talk to the captain on that matter, it would be a good time."

"I will accompany you with pleasure."

I left shortly, to spend the night in an old-fashioned Spanish tavern. All night I was prey to wild or troubled dreams, and always it seemed that a clock was about to strike, ushering in the most critical hour of my life. But there was no sign of it when, at an agreed and common hour, I met Captain Walker at his private dock. Every visible prospect was of a pleasant brief excursion out on the rippling sea.

He appeared in gay spirits. He wore the antique official raiment of the Captain of the Fort—cocked hat, white scarf, long blue coat with gold buttons and epaulets. His gig had bright paint with a striped awning and comfortable seats; the water was of matchless blue; balmy weather lay upon the land without excessive heat; the wind blew mild and cooling. Our crew was of brawny, sun-browned Cubans, most with fine mustachios. Seabirds flocked to see us off, delicate terns to rowdy pelicans; and the wings of gulls flashed like mirrors in far-off sunlight, and great white fishes leaped. On the journey out, Captain Walker discoursed pleasantly and intelligently on the flora and fauna of the islands. He was expert on these matters.

About three miles offshore we came in plain sight of a schooner, spanking in with all her canvas spread. It was the detail that made perfect to the sight this sparkling seascape. When she saw us, she heaved to, and while she waited for us to come up, her crew began to perform a duty which, at first, distance prevented me from distinguishing. I could make out squads of four men each coming up from below, carrying something on what might be a wide plank or a strip of canvas. The object was in each case dropped overside amid a pretty blue-and-white splash of water.

Suddenly it occurred to me that the objects were curiously rigid, black in color, and about the size of human beings.

I controlled my voice with great care.

"What in the Devil are those men doing?" I asked. "I can't make out."

"They are jettisoning a few pieces of cargo that didn't stand the trip."

"Well, there seem a good many. You don't think there's any plague aboard, do you?"

"She'd have run up her yellow flag, if there was. I've counted only about ten. Almost always the ships lose from fifteen to twenty-five. I can't tell you why, except they were weaklings to start with, and the crowding—and the bad air—and the realization that they're going back where they belong takes them off. Yet sometimes burly fellows that you couldn't kill in ten years in the fever swamps go out like a lamp in one night. The cap'n hasn't had a chance to dispose of them before now—I suspect he caught a glimpse of an English frigate."

Captain Walker spoke of other matters. The dumping went on a while longer—my count of the pieces of cargo spoiled and thrown overboard was sixteen—then the procedure changed. Instead of jettisoning the black forms brought up from below, they were laid along the rail amidships. There were about six of these in a row when we came close enough to hale.

"I'm coming aboard and bringing a friend," Captain Walker called.

"I'll have glasses set out for both of ye," roared back a voice with a strong New England twang.

I did not pay much attention. A turmoil in the water on the weather side of the vessel had caught my eye—swirls and splashings not caused by wind or tide, and once or twice the glimpse of a black fin. The sight was in curious contrast—conflict, I would say—with the old and honorable sea ritual observed during our reception. As we mounted the Jacob's ladder, sailors in white jackets and clean kersey breeches stood in the rigging, an honor paid to visitors which was formerly widely practiced but which I thought was extinct. The captain, a bearded New England Yankee with the manner and mien of a deacon, greeted us with a cordial handshake and a hearty, salty voice.

"Welcome to the good ship *Sally Tucker*," he told us.

Strangely, I thought of Salley Sass.

Names were pronounced; hands shaken. The captain was Otis Haverill, of Medford, Massachusetts; and not only the look of the rigging but the clean, trim appearance of his crew showed that he kept a well-ordered, tidy ship. My stomach churned.

"Well, Cap'n, before we sit down in your cabin to a tot of rum, I think Mr. Stono would like to know what you've got in the way of freight."

"Four hundred and five, all in good fettle," Captain Haverill answered. "As for those six by the rail—I told the boys to let you look at 'em, and see if you think they're worth putting on shore."

The six were four men and two women. Captain Walker stepped nearer. The eyes of two of them followed his movements and watched his face; the other four paid no attention. He looked at them with what was no doubt a keen, calculating glance; when he turned back to us he shook his head.

"Not worth their room in a lighter," he said quietly.

Captain Haverill called to his mate.

"Clear the deck, Mr. Thomas," he commanded.

"Aye, aye, sir."

I heard my own voice, trembling a little and strange.

"But, Captain, some of those six have life in 'em yet. Surely they're worth something—"

"Not the expense of digging graves on shore, especially when the undertakers are here, and ready, and free."

He had hardly finished speaking when the first of the six went overboard. The man made no sound as he hurtled down—and a strange and awful silence was on me, too. The sun beat on the deck. The sails flapped in the breeze. Men not busy with the duty whistled and chatted as they went about their tasks. Captain Haverill began to speak of some very old Jamaica rum he had bought at Kingston. As he did so, he began to lead us toward his cabin. And then suddenly, I knew, partly, at least, why I had not moved more strongly to save those six sick slaves from a sudden, terrible death. I would not have succeeded and would have shown my hand. That I must not do until I was ready to play. I must lose greatly before I could win. . . .

A great winning if I won—but only in my heart—or, if the play failed, an unestimably great loss. There was no logic in it. That was the Devil of it. It must be I was not a sharp, but the common sort of gambler who let passion master his mind. This much I knew; I was a true-born son of Charleston, the bastard son of Mason Hudson, the half-brother of Clay Hudson. Faro Jack had told me that he did not know the nature of Fate, nor did I, not the least glimpse, but because of these

bonds it had suddenly closed around me in a strange and terrifying way.

Yet it would be a great play. That I need not doubt. And I
need not be haunted by Faro Jack's observation of great players
dying young.

CHAPTER VII

High Play

AFTER OUR second tot of rum, Captain Haverill named what
he thought was a fair price for his cargo, delivered safe
and sound in the barracoon at Puerto Miramar. It was approximately forty dollars a head—an even sixteen thousand dollars
for the lot—with the provision that he be relieved at once of
the black cattle's keep, and the payment made in full within
three days. Within a month I could dispose of them for two
and a half times that figure. Discounting the import tax paid
directly to Captain Walker and the expenses of their care, my
profit would be at least a hundred per cent.

"I would have to go to Santiago to raise the money, Captain
Haverill," I answered, "so I must ask for four days."

He looked at me keenly with his bright, blue New England
eyes.

"Well, I think you can do it. I'll give you four days. Of
course you understand that if another buyer comes along with
cash in hand—"

"Yes, sir, I do, but in that case I expect the money I pay to
the guards and for other care to be refunded to me."

"That's only fair, and I see you mean business."

"Captain Walker, can you signal in a boat so I may leave for Santiago early tomorrow morning?"

"I can and I will."

"I will pay to you five dollars a head at the same time—a little beforehand, in fact, since it's an import tax—that I pay Captain Haverill."

"That is quite proper," my half-brother answered with a faint smile.

Now we asked to be excused to attend to various duties, and had a pleasant breezy sail into port. Captain Walker—I thought of him constantly by that name, to guard my play—discoursed learnedly on the greatest of Spanish satires, *Don Quixote*. While the character was no doubt overdrawn, he himself had known apparently sensible men who charged windmills. On the dock he took courteous leave of me, and shortly after I saw the captives lightered in. They were transported in batches of six, a continuous hempen line used for each batch, fastened from the ankle of one to the neck of the other, an ingenious arrangement that permitted them to walk at a reasonably fast pace, yet eliminating almost all danger of sudden violence or attempt to escape. When the big doors had been bolted on the outside and the clapboard windows nailed shut and the band of riflemen took their posts, Captain Haverill's sailors returned to their boats laden down with lines. I had expected him to be thus saving of his good hemp, but my heart was lighter to have my expectation proven true.

Still I could not feel the slightest thrill of heroism. My inmost strongest feeling—unless I counted a kind of cold excitement that always took me before high play—was a vindictiveness such as an Indian might feel on a long warpath. Could I still throw in my hand? Yes, because I was a bastard brother; some laws I could not name, but whose verity I could vaguely sense, did not apply to me. But, by the same token, I was free to play. I was risking no one's chips but my own and those Faro Jack had lent to me to risk. So when time moved, I chose to move with it. Walking to the barracoon, I spoke to the cap-

tain of the guard. He did not know English, but a ratty-look-
ing little fellow with an old cap-and-ball rifle as long as he was
acted as interpreter.

"I've bargained with Captain Haverill for his cargo, and
have agreed to pay for its keep, including your salaries, until I
can return from Santiago with the main sum," I said.

"Señor, I feel certain you are making a very profitable deal,"
the captain answered.

"Would you and your men like a small advance on your pay?
Ten pesos apiece, perhaps."

When this was translated, the sun-browned faces beamed.

"We would consider it a great favor, señor, and give you our
hearty thanks."

I handed each of the men a ten-peso note.

"What do you think of this lot, Captain?" I asked, gesturing
toward the barracoon.

"One of the best ever landed here, señor."

"I can speak a little French. Would it be possible for me to
get a message to them? I'd like to tell them that they'll have as
good treatment as they can hope for. I don't want any of them
doing themselves in, during the night."

"Señor, there is an inner door within the outer door, both
front and rear. Each has an iron window for passing in and out
buckets of water and the like. You may look at them and, if
you like, speak to them provided any of them know French.
But that last is rather doubtful."

"My French is very scanty. Perhaps one of you can speak
for me."

All the guards shook their heads. I had no reason to suspect
a trick. The opening in the front inner door to which I was
presently led was about two feet square, and the cracks in the
boarded windows gave enough light—when my eyes had become accustomed to the gloom—to make out several hundred
Negroes, some of them standing in forlorn clusters, some sitting against the wall, many lying down.

"Can any of you speak French?" I called.

Immediately an old man, black as ebony, whom I could imagine as a major-domo in some planter's home of long ago, and a pale-brown young woman came to the opening. Unless I was deceived by the dusk, the latter was quite a beauty. She was tall and lithe, with a dark Semitic splendor in her face; I thought she might be of Arab origin.

"I speak French, monsieur," the old man told me in good accents. "So does the girl called Theba, although that is not her name."

"Has any of you a timepiece?"

As I asked the question, I was watching with the side of my eyes the face of the English-speaking guard beside me. It evinced not the slightest interest or understanding.

The old man was too startled to answer, but the girl spoke, and I could detect the merest stifled wonder in her obsequious tone.

"There might be one, in our band—an old silver watch given by a master in better days—but what would we want of it?"

"It is now a quarter to six," I said, without looking at my own watch.

"The day is nearly done."

"The guards will presently eat supper, and they will have a jug of cheer to make them merry."

"Would that we had a jug, not of cheer but of barest hope, to make us merry."

"Watch your faces and your voices. It may be that during supper, the caps will fall from beneath the hammers of their guns."

"The good God would bless that falling."

"I know nothing about the good God. I do not dare invoke Him. If at eight o'clock the bolts on the rear doors should be slipped back, what then? The night is dark. There are no roads through the forest. Could you find your way to your friends?"

"Some of our friends are waiting at the forest edge even now. They come to meet every new shipment, hoping that a rope will slip—a gun will misfire—and one—or a handful—may go free. It has only once happened at Puerto Miramar. But if you say there is a chance—a hope—we will believe you."

I turned to the guard who was getting a little bored.

"I don't believe I'll sell this girl. She talks with a good deal of spirit."

"She is also good to look upon, señor," the man answered.

"Then be ready," I told her. "I'll do it if I can."

"Will you answer one question, señor?"

"It may be so."

"It is a long time before the hour of eight. Our hearts can shatter from the strain before then. Will you say one word to help me believe? Will you give one reason why you tell us this, so I can hope it isn't the cruelest jest that a slave trader ever played upon his chattels?"

"It is partly a family matter. The main part is to satisfy a grudge."

I turned and walked away, the guard at my heels.

2

When we rejoined the other guards, I had no trouble keeping signs of terror out of my face, voice, and actions. Actually I felt very little, for no reason that I knew of other than my absorption in the game. It was a great game. Perhaps that was why it did not seem so bleak as the games I had played in Faro Jack's rooms. It was no trouble, and rather pleasant, to effect a large vulgar bonhomie that soon put my companions in festive spirit. The jug I sent for was jollily passed. Within half an hour, conversation changed to shouts, and a little after that no one listened to what anyone else was saying. Still, to my disappointment, they did not drink themselves to the ground. These Latins had unexplainable barriers against drunkenness unknown to the poor whites of my own country.

A few natives of the region came up; mostly they were fishermen and small farmers. I served them drinks and they grew mightily jolly in recompense; one of them sang an ancient ribald ballad which the English-speaking guard translated for my benefit, verse by verse. Perhaps one or more of these visitors would be briefly suspected of committing the great offense even now in the cards, giving me a few crucial minutes in which to take to the woods. I had no better plan; I had conceived of no cunning retreat. But I need not regret it; it is not possible to hedge against disaster in really great play. The gambler must use the resources of the moment. He must trust himself as far as he can—that is why gambling is so lonely—and at the bitter last trust to luck.

A solemn, almost poetic mood came over me as the day began to fail. Standing there among my boisterous fellows—or so it seemed although truly I stood alone as on a desert island—I wondered if it would prove my last day on earth. The bet would be a good one for some bystander. I could almost figure the percentage—almost—but not quite. It may be I had made some sort of deal with Death. If so, it had been a fair deal to which I agreed in the secret regions of my soul.

The shadows began to lengthen, to grow, to deepen in tone. They looked like no shadows I had ever seen; and I knew the black cards in this deck were close to my draw. The sun dropped low, then swiftly sunk. Birds passed in headlong flight. They were making their roosts before too late, but it might be I had not made for my roost in time. The jug continued to go round. The guards grew tipsy but without any great slackening of their alertness. The hour was just after seven.

As the shadows deepened, one of the men kicked some dry wood together and lighted a watch fire. At first I thought it would be another obstacle in my path, but I was wrong; in the parlance of the gambler, Lady Luck had given me a smile. The fire did not increase the watchman's vision and instead reduced and narrowed it. No longer were we all in sight of one another. If two men stood a little ways back from the firelight ring in order to tell a joke or share a drink, they became unrecognizable or invisible. And now the rifles, leaned here and there, were no longer conspicuous. Sometimes the firelight burnished them, sometimes they almost disappeared.

Unknown gods! Gods of the lonely, the desperate, and the damned! Gods of children and of humble folk, not the great gods in whose presence you too tremble! I did not mean to invoke you. In all my gambling, I have never asked help from the Unseen; and Luck could smile or frown at me according to her whim. Yet tonight I have somehow bound myself in your name to do this reckless deed, and that binding has lent me new and unknown strength. I do not regret the commitment—I could almost say assignment. It was in some way inevitable—beyond my vision it fits into the pattern of my life and Fate. I will presently stand in great danger, but I am strangely confident, not of success, but of great play. My spirit is exalted but my heart beats slow and cold.

I began to disable the guns. In the barrel of one I poured half the contents of my cup. From beneath the hammer of another I released and let fall the cap. Of the third, an old flintlock, I drenched the priming. The fourth was in an awkward position for me to manipulate; watching my chance, I jammed the barrel end into the mud beside the spring. At the first attempt to fire it, it would probably explode. A guardsman no more guilty than I was innocent could easily be killed, or have his hand blown off. But I could not reckon with such things now. There was no longer any limit in the game.

Time passed. The fifth of the six guns I spiked with a little stick. It too would likely blow up when the trigger was pulled. The powder of the last I drowned with the liquor remaining in my cup.

I glanced again at my watch and the hands stood five minutes to eight.

"We'll have one more round," I told the English-speaking Cuban. "But first I've got to pump ship."

When he translated the vulgarity, it raised a laugh. No one noticed as I slipped off into the dark. They thought I had gone only a few feet. Instead I stole around the side of the barracoon

to the rear door. It was immensely strong and heavy but the
iron bolt slid with ease. In the darkness within was another
door, and high powers of vision came upon my eyes, and when
I opened its iron window I saw an old man and a beautiful
young girl, waiting with an immobility that suggested sublime
patience.

"Is everyone ready?" I whispered.

"Yes."

"When I slide the bolt, give me one minute if you can, then
try to get into the woods without making any noise."

"We will try, monsieur."

I had to use great force to slide the bolt, but it gave at last.
Then I stole back the way I had come. The distant fire leaped
and its black ring of shadows sprang in and out. The guardsmen laughed and talked; I was among them before they noticed
my approach.

One of them joked coarsely in Spanish.

"Pedro says you took a long time," the translator told me.
"It must be your boiler room was flooded."

"No, but I couldn't turn off the tap."

I picked up the jug and began to make the rounds. It was a
curiously noiseless proceeding—none of the men who held out
their cups had anything to say—and my own remarks were soft
and few, unfit to drown out a silence. And out of that silence,
behind the barracoon, there rose sound.

It was not loud but it carried well in the silent night. It
was such sound as light-stepping cattle might make, moving
through brushy cover. The men pricked up their ears; then
one of them made a quick motion and seized his rifle.

"*Diablo!*" he burst out. The rest he said I did not understand.

"What is it?" I demanded of the English-speaking guard.

"We don't know. It's damn queer—"

At that instant the captain of the guard dropped his cup
and darted toward the barracoon. Instantly four of his men
fell in behind him. I thought the fifth would go too, and then

the coast would be clear, and I would vanish in the dark forest, and perhaps my life would be spared. He was a man I had hardly noticed. He seemed the kind always to follow the leader, not one to act on his own account. He was a middle-sized man, rather jauntily dressed.

He took three steps, then glanced at his rifle and stopped. His hand moved quickly and he picked from the barrel a piece of stick I had thrust into it and inadequately concealed. At once the gun leaped and leveled on my breast.

"*Renegado!*" he burst out, with such hate and fury as I had hardly ever heard in a human voice. And then in strange-sounding English, "If they have got away, I kill you!"

3

The fatal card had not yet fallen. The issue of my immediate ruin or repair was not fully decided. The reason was, the guard's watch of me had become impaired through his intense interest in what was happening elsewhere; his attention wavered just a little as he gave ear to the events occurring about the barracoon; and sometimes he cast his eye in that direction. There could come an instant wherein it failed; and then I would strike back. I was not conscious of hope but perceived the possibility of opportunity. . . .

Someone came running. I thought the guard might lose his aim in seeing who it was. Instead it intensified, with the curious effect of him showing dutifulness to a superior. The newcomer was another guard, called Pedro.

At once my watcher, whose name was Ernesto, began speaking rapidly in Spanish. The newcomer Pedro stared incredulously at first, then scowled, and advanced toward me with his rifle raised over his shoulder as a club. He did not strike, though; at the same time he kept well out of his fellow's aim.

"Mon capitán!" he shouted, in the now heavy silence. "Attention!"

"*Momentito!*" someone shouted in reply. A moment later the

capitán and two other guards appeared in the firelight, one of the later being Diego, who knew English. There was a rapid exchange of information, but no break of luck, or shadow of one for me. The men grouped around me but did not get in one another's way; the two or three who semed overcome by passion remained as vigilant as the rest. Two had dropped their useless guns and instead held ready for use a cudgel and a machete. Their excited talk ran on for a few seconds more, Ernesto making the main charge. Only ratty little Diego still seemed inclined to doubt it, and in a few swift seconds this changed completely and he became more belligerent than the others. I knew that if I made a single suspicious or violent move I would be instantly killed.

The captain ordered Diego to ask me a question. He did so, his face pale with fury.

"Why did you let them go?"

"Why should I? Why should you blame me? I had arranged to buy them—"

"You did it. No one else. It was you who spiked the guns. Ernesto saw you meddling with his gun and thought nothing of it. What have you done, Yanki son of a bitch. You have cost the Captain of the Port many thousand pesos. The fame of our barracoon is lost and the ships won't come here any more. I spit on you!"

He did so literally. Ernesto's gun and the club and the knife awaited my reply, poised and ready for instant use, so I made none. There fell a slight pause. I was conscious of the bright and dancing flame and the pretty lights it cast in the brushwood beyond. I saw the men's faces, flushed or pale with fury, and their angry but curiously graceful actions, like those of fighting house cats. This was where my path had led. I had been playing all this while to find myself here. My terror was still not sharp but aching and forlorn. I was more afraid of torture than of death. Torture of a terrible sort was well within the cards. . . .

Diego repeated an order given by the captain.

"Son of a swine, put your hands behind your back."

My mind revolted, for that way lay helplessness. But something more than the glitter of steel and the murderous glow in the eyes of my captors made me submit. I did not know all that went on in my heart and brain. Maybe I thought to lay a chip on time. Time had saved many a man when by all the computations his jig was up. Anyway, I obeyed.

I felt thongs go round and round my wrists. I felt a noose dropped over my neck, and drawn so tight I could barely breathe. After that, the tense figures about me relaxed a little.

"We will now take you into the barracoon, where we will wait the coming of the two captains," Diego told me.

While four of the five guards marched me there, the fifth went to the guardhouse after lanterns. On the way we met the sixth guard, who had tried to follow the runaway slaves into the forest. In the great empty room I was seated on a stool, with my ankles bound. Pietro left to summon my judges; the others sat morosely, talking in low tones. Sitting alone, unquestioned, my mind free to roam, I thought of almost everyone I had ever known. None knew of my swift fall, none would imagine it in their distant scenes, and if they did know, how few would care? Faro Jack. . . . Perhaps Mate Hudson. . . . Clara? If she knew, her interest would be diverted for a few hours from Memphis' games; her mouth would round and her eyes shine with excitement. Mason Hudson and Salley Sass? The threat that had seemed to hang over them had proved a bugbear, and the great oaks still stood, and the lights burned, and the walls were unshaken. For three leagues stretched the fertile rice fields. What was one little avenger compared to these?

After a long time there was a noise at the door. The guards stood up respectfully and all of them looked frightened. Yet when Captain Sidney Walker and Captain Haverill came into the room, they did not storm; they walked gravely and spoke quietly. Not until Captain Walker stood close to the lantern did I perceive that he was under great strain. His color had turned dull white and his soft eyes had a feverish shine and his lips were drawn. I thought very likely he would collapse. If he did, I would not be worse off, and perhaps a chance would come. . . .

With hardly a glance at me, he questioned the captain of the guard. The questioning was long and careful, with an enforced calmness. At the end he turned and spoke to Captain Haverill.

"The men were at the supper fire, the emancipator among them," he said. "They were making rather merry, but they knew no reason not to, with the blacks locked in. They mistook him for a gentleman. I came close to making the same mistake."

"You came close!" Captain Haverill cried, his voice rising. "If you had any doubts—"

"I am speaking now of his station in life. He tried to pass as a gentleman, but I suspected he was an impostor. In the first place, not many gentlemen engage in the slave trade, as you well know. Besides, his manners were a little too meticulous. But I had no doubt whatever of his good faith as a buyer."

"You should have, when he protested putting those sick ones overside. A real dealer would be used to sights like that. I saw something in his face, damn my eyes, but I thought you wouldn't have brought him out there, you who love the trade, unless you were sure of him. Now my charterers have lost a fortune. Who's going to trust me again? My only comfort is, you're in the same boat. You'll look a long time from that conning tower of yours before you see another slaver hove into port!"

"Sir, that goes without saying."

"Maybe it won't hurt you, because you're rich. You've salted away enough that you can go back to Jamaica and live like a lord."

"Captain Haverill, no member of my family was ever known to save a peso."

Captain Haverill turned to me. "Are you a paid abolitionist, or a volunteer?"

"I'm no kind of an abolitionist," I answered.

"Then what did you do it for?"

"I acted on impulse."

"It's going to be a costly one, or I miss my guess. While we're about it"—Captain Haverill turned again to Captain Walker—"has anyone searched him? For money, I mean."

Captain Walker spoke in Spanish to the captain of the guard. Two of the men came up to me and in a matter of seconds found my money belt. Their expression changed oddly when they found it contained an even thousand dollars in pesos.

"It's small consolation, but what it gives you can have," Captain Walker said.

"Less than twelve per cent of what we've paid out. Yet I can't say it's the fault of anyone, except that renegade from Charleston. Impulse, hell! Those slaves promised to meet him in the jungle and bring him a whole lot of stolen money."

"Well, the meeting won't occur. That's my consolation."

Their eyes met briefly. "You know, I wouldn't like to be in his shoes."

"You said his impulse is going to be a costly one, and you're quite right. I'll attend to the matter early tomorrow morning. I greatly regret I'm too sick and weary to give it proper attention tonight."

There fell a brief silence. Captain Haverill stroked his beard.

"I have curiosity to know what you're going to do."

"You have every right to know. My men will take him into the forest. They'll have strong rope and they will find a stout limb. The people hereabouts won't go near the place. I doubt if his bones will be found until long after they've dropped to the ground."

He turned to me and spoke in his soft, pleasing voice.

"In the role of judge—I've appointed myself your judge—I've a few remarks to make. I'm inclined to disagree with Captain Haverill as to the motive of your deed. I doubt if you expect the runaways to bring you money; I think very likely you acted on impulse, as you said. What you must understand is—what you may contemplate as you lie awake, tonight, your last night of life—is that mistaken philanthropy—misguided charity—whatever you want to call it—is one of the most dangerous and disastrous things on earth. More harm can be done by it than by a thousand selfish or even dishonest acts. Thereby the cattle of the earth go free—break down fences—often kill people. The old orders are destroyed. Civilization itself is threatened. Also the charity so-called is itself suspect. Almost always it's a form of vanity. You are one of the vainest young men it was ever my misfortune to meet. It enables you to act the gentleman quite well; sometimes you may even believe your role. Happily your career is going to be cut short. You have reached the end of your rope. Excuse me—one end will be around your neck, the other about the stout limb of a tree. You've danced, and now you will pay the fiddler—rather I should have said you'll dance once more, a very lively last dance which the spectators will enjoy far more than you. With that before you, I expect you will find the night somewhat long. We'll leave you now to pass it the best you may."

He turned and spoke in Spanish to the captain of the guard. The latter saluted with punctilio. Then he addressed Captain Haverill.

"I have ordered all six guards to remain on duty. None are to lie down, and at least four stay sharply alert at every moment. You need have no fear of laxity on their part. They know that this fine imitation gentleman has cost them their jobs—there will be no more black cattle to guard. Nor is there the slightest possibility of his slipping his bonds. My men are especially skilled at fastening them."

As I listened to him speaking, I was thinking of two cards left in my hand. One I could never play. It would be tantamount to asking mercy, which God forbid. The other was a weak card, I could not see how it offered the least hope, it might well shorten my time. Still I decided to play it.

"You spoke of me as a fake, imitation gentleman," I said.

"You're not even that. You lie, steal, and commit murder. You didn't come from Jamaica. You never saw a slave insurrection there, with the murder of your parents and brothers and sisters. Your name is not Sidney Walker. And you're a traitor to your country, your state, your order, and your family."

He waited long seconds before he replied; and I saw his eyes dart to the startled face of Captain Haverill.

"This is quite revealing," he said gravely. "If I'm not Captain Walker, who am I, pray?"

"Your name is Clay Hudson, and you are a renegade from Charleston who had to flee the city."

"What do you think of that, Captain Haverill?" Clay Hudson asked.

"I find it somewhat surprising, but—after all—none of that's my business."

"I trust you'll go with me tomorrow, to see this fellow properly hanged."

"No, sir, I'll ask you to excuse me. I'm a slaver but not a hangman."

"Since he has been so revealing about me, I'll return the compliment. It took me a good while to remember the name Edward Stono—where I had heard it and in what connection—but finally I did. It was the name given to the bastard son of my father by a lowborn Creole woman."

"Devils in hell! That makes him your half-brother."

"Cain and Abel were full brothers."

"Do you mean that you're going ahead with the hanging?"

"I look forward to it with the keenest pleasure. Now let us take our leave."

4

The two captains left the room. Two of the guards stationed themselves at the doors; the others sat against the wall. The lanterns threw a bleak, monotonous light, such as I remembered in the gaming rooms. A wild hope struck me, but I did not let it ingress my heart; I would not give it countenance. I had gambled and lost.

Sitting apart from my captors, my first intercourse was with Death. He did not raise his hand to strike me, yet; it seemed he held no enmity toward me, but I felt that he had claimed me, beyond redemption, and I might as well get used to him. It was a strange task to give the mind. Every way the mind ran, it sought light instead of darkness, it looked for continuity instead of finality. I could hardly force it to accept the situation. The night passing, and then a deeper night at morning, striking suddenly, my own night, my light failed, my own sun gone, but perhaps my stars out, shining, stars I had never seen. That was as far as I dared go in thinking of any future life. I had never thought about it until now and to try to build on it now would seem a weakness. Pride was my great fault. Clay Hudson had called it vanity and he might be right, but I still believed it was pride, however foolish.

The hours passed. Two of the guards dozed, two kept up a desultory conversation, two leaned against the lintels of the doors. It struck me that even the latter were having trouble keeping awake, the rum they had drunk acting as a soporific. I half-wished that I too could sleep. Thus the hours of waiting would seem to be cut short. Yet I remained wide, intensely awake. It was as though my heart kept watching for something that my mind denied. It would not be reconciled to defeat; it dared not hope, yet it would not surrender to despair.

I became slowly aware of a change in my surroundings. At first I did not know what it was; then I perceived, with a stifled heart, that it was only a deeper silence than before. The talk of the two guardsmen had long since died away. They still sat with their heads up, in the same position, their guns in easy reach, but from here I could not tell if their eyes were open; I got the strong, wildly exciting impression that they had closed. The two guards at the door stood just as before, leaning against the lintels. There remained so little to bank on. If this were a game in Faro Jack's rooms, I would be ashamed to lay any kind of bet. Yet my heart said, "Now is the time." If any friend were waiting—if—if—a hundred nos against one yes—now, now was the moment of his greatest chance to help me. One moment in the middle of the night. One little shift of the odds against me.

Then the hair rose on my head, for through the guarded door came the dim form of a girl.

Her hair flowed and her feet were bare. She walked past the man standing by the lintel, and he did not put out his hand to stop her, and he made no sound. She came on, nearer and nearer, walking swiftly but more lightly than any wind. In her hand was a small gleaming thing. In a few seconds more I saw it was a dagger. The two guardsmen sitting upright across the room appeared to look straight at her without seeing her. No one else moved, no one made a sound.

She came close and I saw that she was the girl called Theba. Quickly and with skill she cut the ropes on my wrists and ankles. Then she gave me her hand to help me to my feet.

Their numbness passed off. We walked side by side. Past the two upright sitting guards, nearer and nearer the man standing by the door. As we came close to him she dropped my hand so we could go through in single file. I passed near enough to touch him, in front of his half-closed eyes. He made no sound or movement.

We went on through the outer door. I felt the freshness of the night and saw the stars and the dying red coals of the supper fire. Again the girl's hand found mine. Still we walked in utter silence, but the dark line of the forest drew ever nearer. I thought we would never reach it, that my luck couldn't run that long, but suddenly we did. We dipped into a little dark trail.

For at least fifty steps more we stole our way along, then she uttered a low, sobbing gasp. Into a starlit patch ahead of us stepped the dim figure of a man; waving for us to follow, he began to run at a swift, light pace up a wide, cleared path. Clutching my hand, the girl ran with me, beside me, it seemed on soft grass, into the dark, silent, unknown heart of the forest.

We ran like deer at whom rifles had just blazed. There seemed no limit to the lightness of our feet, to the fleetness of our gait. We followed our leader as her cubs might follow a tigress. We were like disembodied things.

After a long time our guide stopped and spoke in some unknown tongue to my companion. I saw her nod and turn to me, but she could not speak at once for lack of breath. In dimness I could barely penetrate, she put her hands to her breast and looked up to the constant stars as though seeking strength. At last she spoke.

"You are safe now, monsieur. Lugi of the maroons says so. No one can find you now."

5

In only a moment or two more we left the wide path worn by wild cattle, crossed a brook, and came into a narrow trail where we must walk in file. It forked and reforked, climbed a hill, and entered a valley thickly grown to palm and flowering vine, impenetrable to all who did not know its secret entrances and exits. In only a few minutes more we came to a cabana made of palm logs and roofed with thatch. Lugi entered ahead of us and lighted an old-fashioned ship's lantern that was waiting there.

I looked first at his face as the steadying glimmer revealed it. It was the strong, aquiline, brown face of an Indian. Naked except for a breechcloth, his body was a marvel of lithe, compact strength. Catching my eye and smiling, he motioned toward some fruit that had been left on a rustic table—yellow and red and green, beautiful and fragrant to my revitalized senses—and coconuts that had been perforated to emit their milk. By opposite walls were pallets, covered with deerskins.

He spoke in some unknown tongue which the girl quickly translated.

"Monsieur, you are to stay here the remainder of the night with every assurance of safety. In the morning the maroons will come to guide you to their village."

"I have been very lonely, and I wish that you would stay here also, if that is possible," I answered.

"Yes, I will stay."

Lugi smiled and nodded in the doorway, then the night swallowed him. With a bone-handled silver knife that she found on the table, the girl cut several mangoes, handing them to me to eat with a wooden spoon. They had been called the fruit of paradise, but I must soon refuse the offering; then I had her sit near the lantern so I could look well into her face. I had never seen its like. She was of a people and a land of which I had no knowledge. The land was faraway and warm, and the people were of a Semitic race; beyond that I could not even guess.

Her features were of bold free carving, as was her tall, lithe form, and her eyes held a dark splendor I had never seen before, and her skin was a pale, reddish brown.

"It's hard for me to believe that this is true," I told her.

"We were very lucky, monsieur."

"I may call you Theba?"

"Yes, lord. I was called that in Haiti, although my real name is Mariyah, after the beautiful Coptic concubine who was Mohammed's favorite."

"Will you call me Edward?"

"Edward," she echoed.

"You speak French well. How long have you known the language—if you care to tell me?"

"I am glad to make conversation. I too find this very hard to believe. We were both lost—I along with many others—and suddenly we are both saved. I've known French about a year."

"You learned it in Haiti, of course."

"Yes."

"Before that, I think your native tongue was Arabic."

"Yes, such as is spoken in the Libyan Desert."

"Then it must be that you were sold into slavery before you came to Haiti."

"Yes, by my father. He was a great slave trader and catcher.

He had several children by the Arab and Berber women who fell into his hands. When he had made enough money to go and live like a nobleman in his native Oman, he sold us all."

For a moment an intense look came into her face, then a dim and childlike smile played around her mouth, and it passed off.

"What are you going to do now?" I asked.

"I'm going to live with the maroons and help other slaves escape."

"You must understand I'm not a liberator. I believe in slavery as it exists in my native land. If I live, I may become a slave-owner myself."

"One of the maroons, listening at the window when you talked to the captains, heard you say about the same. It doesn't matter now. That part is over."

I looked at her, and pain passed in a zigzag path across my brow, and my being seemed like that I had in dreams.

"Will you eat something, Theba?"

"I ate heartily before the long watch began."

"Have you a husband?"

"No."

"A lover?"

"I had a lover once—but he was killed."

"Children?"

"No."

"Your father is in Oman. Where is your mother?"

"She was a Tuareg woman and was sold to one of the kings of the Nile."

"It's late and you're tired and want to go to bed."

"Not until you do, Edward."

"Will I ever see you again after tonight?"

"We'll be together tomorrow as we journey to the maroon village. But from there the men may want to start at once for Manzanillo. From there you can cross to Jamaica in a sponge boat."

"I wish we could stay together. I wish that was my Fate instead of against my Fate. I have no one else."

"I have no one else either—but it would be against my fate, also. Against what I would have once called *kismet*."

"Will you kiss me, Theba? Please do not do so unless you wish."

"I would like to kiss you, Edward."

She came and bent over me and her lips were soft and warm and lovely upon mine.

"To be kissed—not by death—but by life!"

"Death has gone away—for a little while," she answered.

"But only to return. He never leaves for very long. To me you are the very symbol of life. You're tall and beautiful and proud and brave. Tomorrow we part, but I'll have the memory of you as long as I live. I'll hold it in my heart. It will be with me in many a lonely hour and strengthen me in defeat. I'll see you again as you came into that dimly lighted room, your feet bare, your hair flowing. For that I'll love you always."

She was still a moment, and then she echoed in a strange tone, "Love?"

"What else? What other word could be the right word? Is love so hard to come by? It is the easiest thing we do, we humans —the happiest—and the most sad."

"I will respond to your love, Edward."

"I'm not sure what you mean."

"I mean I will give you mine in return. Is it only for one night? I don't think so. I don't think it can pass so quickly. I think it would be the kind to live in our hearts all our lives. I want it there, Edward, if you do. We have been together so long. We have been so close together. We know each other better than many a youth and maiden who go to the altar. We have run together in the dark. We came face to face with him."

"With whom?"

"I will answer that in Arabic." And when she had spoken some words in the alien tongue, she gave me their English equivalent. "The despoiler of delight. He who puts out the lamp. He who brings the last cup."

"He hasn't come yet," I said, with a sudden exultant thrill in my voice.

"And he won't come, tonight. Tonight the lamp will burn bright, if you wish it. The cup will be the cup of joy. I am a desert woman who can't hide her heart. Tell me if that is what you want."

"Tonight I want it more than anything in the world."

"Then we will be together all the night—deep into the morning when the wild pigeons fly back from the spring where they go to drink—and because of that—wherever we are—we can be together always."

BOOK THREE

CHAPTER VIII

Partial Payment

DEEP IN the morning, when the wild pigeons had flown back from the springs where they had gone to drink, a file of thirty or more maroons came singing down the hill. Their song was very like the wailing work chants I had so often heard raised by gangs of slaves in the Carolina Low Country, its key minor, the refrain essentially sorrowful, the words probably extempore. They were free men, it seemed, yet they remained bound, and I did not know the nature of that binding. I was a long way from Charleston, yet I returned there in the twinkling of an eye. Theba and I would presently go our separate ways, yet either could return to the other in one leap of thought. There was a world of substance and a world of shadows, and these two were inextricably bound.

One of the maroons had brought tortillas, wild-pig bacon, and coffee for my breakfast; another a bunch of cheroots cleverly rolled from the native leaf; the third some deerskin garments and boots for me to wear on the journey through the jungle, to save my own clothes from the thorn thickets and the swamps that we must pass. All were naked except for loincloths and on every face was a broad smile.

157

Without great haste we set forth on our journey, Lugi walking immediately ahead of me, and Theba just behind. After a mile or so, I could no longer see any sign of a path, while the forest became taller, luxuriant, and wildly beautiful. At first glance it would appear impenetrable because of the mesh of vines and creepers, but my companions were jungle dwellers; and Lugi never failed to lift out of my awkward way branches or brambles which the others avoided with slight twists of their lithe bodies.

Royal palms grew everywhere, sometimes a hundred feet tall, and when we gained the hilltops we could see their plumes gracing every vista. Taller than these stood the silk-cotton trees, of unbelievable girth; even so some of them loomed bereft of life, strangled but still upheld by the huge coils of the jaguey liana. Once our line swerved from other living coils. They looked dark except for a soft sheen and were beautifully patterned, and they formed the body of a huge boa that I guessed at eight yards long. But we passed only a few feet from his leafy bed where he lay asleep, digesting an enormous meal, and my companions nodded and beamed at being able to show me one of the marvels of their jungle. This was the mighty *maja*, that swallowed whole goats and wild pigs, but was never known to wind with bone-crushing power about a human being.

Gaudy macaws, uttering harsh cries, and emerald-green parakeets flushed from the tree boughs. The exquisite fairy hummingbirds darted or hovered among the huge purple flowers of the royal piñons. When we stopped for a noonday meal, the forest gave it to us—wild plantains, mangoes, custard apples, and pawpaws, and milky coconut flesh. But at the end of the day's march, we did not gain the maroon village, which Theba had seemed to expect. Actually my fleet-footed companions could have made it with ease, except for an alien of whose comfort they took thought. However, we arrived at one of their pig-hunting camps, where stood a few bark-built, thatched-roof huts. When Theba had swept and garnished the best of these, then stood in the doorway with downcast eyes, I thanked some godlings of happy fortune for the delay.

We arrived at the village in midafternoon of the following day, and at twilight I feasted at a small rustic table set in a breezy bower. The tableware was ancient Spanish silver and the cloth damask, no doubt looted, perhaps amid scenes of brutal murder, from the great *casas* of the Islands. The bloodstains had been washed away, but not from human hands or out of human remembrance, and the end, the final accounting was not in sight, and God only knew where good would leave off and evil begin. The meal, prepared from an astonishing variety of edible substances, was expertly cooked and flavored. I visioned a head cook in some warm, fragrant, clean plantation kitchen, perhaps a mammy greatly beloved and trusted by her "white folks," perhaps a white-haired elder whom the children called Uncle Jim or Sam or George until, suddenly, the incredible rebellion. My heart grew heavy. I had been given a new lease of life, as the old platitude aptly put it, but I did not know what to do with it. I must play deeply, but for what stakes, in what game, against what adversaries?

After the meal came Lugi the chief, accompanied by Theba and a tall bronze Negro, lean as a leopard, with an eagle's face and copper rings in his ears and a remarkable grace of movement. Asking my permission, they squatted on the floor. Their voices and manner and the sheen of excitement in their eyes told me of the gravity of their mission. To my surprise, it was not Lugi who addressed me, but the savage-looking African. I was not able to identify the language that he used—I thought it might be some lingua franca of the Dark Continent. What he said, Theba translated literally into French.

". . . My name is N'kulu and I am a Zulu, and I was born on the middle waters of the Tugela River three years before the faraway King of the White Men gave forth his command that all the slaves of his African domains be set free."

I thought that N'kulu must refer to the emancipation act passed by the British parliament in 1833. Its impact in South

Africa had been enormous, and it had been one of the main causes of the Great Trek of the Boers into the wilderness. He looked about thirty, but he could easily be twenty-five.

"When I had seen the grass renewed sixteen times on the High Veld, and with my spear had slain a lion in sport and an enemy in war, and I had passed under the hand of our witch doctor in the Magic House, I became a gunbearer of a gray-bearded Boer, whom I knew as Heer Piet, and we hunted elephants in the thorn, and Heer Piet sold the ivory for much silver at the trading post at Thaba'nchu."

He paused, and I nodded in token of understanding.

"One day, as we were crossing the Vaal River in time of drouth, Heer Piet found in a sinkhole in the gravel a small, white stone with twelve faces, colder than other pebbles, and greasy feeling. He stared at it a long time, with some passion in his face that I could not read, and then he began to search diligently for other such stones, commanding that I help him. But only in the same sinkhole could we find any, and there only a few. Some were larger than the first, one had eight faces, two or three had more than I could count, but most were rounded, looking like drops of gum from the milk tree. All the next day we searched in vain. Early the following morning, Heer Piet put the little handful of stones in a pouch made of the skin of the hartebeest, and we went our way."

My heart beat no faster, I thought, but with a distinct thump.

"Now it so chanced that Heer Piet had been robbed of his gun and his stores some years before, and trusted no man," N'kulu went on. "So when we came in sight of anyone, black or white, or when we drew nigh a town or a trading post, he would pass to me the little bag of pebbles, and bid me conceal it until he desired its return. Thus I knew they had no little value in his sight, but since he was old and an outlander, exiled from his kind, with many queer notions, I knew not if his sight were true or false—if their value was real or like a dream in the night—and I know not to this day."

In the pause, I asked a question. "Did you and Heer Piet search any more for the white pebbles?"

"I served him only a few months more, but in that time we searched here and there, without finding any."

"Could you, if you crossed the great waters, find again the sinkhole in the river bed?"

"Lord, it might be so."

"Go on with the tale."

"I will, but it is almost done. There came a day that we saw a war party of Basuto advancing across the plain. Heer Piet handed me the little bag, then went forward to parley with the chief. Instead of words, they gave him their assagais, sewing him in and out. Me they took prisoner, and, with no thought of searching anyone so poor, sold me to an Arab slave trader, whose barracoon stood on the banks of the Zambezi. In time I was brought to Mozambique to be resold in Brazil, but the gods and heavy gales caused the ship that was bearing me there to put into Santiago, where I was bought by a planter of sugar cane. In my second year in the fields the foreman guarding our work gang drank too deeply of his jug and fell down drunk, whereupon we fled into the forest. I brought with me the little pouch of pebbles. Thus it came to pass that I have them still."

He fell silent. His bronze face, lean and superbly molded by the stark hands of event, spoke to me of great things I could not understand, nothing of the present matter. Not so the darkly beautiful face of Theba, a daughter of the desert, whose right name was Mariyah, after the illustrious Coptic concubine of Allah's Prophet. Her brilliant dark eyes that I had seen alive and luminous with sudden love were dimmed by tears. She seemed to be waiting for some quite great thing to happen, and the wonder of it was upon her, but I did not know what it was. Lugi the Indian crouched on the ground as still as a form in stone.

"*Bukra!*" N'kulu called to me after the long pause. This was an address I had heard used by Negroes in the Low Country. It was a West African word, I thought, and a title of honor.

"Friend," I answered in English, without thinking.

"It is my wish, and the wish of the people, that I give the little bag of white stones to you."

"Tell me why?"

"Because, first, of the money taken from you by the guards in the barracoon at Puerto Miramar, which one of us watched through a crack in the boarded window. I do not believe that these pebbles are worth so many pesos, but since Heer Piet set such store on them, it may be so. Second, the ghost of Heer Piet often visits my dreams, and he asks me whether the white stones are still in my close care, and what I will do with them, of good usage, that he may rest in peace, and it comes to me that there can be no better use of them than the part payment of a debt owed by my people. Third, my comrades and I have no other need of them, for the forest supplies all our needs, shelter, food, good drink, oil from the corojo palm, cloth from the maya, spices, and medicines. In little hidden clearings we have plantations of bread trees, yams, cassava, coffee, and maize, and bark of the majagua tree even gives us rope to yoke our oxen to wooden plows. Fourth and last, it is all we have to give you, in token of our thanks to you for what you gave to us, and thanks to our gods for what you were spared from giving."

I looked at Theba and spoke only to her. "What I did for you and your people was accidental to a passion. I was serving myself, not you, and deserve no reward. Anyway it was my Fate, and Fate has already rewarded me, through you."

She started to make me an eloquent answer, perhaps as poetic as a desert song. Instead she paused, smiled a dim, tender smile, and spoke very simply. In that instant she made me think of Salley Sass.

"Take it, Edward," she told me. "He wants you to have it."

I turned to N'kulu, once a painted and plumed Zulu warrior from the far-distant Tugela River, tonight my camp-mate and protector in a great forest of the New World.

"Friend, I accept with pride and pleasure."

"Veree good!" he answered with a sudden immense smile,

when Theba had translated. He seemed almost as proud of his English as of making the gift.

It was a small, soft-leather pouch, containing a handful of white pebbles of unknown worth.

2

Later in the night I examined the stones with great care. There were twenty-two in all, about half of which looked like white, petrified gum; the others were distinct and, in some cases, quite perfect crystals with eight, twelve, or forty-eight faces. A few appeared to be cracked and there was a distinct variation in their degree of brilliance as I brought them to the light.

I did not know how many substances were found in the river gravel in a white, crystalline form. They might be some kind of fool's jewel, in the way that mica is fool's gold. Still I was inclined to share the opinion of Heer Piet, a gray-bearded outlander exiled from his kind ere he died on the Basuto spears, that he had made a great find.

I went into a lean-to of bark that N'kulu had raised, and, standing beside his sleeping form, I quietly spoke his name. He came awake and sprang up in what seemed one swift, graceful movement; and I thought it was part of his schooling as a Zulu warrior, the scourge of South Africa, or perhaps as a gunbearer in the thorn to old Heer Piet. At once I beckoned him into the cabin where Theba waited for us. When we had all three lighted cheroots, I spoke to him through her of a matter haunting my mind.

"N'kulu, have you ever gone down to the city of Manzanillo, where the maroons will take me in order that I may sail for Bermuda?"

"Yes, bukra. I have gone there twice, with Lugi and some others, to sell cinnamon."

"Do you know if any of the people called in Spanish *los Judíos,* who will lend money, live there?" For this was not a certainty by any means. Despite their seeming ubiquity, Jews will not make homes in certain cities and towns, often for reasons unknown to other dwellers there.

"There are several, bukra, of ancient and good standing. Lugi says that many of the caballeros could not get along without them."

"When Lugi sends a party of the maroons to guide me there, I would like to have you follow me in the part of a body servant. Is there any way you could get suitable clothes?"

"More than one of our number was a body servant before he escaped into the jungle. The clothes they wore have been carefully put away and preserved. I can—and I will."

"Now I have come to the hard part. I'll put it as plain as I can, and ask you to give me a plain answer. Although you and Heer Piet could find no more white pebbles, such as you gave me, it stands to reason that there are many more, hidden among the rocks of the river beds. If they are what I think they are—what the Spanish call *diamente*—and the Judío of Manzanillo will tell me—I wish to go to Africa, find a great many, and thus obtain much wealth. My hope of succeeding would be far greater if you would go with me. If you did, and the search prospered, I would share that wealth with you. Now tell me, N'kulu, whether you will go."

A very strange expression came into his face—or perhaps there was no expression there at all. I turned away my gaze so he could contemplate the question in privacy; and Theba gave me a smile. Presently N'kulu rose from his seat on the floor and stood in the doorway of the hut, and from the tilt of his head I thought he was gazing through the tree foliage to the big white stars. Those over his head now had once hung low in the western sky—a little northward too, I thought—but he had not forgotten them; perhaps old shaggy-bearded Heer Piet and he had been guided by them more than once across South Africa's great plains. After a while he returned and resumed his seat.

"Bukra, I have no need of wealth," he told me.

"I knew that."

"The Arab slave catchers hunt below the Zambezi. There are

many big and little wars across the Vaal River, and great danger. And we two are not old and half mad as was Heer Piet. We are both young."

"Sometimes it seems I am very old and wholely mad."

"The eve before the morning I was born, a leopard broke into the kraal. All the warriors were away on a cattle raid, so there were none to save our goats but the women, and these hid in their round houses, all except my mother. She took an assagai from the wall and went forth into the pen, and there she gazed into the eyes of Danger, green and glowing eyes, and although the beast snarled, her gaze did not flinch, so he bethought himself and went back to the long grass. Then the witch doctor came, and he made magic and saw the auguries, and he declared that I too would gaze into the eyes of Danger as long as I lived, and it would be my love."

"What does this mean, N'kulu?"

"I will tell you when the wheel turns in my head. I have other loves, men and women, and the sight of the great herds of wildebeests, and of a lion sitting still on a high rock, and of elephants drifting through the thorn. And the fields of kaffircorn ere the harvest, and the dark sky ere the rain. And bukra, I loved Heer Piet, and it is true you are like him in some ways."

"Bah! He was an old, gray Boer!"

"But he was an outlander, exiled from his kind, and so are you. That is the way of many an old tusker, who lives alone in his thorn, the reason being that the herd has driven him forth, or he cannot stand any more the gossip of the cows and squealing of the calves; but sometimes it is true of a young tusker, and then there is no reason that men can know. Where is your herd, bukra? Has it cast you forth? And although old, with watery eyes, Heer Piet could yet see like an *asvegal* across the plain, as far and as sharp as I, who am far from blind. And although his hand shook at common tasks, when he raised his gun it came up as grouse rise from the ground when the serval cat comes nigh, and when it gripped the barrel it was steady as in the coil of an elephant's trunk, and the game, whatever it was, whether a bull wearing ivory, or a hartebeest for our cooking pot, or a *Shenzi* drawing back to throw a spear, it fell so hard that it seemed to bounce on the hard ground."

"When his time came to die, the assagais of the Basuto sewed him in and out."

"Not until he had shot their chief, and clubbed to death three of the warriors."

"As for me, I have rarely held a gun in my hands or hardly ever looked along a barrel at wild game."

"Nor does the young lion learn to kill until he is weaned. Bukra, I have watched your hands and met your eyes, and the wheel in my head has turned."

"Then is the answer yes or no?"

"If you go, I will go with you."

3

A party of ten young maroons was picked by Lugi to take me to the outer edge of the forest that dipped close to Manzanillo. One other, N'kulu, on whose back was a bundle of clothes, would accompany me in a role of body servant into the town, and perhaps much farther than any witch woman in the tribe could vision. Ahead of us had sped a Cuban of the pure Spanish type, an English-speaking fugitive from prison, called Martinez, to spy out the ground and make arrangements for my reception. He would report to the leader of our band at a prearranged meeting place before I ventured down.

When we set forth at sunrise, all the people in the village except the infants and the very old accompanied N'kulu and me to the end of the plantations. At the parting place, they formed in a long, crescent-shaped line and, led by a young Negro girl with a clear, glimmering soprano voice, sang a wild, wailing song, half Spanish, half African. Only the women and girls carried the refrain and gave voice to the long, strange cries; the men repeated over and over a word that sounded like "tembu";

and the low pitch, resonance, and rhythm of the utterance gave the effect of a drumbeat.

Theba and I had already made our farewells in a hut in the village, but when I looked at her and raised my hand she felt the need, as I did, of a parting word. But when she came up to me and kissed me, the word was not *au revoir*. It was *porte-toi-bien*.

"Can't you say till I see you again?" I asked.

"No, Edward, because I will never see you again, except in dreams."

"How can you know?"

"I asked our conjure woman, Hada. She saw you in a vision, and although there was too much smoke and fire to know its meaning, she could not find you in this forest ever again. She said you may walk into the jaws of Death or fall into the pit of Evil. But what we have found in each other, we can never lose. That is the teaching of the lonely desert where I was born."

Some beauty of spirit I could barely divine glowed in her dark eyes.

"I will think of you often, Theba," I told her, as I took her in my arms in farewell. "I will dream of you on many a night. I will live over our great joys."

We parted, and in the afternoon of the third day our party descended the Sierra Maestra into view of the church spires of Manzanillo. At the appointed place we came upon the spy, Martinez, who reported that all was well, and gave me instructions. In three days, two ships would sail. One was a small Cuban sugar boat, the *Santa Clara*. Her captain, known as Escarpelo because of his rough voice, owed a great debt to the maroons and would take me, without charge, to Kingston in Jamaica. The other was a large English steamer, *Maid of Devon*, bound soon for Philadelphia. Once aboard her, with my passage paid, no one would dare molest me or my body servant.

"We have no money to pay your passage," Martinez told me,

"but under the guidance of Fernando—he is the one who will meet you at the cathedral—you might raise enough."

"I will take that way if I can."

"Do not be afraid. This is Manzanillo, which bears the honored title of El Fiel, meaning the faithful."

No other of my companions could speak either English or French, but their strong handclasps and broad smiles were part of a universal language older and more open than either of these. Two or three gave me good-luck charms associated with voodoo. Since my clothes had been brushed and cleaned, I was able to dress respectably and inconspicuously. When N'kulu put on the white jacket and loose cotton trousers of a body servant, he looked quite domesticated—a far cry from the lean savage of the woods. As the light failed none looked at us twice, and no one spoke to me until, at dusk, what appeared to be an old beggar approached me close by the high-towered cathedral.

We followed him as we had been told to do; he led us to a house of middle quality enclosed by an ancient stone wall. There my old beggar turned into a pleasant-appearing Cuban, apparently of pure Spanish stock, no older than forty-five; with him dwelt a handsome woman whom I took for a quadroon, and a young man and a young woman of mixed blood. The family was apparently prosperous and of good standing in the town, and my curiosity was aroused as to what possible bond they had with the maroons, but they did not tell me, and I could not bring myself to ask. I noticed that the woman had been branded by a triangle within a circle on the back of her hand. It was a deep and indelible burn, and that she had had a tragic history I could not doubt.

4

When I had bathed and shared the family's spicy Spanish supper, I asked my English-speaking host if I could be taken, early in the morning, to the shop of a pawnbroker of good reputation, liberal as possible, and speaking either English or French.

"If the business involves as many as a hundred pesos, such a one will come here to see you, not tomorrow but tonight," my host answered.

I asked that he bring his best magnifying glass and most delicate set of scales. The young man left the house; and again the tempo of events began to quicken. Within the hour arrived a bearded Spanish Jew, Señor Augustin Marcel, who reminded me of some Italian Jews, of high and ancient standing, whom I had known in Charleston. His bearing was dignified and his manners impeccable.

When I had looked to the window shades, I took from my waistcoat pocket a white pebble selected from my antelope-skin pouch. It was not as large as two or three of the others, having about the diameter of my little fingernail, but its eight sides were smooth and quite perfect, and it was the brightest of the lot. This I put in his hand.

He glanced at it curiously, then with growing amazement. Taking it close under the lamp, he affixed his eyeglass and scrutinized it minutely. At last he raised almost incredulous eyes to mine.

"May I ask, señor, if this stone came out of Brazil?"

"No, sir."

"Well, I didn't think so. It hasn't quite the appearance of a Brazilian stone. I won't say it has more fire—or less—but its water is somehow different. Would you care to tell me from what mines it did come?"

"From none that I know of. It was found in South Africa."

"You mean Asia. There are no diamonds in Africa."

"I am repeating only what was told me."

"May I weigh the stone?"

"Please do."

He dropped into one pan of the scales small cubes of brass weighing something less than four grains each. The beam tipped as he put in the eighth.

"Something over seven carats," Marcel told me. "That is as close as I can come with my present counters. Now I ask that

I take the stone home with me, to scrutinize in daylight. I'll give you my receipt, valuing the jewel at a thousand pesos, although, actually, it will not bring so much. I'll return with it tomorrow morning to offer you a loan on it, or to purchase it. Whichever you desire."

"I gladly agree."

"I failed to state that Fernando, your host, will assure you of the validity of my paper."

"Sir, I don't need the assurance."

He seemed pleased and took courteous leave. In the morning he returned, and offered to lend me five hundred pesos on the stone, or to buy it outright for seven hundred. I accepted the latter.

"Mark you, Mr. Stono, it would bring somewhat more in Amsterdam or New York, possibly in Havana. There are no cutters here."

"Would you name me a reliable buyer in New York in case I have other stones to sell?"

"With pleasure. He is one of my nation, indeed a distant kinsman. Moreover, if you care to show me the stones, I can make a good guess at what he will pay for them. At least I will tell you what I would pay, if most of my money was in hand and I had his heavy purse."

So I showed him the twenty-one stones I had left. He examined each one with his glass, quickly but carefully. Then he removed it from his eye and gave me a happy smile.

"Mine is the best of the lot," he told me. "Only one of the others approaches it in worth. Still they are finer than any run-of-the-mine I have ever seen, and I am mightily curious as to the field that produced them. I estimate their weight at one hundred and ten carats, and I think you can safely count on forty-five hundred dollars for the lot, and a good chance of getting five thousand."

"No more than that?" For this was only a doubling of the capital I had started with, and I owed nearly half of it to Faro Jack.

"Say forty-five or fifty dollars a carat. That's a high price for rough diamonds, and, mark you, young man, that comes to seventy-five thousand dollars a pound!"

When I stared at him, and perhaps he saw a fever reddening my face, he could not refrain from baiting me a little more.

"We Jews know about jewels. Ever since we went into exile we have dealt with them—you see, we had to be ready to run at any hour of the night, with what goods we could snatch up—and perhaps the two words are connected. But even we did not suspect there are diamonds in Africa. If I were a young man—footloose and free and knowing the way—I would go and look for them."

He wrote down the name and address of a kinsman in New York; and after counting out seven hundred pesos he shook my hand and departed. Suddenly I was satisfied with the present prospect of only a small fortune; nor was it a case of sour grapes. To lie to others is excusable and often commendable but no good gambler may lie to himself for that is the part of a sucker, and that way lies ruin. I did not want to stop before I was twenty-five and be a little planter, a petty gentleman, all my days. As it was—but let me dream awhile. There was almost no horizon to those dreams!

My first act was to give Fernando fifty pesos for his good care of me. If he used it to help runaway slaves, which I could hardly question, it was his business, not mine; and consistency had never been my long suit. I remained a Charlestonian of deepest dye, but if necessary—as most men find out about themselves—I could on occasion run with the hare and hunt with the hounds. That way, between the Devil and the Deep Sea, we manage to live on.

CHAPTER IX

Young Moon Setting

M Y JOURNEY from Manzanillo to New York, with the business and pleasure involved, and my leisurely return to Savannah, occupied nearly three months. Señor Marcel's guess at the market value of my diamonds turned out fairly close, and on the low instead of the high side, as I had feared. After pocketing for some unknown future use the stone he had told me was the second best in the batch, I received five thousand six hundred dollars for the remaining twenty. During the transaction I was straitly and cunningly questioned as to their source. Since no one believed my story of their being found in South Africa, I thought best to stick to it, in the spirit of Charleston salt-water fishermen who always gave Bull's Island as the scene of their big catches brought into port. The shrewd questioners grinned the same as had the dock loafers. But one of them, a famous expert and cutter fresh from Amsterdam, solved the mystery to the satisfaction of all.

"Dese stones, dey coom from de Kapuas Valley in Borneo," he pronounced in a thick Dutch dialect. "For fife dollar, I name you de werry mine. I do not blame you, Heer Stono, for telling de little yoke, but I vill eat all de diamonds ever found or ever vill be found in Sout' Africa. You see, mine friend, de geological formation is all wrong."

When I arrived in Savannah, I had three drafts on the greatest of New York banks, the first for two thousand dollars payable to John Fargo, whom I knew as Faro Jack; the second for the odd sum of two thousand seven hundred and sixty dollars made out to me but endorsable to any other in case of certain eventualities, and the third, the balance of the sum, payable to either N'kulu or myself, according to which lived the longest. I could not forget Jack's utterance regarding the short life of great players. I had played greatly once, and the game had come wondrously nigh to being my last; and the present cards were pregnant with even greater games.

From Savannah we went by river steamer to Augusta; from where inquiry led us to an old millpond on a tributary of the beautiful Ogeechee. The millhouse had been turned into a cottage with genuine flowers growing about its door, and it seemed that the story of John Fargo, alias Faro Jack, had turned out almost unbelievably right. The pond teemed with the bass and bream, catfish and 'gators and terrapins, herons with the shining whiteness and serene flight of angels waded its shallows; redbellies and even shad made springtime rushes into the spillway. The flowers were tended and the cottage tidied by as pretty and trim a brown-skin girl as I had ever seen. Although she had emancipation papers taking effect the moment Jack died, she was in no hurry for that event; he had bought her out of a cotton patch, she doted on catching and eating catfish, and her expression as far as I could tell, was one perpetual beam. All this, and the garden and cornfield, Jack showed me in great pride. If I thought he would be chafing at the bit for the smoke-filled garish rooms of heartbreak, I could think again. The nervous glint was gone from his eyes and his manner was so mild that, barring the brown girl and a small whiskey still, you could mistake him for a retired deacon. However, I was too good at reading faces not to notice now and then a fleeting deep anxiety that just now he wished to forget.

Not a single deck of cards could be found in the whole layout. My questioning him about this oddity brought out a strange and chilling fact.

"You haven't even an old pack for you and Cassie to play seven-up?" I asked, in the way of teasing him, as we sat on his little porch overlooking the water.

"I threw it in the lake a month ago."

"Did Memphis—or some other old competitor—pay you a call?"

"It wasn't Memphis—or no old competitor neither—but I had a caller, and he taught me a lesson."

"For how much?"

"I hate to tell you, but I will. I declared a thousand and so did he. I thought we were both cracking a joke. But he took the thousand."

"That reminds me." I brought forth and handed Jack a draft for two thousand.

"Good God A'mighty!" he broke out, when he read the figure.

"I haven't included any interest."

"I don't want no interest. I don't want the principal, unless you can spare it." Although he had a gambler's face, he could not keep out an intense hope.

"I've nearly twice that much, clean profit."

"Are you lying to me, Edward? You never did."

"No, sir."

"Well, then, you haven't any idea what you've done for me. I've got the rent from some property in Augusta, but I went in debt to pay for this place, and I'd raked up a thousand to pay it and then lost it, sucker that I am. What was I going to do next? Damn my soul, if I didn't think of selling Cassie—and that would have damned my soul, forever amen. It scared me so that I gave her those freedom papers, signed before a notary, sealed by the court. Remember I believe in the human soul, its blessedness or its damnation."

"I remember that you do."

"What was left but hiring a couple of grubby rooms in Atlanta—I was too proud to go back to Augusta—and run two-penny games until I got in the clear? But I hated the thought of it, and now, by all the stars that shine, I don't have to! What a piece of luck! My God, what a trick of Fate! You see, Edward, I didn't expect your return for years and years. 'Fact, I wasn't at all sure that you were alive. And so many of us come back broke. Broke of pocket and sometimes broke of spirit. They were laying for you, Edward—the bad cards, I mean. You were so young and so proud. Instead, you came back a winner and paid a debt I never thought I'd need. But watch out, or they'll get you yet."

"What got you that night, Jack? It wasn't your sixty years. Your eyes are still bright, your hands steady—"

"It was whist, played with the greatest skill—backed by one of the wickedest brains—I've ever run across."

Jack often used "wicked" to mean dangerous or merely very competent. But I detected suppressed excitement in his voice and countenance—a wonder was upon him greater than that of the return of his bread cast on the waters—and I knew I had not yet got to the bottom of this affair.

"He said he was traveling through the state, looking up routes for new railroads," Jack went on. "But the real reason he came here was to inquire for you."

"For me," I echoed after a long pause.

"He said—and his eyes shone like a fox's in the shine of a pine-knot pan—that he knew your brother, in Charleston. I said that you hadn't any brothers that I knew of; he answered that I hadn't been very frank about my history, and since I didn't like the smell of him—I just put it that way, but the fact is, he wore some kind of perfume—I shut my mouth."

"This was a month ago?"

"Yes."

"What name did he give?"

"Mr. Henry. That was some kind of a joke. An ornery one, unless I miss my guess. He was a very handsome man about forty years old, with fine clothes. The odd thing about him was—one of the odd things—he scared the wits out of Cassie."

"How?"

"I don't know and Cassie doesn't either. Every time he looked at her he gave her a little smile that came straight out of hell."

I was almost at the bottom of it now. I was not excited, though; I had only a sense of the turning of Fortune's Wheel, of cards shuffling and falling in a game that had started and could not be stopped until its end; of Fate that rode the rawboned horse of Death.

"How did he look?" I asked, when I had the heart.

Jack had card sharp's eyes and would tell me true.

"It's a question I hate to answer, but I will. Although a whole lot handsomer, he looked a lot like you."

"Had you ever seen him before?"

"I wasn't sure. I'd forgotten his name but remembered he came from one of the great Charleston families. I think he left town about twenty years ago under some kind of cloud."

"I get the point of the joke of him calling himself Mr. Henry. His father was a great admirer of Henry Clay—in spite of Clay being a political enemy of Calhoun, and favoring the restriction of slavery. In fact, he named his son after him, but the son doesn't favor its restriction; he favors its universal application. Still it wasn't a very good joke. I doubt if any of Clay Hudson's jokes are very good."

"That was who I meant," Jack said quietly.

"I think he intends to play an extra good one on me, one of these days. Much better than taking me for a mere thousand dollars at whist. I wish I knew what it is. I'm going to have to be careful."

2

Returning to Augusta after my happy visit with Jack, I did not try to find Clara Day. It would have been an easy search, provided she had not taken herself off—following some lover, perhaps, or the strong smell of money—or had not been taken off by a spell of fever aggravated by late hours, a knife in the breast, a spoon-ful of poison, or some other sudden accident to which the Clara Days of this world are especially liable.

The month was March—not yet its ides, only its beginning. In Augusta spring had not made up her fickle mind to set in or to wait awhile, warm, bright, heavenly days alternated with days of blustering wind, gray days, days of bitter frost, but as the screeching train came down from the low hills and the trees took more and more to wearing cloaks of Spanish moss, there came a sheen of green upon the landscape, the sky looked more serene, a greater number of dark-skinned fishermen waited for us to pass before they resumed their places on the bridges, and the season was a fortnight and perhaps a whole month advanced. At length we steamed and tooted our way into the beautiful, ugly, noble, infamous, good and evil but always valiant city of my birth. Still I did not know what in the Devil I was doing here, or what he would do to me.

Perhaps I had no choice. The cards fell in a certain way; I must play them or pass; with God looking over my shoulder as I thought He did all men, I dared not stack the deck. Anyway it so happened that I inquired of an elegant, ebony-black door-man, who would be certain to know, whether Miss Salley Sass—or perhaps her name now was Mistress Mate Hudson—dwelt with her kinsmen at the Hudson mansion by the promenade, or whether she was still at Hudson Barony, or somewhere afar. He gave me a full answer in rich Gullah.

"Sah, she's still Miss Salley, but de ol' butler, Nicodemus, he tell a frien' o' mine 'at it may be any day now she'll change up. She livin' at Mr. Benson's house—he de white fo'man—while de hands fix some new flo' in de big house. Mas' Hudson, he at de town house. Dey say he won't stay much longer, 'cause it done been bought up. Mas' Mate, he off in Alabam', seein' about de land Ol' Miss got out there."

"Where Master Arnold and Master Clay?"

"Mas' Arnold, he at his own house in de town." Then, con-fronting a subject that he did not like, "Mas' Clay Hudson, he stay at de hotel las' week, but he gone somewheres now, and I don't know when he be back."

Luck was with me, I thought, that both Mate and Clay Hudson were presumably out of town. Mate was my friend—I could not think of him otherwise—but he had never mentioned our blood relationship, and it was in keeping with his character not to know it. He possessed and would ever retain an innocence that I had lost before I was ten years old, and which Salley, by what imparting of what serpent I knew not, might never have possessed.

In my room I wrote a careful note:

Dear Salley:

Would you and Mr. Mason Hudson the elder give me a few minutes in the very near future? I will meet you at any hour and place that you appoint; if tomorrow is sunny and warm, I take the liberty of suggesting the Battery at four in the afternoon. I consider the matter of considerable importance and I hope you both will regard it favorably.

I remain, ma'am,

Your well-wisher,
Edward Stono

A free-born stableboy agreed to deliver it at Hudson Barony for one of my Spanish pesos now changed to a Yankee dollar. At evening he brought me Salley's answer—a single line on lavender scented notepaper that her uncle Mason and herself would keep the rendezvous unless unforeseen circumstances interfered. I went to bed excited, perplexed, half-proud, half-ashamed. The day broke on a clear sky, and the warm sun followed soon.

When I had dressed, I went forth to make pilgrimage to our old house by Upper East Bay. We had never owned it, only rented it; and no doubt some poor whites of the Quarter occupied it now; still I felt compelled to gaze at its shabby exterior and, if possible, enter its bleak rooms. To my great shock, it had been destroyed by fire. Literally nothing was left of it but a dozen stones on which its sills had rested and the remains of a stone chimney. Then, as I gazed upon these remnants, something very like relief swept through me. There was fire and smoke in the vision of me seen by the witchwoman of the island; and fire and smoke had set me free from one chain of the past. I was no longer dubious of the decision I had come to, and no longer ashamed. Instead of dreading the meeting in the Battery, I looked forward to it.

The hour drew near. I sat on the very bench where once I had told secrets to Salley Sass, where she had turned her proud black head and kissed me. Almost on the moment, she and Mason Hudson appeared. My father wore the long form-fitting coat, tall hat, stock, and tight gray trousers associated with my remembrances. Although past sixty, he gave no sign of declining years; his back was straight, his head high, his carriage slightly and deliberately grand, his countenance beautifully molded by the hands of Time and more distinguished than ever—if my eyes told true—and they almost always did. About him hung an air of elegance he would never lose. In shabby clothes and with a dirty face he would still inform us instantly of his rank—us poor whites of Upper East Bay—and of our own rank.

The money Salley had spent on her attire was little, but it had gone a long way. Her many-gored skirt with its flaring bottom and close-fitting jacket with creamy lace at its collar and cuffs matched and were as seasonable as the dark-green foliage, not flamboyant yet of first-venturing spring; set perkily on her black hair was a sailor hat of straw.

I looked at her, halfway hoping she would be changed, aged a little, looking more like other people, not so set apart. Instead the quiet magic was on her still. I had never seen such a superbly cast female face; its only counterpart in a male face had been that of her cousin, Clay Hudson. A bad strain of the high Ashley blood had beautified them both. Hers was a dark beauty, lent by the thick forest and deeply shaded rivers of her native Edisto, and recalling to lonely-hearted men long-ago dreams of love, that never would and never could come true; and bringing to men like me, who disavowed such dreams, immediate leaping lust. Her eyes were pale brown, her lips dark red. Only when she smiled was the sharp pain of seeing her relieved. Then her face took on a childish lighting. No longer a witch of the woods, too beautiful and too still to be human, she became only a highborn daughter of our Low Country, with some evil in her.

My father, Mason Hudson, waited with his hat in his hand for her to greet me. It was only a wild aberration that I thought of Mate Hudson, pausing politely, while Clara Day mounted a flight of stairs in Memphis' gaming rooms. But this now was more than Low Country chivalry, ever somewhat overdone in this New World anomaly that was Charleston, this transplanted Versailles a century out of date. He was reminding me—perhaps only himself—that he had not acknowledged me as his son.

3

"Edward, I'm glad—and a little surprised—to see you," Salley said.

"I don't see why you should be either one."

"Well, I can't explain the first. Perhaps it's just that you don't appear as frightening as I half-feared—as you, yourself, threatened to be, if ever I saw you again."

Salley had a natural impulse to break ice at once. It might be her most aristocratic propensity. Certainly she did so not in malice but to establish truth, without which no one could feel free. I could not deny I felt greatly relieved.

"As for my surprise," she went on, "I certainly didn't expect to see you this soon—and quite likely never again. You don't play it very safely, you know. But you want to greet Uncle Mason."

"Sir, you're looking very well," I said, when we had shaken hands.

"Thank you, Edward. I can say the same of you."

"A great deal nicer, to tell the truth," Salley added. "The last time—but of course conditions were at their worst, that night. I'd think something very pleasant has happened to you since." She looked at me more closely, her gaze wide and direct. "And perhaps some things not so pleasant."

"May we sit down?" I asked. "What I have to say takes only a few minutes—"

"I think we'd better. Things you say have a way of taking my breath."

She sat on the nearest bench, my father and I on either side of her. All three of us appeared very calm; although none of us came near it. I knew my own feelings and I had sat with too many adversaries at high play to be deceived by others.

"First, I would like to ask a deeply personal question," I began. "I don't think the answer to it will affect what I wish to do, or give me more, or less, justification, but I'll feel better, knowing the answer—that there was more logic in it—and there's very little at best—or that I went ahead anyway. I guess that's not very clear. I assure you, though, that you won't regret telling me. I came to meet you in peace and in contrition."

"I accept that assurance," my father said. "What is your question?"

Salley started to say something too—I thought it would be a kind thing—but she closed her warm-looking lovely lips, and I saw them, and thought of our last kiss, the second of only two, and I could hardly speak at all.

This little park, somehow the epitome of Charleston, was where Mason Hudson gave me my first book. Here I had first met Mate Hudson, with a kind of beauty in his face and loneliness in his eyes. What I was about to do, I might be doing for Mate's sake. I might be doing it for vanity, although that might be only a cheapened name for pride. Anyway I would be doing it for my heart.

The trees were budding, and this was March, and our lovely Southern spring was breaking fast. Fast as the beat of my heart, I thought. But as I sat here with my betters, my voice was calm, and my manner was that of a gentleman.

"Will you kindly tell me whether your investments in Alabama have prospered as you hoped?"

"Not as we hoped," Salley answered before my father could speak. "The crop we planted last year was a failure because of drouth. The drouth was confined to only a few square miles—nothing like it had ever been seen before—but our land happened to be in the middle of it."

"Had that anything to do with the selling of your house in Charleston? I heard it had been sold."

"We didn't sell it. We should have done so years ago—and now we've lost it. My cousin, Clay Hudson, bought up the mortgages and foreclosed. Uncle Mason and Aunt Mildred have until May to get out. Clay was very gentlemanly about it—he is the most polished member of the family—in that respect he reminds me of you. Like you, he deals in facts."

"I deal cards, which are only numbers of agreed value. Gamblers live in a world of half-fact, half-fancy. Also, I deal in myth, as you well know. And I wish to remind you that I'm not an accredited member of the family."

Mason Hudson had changed color but I thought he blessed Salley for her frankness. The ice was indeed broken. My heart lifted.

"That last was unavoidable, Edward," he said quietly.

"I know it was. I can go ahead now. Salley spoke a while ago of what I had told her the last time I saw her. Of course, sir, she told you."

"No, I didn't," Salley said.

"You didn't!"

"What would be the use? It would worry him, and he had enough worries. Either you could carry out your threat, or else it was a false alarm. I don't know yet."

"I'll tell you now. Sir, when I came to the Barony that night, I was not in my right mind. My mother had just died in squalor. She had received ten dollars a month from you, and with her sewing—"

I was strangely interrupted. My father spoke in a low, shaken voice. His face turned swiftly gray.

"Did you say ten dollars?"

"Yes."

"Edward, I sent twenty. Even that was a pittance, but it was

all I could do. You won't believe that. I, master of a great plantation, a slaveowner, and all the rest. I was trying to guard the
secret. I never knew how to manage. There were so many calls,
all of which seemed important. I'm only making matters worse—"

"No, you're not. Anyway it was more than most men, even
most gentlemen, would have done, unless they were forced to.
Of course your messenger took half. Sir, you were at fault in trusting a man like that. But you couldn't come yourself—and you
didn't want anyone else to know."

"He is a devil!"

"Granted, but he had something to do with my cure. When I
came to the ball, I told Salley that the Hudson family and I were
going to change places. I would own Hudson Barony and the
town house; you and the others would live in shacks and see how
you liked it. Even then I didn't for a moment think of it as
justice, even the Mosaic law of eye for eye, tooth for tooth; I
intended to bring it about for my personal satisfaction, an act of
malice. Very naturally, Salley didn't think I could succeed. One
little bastard, matched against the power and glory of the Hudsons—those were her words."

"I was more frightened than I let you know," Salley said, not
looking me in the face.

"You should have been. I meant it very seriously—and I am
a gambler who will risk high stakes. I lived to see the folly of it,
and now I've reached a quite opposite state of mind. I'm more
proud of my mother than ever—the long brave fight she made—
and have accepted the fictitious name she gave me as my real
name. I want to start from scratch. I don't want to be a half
Hudson but a whole bastard. I don't want her to owe any obligations for an act which she did of her own free will, and I don't
want to inherit any obligations, good or bad. I wish to make one
settlement, then close the door on the past. I don't want to feel
any more dependence. I wish to be entirely free."

The reason Salley did not look at me was that her eyes had
filled with tears. I did not know their meaning. But my father's

eyes were fixed steadfastly on mine. His soul was in them, and I almost saw its shape.

"I am not sure—that I know what you mean," he said.

"I do, I think," Salley said.

"I have here a draft on a New York bank for the sum my mother received from you in twenty-three years. It is true that you paid out twice that sum, but the other half was lost through no fault of hers—indeed through your own mistake in choosing an agent. I wish to endorse it over to you. For the interest you took in me —the books you lent me—I can give you only thanks."

"Edward, you cut me to the quick."

"I don't mean to, sir. I'm doing only what it seems I have to do, according to my conceptions, to gain the freedom that I need and want."

"Take it, Uncle Mason," Salley broke in. "He wants you to have it."

Time rolled back his scroll. When Theba had spoken thus of my accepting N'kulu's little bag of jewels, she had reminded me of Salley. Now Salley reminded me of Theba.

"How can I?"

"You owe him his freedom, if he wants it. What claim have you got on him really, except the money? And if you won't take it for his needs, take it for ours. It means we can plant another crop."

Her voice broke and she rose quickly and walked a short distance away.

"Edward, I am not a clever man," my father told me. "I'm not an understanding man. I find in times of great perplexity I have to be guided by others. But I wronged your mother—I wronged you—and to take back the money with which I tried to atone—"

"I don't know that you wronged either of us," I said, when he paused. "It is over my head as are all the other mysteries of life and death. But I know that except for you I would never have been born. I would have been non-existent. If that will help you any in doing what I ask—"

"You *ask* it?"

"I entreat it, for my heart's need."

"Then I will."

I took out the little slip of paper with the small inkhorn and pen that I had brought, and wrote on the back of it. My hand shook when I held it out; with a shaking hand he accepted it.

He rose at once. "Edward, I wish you good day," he said—the only suitable thing to say, I thought.

"Thank you, and will you tell Salley I'd like to speak to her a moment more?"

"Of course I will, and I'll wait for her on the High Battery."

He walked off, his back straight and his head high, and spoke briefly to Salley. She returned to where I was standing.

"What is it, Edward? What do you want of me?"

"I'm a free man now, and I ask you to marry me."

She looked at me steadily and long.

"Come out to Hudson Barony tonight," she replied. "I believe —I'm almost sure—that tonight I'll give you my answer."

4

Chances were, I thought, that Salley would receive me in the little parlor of the foreman's house. The fact remained that I was going forth to sue for her hand in marriage, a mission of great moment, so I dressed formally in a broadcloth evening suit and ruffled shirt I had bought in New York to replace the garments I had lost. Again I hired the fast team from Bailey's livery stable. Although N'kulu knew next to nothing about guiding vehicles, he had ridden horses, possessed strong hands and a commanding voice, and was correctly dressed as a body servant, so without great compunction I let him drive. Happily he got through the Charleston evening traffic without accident. Once on the open road, he was in his glory.

When we turned into the avenue of ancient live oaks there gleamed through the foliage a light in the window of the Big House. It winked out and came again, and I followed it, and gave no further thought to the foreman's house standing half a mile beyond, except to wonder at my own faithlessness in Salley's *savoir-faire* by ever doubting the dignity of my reception. Every form would be observed, every detail have a correct aspect. If half the floor had been torn up, there would be no sawdust or kegs of nails on the part remaining, only the warm glimmer of the lamps.

My suit might be dismissed—I had no real reason to think otherwise—but this was no fool's errand. If it were, she would not have bade me come.

The old butler, Nicodemus, answered my knock. He bowed low, we exchanged a remark about the weather; with impeccable mien he led me into the drawing room where three big logs blazed crackling on the hearth. There he bade me wait Miss Salley's coming. It would not be long, he thought, and I could warm myself after the cold ride. Meanwhile I was marveling at the lovely multicolored flame. This was salt-impregnated driftwood hauled from the beaches, which Low Country hostesses burned only at intimate gatherings, usually of family importance. It caused me to wonder greatly. I knew so little about Salley; all that I really knew of her was her dark and thrilling beauty. There might be more luck in the cards tonight than I had dared imagine. There might be more good fortune in my Fate than I had ever dreamed.

She appeared in a few minutes, quietly, at once lovely and tranquil, as bringers of happiness come to us in dreams. The signs of good fortune multiplied. With the full skirt of black velvet she wore a lace bertha dropped off her shoulders, with short, puffed sleeves, whereby their exquisite rounding became glossed by the firelight, warm and dark, and her eyes were beautifully matched, and the first swell of her breast was shown by the low bodice, for the pleasure and excitation of my gaze only. Beside the fireside chair from which I rose stood a large, high, old-fashioned footstool. It was here she chose to sit, a little lower than me, and in my easy reach.

In the way of visible amenities there was only Nicodemus who came only a moment after her entrance, and by poking the fire and turning over one of the logs caused a greater play of its rainbow lights. He went out, and I took her beautiful long hand in mine. It felt firm, and its countless small muscles were well developed. I visioned her fishing with a hand line for red bass when she wore pigtails, the surf crashing about her knees. Since then this hand had performed many a useful task.

"Have you decided yet?" I asked boldly, after a few minutes of trivial conversation.

"How could I, when you've been away two years? No, that's not the reason. You've prospered, financially—I believe that's the polite word, though it isn't very polite—and personally. You are certainly far more eligible than when you left. Did you make the money gambling?"

"No. I'll tell you after a little while how I came by it. It was a kind of a windfall."

"Have you got a lot more? You see, I have no father to put the proper and quite rightful questions; and Uncle Mason couldn't put them. Even when poor people marry, the father has the right to ask if the suitor has a good job. In the aristocracy, money is among the primary considerations. The estates mustn't peter out; they can only be maintained by advantageous marriages. Otherwise it's a case of shirt-sleeves to shirt-sleeves. I'm a poor one to talk, because I'm a pauper; still my position ought to be worth a mighty lot. I mean—to balance against the riches of a suitor without position."

"Do you talk that way—blunt, to say the least—as a kind of performance, or does it come natural to you?"

"You like to have me talk this way. I discovered that long ago. The reason is, perhaps, that your own shortcomings—your gambling and your bastardy, for instance—seem so much less damaging when they are spoken out loud than when they are whispered. Besides that, I'm inclined to be an unusually honest and direct person. I've had to compensate for some bad blood, and I got practice in it from talking to Papa like a Dutch uncle. That was the only way I could get anything out of him, even money to buy food. He rather fancied himself, you know. His

father was a Sass, he'd married a Salley, and his mother was an
Ashley, although of the wrong branch, so I had to keep reminding him that he himself was a rotter. You're not, Edward. Don't
take it as an implication. And now answer my question. Believe
me—if you want to marry me—it's terribly important."

"I've got something over a thousand dollars."

"Oh, is that all?"

"But I may have a million dollars at this time next year."

"Then I'd better wait till then, to make up my mind."

"Maybe ten million. Possibly a great deal more than that. Instead of three square miles of rice fields, I may have thirty miles.
I may be the richest man in Carolina—richer than Cornelius
Vanderbilt. Do you think in that case any of your friends would
give a damn whether my seamstress mother was married to my
father? But you can't wait till then to make up your mind.
You've got to take me while I'm on the make, or not at all."

"That thrills me—a little. I don't know why."

"In the meantime I can offer you a great deal of excitement.
I'm going to sail for South Africa in a few days, and as my bride
you can go with me. When we get there, we'll look for diamonds.
I know that diamonds are to be found and I know where to look
—knowledge possessed by no other white man. We'll live and
travel in an ox wagon. I have enough money to grubstake us well.
We'll eat mainly wild game and we'll run into danger from
savage tribes and wild beasts. If we strike it rich—then I'll be
content to return to the Low Country and make the biggest
splash in its recorded history. If not, we'll go and do something
else."

"That has a wonderful ring to it. You are a very effective
suitor. If it wasn't for Mate—"

"Also I'll give you this, and all that goes with it."

I leaned down a little and took her beautiful face between my
hands, and they felt the beauty of it and the gloss, and my lips
knew and conveyed to me a beauty and ecstasy beyond telling,
almost beyond belief, as they pressed and then captured hers.
When she became conscious of losing her safe bearings and tried

to draw away, I held her in a tightening grasp. Her lips parted and I felt her breath quicken. But as suddenly as I had seized her, I let her go. I was impelled to by the same instincts that made me a successful gambler.

"There's a lot of evil in you, Edward," she said slowly, after a long pause. "I didn't feel it in your kisses, but I see it in your eyes."

"There's a lot in you too, Salley. You came by it more naturally than I did."

"That's one reason I love Mate."

"I think you could go on loving him—in the way that you do— and still be happy, married to me."

"Maybe I could. But he wouldn't be happy. I think he'd die soon. Let that go for the minute. Where did you hear about the diamonds?"

"From a runaway slave."

"You didn't help a slave to run away—did you?"

"Yes, a lot of them."

"Isn't that treason to all we stand for?"

"Not under those conditions."

"Was there a woman involved? I have a feeling that there was. I thought that was what brought the change in you I saw when we met in the park."

"A very beautiful young woman. She was an Arab girl who had been sold into slavery by her slave-catcher father. She was as tall as you, darker than you, as beautiful as you. But she had to go her way and I had to go mine."

"But not at once."

"No."

"Not for several weeks—or months."

"No, only a few days."

"She couldn't have wrought that change in you unless—"

"Of course not."

"Do you want to go back to her?"

"What she gave me was so perfect—so satisfying—that I can go back to her instantly. She promised me that, and I find it's true."

"Was she more of a woman than I am?"

"How can I tell you at this stage?"

"You know, Edward, that makes me very jealous. I'm not jealous of the Charleston women. They're beautiful—accomplished —highbred, but they've been so carefully sheltered that they've become too refined. Mate doesn't want any of them. I mean, he hasn't any powerful need of them. He wants—and needs—only me. I want you to want and need only me, not in the way that Mate does, but as your woman. Yet this swarthy Arab girl—"

"She wasn't much darker than you. Once, at least, she reminded me of you. She had long dark hair and very light feet and there was a splendor in her face and she came of a more passionate race."

"I don't think she did." And as I looked Salley in the face, her gaze fell and the color mounted fast in her pale-brown cheeks.

5

I lifted Salley off her stool, and sitting down again held her in my lap. She was warmed and aroused and vulnerable, and partly because of the forces awake and fierce within me, and partly to gain my ends, I made reckless love to her. For a little while we were more in conflict than in union. She took pleasure and perhaps pride—strange and inexplicable is the human heart—in my desire; but also satisfaction in resisting it. But the cards of life were stacked against her. Her eyes changed shape, and darkened as her pupils became immense, and were lighted deep within, and the longing in her face became manifest in beauty which not words or even thought could measure, the linking of poetry with passion that is one aspect of human love. The fire threw many-colored lights. The darkness lay outside the windows and the house was silent and in the great river the tide rose with irresistible power, and a night bird cried, and the mystery of being was deep and full upon us both.

She drew back, and covered her breast that I had bared, and her face was luminous with desire.

"Pull the bell cord, Edward."

"If you like."

"I'm only going to tell Nicodemus that we can watch the fire and for him to go to bed."

"Very well."

"It will only take a minute. If that minute breaks it up, it isn't worth keeping anyway. It isn't the real thing."

I rose and pulled the cord. When Nicodemus came, she was standing by the fireplace, and she spoke to him in the deeply friendly voice that masters and mistresses employ to their trusted retainers. He stirred the fire again, and withdrew. She remained there, motionless, fully a minute more. Then she came back to me and put her arms around my neck and kissed me.

"Do you love me, Edward?"

"Yes."

"Will you always love me, even if this night is our lone and only night?"

"I always have, and I always will."

"Come with me then. Walk quietly."

She took me by the hand and led me out of the room. We went into the hall and climbed the high, wide, dimly lighted stairway. At its head she led me into the dark passage, then opened a door. A low fire in the fireplace, not long ago tended, flung a dim, uncertain light on a tall chest, chairs delicately wrought in dark-red mahogany, silk curtains, and a canopied bed. There was a faint, agreeable, flower-like smell I could never forget. The window opening westward revealed the young moon, sharp-edged and bright as a sword.

"When will it set, Edward?" Salley asked.

"In about three hours."

"If you wish, you may stay till then."

"I wish it to be in earnest of our staying together always. Again I ask for your hand in marriage."

"I can't promise you yet, Edward. I'll try to tell you before you go."

"Then I've got to ask you something else. Maybe it will stamp me as a vulgarian. But I've always thought it concerned a right thing. You know I dreamed of being a gentleman. No matter what I do, I can't quite waken from that dream. My mind is confused by it, but a few old concepts, rules you might call them, still operate. You are a great aristocrat. Somehow that enables you to make your own rules as long as no one is harmed. But I've got to stick to the book."

"That is very touching, Edward. I wish I could promise to marry you. I'd love to go to Africa with you. But I'm not sure."

"You know what I want to ask?"

"Yes. If this is the first time."

"You know it's none of my business?"

"I'm not sure about that. Everyone has the right to do what he thinks he must do, to stay out of hell. If it seems right to you to ask me, do so, and I'll tell you."

"Would it be the first time?"

"No. It would be the second time. The first time was with Mate."

"I didn't think that Mate would break that old rule. I thought he would be less likely to than I."

"We were both very young—on the beach—and I tempted him."

"If Mate loves you as much as I do, he would have won you by now."

"That's not fair. It wasn't his fault. I'm the one who waited —and I think for you. Now do you want to try to prove it, or go back? It would be safer to go back. Not for me, but for you. The danger is very great. You may never be happy again— after tonight. The invitation may again be withdrawn. Do you remember?"

"How could I forget?"

She came close to the fire, then turned and looked at me. "Well?"

"I love you, Salley. To use the talk of the tables, I call you."

"I hope that you win."

The moon dropped slowly. Everywhere she looked, there were

scenes reflecting the drama of life, the beauty of love; but I thought she kept a special and benign watch through our window. She shone on the broad reaches of the river, and there the fish fed fiercely, ere the fast of darkness. The season was early spring, and the strong passionate resurgence of life moved in every trunk and shrub and blade of grass and heart. This was the South, beloved of the sun, the warm land peopled by a fervent race. I was its son and Salley was its daughter, and in loving each other we loved what had shaped us. I will be true to you, Southland! I will not be seduced by the gnawed-bone morals of the cold North. The daughter of the green and fertile island lay in my arms. The darkness of its forest and of its deep slow-drawn rivers was echoed in her hair, reflected in her face.

That beautiful face that flung beauty into mine! The ecstasy of being, not half-drowned in piety, entangled by texts, not shivering with cold, but luminous and leaping, young, scornful of Death; you I have tonight. I know the bliss of love, I have plumbed, although I do not understand, the mystery of eternity. Yet the moon falls, cutting off the minutes, measuring time. Moon, stand still a space. Wait, Time, a little while. Death, I will make a bargain with you, one that will profit you well. Good and Evil, I cannot tell one of you from the other, but I will divide between you all that I have. Love, do not turn away. Luck, I have never invoked you before, I was too proud. Tonight stand by me.

But the moon set. There was darkness in the west except where small stars shone, eclipsed until now. I rose and stood at the doorway. Salley came to me and took my hand and talked plain as was her wont.

"I love you, Edward. I've loved you from the day I met you on the beach. But I still love Mate."

"You'll have to choose between us."

"I can't, tonight. You're my mate, but he's my Mate—I wish it didn't sound so clever."

"Give me my answer, Salley."

"It's the wrong time for both of us. The moon's set. The fire's almost out. The breeze has brought up the swamp damp and I feel cold and guilty. If I answered you now, it would have to be no."

"When can you answer me yes?"

"Perhaps tomorrow morning, when the sun comes up. Give me that little while, so I can be sure. I promise I'll write you."

"Good night."

A few coals still glowed in the small fireplace. By their glimmer I found my way out the door; and, by a reflected gleam from the fire in the drawing room, down the broad stairs. The front door opened to my hand, closed behind me.

The stars were over me now, distant, and very cold. But surely there was one of them, somewhere in the great assembly, that boded well for Salley and me. It knew the word she would send tomorrow. It bade me be of good cheer.

6

I rose and dressed soon after sunrise, glad of the new day, feeling that it would be a different kind of day than I had ever known before. I felt sure I would have till high morning, perhaps until deep in the afternoon, for Salley to keep her promise; but I would not be impatient, I thought; I could sympathize with her dilemma; I could partly grasp what a feat of will was demanded of her to break with her life's ways and promise to marry an outsider. But the die was cast, the cards were dealt; and by some hard-bitten habit of mind I did not succumb to fear.

I walked awhile before breakfast, about the quiet, time-honored streets, and did not go into the dining room until after nine. Just before ten I was sipping coffee and reading the morning newspaper when one of the Negro postboys approached my table with an envelope in his hand.

"Mas' Stono, de letter come for you at haf-pass eight, but we couldn't find you no place."

"That's all right." I handed him a coin.

"You want me to wait for de answer?"

"No, you can go."

I opened the envelope with care. The faintly scented sheet bore the heading, simply and beautifully engraved, "Hudson Barony." The handwriting was familiar, clear, and fine. It read:

Dear Edward:

I watched the dawn break and came to my decision. I hope if your sense of loss is severe you'll stand to it as you've stood to other losses, like the great gambler you are. Mate needs me more than you do, and I can't go back on my own.

In fairness and I hope in kindness to us both I am acting immediately. Mate is going to meet me in the chapel of St. Michael's at half-past nine this morning. We join in inviting you to come, and if you do, we will consider it an honor and a happy augury of the future.

Faithfully,
Salley

I looked furtively about me, as though I were committing a shameful offense. No one was looking at me; everyone was busy with his breakfast or his newspaper or his score. I could lay my head on the table, and no one would take immediate notice. Actually my swimming head was my only physical symptom of shock. But when I started to get up, I was afraid my knees would buckle and I would fall.

I walked stiffly from the dining hall. My vague intention was to make for my room, if for no other reason than to get out of people's sight, to hide what I could not change. But by the time I got to the stairs my thoughts were flowing in a confused rush. An obligation to act was upon me, I felt its growing weight, an action sustaining of my dignity, even my manhood. Suddenly I knew what it was. Late as it was, I must try to accept Salley's and Mate's invitation.

No gentleman or one who aspired to that estate could do otherwise.

So I turned and made for the outer door. A Negro servant bowed low; I saw him and waved my hand. I began to think about my clothes. I always dressed carefully, with a touch of elegance avoiding dandyism, and my silken stock was spotless and my boots newly blackened. My coat was buff and I wished I could change it for a black one, but there was no time to spare. I took the nearest of a line of waiting cabs.

"Drive fast to St. Michael's Church," I ordered, my voice shaking.

He gave me one odd, sharp glance, then whipped his nag. I still could not think straight, but I listened to the regular and pleasing rhythm of hoofs on the stone and looked at the signs of spring, the great houses and the small, the people hurrying, the other traffic, the unceasing inquiries of the street dogs, until we came in sight of the ancient edifice. Perhaps a dozen empty carriages were being held by Negro drivers. Messages had flown fast this morning, to assemble even this number. I got out and bade the driver wait. A footman directed me to the chapel door. It was open to the spring sunlight, and a voice intoned within.

"So I pronounce you man and wife . . . now let us pray."

The murmured prayer cured my confusion only to give passageway to my blocked emotions. Even before I saw my lost one, Salley, rise from her knees, I looked at Mate Hudson, his face white, an incredulous wonder in his dark eyes, his actions unconsciously graceful as they always were. One thing I had to be thankful for, I thought; one little mitigation of the crushing force of the blow. It was Mate, no other, who had beaten me to the prize. It was not someone who had spurned me but one who had given me his friendship, as far as his lonely soul would let him—except for Faro Jack, my only friend. Then, steadied and sustained, able to see clearly and truthfully, I looked at Salley.

The beauty I had seen last night burst over me like a wave of the sea. That was my only claim upon her now.

The witnesses—and that was what they were, representatives of the *ancien régime,* who had just witnessed the linking within church and state of the lives of two of their own—converged on the pair to kiss Salley and shake Mate's hand. More people were weeping than I would expect in this proud lot, especially considering the simplicity of the ceremony, most of its usual accompaniments of color and sound and symbolism omitted in Salley's haste. How had I ever dreamed that she might marry me?

My turn to speak to her came at last—the turn of an outsider. But her eyes filled with tears as they met mine, and her lips pressed mine in such love as she could give me. It had not been enough. Once she had invited me to a beach party—I was sixteen, with every nerve raw to the winds of the world—but the invitation had proved invalid. . . .

"I'll always thank you for coming," she told me, choking. For the *ancien régime* of the Low Country had not hearts of stone.

"Edward, do you remember—at Memphis' joint—I said my luck would never turn?" Mate asked, his voice deep and glowing. "Well, I was wrong!"

Mason Hudson would have spoken to me too, if I had turned to him. He was deeply moved, and my coming here so late, a black sheep of his own begetting, may have undermined him still more, for there was irresolvable conflict in his face. I bowed to him and to his wife, the latter answering with an ambiguous nod of her head. Jeff Legare, who had served as best man to Mate, gave me a big smile, and even Arnold Hudson would not rebuff me, and Clay Hudson had not joined the company. Still I longed for flight. Unseen in the press of friends and kinsmen warmly greeting one another, I slipped out the door. No one saw or called to me, as I hurried around the walk to my cab; no knowing white-powed sexton questioned my right to be here. I dropped into the cushioned seat. It was in the way that men slipped down into their deathbeds, I thought, when they were old, not young men like me—sorry to leave but glad they need not stay.

"Take me to the hotel." My voice was steady and cool-sounding. Losing gambler that I was, I could still bluff.

7

When I had gained my room and locked its door and paced its floor for two hours, I had arrived at what seemed one important decision.

I would not go to Africa. The way was too long, the search for diamonds too uncertain. I would become a gold-seeker in the new camps of the West, but not by delving in the gravels or blasting the rock. I would pit my prowess at the poker and black-jack and monte tables. I would play against the deadliest sharps that had ever crossed the river, I would take a woman to stand behind me at the games, satisfy my needs in my hours of leisure, and perhaps give me a ration of beauty and even of tenderness. I would fight for survival but not scheme to live long.

Still I could not decide whether to go by sea except for a short rail passage, as to Panama, or to travel overland through our own tremendous West. By either route I would find sharps to keep me in practice. Actually I did nothing to further either journey.

The day I lost Salley and on the following day I read a good deal, daydreamed futilely and long, and, oddly enough, slept much and very deeply, as though I had been drugged. I hardly left the hotel, partly because there was nowhere I wanted to go, mainly perhaps in a not quite explainable dread of encountering any of the other Hudsons, Mason, Mildred, Clay or Arnold, or Butler Mims, or the rascally lawyer, Matthew Whitlow, or even boyish Jeff Legare. On the morning of the third day, a room servant brought up a telegram. I did not doubt the message was from Mate and Salley, dispatched from a wayside station on their bridal journey.

But the telegram had been filed in Augusta, and my eye, leaping to the signature, found the single name "Jack." It read:

Arriving tonight. Wait for me.

I realized neither relief nor disappointment, only a glow of gratitude for the steadfastness of Jack's friendship.

When I met the night train from Augusta, there was Jack's real and sturdy form on the steps of the car. We got in a cab, and saying very little made for my room. There I set out rum and water, and a cold but nourishing supper. When he had washed off the dust of travel, it did me good to see him eat and drink.

"I read in the Augusta paper the Charleston dispatch about Salley getting married," he began. "You said you were expecting it but I knew you'd take it hard."

"Middling hard, Jack," I answered.

"Well, I didn't lose any time getting here. As a gambler, your forte had never been to play safe. You're a very intense man, sometimes you strike me as a desperate man. I doubted if you could think this over coolly, so I did some thinking for you."

"Great God, I want to hear it."

"Remember, when I first proposed that you give up hanging around supported by your mother, both of you dreaming of you being a gentleman, I quoted Shakespeare at you. I said to you, 'Get money, get money, get money.' He's the most quotable fellow that ever lived, I reckon. He's got every human problem and situation ready for your tongue, although I don't know one example out of a hundred. But I do remember five words from the great soliloquy in *Hamlet*, when he listed the 'slings and arrows of outrageous fortune' that often make men want to jump forever and forever in the river. The one I mean is, 'the pangs of dispriz'd love.' "

"It's very well put. To love a woman—to fight against and can't help it and then yield to it, head over heels—and have that woman not give a damn."

"I don't say Salley didn't give a damn. But she loved Mate in a way that makes a woman decide to get married. It was a great rebuff to you. No one, not even she, knows how great. I come the nearest to knowing, because I know your dream. She was the center of that dream. You lose her, and you lose it all. And, Edward, you've lost her."

Suddenly I perceived that I had not quite accepted this. The reason I had slept so deeply was not to see it in my dreams.

"She and Mate are married, till Death do them part," Jack went on. "You're not accepted as a gentleman in Charleston— nowhere are you so accepted, unless it is in the forests of the maroons in Cuba—but you're too much of one to try to part them, or win her away from him. Edward, when I proposed that you become a gambler, taking advantage of quick hands and mind and lightning-quick eyes, you didn't decide right away. When did you decide? What made you decide?"

"When I got the note from Mildred Hudson that I wasn't wanted at her party."

"You became a very good gambler. Not one of the famous but a highly able one. Now you've found out you're not wanted as Salley's husband—not wanted enough for her to take you instead of Mate. She doesn't love you enough, or you're not good enough for her. Both of 'em hurt, the second hurts the worse, but that might not stop it from being her true opinion."

"I know it's her true opinion."

"So what are you going to do now?"

"What I did before, except I'll be a bigger gambler than before. I think I'll go West. There I'll play against the biggest there are."

"That's not very big—if you're talking about draw poker and stud, twenty-one, whist, three-card monte. I want you to go on gambling—that's your calling—that's your nature—but for far greater stakes than the rolls of your opponents at the gambling tables. Listen to me, Edward. Did you know there are prizes greater than being a gentleman? I mean the kind of gentleman you wanted to be—a plantation on the river—Saint Cecilia—all the rest of it. And do you know that with enough determination—luck—and courage those prizes are within your reach?"

"Name one of 'em."

"Leadership is one. To be a leader of men. To be a great builder is another. To found a house in a new land. Perhaps to help build a new nation."

I took Jack's hand and shook it. It was only a little sign that I appreciated his sincerity and would be forever grateful to him for showing me his best.

"I kind of thought you would think of going to the gold camps," he told me, in lowered tones. "That's the reason I got a hump on, getting here. Instead of that, I came to urge you to keep to your plan of going to Africa. But enlarge it about ten times."

"Take a drink and tell me the rest."

He downed a tot of rum and turned to me with glowing eyes.

"When you talked to me about finding the diamonds, you the same as told me what you wanted of them. To come back to Charleston and have the finest barony of all. Now I want you to go without any thought of coming back. Wash your hands of Charleston, except for your happiest memories. Shake its dust from your heels. Hunt for your diamonds, but don't think yourself defeated if you don't find them, and don't hunt too long. Remember that old man—N'kulu's master—he couldn't find them. He recognized one when he saw it—he knew just where to look—but he couldn't find any more. But there are things in South Africa ten times greater than diamonds. I've been reading about the country—pining for it some—ever since I was a boy. In the first place it's as big as all outdoors—big as all the United States west of the Mississippi. There's more game than Bridger saw when he first went to the Rockies. In all that vast territory there are only a few thousand white people. Instead of a plantation of so many thousand acres, you can have a ranch that a good pony couldn't cross in a whole day."

When I kept silent, he said a characteristic thing.

"A ranch with lions on it."

I did not try to stop that ice and fire from running down my back.

"I want you to gamble as you never gambled before," Jack went on. "For life, I hope for love, for happiness, for fortune. Not with little pasteboard squares with marks on 'em but with savage men and beasts, dangers, deserts, mountains; and I want you to use all those powers you need at the gaming tables, but better and stronger and bolder." Strong and bold was his voice as he spoke right at me. "Do you hear me, Edward? Do you call me?"

"I call you, and raise you."

He had turned white, and, to cover up, he groped in his pockets, bringing out an odd assortment of personal belongings, pencil and ticket stubs and crumpled bills. "I've got it somewhere," he said. "A fellow on the train gave it to me. Here it is," he went on triumphantly, displaying a page torn from a notebook. "The name of the vessel is the *Santa Lucia,* and she's a stout little Portugee, and she'll sail on the tide three days from now, bound for Lisbon with a cargo of sea-island cotton. From Lisbon there are flocks of ships that put out for Mozambique."

"Speaking of the tide"—I sniffed the air that smelled like a fresh-dug bushel of clams—"it's about low."

Jack and I walked out on a little porch overhanging an alley. The breeze was up over Jim Island, as the colored called it, and it had skimmed away the clouds that had created a red sunset, and the stars shone in great array.

"One of those is for me," I said. I pointed to the east from whence stars rose.

"Yes, but maybe I spoke too big about the ranch. I won't renege on it, but I'll hedge it. You may not win anything you can write a deed to. But you'll play high, wide, and handsome—to use the language of those Frisco sports—and if you ever come back here—and I don't rule it out—it may be your Fate will bring you back—I think you'll have something I greatly admire in a man."

"What would it be, old man?" I asked, after a long pause.

"Size," he answered.

BOOK FOUR

CHAPTER X

The Raider

THE USUAL ROUTE from America to South Africa was to Capetown by way of England. The route I took, by way of Lisbon, and then aboard an auxiliary steam trader bound for Mozambique, had several advantages. I rode on no great Indiaman, but the snug, seaworthy Portuguese ships had the shorter way, were almost as fast, and charged a good deal less. There were no royal governors that I need impress, not even haughty army and navy officers, so I spent my spare time learning Afrikaans—the Dutch dialect that N'kulu had picked up from Heer Piet. A harsh and, to my ears, outlandish tongue, with many guttural sounds, still it covered nearly every detail of the African scene, and knowing it ahead of time would stand me in good stead when my search began.

Big Indiamen touching Capetown take off by the shortest route to Calcutta, but little Portugee making for Mozambique would touch Delagoa Bay, actually the back door of the Transvaal, whereby I would save hundreds of miles by ox wagon in gaining my hunting ground.

Capetown lay almost exactly as far south of the equator as Charleston was north. But the weather being just reversed, here the mild winter had set in, bringing gray days and sharp winds; while there the land lay in the lap of voluptuous July. The short, broad-nosed Hottentot men, related to Bushmen, and their heavy-rumped women looked a poor substitute for our shapely West African Gullahs. Many old Dutch settlers lived stodgy, stingy lives, torn between piety and greed; the English were mainly remittance men, stuffy officials, or fortune-seekers, with few of the graces of our gay, suave Charlestonians. However, of all the emigrants, the Americans appeared the worst. A good number of them were sailors who had deserted their ships and taken up with Kaffir women and Cape brandy.

Trying to raise money for his passage home on a French ship, an intelligent-looking Parisian offered for sale a firearm the like of which I had never seen. It was what he called a pin-fire breech-loader. Bullet, percussion powder, and charge were contained in a single copper shell, from which a tiny pin thrust upward through a notch to be hit by the hammer. Some care was required in loading the piece, yet it could be done quickly, and the ball weighed an ounce, heavy enough for the largest African game. Yet the Dutchmen and Englishmen who viewed it shook their heads, whispered behind their hands, and remarked that percussion-cap muzzle-loaders were good enough for them, always had been, always would be.

"This rifle was made by Houiller, the greatest gunsmith in Europe," the Frenchman told us. "It cost twenty-five hundred francs—a hundred pounds. Yet I will sell it for fifty pounds to the first comer and throw in a hundred rounds of ammunition."

"May I shoot it?" I asked.

"Yes, you may."

Atop a tower moldering into ruin, once some sort of town-crier to the early Dutch settlers, hung an iron bell. I leveled on it, and the sight of the other loafers scampering in all directions helped me to brace my nerves and take a quick, good sight. As I touched the trigger, I was whirled half-around as by a mule kick, but the bullet was out and gone long previously, and the bell that had not given forth one clang in the last century spoke out in a kind of eerie toll.

"That gun is accursed!" a bearded Dutchman cried in Afrikaans.

"I bloody well believe it," an Englishman said, in his own argot.

"Look you. It is a good cable's length from here. Whoever heard of a ball holding true that far! Young gentleman, it is a sign. Have naught to do with newfangled things; stick to the old and tried. The bell cried out someone's death, yours if you buy it, the buyer's if you sell it. I would not take it for a gift. I would not fire it if you give me fifty pounds."

"Thank you, Mynheer. I do not say you are wrong. I think quite likely you are right. Still, it is my fortune to buy it." And I counted out the Frenchman fifty pound notes.

2

Time passed, event moved, we met obstructions and delays, and made the usual number of mistakes. The consequence of all this was one day we found ourselves gone from the sleepy town of Lourenço Marques, and following wagon tracks on the bank of the Maputo River, bound for the Blue. "We" were now N'kulu, his old, rank, and remarkably handy tribesfellow named Kininni, myself, twenty-four oxen, with wide, sharp horns, lean, tall, and quick as Texas cattle, and a shaggy, low-bred nag, with spirit showing in her eyes and ears. Except for the absence of household goods and slaves, you could mistake us for *Voortrekkers*. Actually we were quite respectably outfitted, with a stout canvas-covered wagon, tools and spare parts, the biggest washpans in town, the purchase of which had impressed the perfumed Portuguese dealer, corn to make mealies, salt, onions, tobacco, and coffee, and a jug of the wicked—this was Faro Jack's word—Cape brandy. As we moved up out of the cold south, the weather waxing hot, N'kulu and Kininni wore next to nothing. I had a supply of straw hats, and pants, shirts, and shoes of soft, tanned buckskin. We got our meat with a smooth-bore muzzle-loading musket, firing a two-ounce ball.

N'kulu loved every sun-baked mile of the long trek, because he was getting home. The blacks whom we met recognized him as a Zulu and either made blood bond with him by many a queer rite, or placated him lest his horde of plumed, blood-thirsty tribesmen lay in hiding behind the nearest *kopje*. As for me, I was becoming an expert inspanner and outspanner. Charleston had turned into an impossible dream of the night. Salley came to me but rarely, and even then I could hardly believe in her, she was so lovely and so cool.

I had never but the vaguest notions as to where we were. N'kulu and Kininni found their way by guess, signs left by ear-lier travelers, and more or less imaginary landmarks. Mean-while we were not completely exiled from people whom I could loosely call my own kind. These were the hardiest and most venturesome of the Voortrekking Boers, who, frightened of seeing another rooftop, had brought their flocks and herds from one lesser wilderness to a greater until they had reached this Ultima Thule. Even so, we could travel all day and sometimes half a week without seeing a single kraal.

I did not seek out these settlers. Almost always they were hospitable, but they were also God-fearing in a fearful degree, reading nothing but the Bible and mainly those parts dealing with the wrath of the Lord. I preferred the company of my vivacious Zulus. Anyway I had no plausible excuse for my presence in these parts.

We had seen wild animals on the first day we left Delagoa Bay. South of the lands once held by a black king named Swazi, they increased in unbelievable numbers. There were not only springbuck and steinbok, but quaggas, eland, gnus, hartebeests, buffaloes, and magnificent kudus. Once we passed a whole army of baboons, and I feared for our outfit, they seemed so bel-ligerent. It became a common thing to make out a leopard stealing away in the grass; the songs of silver jackals and spotted hyenas bewitched the night; and now and again an incredible aardvark ambled across the road.

I had not fired the fine French rifle since I had left Capetown, partly to save ammunition, partly because I distrusted its unfamiliar mechanism. But it needed a blooding, N'kulu said—as his spear had been blooded when he became a warrior—and the strange gods of the veld, like no gods that ever were, mean and mischievous and often deadly, but sometimes marvelous and magnificent, provided the opportunity.

We had had a long and grueling day, trying to reach a water hole, and had kept on beyond sunset, beyond twilight, because of an immense ascendant moon. There are no moons in my experience or in travelers' tales like the moons of Africa. They are larger, grander, and more luminous than any on earth. Then we made camp in the soft and perfect light. It was a scene of great peace, one to warm the heart and reassure the flagging spirit. Nothing but happy things could occur tonight—deep feeding for man and beast, and deep sleeping.

Then from nowhere appeared a lion. He was suddenly in our midst, virilely maned, huge, insolent, walking with a princely stride. He walked up to one of our oxen, a big cow called Maria and, while she stood transfixed with terror, gave her a little blow on the side of the neck. She fell down dead. The lion stood over her, and took several seconds to set his teeth in a way convenient for him. During these few seconds I was clawing in the wagon for the pin-fire rifle. It happened that N'kulu had fired the muzzle-loader only a few minutes before, employing his last ball, and not having gone to our store had left it unloaded.

By the time I had clutched the pin-fire the lion was disappearing at the edge of vision, the ox in his jaws. She weighed at least twelve hundred pounds, he not more than half as much; but he walked away with her as a man carries a rather light but bulky and awkward load. He had his teeth set somewhere in her shoulder. All four of her legs hung on his right side and dragged on the ground and made a little cloud of dust visible in the moon.

I opened the breech to see if the pin-fire rifle was loaded. It was, the little pin in place, but the extra shells were God knew where.

"I'm going after him," I said quickly in Afrikaans. "You two stay here and guard the other oxen."

For male lions do not always travel alone. His lithe wives might be somewhere out in the dark, lusting to make a raid; or perhaps he was a member of what the English called a "mob," hunting with remarkable co-operation, the terror of every living thing on the veld except the elephants and rhinos, who walked wide for no lion ever whelped, and except for little jackals who could hide behind the rocks.

"Do not so, bukra," said old Kininni. "You will be killed."

"If he is to be killed, why, then, he will be killed," N'kulu reproved him. "Anyway it is his Fate to go. I can see it in his face."

I did not know where N'kulu got his idea of Fate. Mohammedanism had never touched the Zulu tribes as far as I knew. But they were curiously like Moslems, in warlikeness, honor and personal bravery, and ten times their equal in cruelty. I needed the same philosophy as I left the camp site and pushed out into the moonlit veld in pursuit of the thief. His shape was still vaguely visible to my stimulated vision. But it was not nearly solid enough to see over rifle sights.

Ahead of me he walked, behind him walked I. I dared not run for fear of falling into ambush, and our walking gaits appeared identical. In a few seconds, I was all alone with Africa and her prodigious lamp. I had one load in my gun. When Dutch boys go hunting, their fathers give them only one load. Their purpose is no doubt economy, but it has made the greatest race of marksmen the world has ever known. How many loads did the lion have? Only one—to run at me, knock me over, and kill me.

That was not what steadied me the most. It was thinking of

a she-oxen named Maria, who had never harmed a living soul, who all day long tugged in her yoke for the right to food and rest when darkness fell, herself suddenly pitched into utter darkness by that arrogant invader. He had walked up to her and killed her. I was going to walk up to him and kill him if it were possibly in my power. I was badly frightened of the moonlight and the grass and the solitude, and the thought of Simba, the male lion, the great killer, a vague shape in front of me, but it may be I did not treasure life as much as most men, and that might be because I was a bastard. No arrangements had been made for me. I was an interloper—or, it might be, because I was a gambler.

Salley had been mistaken when, after I had promised to save Mate from Memphis, she had told me I might feel like a gentleman for the last time. I felt like one now. It was a wonderful feeling. The cold in my heart could not subdue the glowing in my soul.

Perhaps two hundred yards from the camp the lion became annoyed over my following him. He did not like to have anyone question his sovereignty of the veld. He dropped the oxen and disappeared in the thick grass. But I had not the slightest notion that he had abandoned his prize; he was waiting and watching to see what I would do; at a moment favorable to himself he would do something. I pushed on, and soon came to the carcass. I stood over it, the rifle ready in my hands. I was quite sure that the lion would not keep me waiting very long. He could not abide seeing someone other than himself in possession of his prize. The trouble was, I did not know from which direction he would make his entrance on the scene.

It was like the end of the betting in draw poker. I had bet very high, all I had in fact, on what I thought was the winning hand. Say it was three aces, but a full house or straight or flush could beat me. There would be no way of knowing until my opponent laid down his hand.

There ensued a second or two of ineffable suspense.

Then out of the moonlight came the lion, his head down,

his tail rammed out, his legs driving like pistons on a steam engine. I did not see him until he was within forty yards—in spite of the magnificence of the moon its beams were dim— and then it seemed I barely had time to level, aim, and touch the trigger. As I touched it I felt a lack of confidence. It was a newfangled contraption; unlike our good old muzzle-loader; it was untested.

But the night roared, and the powder smoke blinded me, and when it had drifted away I still could hardly believe that the gods had not taken this beautiful chance to put me where I belonged. Instead, I still stood by the dead oxen, blood in my veins, sense in my brain, light in my eyes, strength in my muscles, Edward Stono, a living man; and ten feet from me, quivering in death, lay the lion.

Maria, you are avenged. So, in some infinitesimal measure, are all those who are faithful and guiltless, who toil all day only that they may have a little rest and food when the soft night comes down.

CHAPTER XI

The Rider

FOR A MATTER of six months, I gambled against the secrets of the river bed. Twenty miles up and down the Vaal from the rocky reach where Heer Piet had found diamonds, I washed the gravels for the small, cool, greasy-feeling crystalline pebbles with a dogged patience that made restless N'kulu stop, stare, and sigh. I did not win the bet, and, in gambler's parlance, got no run for my money. I looked everywhere that heavy sediment would settle, but found not even a flake. Every day seemed to end precisely where it began.

Moreover, the life of adventure that Faro Jack foretold for me only halfway came to pass. When in need of meat, I shot the first buck that walked into my sights. Abundant driftwood provided for good watch fires, so lions did not haunt our camps; and when we ran into them in the grass, they usually tried to bluff us or made off. By never arguing with the elephants, always giving them right of way, we kept from waking their titanic wrath. There was no known means of appeasing a truculent rhino, but we did not see many, the land was not brushy enough to please them, and thrice we gave attacking beasts the slip, and only twice had to shoot for our lives.

The natives who passed our camps were hunters or traders or pastoralists in league with the Dutch, and never made us any trouble, and often sat through most of a night with N'kulu and Kininni, jabbering and sucking marrow bones as though raised in the same kraal.

The land was always wonderful, the river brought new sights, and I greatly relished being a diurnal creature instead of a nocturnal one. I thrived on the labor, grew lean and nearly tireless, and almost without knowing it became not an expert marksman, like so many of the Dutch, but a good, quick shot. However, the time had come to change grounds. Perhaps a search for some other source of wealth, gold or ivory or perhaps some wide fertile valley not yet claimed by the Voortrekking Dutchmen, might be indicated soon. So on a pink and pearly morning, we inspanned and trekked.

Making for a strip of land ceded to the Dutch, we pitched by a stream called Klipspringer, deeply eroded and subject to high floods. For once we were only a mile from a farmhouse— almost near enough to smell mutton stewing—but no other homestead lay within twenty miles.

The farmer, whose name his cattle drovers gave as Jan Du Piel, had been a Voortrekker under the sturdy Potgieter, but he had broken with his leader, had quit the settlements of Lydenburg and Zoutpansberg, and with his daughter had become an outlyer here at the brink of the Blue. A wandering Bastaard dye-seller, part Dutch and part Hottentot, lately and more politely known as a Griqua, warned me to walk wide of him.

"He is greatly incensed at Jehovah—this being the name of his god—for not giving him sons," the Griqua explained.

Loafing in camp about sundown, I noticed a herd of milk cows being driven toward the kraal by a small but easy rider in a straw hat. I waved in salute, whereupon the rider's pony headed my way, and the cows lowered their heads to graze. As the rider came near, I made her out, first, as a towheaded child, then as a flaxen-haired young woman certainly sixteen, quite possibly as old as nineteen. She rode up, and most pleasant perceptions trickled through my mind.

This girl had been raised on the veld. Almost certainly she had never opened a book except the Bible. Probably she had never been taught to read; she had never seen a picture or heard a verse of poetry unless it was a forbidden song by a black woman; most of her life had been spent in the saddle, eating a spartan diet, sleeping on a bed made of strips of raw-hide, walking on earthen floors, never in this world seeing or touching the slightest luxury or any man-made beauty. She had been born since the great trek from Cape Colony. A few times a year she went to "meeting," and listened to a minister picture the horrors of hell. Then what in the Devil had put such prettiness in her face and charm in her small, lithe form? It could be nothing but the native grace of that frequently monstrous, sometimes divine, human race.

Her hair was parted smoothly in the middle and dressed in long, glossy braids. When the sunlight hit it fairly—for she removed her straw hat to show it to me—it shone like the most delicate and forever unfindable gold. Her eyes were ineffably blue, the blue of the African sky seen in patches among white scattered clouds. They were probably common eyes, nothing to excite the artist, but for the present at least they glimmered with excitement—no doubt I was the first western European of something like a suitable age she had seen in half a year. Anyway I was not sure of the commonplaceness of her eyes. They were oddly set and had a direct and an intense glance. If they had never looked into a book, they had looked deeply into Africa. She cast them once about my camp, and I had the notion that she could enumerate—and evaluate—everything in it. They were the eyes of someone intensely alive. I knew about intense life, for I had felt it when Theba had rescued me from the barracoon, and again, when, half a year gone, I had stood beside a dead lion.

Her face was somewhat broad. I was glad of that, when she smiled—there was so much room for the smile, and it was so

childlike and beaming. Her father being a fanatical Dutchman, dead against all fleshpots, had set no bleak asceticism in
her sun-tanned face, and instead there was wonderful earthiness
that stirred my pulse. Her lips were full and rounded. Her
brown neck, which had been snow-white to start with, was
small and lovely and, I would almost think, highbred. Best of
all, she was a woman, and this semi-desert, this arid, hungry
wilderness had not deprived her of it. She was about five feet
five, I thought, taller than any *vrouws* I had seen in Capetown,
taller than any bespangled native girls except a few highborn,
long-shanked Zulus. But every inch of her was female, and the
man who could not see it and rejoice in it was not a whole man.

She was shy and likely to be tongue-tied so I spoke first.

"Thank you for coming to visit a lonely traveler," I told her
in Afrikaans. "My name is Edward Stono. What is your name?"

"Mine is Trudi Du Piel. Are you of Dutch descent?"

"No, I am a Yankee."

"But you speak Afrikaans like a native!"

"I had a good teacher."

"Is your wife here? I don't see her."

"I have no wife."

"You are quite old not to be married. Most of our farm boys
marry at sixteen."

"Then you too are old not to be married."

I meant to speak lightly but a shadow came into her face,
and it was not dispelled until I showed her my lionskin, spread
on my pallet.

"Have you ever killed a lion?" I asked.

"Yes, Mynheer."

"A rhino?"

"Yes, Mynheer. Will you show me your guns? I heard that
the English—but you are Yankee—have very fine guns."

So I showed her the muzzle-loader and the pin-fire rifle.
She gave the first only a casual glance, but the latter fascinated
her. "I have never seen such a gun," she burst out, when I
showed her how it was loaded.

"Would you like to shoot it?" I asked.

"I would like to, but I won't waste a cartridge. And it must be that you shot the lion with the muzzle-loader, for there is only one hole in the skin."

"No, Trudi. One cartridge did the trick."

"Then it must be much stronger than it looks."

"I think it is."

"If you want me to shoot you a buck—tomorrow, I mean, when I take the cattle to pasture—I will do so gladly."

"How would you bring him into camp?"

"I would put him on Johan's back and walk." Johan was evidently her gelding. "And now I must go home, for the sun has set."

I could not let her go for a while yet. I brought out a tin of sugarplums and a flask of mild, sweet Portuguese wine, brought all the way from the colony. Her face lighted like a child's. I had never seen a more beaming smile. Before we knew it, the shadows had grown quite long.

"Oh, it's getting late!" she cried suddenly, leaping to her feet.

"When the time comes, I'll take you home."

She looked startled—perhaps a little frightened, although this young horsewoman with hair the tint of wheatstraw was hard to frighten, and I must remember that in my dealings with her, for even a little fear manifest in her might indicate the presence of a full-sized danger—then speculations I could not read came into her limpid eyes. They reassured her, I thought; still I could get her to stay only long enough to finish her drink. When she mounted her pony I noticed what seemed to be an ancient flintlock in her saddle scabbard. I remembered a lion that had walked brazenly into camp in light hardly dimmer than this, so I put the pin-fire rifle, loaded and ready to go, in my saddle scabbard. She rode in and out of the scattered band of milk cattle and almost instantly, it seemed, collected them in a tight herd. If I had ever seen a better rider, it was someone born and bred and raised on a horse on a great

Low Country plantation; and he would have merely more style, not a whit more ease, grace, stability, and mastery of his mount. She did not ride like a Valkyrie. They were poetic riders of the sky, who sung from horizon to horizon. She rode like a farm girl who must cover rough ground, meet with constantly changing conditions, look out for her own neck and her horse's, and in the shortest possible time. Not only her hands but her whole body was sinewy. Thinking of its woman's shape, a warmth crept through me, and I was hard put to it to pay attention to her innocent remarks.

Trudi! The African sun had set, just now, but it was stored up inside of her. Her pale skin had invited its entrance; and what a mate she would make for a young Afrikander, unknown to any fare but meat and mealies, who must people his broad lands! What was there to keep me from taking that part? Why was I ineligible to take a daughter of this broad and sunny land? Nothing but a dream as lost and gone as any in the night.

I rode beside her presently, our stirrups almost touching. The intense blue of her eyes had slightly darker rims, not their only mystery. Africa itself was in her, the golden grass and the fierce sun and the long horizons and the danger and the death; she knew about lions, and great elephants raiding the cornfields, and baboons that must be massacred to save the crop, and the dreadful swarms of locusts. Like Africa herself, she was a bottomless well. She seemed so limpid but really she was so deep.

I had laid the ghost of Salley long ago. Now I was tired of traveling alone. It came to me, as both an intuition and an inward force, that I would like to woo this gold-haired girl of the veld and wake the primal passion under her soft, tanned skin. I would like to woo her in the grass, and in the thin shade of the mimosa, and perhaps I could win her, and then—so strong was my vision—keep her always. It might be that my luck had changed. It might be I had made a find richer than diamonds. Who would stop me from spending my days in this new and burning land, if here lay happiness and fulfillment?

I was dreaming, but, for the first time, what real, unfantasti-
cal dreams!

2

"You can go back now," she told me.

"No, I'll take you to your door."

"There's no need of it. I can see our chimney from here.
The grass is too short for lions or even leopards. Thank you
for coming this far."

"I want to go all the way."

She hesitated, then nodded. It was not an easy, careless decision, a letting-slide as when, a few minutes before, I had
asked her to stay awhile. Instead it was feat of will. She was
facing costs, and, rising above that, defying consequences. I
would not have known it except for the training of my eyes
at the gaming tables. And this was a good deal higher play than
I had guessed.

Suddenly I was frightened, because I knew that my companion had decided to face and challenge a very real danger.

We drew nearer the homestead. It would have been bleak
enough in the genial sunlight; now, in this suddenly chill twilight, grayness everywhere, not one bright living tint to cheer
the eyes, it appeared desolate in the extreme. The tall figure
by the gate was a man, very lean and erect, wearing a tall hat,
an oddly cut coat, and a fringe of gray whiskers around his
chin.

Trudi turned to me and looked me in the face.

"You'd better go back, now," she said.

"No, I'm going with you all the way."

"I think you may be sorry but I thank you just the same."

So we rode on, a little closer together than before. We came
up to the watcher, and I had never seen such an austere human
being. Africa can humanize a person, I thought, by constantly
pitting him against ruthless nature; but, with a slight change,
it might denaturalize him. This was no doubt Jan Du Piel,
whom I had heard hated Jehovah for not letting him beget

sons. I thought to speak to him, some kind of a civil greeting, but when I saw his face I knew he would regard it as a weakness, so I kept silent.

"Trudi, tell this young man to go his way," the Boer commanded in a cold, level voice far more ugly than the snarls of a hyena. "Then drive your cattle into the kraal. Then come yourself to the stable."

There fell a brief pause.

"To the stable?" she echoed.

"You heard me, Trudi."

"You're going to do that—again?"

"You've disobeyed my orders by loitering—visiting this man's camp, if the signs tell true—and you're to be punished for it."

"You can't. I'll not stand it."

"You're my daughter, and you'll do what I say, and if you dare dispute me you'll get twice as much."

She paused, considered, then spoke in a low, clear voice.

"Unless you promise not to do it—never to do it again—I'm going to tell him."

"By all means tell me, Trudi," I said quickly.

"You'd better not! By all the saints in heaven and the devils in hell—"

"Better than that I'll show him."

In one leap she was off her horse. Her hands flew and she peeled off over her head her buckskin shirt. She had turned her back to me, not in modesty, but so I could see more plainly what she wanted to show me; even so I knew her for a woman with a knowledge deeper than before, and that helped her cause.

Across her back were many narrow stripes, some of them not healed, such as are caused by the kiboko, the cruel rhino-hide whip.

"It won't happen again," I told her.

"What do you mean, you son of Beelzebub?"

"It won't happen again. You'll never lay a whip on her again."

"Who'll stop me? She's my daughter. If I'd laid the lash on her faithless mother, she might be in heaven today, instead of burning in hell. I'll whip her as I think she needs it, as many stripes as I choose."

"Not even one stripe."

Jan Du Piel reached behind him and drew from a hip holster a horse pistol cocked and primed. I too was on the ground by now—not remembering how I had got there—and I struck the barrel with my quirt, knocking it out of his hand. Trudi picked it up and ran out of her father's reach. For a few seconds all three of us were immobilized. The fault was mine—I did not know what to do next. But the solution was so simple, and it rushed into my brain like a spring freshet into a dried-up water hole, and I spoke without effort or need of second thought.

"Get on your horse, Trudi, and we'll go."

"If you like," she answered.

"It's not her horse," the Dutchman broke in harshly. "It's my horse. It's my gun too. She hasn't a thing of her own, even the clothes on her back. If she's going to hell with you, and that's where she belongs—where her mother went before her—you'll have to pay for them."

"How much? Trudi, you know their worth. Set the price and I'll pay it. I've got a hundred guilders—forty Cape dollars—in my poke."

"That's just right," Trudi answered.

"A hundred! That's hardly nine English pounds. Three hundred would be cheap—"

"A hundred is the price set. Will you take that, or nothing?"

"I'll take it, may devils wrack your souls in hell for evermore. May your crops fail. May the lions kill your oxen and the hyenas pull down your sheep. May the murrain come to your herds and the rats raid your barns. May you wither away with sickness. May the blacks bring you to torture. May the black mamba bite you while you lie asleep. May the tsetse fly destroy your brains. Death and torment to you both, son and daughter of Lucifer. I hate you. I hate all mankind. I hate God."

But he took the forty Cape dollars I handed him in a little poke, and he was counting them over and over as we rode away.

3

My camp was at the edge of some thorn thickets, close to the stream. Below and above, where the ground was more open, 'mpalla came to drink, quaggas and zebras, gazelles with soft eyes and ever lifted feet, hartebeests, and sometimes oxlike eland. These visitors had all gone by the time we reached the wagon, but the jackals had crept down, yapping, hyenas met and howled, and far away a lion gave forth rhythmic grunts. Listening to these sounds, meanwhile preparing for the night ahead, Trudi and I need not as yet confront the future. Without trying we avoided making an issue of our being together, alone, and far away from everyone except our two black men and the beasts of the veld.

I was busy, looking after the oxen, and she saw to the cooking of the evening meal. We ate it on the ground, sitting opposite each other, looking now and then at our small fire, because we could not afford a big blaze in this grassy country so bereft of fuel. We had scarcely finished when she, N'kulu, and Kininni cocked their heads in the same way, at the same angle. Their eyes met one another's but did not meet my eyes because I was an alien, not an African, and did not know the swift leap of thought between them. Trudi smiled faintly and nodded. The tension in the two black faces immediately eased. Into the firelight walked a young Negress, her breast and thighs covered in the way of a domestic servant, but with wire bracelets on her wrists and ankles.

"M'sabu!" she said to Trudi, looking her in the face.

"Mynheer, this is my household wench, whose name is difficult in Afrikaans, but whom you may call Hagar, after the handmaiden of Sarai in the Good Book."

"Did your father let her come?"

"Not he! But she belongs to me—my Aunt Wilhelmina gave her to me, and I think—" She paused, and began to speak to the Negress in some African tongue. When the short parley was over, Trudi turned to me again, childishly pleased. "Hagar said that she hid, and my father could not find her, and when the darkness fell she ran away."

"Wasn't she afraid to cross the veld at night?"

"She was more afraid to stay."

"Will your father come seeking her—or you perhaps—during the night?"

"No, he has cursed me, and that is the end of it, and he would never take me back, even if I would go, and I never will."

"Where do you wish to go? But your heart is troubled to-night, and no doubt you'd rather wait till morning to speak of it."

"By your leave, Mynheer, I will speak of it as soon as Hagar and I make the beds for the night. By then the fire will burn low, and the veld will grow quiet, and I can speak free."

"I want you to feel free, Trudi."

"I've never known such a thing between man and woman."

"You know it now. Make the beds of 'mpalla and hartebeest skins—I have enough, saved for making clothes. N'kulu and Kininni will sleep where they please."

I did not appear to watch her, but I saw her lay out the best and softest skins for me, then make a pallet for herself some few feet distant from mine, and another for Hagar literally at her feet. Before long, she returned and took a seat beside the fire. Hagar remained in the shadowy background.

"You asked me where I wished to go," she said. "Before I can decide upon a place, it would help me to know where you are bound."

"No place in particular. Any place my road takes me."

Her eyes brightened like a gypsy's. "Mynheer, are you seek-ing land, as do the Voortrekkers? To make a great farm, perhaps, with many kraals and cattle? Or are you, as some of the outlanders, seeking ivory or gold?"

"I am seeking my fortune, by any means within the white man's law."

"Do you expect to pass before many months by Port Elizabeth?"

"That would be a journey of many weeks. It is not in my plans, but—"

"There is no need of taking it now, if—if you have other plans, and my presence in your outfit is no trouble to you," she broke in at once, hurriedly and stammering. "I will tell you what I started to. In Port Elizabeth lives my mother's sister, who, when you pass that way, would take me to live with her. I am eighteen, a virgin, unwedded, unbetrothed; and among the young men, friends of her sons, in due time I would find a husband. But if I am welcome in your camp, going on as we have started, I too would like to go where the road leads. Truly I would like to see much more of Africa before I settle down— for there is no land like it in all the world. And, Mynheer, it is not a boast that I would not delay your journey, and indeed might even help to make it prosper."

"How is that, Trudi?"

"I can inspan, outspan, drive, pitch camp, cook, make clothes, and get meat. I know what tribes are friendly, which are treacherous, and which are hostile. I can tell good country when I see it, and I know what parts have lately been forsaken by the Doppers, where land can be obtained free, or bought very cheap. I can read sign of distant water and good grass; I know the belts of the tsetse fly, having listened to the talk of the Voortrekkers; and I have heard of certain regions where elephants are numerous and good ivory is common. It would not matter to me if we journeyed a whole year—or as long as you wish. And if I can help you, as I believe, it would give me great happiness."

"Do you wish to tell me why?"

"Yes, I wish to tell you. Because when you came close to

the farmhouse, and I warned you to go back, and you yourself felt the danger, still you came on."

"That was a little thing. Any gentleman—" I stopped, for I remembered that my doings in this connection were all done.

"Remember, I have never seen a gentleman before."

"Apart from that, I offer you a place in my camp as my companion. We will trek about the country, seeking gold, or ivory, or other precious stuff, or fertile land fit for grazing cattle and sheep. But if we find none of these, it won't matter to either of us, for I too wish to see the great land of Africa, and if we take a year to do it the time will be well spent. I will give you work to do and make many calls on you, but our main business will be enjoyment. And I won't make any call that you don't wish to answer."

"That would suit me very well, Mynheer."

"If it should so happen that we would become lovers—" I paused.

"In that case, it would so happen."

"In America, before I set sail, an old dear friend foretold me many good adventures. For a long time the augury was but half-true, but now it comes to me out of the night that my adventures in Africa will be more thrilling and more meaningful than he imagined. I am a gambler by calling, and lately the luck has run against me. Now I have a *hunch*—that is a word meaning an intuition—that my luck will be better than I ever dreamed."

4

After Trudi's coming, I forgot what it was to be lonely. She was my companion. On the long trek or the short trek, in the evenings about the fire, or in the wonderful clear fresh mornings ere we began our day's endeavors, washing gravel in the creek beds, hunting, eating our simple meals, outspanning and inspanning, making or breaking camp, I knew the warm and joyful sense of her nearness to me. It was a different kind of nearness than I felt in N'kulu. He looked upon me as his master, a sort of deputy of Heer Piet whose bones were gnawed and scattered by jackals old and gray or dead; besides, he was a Zulu, his identity bound up with much that I could never share. We enjoyed each other's company, especially during any arduous or somewhat dangerous activity, and were fond of each other; but could not enter the mysteries of friendship. When Trudi was with me, I felt that we were not two people but one person with two sides. We need not talk at all to be aware of our close bond. We need not touch each other, but often I took her hand and held it close.

We were companions, and I wished we could be more. It seemed strange for her and me, a young man and a young woman on the limitless veld, to stop with that—at least to rest with that for the time being—yet when I looked at it squarely with my own eyes, not borrowing the eyes of others, it lost its seeming strangeness and became as commonplace and as natural as our diet of meat and mealies. I had not yet fallen in love with her in the way I had loved Salley. This was the present status. Neither of us had come to any clear decision about the future. Often I felt desire for her, but I never saw the least sign of reciprocation on her part. She wanted to be free to travel back and forth, up and down the veld. She was a bird new-freed from its cage, and with a good wild bird to fly with.

All that she had told me that she could do, to make herself my valuable partner, she did exceedingly well. I found I could rely on her, and I need never give the matter a second thought. Moreover, her timing, regulated by her energies, was unfailingly superb. One incident of the camp ground illustrated it well.

We were moving north—our general direction—intending to search the gravels of a turbulent tributary of the Vaal. Because we had found a good site about noon, close to a village where we could buy fowls, millet, and yams, we had outspanned under the burning sun and were rather lazily going about making camp. Presently N'kulu made a rather odd find—a human skull. Immediately after the midday meal, when I was lolling on an eland skin, and Trudi was sitting beside me making a buckskin shirt, Kininni reported the discovery of an almost complete human skeleton, its bones gnawed not quite bare only a night or two before.

"I'm afraid we're going to have to move camp," Trudi told me.

"Because of a few bones?" I asked.

"Because we've happened to hit the village cemetery. It's a Shenzi village. I knew that from the look of it. A good many of the Shenzis don't bother to bury their dead—they just carry them a mile or so, and leave them. That attracts all the carrion-eaters—not only vultures but maribou storks, hyenas, and jackals—the rabble of the country—and also—I hate to say it—lions. I saw more lion sign about than I liked. I thought it was accidental, but it wasn't."

"Let me finish my pipe, and we'll move."

N'kulu, Kininni, and Hagar got under the wagon—they preferred that shade to that of the dwarf mimosas—and Trudi hastened to complete her sewing. Hardly a moment later she leaned toward me, very slowly, and whispered in my ear.

"Lie very still a moment, will you?"

"Yes."

At once she turned and began to creep toward a thorn tree, against which leaned our smooth-bore musket. The grass was not high, yet I could distinguish her movements only by the little waving of its tops. In a moment she came creeping back. Very slowly she rose to a sitting position, the gun handy in her arms. As it came level, she touched the trigger. After its deep-throated roar, she turned and gave me one of her quaint smiles.

"If you want to go and look at him, you can. He's only about a hundred feet."

"What?"

"A lion. A big male that you'd never think could creep through grass this short. I've heard that lions that hang around native graveyards—a polite way to put it—get awfully bold, but

I certainly didn't expect one of them to try stalking us at high noon."

"Why did you tell me to lie still?" I asked, when I could get my breath.

"I didn't want to trip his trigger. I mean, he was already much too close when I saw him—hardly fifty yards—and a sudden motion by either of us might have made him charge. I thought I'd better crawl to the gun, even though it took a little time. Donner Blitzen, but it seemed a long time!"

5

I went to look at the lion. He had been shot through the neck, and, already belly-down in the grass, had made no motion other than drop his head. Then and there I got the pin-fire rifle, as well as its supply of cartridges, out of the wagon.

"I wish to make a trade with you, Trudi," I told her.

She did not speak aloud but her blue eyes spoke to my great pleasure.

"I wish to trade this gun for your old flintlock. You're the best person in our outfit to have it—in fact the only one fit to own a gun of such excellence. Will you trade?"

"Yes, Mynheer."

When she took it, there was so much joy in her face and her great glance at me was so thrilling, I could not refrain from taking her briefly in my arms. Briefly her lips pressed mine. It was our first kiss. Her lips were rounded, full, and wide, and imparted to my lips and hence to my consciousness a knowledge of her I had not had before, and which even now I could not think through, let alone express in words. It had to do with an immense vitality, but of a female order. Perhaps it was a yet-unawakened capacity for love. Why not, when she had always lived in the sun? She was born blond, yet the sun had not spared her his intense beams. Her father, Jan Du Piel, needed hanging, and her mother, Africa, was accursed by the prophets of old—*Woe to the land shadowing with wings beyond the rivers of Ethiopia*—yet together they had endowed her with a passion for life unknown to the tame peoples. She was a Voortrekker beyond a doubt. My luck had turned at last—but I must not ride it too hard.

That evening I spoke again to Kininni of a matter he had causally mentioned some weeks before.

"North of the Limpopo, north of the Sabi, there is a greater river than both put together, flowing generally eastward, from the hinterlands of Angola to the provinces of the Portugee at Mozambique."

"Bukra, that is true, and the river is called the Zambezi."

"Before I left my abode, far across the western sea, there came word of an English doctor descending that river and finding a great falls, which he named for the white Rani of his native land, England."

"They are such falls as few human eyes had ever seen."

"Suppose we struck the old Arab trade route which skirts the edge of the Kalahari. In how many days could we come upon the falls?"

"Lord, it is a long way. If you stop to search the gravels of the dongas—God alone knows why—it might take us a year. If we journeyed steadily, outspanning every night, inspanning every morning, I judge we could make the journey in two moons."

"Is there plenty of game along the way?"

"Yes, bukra."

"Is there enough water?"

"At this time of year, and for the next four moons, there is enough."

"May we buy corn from the villages?"

"If they do not give us their spears to eat, instead."

"How great is the danger?"

Kininni scratched his head long and thoughtfully.

"You ask, bukra, and I will answer. May the gods guard my tongue, lest I lie. If we went with a hundred men, each with a firearm, the danger would be small. If we went with ten men, likewise armed, the danger would be great. But when one white man and two blacks, one white woman and one black, journey in one wagon and on their horses, there is danger from lions—from elephants—from rhinos—maybe from fever, but from men there is almost none."

"Why is that, when we will come close to the kraals of the fierce Matabele driven from the Transvaal by the Boers?"

"Remember that the fierce Matabele are only Zulus, as are N'kulu and I. And why should they kill us, bukra? They know we have not come to take their lands, five of us against five thousand. We have nothing that they want—they do not know how to use our guns, and they have cattle in plenty. Did not the same doctor who found the great falls cross the Kalahari, even to Lake Ngami, nigh ten years past? The great Moffat *bwana* goes at will to the court of the Matabele king. Still there is no telling. Often men kill because they know no better, as dogs kill sheep. If you want safety, you must go to Capetown. But that too is a long way!"

"Nay, we will go and behold the great falls of the Zambezi, the wonder of God."

He stood straight, with a little proud squaring of his shoulders that meant more than words, his eyes on mine. When I confided the plan to Trudi, something very like fear came into her face, but it was not fear; it was only awe. Happily she did not believe in a god in whose image her father had been created; in some childish desperation she had sought a deity who smiled sometimes, who liked the bright faces of little children and whose heart warmed to human hope, and she had found him, perhaps in the huts of the blacks, perhaps in the hills bathed in morning mist; and perhaps she had entreated him that she might go adventuring into the unknown North, but I doubted if she had ever asked to lay eyes on the great Zambezi.

So we set forth, Trudi, N'kulu, Kininni, Hagar, and I, and the oxen who knew naught or cared naught where we went, because their toil would never end until they died, and the two horses. In due course we came to the old trade route, running north beside the vast Kalahari, the great plateau of south central Africa. Sometimes the veld made deep inroads into its red sands, and here the wildebeest and springbuck roamed in immense herds, and the giraffe and the white rhinoceros showed their grotesque shapes; and sometimes the red sands ran deep into the grass, and here there was no life except the adder and the secretary bird, and we must dig for water in the beds of the dry dongas.

There was not a single day uncrammed with incident or adventure, hardly ever a long vista that did not make our eyes kindle with anticipation, almost never a night that we did not bless the watch fire, the cooking pots, and our lowly beds.

During the journey there came upon me a fever, usually low and lingering, sometimes high, that only hard work and deep sleep could slake. It was the fever of a man for his mate. But it did not yet flush the bright brows of my companion, and anyway she was forbidden to me yet. There was still a contract to be fulfilled. I did not exactly know what it was, or completely believe in it, but I knew the penalty of its breach. That knowledge lay deep within my soul.

When after many weeks we had skirted or crossed the foothills of the Matapo range, we came into the watershed of the Zambezi. Traveling northwesterly at the edge of the grass, and directed by sheep grazers with whom N'kulu established some bond of language, we began to hear a low-pitched, slowly loudening roar as of distant thunder. Then, on an afternoon, we came in sight of the mile-wide river. It flowed serenely, blue as the sky, over level rock; its valley was wide, bordered by low hills; very little forest obscured the view although a cluster of wooded islands set in the river itself and their number seemed more as we gazed downstream. But there was nothing yet to account for a roar as of doomsday and a great cloud of rainbow-colored spray. From our viewpoint it seemed that the easy level flow was endless and immortal as time itself.

But when we ventured farther down the bank we discovered a continuous cataclysm, a scene first described to the civilized world only the year before, unsurpassed in grandeur. Suddenly the great river poured over the brink of a precipice into a vast, gloomy chasm. At every beat of the heart an immeasurable mass of water—probably a million gallons—leaped down and out of sight. The roar extinguished all other sound and continued on forever, giving the effect of some other world where there was no sound, or any living creature with the power of hearing. I felt in the midst of a supernatural silence. I turned to talk to my companions, but it was no use.

CHAPTER XII

The Discovery

MANY TALES were told of Neapolitan peasants herding their goats and tending their vineyards within a stone's throw of the vast maw of Mount Vesuvius. I thought of this in connection with a Bantu village just far enough upriver from the falls that the people could communicate by shouting in one another's ears. Moreover, since some of their pastures and maize fields lay on the opposite side, they thought nothing of crossing back and forth in boats. There was no considerable danger, they said. The river flowed like any other river, tranquilly and majestically, unwarned of its impending fall, not even quickening its pace, until the second of its doom. And because of the blown spray, the crops never failed from drouth.

If it were the wish of the *bwana*—I thought this last must be a Swahili word, brought by the Arab slave traders from their beautiful coastal cities on the Azanian Sea—they would take him and his M'sabu and his boys to an island near the brink of the falls, from which they could gaze down upon the fullness of its wonders, leave them there while they attended to their flocks and herds, and come for them soon after moonrise.

Trudi was eager to accept the invitation—and she had long

231

ago learned to trust the prowess of the people and to rely on their capacity to survive—so I, relying on Trudi, gave ready assent. We pushed out in big, awkward-looking bateaux that the blacks handled with assured, long-practiced skill. But when the chief had landed us on the island, with a two-quart bamboo stein of palm toddy, our three dark-skinned followers showed no inclination to come with us.

Kininni fingered the talisman that he wore on a wire at his throat. N'kulu made a sign with his forefinger that I had seen him draw only once before—it seemed to be a circle enclosing a triangle. The most seriously affected was Hagar. She could not bring herself to look at Trudi. She was close to tears and I thought that her conscience hurt her as no man's ever could.

But the boat had hardly pushed off when Trudi and I were glad of our aloneness. It was adventurous without being frightening, moving and mysterious, yet warmly companionable. The treeless island comprised about three acres. The grass was as rich and thick as an unmowed lawn in front of a Low Country mansion, kept eternally green by the intense sunlight and the blown spray. The latter dampened the whole scene but did not wet us; and there was a rainbow every way we looked. The lower point of the island looked down into the gorge into which the vast flood poured with everlasting thunder, and the poetry of Poe and Coleridge came to my mind; while I fancied Trudi, who had never opened a book except the Bible, thinking of the mysteries of the Apocalypse.

We sat in the grass, our wonder never dying, ever renewed; and the feeling grew upon me of being alone in the world with my pale-haired Voortrekker—a world even now, this minute, in the process of creation, with new-raised mountains and great waters flooding and roaring, a world we had searched for and found far beyond the barriers of all other worlds; and it was like a dream from which I could not quite waken. Then a strange thing happened. She called my attention to what I thought at first was one of the village oxen, swimming the river above the island. Then the beast came to shore, sturdily wading through the shallows until his whole form loomed before our gaze; and he was not an ox but a wild Cape buffalo, one of the most formidable of animals, with heavily bossed, wide-flaring horns. We had no guns and if we waked his berserk fury he could easily kill us both; yet it did not occur to either of us to feel afraid. Instead our hands clasped and we watched him in delight. He in turn lowed impatiently at what he considered our intrusion in his private domain; then, discovering we meant him no harm and expected none from him, he could not resist lowering his great head and snatching a mouthful of the succulent grass.

For nearly half an hour he lingered at the opposite end of the island, not quite reconciled to our presence but reluctant to take his leave. Then again he entered the flood, and we only caught glimpses of his big horns and thrusting muzzle as he swam to shore.

By now the sun was going down amidst flaming clouds, and the rainbow mists lay everywhere over the water and land, drifted, and spread and changed; and we gazed down upon the deep-blue flood above us, majestic and serene, then into the black tumult in the gorge below. The many-colored mists changed to luminous silver as the sun set and a huge and incredible moon rolled up with mighty force over the eastern hills.

I drew at Trudi's hand, and she came closer to me. It might be that on the sixth day in Eden, God had not yet completed all His vast works, perhaps the mountains spouted fire, perhaps the sea and the land had not finished their division, or even the light from the darkness, so the two wonder-struck human beings sitting there could hardly believe in the wonder of their own creation, and when the man drew at the woman's hand, she needs must come to him. Trudi came, and lay across my breast. She was very like Eve, I thought, in her innocence and wisdom, in beauty that no rainbow mist could equal, in strength, and in wile.

I kissed her wide full lips. In a little while they parted in

warmer welcome of my kiss. This moon made me forget a setting moon of long ago. The moonlight flooded the whole scene,
white and magical as that which once had shown me a lion in-
vading my camp. Silver-white in my arms lay my captive, although I thought there was still a tint of pale gold in her long
hair, and the deepening darkness of the sky was reflected in
her eyes. I wished she would strip off her buckskin shirt, not in
shame tonight but in pride, and she would become my woman,
and the great surge of the river would solemnize our mating,
and we would be given a glimpse of eternity in the waters falling without end; and how could any man-made temple be as
hallowed as this river-girt island under the moon, or any scene
as sublime?

We would inspan and outspan the length and breadth of
Africa. She would bear young with the wild of the river in their
hearts, the sweep of the veld in their souls; and I would have
no more to do with Charleston and its tangled things; and I too
would be an Afrikander, forgetting my mother tongue, while
our cattle thronged our kraals and our sheep grazed far. I would
search no more for tiny crystals in the river gravels, of good
only to tame folk in distant, crowded cities, and for kings and
dukes and women of fashion, and instead I would seize upon an
empire of my own, ten leagues long, five leagues wide, with
grass and forest and springs, hills and valleys, rocky *kopjes*
where lions dwelt; and my children and my grandchildren
would have it for their domain.

We would hunt together in the high veld and the low veld
and the middle veld of the thorn and mimosa forests. We would
despoil the elephant of his great ivories, and the white rhino of
his precious horn, and the bucks of their soft skins and muscle-
building flesh.

The bond would be made now. I would renounce all other
bonds. Trudi, will you be my woman? Will you take me for
your mate? I love you, Trudi. Alone, neither of us is anything,
only casuals of the night, but together we would be uncon-
querable.

My thoughts moved so strongly that my lips shaped words. She could not hear them, but she felt them against her lips. It seemed to me that she drew back a little, her eyes searching mine in the silvery light.

"What is your trouble, Edward?" she asked, her mouth pressed against my ear.

"I have none, but wanting you," I answered in the same wise.

After a long pause, she addressed me again. "It is a guilty wanting that I can't gratify."

"I love you, Trudi. I swear it by the river."

"The river falls. You must swear it by the sky, which never falls. You know that, no one better. I think that is where your trouble lies—something from long ago. But wait a little while. Perhaps all will be well."

"I can't wait. The moon is up and will soon start to set." So I spoke, not knowing my own meaning.

"Yes, and it shows the boat putting out from shore."

She kissed me with great tenderness, and rose.

2

The falling waters, with the power of a hundred thousand elephants and uncountable plow beasts, had gouged out of the rock a narrow gorge, through which they burst with unimaginable violence, scooped out a swirling, boiling whirlpool five hundred feet across, and chiseled out a Z-shaped canyon, dark and eerie as Xanadu's, forty miles long. If there were diamonds in the rock, surely the cosmic cataracts would uncover them, wash them down, and dump them among the sedimentary gravels. So I gave up my notion of giving up my search, and we inspanned for a trek eastward, and began to sample the rock at favorable-looking places from the foot of the trough to the mouth of a northwest-flowing tributary that we could not ford.

Trekking up the waterway in search of a crossing, often a big donga—the child of the child of the old grandsire Zambezi—forced us many miles back into the veld. So our reunion with the river was an ever-recurring pleasure. For the rest, it was the happiest trek we had yet made, promising we knew not what. There were the usual number of delays, but we did not mind; except at good grass and water, we were never in any great hurry to arrive anywhere. Every day the sun rose and shone; in the twilight there was almost always rest and food for all. The land remained unspeakably wonderful; all five of us humans stayed marvelously alive from the sun-bleached tops of our heads to the tips of our toenails. I could not speak for our two horses and score of oxen, since they had their inmost being in a world I could not enter; but they were lean, in good appetite and health, and apparently never reluctant to start the next day's march.

An event that began as another mishap, only to deepen in complexity and significance, occurred less than four weeks after our visit to Victoria Falls. The moon had rounded, but was not quite full, and it heaved up in a pale-blue east nearly an hour before the sun pitched down in the golden west. I had ordered our gait quickened as much as the tired beasts and the rough ground would stand. The reason was a dun-colored cloud that was quickly spreading across the sky before a brisk wind, not yet high, out of the Matapo Hills. I intended to pitch at the first donga with a trickle through its sands, or at a "pan" if the water were not too brackish, or even at a water hole with white bones at its bottom and black scum on its top. The reason was, the wind was slowly but steadily rising. The veld here was open, the high veld without trees, whereby it would sweep free. And our oxen could stand up better to a gang of lions shadowing them in the grass than to a howling wind.

Suddenly, with only the briefest warning, it struck full blast. One minute I heard its low, deep-toned whistle in the distance and its singing swish across the grass; the next we were in the midst of it, buffeted by an unseen foe who seemed to attack from all directions at once. As usual, Kininni was driving, N'kulu and Hagar rode in the wagon; Trudi and I were on horseback. All the beasts were simultaneously panic-stricken;

but although Trudi and I could exert some mastery over ours, Kininni's control of the oxen was instantly lost. He could only hang on as, making nothing of the heavy brakes, they galloped across the plain.

They would not go far, I thought. The labor was too great. In the meantime, though, they might leap and stagger across a watercourse that would break our wheels. Instead, another misadventure, never coming our way before, changed instantly the shape of the night's event. A great gust of wind broke some of the thongs that fastened to its frames the canvas covering of the wagon. It broke loose at the windward side and began to flap; in a few seconds more it tore free like a sail from a mast in a heavy gale and, with the wind in it, began spinning and rolling and tumbling across the plain.

It was the roof and side walls of our house, our protection against weather and wild beasts, the comfort of our followers, and an irreplaceable essential to our trek in this unpeopled land. Without stopping to think or taking note of any landmark, Trudi and I followed its grotesque flight. Across this stretch of level ground, it traveled at devilish speed. We had to gallop our horses to keep in sight of it. At a distance it looked like an enormous dirty-white bird flying close to the ground.

More than once it settled and lay still, only to take off again before we could get hand on it. Its flapping fantastic flight threw into panic a herd of zebras, already frightened by the gale, and it seemed to be chasing a family of sable antelope, a beautiful buck, his doe, and two calves—the first I had seen in this part of Africa—and what sense they made of the persistent pursuer, a visitant indeed from some unknown world, was beyond human wit to imagine. I think that Trudi and I trailed it about two miles before it stuck fast in the spinny of low thornbushes. We seized it with the determination of a gentleman retrieving his topper on a gusty day on Meeting Street, only to look across into each other's widening eyes.

The windstorm was passing—I could already detect a diminishing of its force. The dun-colored cloud was unraveling into swiftly drifting skeins. The fact remained that we had broken the first rule of the Voortrekker, in becoming separated from our outfit. Any way we looked we could see herds of game— wildebeests, hartebeests, gazelles, zebra, eland, and giraffes—and nothing else but the wild, unpeopled veld. The sun had already set. The night would drop down upon us like vultures on a carcass. Haunted by danger in many forms, it would immobilize veld-wise N'kulu and Kininni as surely as ourselves. The only comfort I could think of, for the moment, was the rising and radiant moon.

Trudi was appraising the situation as correctly and more coolly than I.

"Edward, have you any friction matches?" she asked in an easy tone.

"No."

I had carried none, in fact, since a portion of our precious store had been wetted and ruined in a sudden shower nearly a fortnight previously.

"Well, I guess it doesn't matter. There isn't any fuel—and we haven't an ax."

I glanced at her saddle scabbard. It was empty, for the simple reason that she kept the newfangled pin-fire rifle in the wagon, afraid that a tight brush in the thorn thicket would damage its mechanism. However, I had the old smooth-bore in my scabbard. It was loaded, and I had two extra slugs and some powder and caps.

"We'd better forget about that gun," she said, reading my mind.

"It would be a protection—in the last ditch."

"We don't want to get in the last ditch. If you should wound a lion with it—or a rhino or a buffalo or a leopard—not to mention an elephant if one comes along this way—we'd be in what the English call a pretty kettle of fish."

"Well, what are we going to do? I object to being eaten, at least without a struggle—"

"Edward, will you leave this thing to me?"

"With all my heart."

"Then sit down and we'll talk."

"It seems an odd time, but—" Trying to grin, I sat down in the grass. She dropped down beside me.

"Edward, have you anything to eat?"

"Yes, some dried eland beef in my knapsack."

"Good. My canteen is almost full of water. Edward, I've talked to many an old Afrikander, and I'll tell you exactly what I think we should do."

"Please start as soon as possible."

"About being eaten. You mean of course, by lions. This is the wild veld. There's no reason to fear man-eaters this far from a village. The lions around here are respectable lions. They live on the game they know and avoid the kinds they don't know."

"How about leopards?"

"They're not as trustworthy, but, on the whole, the same holds for them. Now it may be that horses smell very much like zebras. The first thing to do is take the bridles and saddles off our horses and turn them loose. They may find their way to the wagon in the dark. At least if a lion or a leopard starts to stalk them, they'll have a fighting chance. In the morning we can make a fire with a wooden drill. I know how, although it takes a full hour, and it is a wearisome job. N'kulu will see the smoke and come for us."

"I'm not worried about our being found—if we can get through the night."

"The next thing is to make ourselves as comfortable as possible with this canvas, then go to sleep. I'll tell you as near as I can hit it—where our danger lies. It won't be from lions or leopards. They're not coming near two strange motionless beings rolled in canvas. That is—I don't think they will—at least closer than fifty feet. Remember they will be able to see us perfectly well but will have no clear recognition of us. Buffaloes will walk wide of our smell. Human beings must smell like the devil to the wild things. Elephants might come up, but I don't think they'll go into a rage and trample us. The elephants around here have had very little to do with human beings—I think they'll go on about their business. That leaves only rhinos. And rhinos—as you know—are unpredictable."

"What would be your guess of a rhino's behavior?"

"I think he might snort and stamp, but if we keep quiet he'll go away."

She looked at me earnestly, anxious for me to believe her, her eyes clear and candid.

"Under the best of circumstances," I remarked after a long pause, "it's going to be quite an adventure."

"Maybe not. Maybe we won't have any visitors but jackals."

3

Trudi was wrong in this last respect. We had hardly spread the canvas, leaving a fold on either side for our cover when the mountain chill crept down, when a small herd of buffaloes came striding into the dying wind with their muzzles thrusting; and, at sight and smell of us, thundered away snorting. The day died so peacefully that we could hardly say when the last of its light expired and the silver gray of the veld was moonlight only. We had a sense of expanding vision. The reason was, of course, there was no firelight to dim our eyes; although actually we could not see nearly as far as we thought; a shadow that looked to be a hundred feet distant was hardly thirty. Still the night was a notable one, the air changed by the wind, the dying of that wind leaving the animals restless, many of them finding themselves after their run on unfamiliar ground; the moon high, bright, and potent, the old magics working strongly, the spell of Africa, which no man can explain any more than he can deride it, laying thick upon the land.

For once, at least, my perceptions were sharply alert to the mood and music of the African night; my soul was wide open to its mystery. I was not in camp or on the way to camp; none of this moonlit savage sweep I had made my own; I was a visitor, a stranger, with nothing possible to do but watch, listen, and surmise. I was not the dominant animal, making my way at whatever cost to the inhabitants; in a certain sense I was at their mercy. Forces out there could move in upon me but I could not move upon them. I was subject to the night and hence to Fate in a way I had never before felt. I wondered what feelings crowded the vital, palpitant heart of my companion.

As we ate dried meat and drank from her flask we spoke very little, and then in hushed tones. Maybe we would be safer if we shouted. The idea came to me that we should do everything we could to emphasize our difference from the dwellers here, our humanity that just now was an idea strangely hard to grasp. But I had agreed to leave everything to Trudi. She had talked to many old Afrikanders; she herself was a young Afrikander who had stored away much lore and had many true feelings about the country. I would follow her lead. I would do what she thought best.

But there was one factor in the situation, one force, that I did not think she comprehended or perceived. It was an outlaw now, I thought, but that did not reduce its power. As she sat near me, in arm's reach, the moonlight on her face, I was more taken by her than ever before. My desire for her grew upon me until it possessed me wholly, leaving room for no other desire. I could not think of the future. Actually it seemed that there was none, that time had stopped, and there was no world other than this gray world of grass, great scattered stars, moonlight, loneliness, and wild beasts, with her somehow its child, and my sought-for prize. The shadows lay thick about me. The lonely miles ran unmeasured. There was no sound.

Above me the great stars shone, and would be shining a million years from now. But this *now* was mine—ours if Trudi would share it with me. The immensity of dimness and solitude had not sapped at my life. I felt it throbbing in my fingertips. She too was alive as the unseen creatures roaming the veld. Could I make her grasp the *now*? The rapture of one moment, the sense of being, the ocean sweep of desire?

Then out of that deeper darkness, into the misty moonlight, emerged three shapes. They were not attracted to us. They were only passing this way. But when they saw us, seated on the canvas, all of them stopped and gazed. I saw now that they were big male lions, with heavy manes. As they paused, they proposed prodigious latent power. One of them—the youngest, perhaps, growled in low, deep tones.

"Don't shoot," Trudi whispered.

I heard her in the silence and I sat still. The three beasts gazed for perhaps half a minute, then one of them—the oldest, perhaps—continued on his way. His companions joined him. On they strode, out of the moonlight, out of our vision, into the farther shadows.

When I looked again at Trudi she had removed the pin that held her hair in a glossy knot at the back of her head and let it stream about her shoulders.

"Now?" I asked. I could hardly speak but she understood.

"Yes, yes."

Our hands flew. In a moment she lay gleaming. Her pride in her beauty revealed by the moonlight was greater than the pride of the lion in his strength. I saw her lips faintly curled and her wide-open luminous eyes. I saw her shaping more tender and touching than a gazelle's. The moon rose higher; the stars looked down; far away some jackals began to bark and that caused an old gray hyena, divorced from his pack, to wail and sob, then break into horrid laughter. Other hyenas replied. Now the veld was awake and alive. But no wakefulness was as great as ours, no life as intense.

Did they know beauty, our companions of the night? The sulky rhino, the glowering buffalo, the stealthy leopard, the prideful magnificent lion, the elephant serene as the clouds of heaven until his wrath broke? Did they look up to the illustrious moon and wonder about the stars? It came to me that they did not, but they knew the tragic splendor of existence. They knew its travail, and some of its ecstasy.

We were one tonight. We had established some great, ever-

lasting bond. No lovers were ever more fortunate since that forbidden hour in the Garden. There was nothing tawdry, nothing base; the sky was over us, the moon shone in glory, the stars
burned far off; the secret was almost whispered in our ears;
everything had meaning if we could only grasp it, the silence
and the shadows and the solitude, the beauty and the bliss. The
hyenas laughed and sobbed. The little jackals barked. Far away
a lion roared, declaring his kingship of the plain. I did not
know what life was, or what it meant, but it was no small mystery, no trifling boon.

CHAPTER XIII

The Stalk

THE NIGHT was long, blissful, and epochal in our lives, and we spent it in each other's arms, sharing each other's sleep or wakefulness. Sometimes we were wakened by the drama of the veld that happened to come close to our bivouac. A jackal tried to steal my haversack, containing some dried meat we had saved for breakfast; a loiterer that we both thought was a leopard crept with not quite perfect silence through the thorn; a herd of zebra, stampeded by lions, broke across the donga, and a terror-stricken colt sprang by us almost in arm's reach. Yet I cannot say we were ever greatly afraid. There was a wonder of life upon us that precluded fear, even fear of life's sudden and violent stop in the African night on the open veld.

We saw the moon drop behind the hills, and there set in a brief interval of intense dark, with a great showing of the stars, before it began to roll back and give way to a barely perceptible grayness, preluding another day. Mistlike it paled and spread. Earth-vision came back to our eyes. Then we watched the tranquil, common, miraculous birth of morning. Color returned; landmarks stood forth; distance was recaptured; and the vultures flew forth to see what the night had brought them, and we thought of the wild hunters driven by heaviness of limbs and belly and heart to their dull lairs, although we could not see the slightest movement in the grass. Except for one herd of quaggas a long way off, our companions of the night had deserted us. Thank the blue skies that never fall, we still had each other.

Trudi began to make a wooden drill to spin with a string and make fire. I thought we could find a quicker means, so I cut off a little canvas that could be spared, doubled it and redoubled it with a salting of gunpowder, and, when kindling was cut and ready, fired into it. It began to smolder with a distasteful smell, and by blowing upon it we could have no doubt started a fire. The effort was suddenly needless, because Trudi's quick eye caught sight of N'kulu, approaching on horseback across the plain; and a moment later I made out the wagon, a mile or so at his rear.

I came quickly and took both of Trudi's hands.

"Isn't Zumbo the nearest European town?" It had marked the last westward shadow of Portuguese colonization.

"Yes."

"Is there a Dutch church there?"

"There was—the last that I heard. It may be that the Matshangana have come again. There's been talk of it." This bloodthirsty tribe had decimated most of the river towns twenty years before.

"Well, we're going to try to get there. If we can't make it, we'll go elsewhere. We'll look for diamonds on the way. If we find any, even a few, they'll come in handy for buying cattle and sheep and Kaffirs and equipping our farm. If we don't, we'll take up land in the Transvaal, and begin the best we can. In any case, we'll be man and wife long before then. Our children will have a name and can hold up their heads anywhere they go. Does that suit you?"

Her smile was broad although her eyes filled with tears.

"We won't find any diamonds, but we won't need any now," she answered.

So we waited, properly, for keen-eyed N'kulu to ride up. He looked from Trudi's face to mine, and the impassivity of his own face was not as perfect as usual.

"Hagar as well as Kininni are in the wagon," he reported blandly. "Both horses are safe, and so are all the oxen. It won't take long to put back the canvas. The evil spirits struck at us, but the good spirits came to our help. And for that I will make offerings to them all my days."

"I will do the same, the best that I know how."

We were wonderfully happy, we five people, two whites and three blacks, with our wagon and oxen and horses and guns and adventure, and the vast spaces of Africa in which to have our being. We were making for Zumbo on the Zambezi; and we could have got there in no time by trading our outfit for native boats, but instead we chose to go by land, encircling the great tributaries until we could find a ford, and thereby we spent our days on the high veld, the middle veld, or the low veld, and our nights under the stars; and almost never did we cross another wagon track; and for days on end we did not come in sight of a native village. Our fare was meat and mealies and, very occasionally, roots and berries which one or other of the three Negroes identified as being good to eat. Here and there we looked for diamonds without finding a chip of one, but quite frequently we found ivory, almost imperishable among the moldered bones of a great bull, and the tusks that we added to our growing store would bring something like a Portuguese peso a pound at the river town, enough to replenish all that we had expended for gunpowder and corn and the few other things that the land did not supply.

The wonderful land! It was rugged, sun-baked, and lean, very rarely cool and green with forest, but it suited perfectly us rugged, sun-baked, lean travelers upon its illimitable veld. For one thing, there was no safety. A constant alertness was demanded of us, and that kept our senses sharp and our nerves in tune. There was always the possibility of a war party of Matshangana, starting out on a raid and wanting a good augury of victory, wetting their assagais in our blood for the fun and Devil of it. Manikusa, their king, was an old man, and it was said that he could no longer control his plumed and painted warriors; so we journeyed many a long mile out of the way to avoid their kraals. There were tsctsc flies that could kill a hulking eland as easily as us; and there were elephants and rhinos in the thorn, buffaloes in the wallows, lions and leopards and black mambas in the grass.

But there were also herds of high-jumping 'mpallas, little gazelles with whirling tails, hartebeests that stood foolishly and gazed, and wildebeests that ran in frantic half-circles like Western bison. We got on good and almost intimate terms with giraffes, and wished to borrow their long necks to spy out the plains. We slaughtered an eland now and then, and stopped and smoked the meat, for we could never tell when we would come on hungry country. We enjoyed the sight of steinboks, klipspringers, water bucks, roan antelopes, quaggas, and zebras, but we stopped and stared when, now and then, we came in sight of the marvelous sable antelope, handsome beyond belief, or the great kudus with twisted horns. To hyenas and jackals we paid scant heed—they could not help being scavengers of low degree—but when we spied their cousins, the wild dogs, the most pitiless killers in a pitiless land, we stalked them with our guns and laid some of them low.

2

One fresh and fragrant morning, about two months after Trudi's and my bivouac on the moonlight veld, she had something important to tell me. I knew it from the look on her face and the way she tagged after me as I went about my chores; and when I walked down to the spring she came with me. Her conduct was dignified in the extreme—she could pass for an Afrikaans *vrouw* of the strictest sect—but there was a pronounced shine in her eyes.

"When do you think we will get to Zumbo?" she asked, in carefree tones.

"At this rate, just about never," I answered, wondering at her.

"In three months, do you suppose?"

"Perhaps. I didn't know you were in a hurry."

"Well, we're to be married in Zumbo—are we not?—and I don't want those fat Portuguese women to laugh at me."

"Why should they laugh?"

"Why shouldn't they? The only thing missing from the joke would be a father with a gun. In three months—well, not one of my skirts will fit me."

I sat down, partly from weakness, and made a little sign she knew, and she came and lay in my lap. When I had kissed her to my heart's passing content, she blurted out her triumphant story. Even a month ago she was sure—the mealies had lost their taste, she could not tell eland meat from wildebeest—she dreamed constantly of long strings of fish—she craved pepper sauce—her nipples swelled and itched. She had not told me then lest she be mistaken, and I build in vain. Now she was sure. But there was nothing remarkable about it. Fertility was the order of things, in case of both man and beast, in sun-burned Africa. A Boer husband, being told such news, would barely take his pipe out of his mouth to listen. Unless one of us came to an early death—and I remembered, and could not forget Death's ubiquity in this vast, new, half-peopled, accursed and blessed land, how he was the greatest Voortrekker of us all—why, it would be only the first of many.

"Will it be a son or a daughter?" I asked.

"How would I know?"

"You have already asked Hagar, and she has told you."

"Hagar is a Kaffir woman. I don't believe in her signs. Now in a few months, I myself can tell—by the way I carry him, whether high or low—but you would think me a fool to put any faith in an ostrich hen taking off while the cock stayed and strutted, or a male hyena coming into camp in broad daylight, and stealing some meat I had just dressed. Now there was one sign which, although I do not believe in it, is in good repute with the Boer women as well as with the Kaffirs. In the week of my conceiving—and Hagar and I too know what week it was—three times a bull elephant moved up out of his herd to trumpet at us. Not once did an old cow give the warning. It may be so—or—it may not be so. All that I know is—as sure as the grass will die and the rains come again—of us two, there will soon be three."

"All I know is, we will make a little haste to Zumbo."

We did so, and came to the ancient Portuguese town in a little over a month. It stood at the very edge of white man's country, at the mouth of the great south-flowing tributary known as the Loangwa, as long as the Hudson, and which is said to rise beyond the farther reaches of Myasa Land. In some respects the town was thriving. There was a lively traffic between the Portuguese traders and friendly tribes of natives for ostrich feathers, ivory, and slaves, the latter mainly captives of the Matshangana. Yet I could not escape the feeling of it hanging on the edge of an abyss. Out of the west poured the great Zambezi, becoming even greater with the influx of the Loangwa; and vast countries lay out there, peopled with blacks and wild beasts, and only a few adventurers dared pass the confines of the town.

The merchants with their gold seals took little interest in Trudi and I. We had seen the Great Falls of the Zambezi, we had crossed the red sands of the Kalahari, we had lived and thrived in black kingdoms where, according to legend, every white throat was quickly cut; but we had a small, cheap outfit, and nothing to sell but a few tusks. Meanwhile, though, we looked at them with a certain condescension. They knew nothing about Africa and it was useless to try to tell them. They had never seen the herds of wild elephants drifting silent as smoke clouds through the thorn. When the sun set and the moon rose and the dark was bewitched with silvery light, they went inside their houses and closed the doors.

It turned out that we had arrived at Zumbo at the wrong time. Heer van Lydeck, the pastor of the small Dutch church that had found root in this foreign soil, had taken off for Sofala a few weeks before and would not return for another month; meanwhile, there was not a single ordained minister or lay figure in the town who could perform the Protestant sacrament of marriage. For my part, I would have liked to have the rite performed by one of the old kindly Portuguese priests; but it would be outside his province and authority, even if it were his desire, so Trudi's and my only choice was to await the minister's return. Meanwhile, there were tributaries of the Loangwa whose gravels I wished to scan.

What seemed a far more minor matter, yet which caused me a deeper uneasiness, was the circumstance of our arrival in Zumbo during the stay of a party of men known far and wide as Harvey's Hustlers. There was nothing especially unique about them. Small gangs of adventurers had begun to operate throughout South Africa, mainly renegade Englishmen and Boers, who managed to play both ends against the middle in the various native wars but whose main source of living was an illicit trade in slaves. Harvey's band consisted of only six men, including himself, yet I had heard of them first in Delagoa Bay, and some farmers I had met muttered about them in hate and fear.

I came face to face with them in the main trading post of the town, sitting about a table drinking Cape brandy. They were quiet enough but their expression and manner breathed arrogance and cruelty. A Portuguese half-caste clerk, called Alfonso, speaking oddly accented but fluent English, took pleasure in identifying and portraying for my benefit its various members.

"Harvey is the one with the red hair," he told me. "I think he is a Scot, but he came here by way of Australia, and many say he is a fugitive from Botany Bay. He is a wonderful shot. He boasts that he has killed eighteen Kaffirs and four whites, including a woman who was false to him. Notice the gold ring he wears on his right hand. It is shaped like a serpent and identifies him in any company, but he doesn't care—it is his boast!"

I noticed other signs of natural leadership, including the boldness of its ready assumption, with quick and positive answers, in a low, resonant voice, to his followers' remarks. A little over medium height, he was powerfully built, quick of movement, with restless energy; and his most outstanding feature was very bright, light-colored eyes with the intense marksman's glance.

"Why don't the authorities hang him?" I asked.

"The authorities, say you. Who are they? Who rules South Africa, now that it is divided between the English, the Boers, the Portuguese, the Germans, and half a dozen native kings? No one dares restrain him, much less hang him. And his main lieutenant is the Arab, Mustapha, sitting at his right. Next to Tippoo-Tib, he may be the most successful slaver in South Africa."

Alfonso went on to tell me of the other four. One was a burly Boer, called Fritz. One was a small, dark, graceful Portuguese, named Bernardino. Still another was of Irish antecedants, gentleman-born according to his appearance and manner, but with a slow, evil smile; he was known only as Sligo. The last was my own countryman, and a Southerner, I thought, to judge by his olive skin, brown eyes, slow speech, and high spirits. His companions called him Culpepper, whether or not for the old Virginia town Alfonso did not know. He was the only one of the company who, obviously, had drunk more Cape brandy than he could control.

"What are they doing here?" I asked.

"Resting—between enterprises," Alfonso answered sonorously. "Perhaps they will soon take off for Capetown. Harvey has a woman there, I hear—one good to look upon, who works at White's."

I did not wish to become involved in their next enterprise, however minor. Then and there I gave over for the present a trivial, although pleasant dream of having my last diamond, almost as good as the one I had sold Marcel, sellable for about five hundred Cape dollars, set in a ring or a brooch or a pin for Trudi by a clever Dutch goldsmith in the town. Harvey's Hustlers might quite possibly hear about it and they might be so down-at-heels that they would condescend to take an active interest in it. Anyway Trudi would not know what to do with such a ring, pin, or brooch, except to love it very dearly and carry it in a packet at her throat and sleep with it at night. I had already learned she had never owned one single bauble that could be called jewelry; her father associated such with the Whore of Babylon. Actually she had never had a real doll either, only a wooden mannikin carved for her by one of the Kaffirs, and which she had hidden from her father. However, if the skies did not fall too soon, she was going to have a living, breathing doll to make up all her loss.

Indeed, after a close survey of the six bushwhackers—from whom our party had no real protection except our rifles—I thought best to get shed of their company as soon as possible. To that end I spoke freely of Tete, four hundred miles downriver and at present the liveliest of the Portuguese settlements; and since it lay below Kebrassa Rapid, the journey was frequently made by land in ox wagons. Once clear and out of sight of Zumbo, I intended to double back to the Loangwa, whose gravels seemed more promising than any I had sampled.

We completed the maneuver, and after five days' journey found a beautiful camp site at the edge of Basenga country. On a day that a caster of my horoscope, supposing I had ever dealt in such occult matters, would have marked with an esoteric mark which only he could read, all my companions took themselves off in search of an "elephant graveyard" which a wandering Shenzi root-digger had told N'kulu lay only ten miles distant.

Like most Afrikanders, Trudi believed in elephant graveyards. The belief centered in the notion that wild elephants, sensing the approach of death, went off to certain grounds to breathe their last, and their tusks could be found there in wealth-bringing numbers. I did not believe the story, not through lack of wonder at this most amazing and inscrutable of beasts, but because we ourselves had found tusks the length and breadth of the veld; but both N'kulu and Kininni thought it very likely, and their boyish eagerness to go with the M'sabu and Hagar was stronger than I could resist. Anyway I was not willing for them to undertake the little trek alone.

So they went forth happily, Trudi on horseback, the three blacks in the wagon. Apparently they had not the slightest doubt of coming back with the wheels creaking and the oxen groaning from the load of ivory. As for me, I was rather glad of the free day. I meant to go to a small tributary of Loangwa, deeply scoured and subject to great floods, and to wash its gravels for small crystals, colder than most pebbles, and greasy to the touch. I rode my horse, and brought the old smooth-bore musket in my saddle scabbard. Besides powder and balls, I had one of the washing pans, and plenty of dried meat for my day's fare. After tying my horse in a small spinny of dwarf mimosa trees, I went quite hopefully about my search.

I did not believe in elephant graveyards but I had never denied what could only be called human intuition. The day had seemed a strange one from the moment of its breaking until now. I could not pick out a thing wrong with it; the birds and animals behaved in their usual fashion; yet the heat and the flurries of breeze and the shadows on the rocks and the silent flow of water all seemed to be a little off-center, slightly distorted in some way, as things appear in dreams; or perhaps I was slightly feverish from a touch of malaria, or maybe I had been bitten by a tsetse fly, and this was the beginning of the swift decay of my brain.

My only main concern was for my companions. Although they had struck off alone onto the veld a hundred times before, today was the day I should not have let them go. Africa was an accursed country—Isaiah had said so in some of the most ringing words ever written in Hebrew. Maybe the Devil had

created it out of the residue of the rest of the world's creation
while God's back was turned. These great rivers, these endless
plains, this forever grass, the *kopjes* and the sudden luxurious
dongas and the lean thorn. Africa had been too good to us
lately. She was up to something, and I wished that I knew what.

Africa, don't strike down Trudi. Take me and N'kulu and
Kininni and even Hagar, we are grown up, we have lived devilish long already, we are the run and ruck of black and white
people whom the Devil can't hurt very much, we are cannon
fodder in the war between good and evil; if we die, to hell
with it anyhow, the grass will come up just the same after the
rains, the little zebra colts will chase their mothers, the wild
pigeons will hurtle by in the twilight, the evil spirits will not
meet in great festivity for a victory won. But Trudi is different,
she is unique, I found her in evil's very den, yet her eyes were
blue and her hair golden and her heart high. I don't know her
to this day. I have no idea what goes on in the mind within
her mind which is her secret self. I have won her love and her
favors, to which I have no more right than to a gift of wings
by a visiting angel. Don't do anything to stop her wide, slow
smiles. If I can't have her, I'll not protest; she is too much luck
for a gambler like me who figures the percentage; but let her
live on under your fiery sun; let her ride like some strange
yellow-haired centaur until her labor pains begin, then let
her give birth and keep her living, breathing doll without too
great a price.

But thinking this, I kept on washing gravel. No, I would not
yield to these superstitious apprehensions; I was an American,
a Southerner, a Charlestonian, a civilized fellow, with some
pretensions to being a gentleman, not a savage living in a beehive house in a nameless village. Perhaps I paid more attention to the business than usual. It was nearly noonday now,
there was nothing to fear from lions or leopards; and no cover
for elephants, rhinos, and buffaloes. And so it was that a human
voice, rising suddenly out of the low thickets on the riverbanks,
a voice speaking English, shook me to the marrow of my bones.

"Put up your hands, you Yankee bastard," the voice commanded.

I turned in that direction. I could see no one.

"Are you addressing me?" I asked, as though I were drunk. "If so, you've made a mistake. Bastard or no, I'm no Yankee."

Farther down the bank, someone laughed rather shrilly.

"He's got you that time, Sligo," the laughter said. "He's no more a Yankee than I am, but if he doesn't put up his hands by the time you can count ten, give him a two-ounce slug through his gut."

I waited hardly a second, then put up my hands. It did not seem likely to me that Sligo would shoot—there are few things as valueless as a human corpse—but authority rang in the voice and for a second or two I thought it might be Harvey's, although it had a Virginia instead of an English or Australian accent; and I did not know the game, its rules, or its stakes. My gun was leaning against a rock about twelve feet distant. Unless I missed my guess, I was one against six.

But only five came out of thorn through which they had stalked me with consummate care and skill. The missing one was none other than Harvey himself—I looked in vain for his red head and compact form in the shiny-eyed quintet. It struck me then that this was only a minor enterprise on the part of his hustlers—he had probably sent them out while he remained in Zumbo with a bottle and a half-caste woman—and that might mean that I might not be murdered, only beaten and robbed—but there was something wrong with that argument. I could find its flaw if I looked carefully enough.

The five came up to me, and I could tell by the way they kept out of one another's sights that they were used and trained to concerted attack. Instantly I identified every one. I had not forgotten a single face or any fact of the brief account given me of them by the Portuguese half-caste named Alfonso. The name of the handsome, hirsute Arab was Mustapha. If ordinarily second in command, he would naturally be first in his chief's absence, but evidently he had yielded the office to the

American called Culpepper, probably because he could not speak English. Sligo was the renegade Irish gentleman with the slow, evil smile. The burly Boer with gross features was called Fritz. Bernardino was a small swarthy Portuguese with grace in every movement.

It was Sligo who came closest to me—too close for his own safety, except for the gun barrels of his fellow bushwhackers leveled upon me with long-practiced ease. I did not know his intention, but I felt the cold, swift surge of terror. In the middle of one of his smiles—without crossing the aim of the guns—he struck me a short, terrific blow on the side of the jaw. It was as though he had a rock in his hand, and I went down like a polled ox. Although I did not quite lose consciousness, when again I realized time and place, the scene had changed. I lay in short grass, some sixty yards back from the riverbank. My hands and feet were bound by rawhide thongs to deep-driven pegs—in the jargon of the English army I had been "pegged out." My five captors stood about me, talking jollily in Afrikaans, meanwhile waiting for me to regain my wits.

"He's all right, now," Culpepper remarked. "Sligo, find out what we want to know."

"You heard that?" Sligo asked.

"Yes, sir."

"We've been watching you wash the gravels. In fact, we heard about it before we came to Zumbo. What are you looking for?"

"I'm looking for gold," I answered promptly. "The rivers here are very like the rivers in California—almost drying up in summer, high in flood."

"He talks well," remarked Fritz, laughing.

"Where do you expect to find it?" Sligo went on. "You must have some clue."

"I look at the foot of rapids and in eddies where heavy minerals would naturally settle."

"Have you found any yet?"

"No, sir, I haven't."

"Search him, Bernardino," Culpepper commanded.

The little Portuguese did so. When he opened a little gazelle-skin bag I carried in my shirt pocket, at first he stared dumb-foundedly at the pebble-sized stone it contained. Suddenly his dark skin flushed, his eyes widened and shone, and he passed the stone to Culpepper in stunned silence.

"Great God, it's a diamond!" my countryman broke forth.

"It couldn't be," Sligo answered angrily. "Everyone knows there are no diamonds in Africa."

"Look at it, you Irish fool!"

Sligo took it between his fingers, examining it with what seemed expert care. His eyes bulged strangely, then he turned on me with a malignant expression, frightening as any human look I had ever seen.

"Where did you get it? Speak up."

"A native found it, somewhere in Cape Colony."

"You're lying. It was found close to here. Well, you'd better not lie to us. Fritz, you and Mustapha bring a big rock."

"How big a rock?" Fritz asked with terrifying calmness.

"I said a big one. As big as you and he can carry. Two or three hundred pounds."

"What are you going to do?" Culpepper asked. It was his last attempt to resume a command that everyone here perceived he had lost.

"Evidently you don't know legal procedure." Now there had come a new note in his voice, one which he thought was hu-morous and which I recognized as exultant, a voice heard in drunken men but almost never unassociated with cruelty or violence. "Haven't you bloody Americans ever heard of Old Bailey? The wardens had a way of getting confessions, they did so! They used it with the law's consent till only a few years ago—I dare say they still use it on the sly. Leave this thing to me. Fritz, you and Mustapha hurry up with that rock. I'll teach you blatherskites something before we're through."

He had not taught me anything yet—I already knew of noth-ing quite so vicious in the whole tainted human family as a renegade Irish gentleman—but he had told me something. It was, very simply, that my appointment was not only with torture, but with murder. The latter went without saying. It was an outcome as fixed now in the minds of these five bushwhackers as in my own mind. The reason was that, no matter what I told or did not tell, in the end they would not dare let me remain alive. They could catch slaves and by greasing a few hands sell them to Arab dealers; if they whipped some of them to death, the evidence could be easily concealed, the matter buried with the bones with only hyenas to dig them up and gnaw them. But I was a citizen of a distant but redoubtable nation. An American consul had his offices in Capetown; English governors must answer to foreign offices in London. I might have more money than they guessed. I might have influential friends.

I could not keep my brain from arriving at this obvious conclusion. At the same time I could not keep from remembering that once before I had been sentenced to an ugly death, only to be rescued. But before there was sheltering dark into which to leap. Now I lay in a blaze of sunlight, on an open prairie almost naked except for patches of low scrub and scanty grass. I did not have all night for my luck to change, for wonderful cards to begin to fall; I had no more than an hour or two at most, and perhaps only a few minutes. The time seemed to rush as Fritz and the glowering Arab arrived with the rock. They had got it from rocky ground about fifty yards distant; by their grunting and straining it must weigh three hundred pounds. Oddly enough, I had a good idea what they would do with it. Somewhere—sometime—I had read about Old Bailey.

"Lay it square in the middle of his belly," Sligo directed.

It was done. Because at first I braced my muscles against it, I was aware of no great pain. But this could not last long.

"Where did you find that diamond?" Sligo demanded.

"It was found by a native in a washhole in the Vaal River."

"Why aren't you on the Vaal, looking for more?"

"I looked carefully, but couldn't find any more."

"Culpepper, you and Bernardino bring another rock."

Used to obeying orders, the two went off. The others waited and the Arab told a joke in broken English, but Sligo did not laugh at it; it would be beneath the present dignity of his captaincy. I remembered that I had seen these five men only once before. Their roots and my roots had no mutual ground; they were as much strangers to me as would be a mob of lions. There was no heritage of hatred between us. They were killing me for the sake of a little carbon crystal. It was not a fitting end to my adventure. I deserved better than this of the gods; I had striven hard, and now and again I had acted gentlemanly. Yet there was the blue sky, with its ever-watchful vulture; there was the sun blazing in my eyes; around me grew the mean thorn and the yellow grass; and the growing pain in my belly did not quite banish its sickening cold.

Help, if you are going to come, come soon! If there is no help for the seamstress's son, for a bastard named Edward Stono who tried to go too far and to climb too high, may the dark come quick! The great players often died young, Faro Jack told me so. Maybe I was not a great player, only a piker, the word used by the Forty-niners in Panama; but many of that ilk likewise died young. They did not like it any better than the great ones. They were as cold and forlorn and lonely in the deeps of their souls. Yet almost all of them stood up to it, when it became unavoidable. It might be vanity, but, again, it might be pride.

Culpepper and Bernardino came grunting with the rock.

"Lay it on his chest," Sligo directed.

They did so, and its weight was over two hundred pounds. It had a sharp corner that dug into my breastbone; I could hardly lift my chest to breathe.

"Where did you get the diamond?" Sligo asked me.

"I've already told you."

He looked up, with his slow, evil smile. "You bullies bring more rocks. I'm through wasting time on him. My patience"—and this sounded so well that he repeated it—"my patience is exhausted. We'll put 'em on his legs and arms as they used to do at Old Bailey. We'll find out where that diamond came from, and why he's washing this stinking little donga. I think a hundred-pounder on his head might help him remember. If it doesn't, I know one little trick. I hate to play it on a white man, it's a trick too good for Kaffirs, but he seems to want it—"

At that instant the top of his head flew off, looking oddly like a chip when one is cutting wood, and he whirled around very strangely and fell down. About the same instant—out of some thorn or grass not far distant—came the loud roar of a rifle.

In the next few seconds only one of this five left alive remained motionless and silent, and I was that one. I could not help myself, being pegged out and weighted down with five hundredweight of stone. The other four became violently active, yet with a curious dreamlike lack of consequence. Both Culpepper and Mustapha snatched up their guns, which were near at hand; then stood pivoting back and forth, looking for a target. I saw both of their faces and there was something irresistibly comic in their popping eyes and ghastly gray faces, despite their undoubted bravery. Oddly enough, Bernardino fell flat. Probably he had done it in some shooting affair long ago, and it had saved his life, and he could think of nothing else. Fritz broke forth in an Afrikander howl. The words made sense, but the complete absence of expression on his face, as though it had changed to wood, gave them an unforgettable oddness.

"Where did it come from? Tell me, Dummkopf. Where did that shot come from?"

No one could answer. The seconds ticked off, and I think a little hope was born in the hearts of the two riflemen; it might stand to reason that whoever fired the shot was now sneaking away through the grass. But disillusionment came soon. Mustapha the Arab never experienced it, never knew it; but the three others could tell him about it, if they should meet again. A black spot appeared suddenly on his forehead;

at the same second the rifle boomed. Mustapha appeared to keep his position, his rifle thrusting, for a long half-second more; then he pitched forward and down.

"Oh, God!" cried the man called Culpepper with what might be easily mistaken for fervent piety. But when he looked for the way to run, he could not find it. When he tried to remember which way Mustapha was facing when the bullet struck, he could not remember.

"Rush him, before he can load again," cried Fritz. "He has a double-barreled gun but he can't shoot again—"

No one believed Fritz; at least no one would follow him on the brave venture. Fritz alone ran forth, howling, in the general direction of the fire; now I could understand how such a seemingly stupid man could have a place among Harvey's Hustlers. He ran about forty yards, a formidable figure, brave as a lion, perhaps, but more suggestive of a rhino charging, before the gun roared for the third time. He toppled sideways, indicating that the bullet had struck him in the side of the head. Then there was a sudden silence. The only movement was that of Bernardino, creeping away on his hands and knees. Culpepper was watching the grass, ready to shoot at its first movement. He too was a brave man.

"You're next, Culpepper," I told him.

"Then, by God, you're going with me."

He turned and raised his gun barrel, intending to brain me. He was not quick enough, for a rifle roared, the piece dropped from his hands, his face was flooded by a great gush of blood, and he dropped down with his friends.

Only Bernardino was left. He was still creeping through the grass, but he had gained a little distance, and suddenly he trusted to speed. Leaping up, he ran away from the fire. I had never seen a human being cover ground so fast. In a few seconds he was more than a hundred yards from the scene of slaughter. Hope would be rising in his heart by now; he was going to make it; he would live on; of all those so vividly alive a few seconds ago, he was the lone survivor. No one could aim true at this range; no bullet could carry death this far.

Perhaps he was naming over his long-neglected saints as a rifle boomed once more. Far out on the plain the little, scampering figure seemed to stumble. He fell with his legs and arms wide-stretched. That he was head-shot I did not doubt.

Then a wail rose in the grass in front of me, and up out of it sprang Trudi, her rifle in her hands, and she came running toward me, bawling like a child.

CHAPTER XIV

I Did It All Alone

ALONG WITH our activities, fairly brisk in the next few days, there came to pass a mystery that I have never solved. After her crying spell, Trudi got in the wagon and went to sleep; on awakening it seemed that she had forgotten the desperate drama in which she had played the main part. She never spoke of it again or indicated any conscious knowledge of its occurrence; no doubt she was suffering from shock; and for several nights her sleep was troubled by bad dreams. The only help I knew for the latter trouble—and to my great joy it seemed to work—was to hold her fast in my arms.

None of us mentioned the matter to her, whether a wise course I did not know. After leaving the scene, none of us ever returned to it. We did not give Christian funerals to the victims of the brief and positive gunfire; we gave them African funerals. Before leaving the scene, N'kulu retrieved my diamond from Sligo's pocket, and I unleathered and set free five horses tied behind a thorn thicket. It pained N'kulu and I think Hagar to leave five good percussion rifles where they fell; Kininni cared for none of such things. Our point was not to conceal evidence of what had happened, but to call no attention to it.

The veld had swallowed up more than one vivacious party without anyone ever to say what had become of them.

Meanwhile I did not forget that when we had first laid eyes on a party of bushwhackers, it had numbered six, not five; and its leader, a red-headed man of parts, remained unaccounted for. His name was Harvey. He had come to Africa from Australia, probably a convict settlement. A successful slave trader, he was no doubt hand in glove with some important Portuguese officials; and the tale of his participation in various native wars could mean that he had influence with some kings and chiefs. Within hours he would be wondering what had happened to his band. Their loss might put a crimp in him; he might be afraid to bluster any more and he would vanish in the Blue. But he might be a zealot of some kind, so we inspanned and we trekked without delay.

In the next month we saw large regions of Africa. My excuse for keeping to our rough, jouncing way, instead of outspanning for a good rest, was always a river, a creek, or a donga not far off, whose gravels I wished to sample. On the whole we kept to the high veld, where there was almost no timber, but great visibility and maneuverability. We were hundreds of miles from the scene of execution, in the vague frontiers of Matshangana country, before I felt sure all danger of retaliation had passed.

Now we could outspan for a good rest. There lay the wide plain that a jackal could hardly cross unseen; nearby was a "pan" of remarkably sweet water. True, I did not like the country, for no reason better than its looking ugly to me, with its short, half-dead grass, patches of red sand, dwarf thorn, and—which must be temporary—apparent lack of game. There were plenty of hyenas and jackals and fox, more villainous-looking wild dogs and grotesque aardvarks than I had ever seen in one area; and the skies were dotted with vultures and the grass alive with snakes, but I looked in vain for a single herd of wildebeests, quaggas, zebra, ostrich, 'mpallas, hartebeest, spring-bucks, eland, or kudus. Maybe it was the wrong day. Maybe a hunting party of Basenga had come through here lately. I did see a white rhinoceros, and one she-elephant. But the former was running off as though the Devil were after him, soon lost in clouds of dust, and the latter was so tall and gaunt and wasted that I thought of her as a death-elephant, bringing a message from her infernal master.

We made camp, and ourselves as comfortable as possible. By loading the smooth-bore with small shot, I shot enough guinea hen to give us a meal of fresh meat. In the middle of the night, Trudi wakened me with a long kiss. A weak and waning moon was just rising over the plain, but the stars blazed in splendor; and as the jackals laughed and sobbed, she and I recaptured the wonder of our night on the veld, after the wind had died. It seemed that truly her lithe and lovely flesh had become one with mine. She was my appointed bride. I had found her here in emptiness and silence, on the endless plains. The life of my life was expanding within her womb.

"Where are we going, when we leave here?" she asked.

"We can go back to Zumbo. The minister will be there by now. I want us to be married. As you said—we mustn't let the Dutch *vrouws* laugh too long."

"I don't want to go there."

"Then we will go to Lydenburg or Pretoria. What does it matter where?"

"Don't you want to go back to—what is the place?—and leave me here?"

"Charleston? No, I'll never return."

"There is a girl there. You've spoken of her once or twice. She is very beautiful and highborn."

"Her name was Salley Sass."

"Do you still love her? If you do, take me to Port Elizabeth and leave me with my aunt, and go back to her."

"Trudi, I don't think anyone ever quite gets over being in love. It changes every cell of the body. But she married another, and now I'm free of her. Sometimes it's a wonderful thing to be free of those you love. I don't have to woo her any more. I don't even have to think of her. Now I'm in love with you. I don't want to be free from you—I want to be bound to you—the more bonds, the better. Will you love me always? Will you never leave me as long as you live?"

"I'll love you as long as I live. But tonight the jackals sing of Death. I can hear them."

"Their song is the same as always. This is Africa, where Death is always just at hand, waiting in the grass. But both of us have the capacity to survive. We are fit to be Afrikanders. Will you join with me, Trudi? I won't feel satisfied until we've knelt before a minister—and gone through the old ceremony—and taken the vows. Then I'll tell you what I want. It's not diamonds and it's not gold, and it's not to be a gentleman in Charleston, or to own a great plantation. I want an African farm. I want sheep in the fold and cattle in the kraal and babies in the cradle. When can we start, Trudi? I've found myself at last. Where in all this vast Africa shall we go to make our home? The diamond I have will bring four hundred, maybe five hundred Cape dollars. I have a little more, besides our outfit. All my life I've followed will-o'-the-wisps. Now I want something real."

She considered a while, noting my wild, half-formed thoughts, not blaming me for them, drunk as I was from the night and the freedom and the exultation of life itself, but not letting them cloud the clarity of her ideas. At last she answered in her own steadfast way.

"Edward, I think we had better go to the Transvaal frontier. Many of the Doppers are leaving their big holdings, and going into Bechuanaland to start new, and a little money will buy a great deal in land and kraals and even cattle. Tomorrow let us inspan and see what we can find."

Happy, we drifted off to sleep. Later a bleak dream moved upon me like an evil spell, and all my springs of joy were poisoned, and I wandered all alone in an infinite gray landscape. When I called to Trudi again and again she did not answer. Then it must be that I moaned in my sleep for suddenly her arms were about me, her kiss warm and living on my lips, and I knew she was with me still, and that was more joyous than life being with me still. In a way they were the same. When I was in her arms, I felt the flush of life. I grasped the enormous void between being and non-being. I had little need of other victories; the vanity that Clay Hudson had seen in me required little food; my spirit rose out of me and soared.

Even so, the morning just now breaking, the merest gray cast on the face of the landscape, conveying not yet color or depth, but only the outline of things, seemed unaccountably sinister. Thank God we were breaking camp today. The sooner our wheels began to turn, over rocks or anthills or endless grass or the barren red sand, that much quicker I could know that a curse was lifting off me, or that it was imaginary to start with. Africa! Perhaps this was its dark heart. Maybe we had stumbled on it, a *land shadowing with wings beyond the rivers of Ethiopia.* The vultures were not up yet, but soon their shadows would flick across the ground.

2

"Eat your mealies and meat and inspan as soon as possible," I told N'kulu.

"Bukra, the meat is all gone."

"We'll get more before the day is out."

The day had hardly begun before we saw our chance. Before the sun had burst up, blazing, over the eastern plain, N'kulu made out a herd of eland about a mile away. Eland was the best meat in Africa. Unlike that of most of the smaller bucks, it was not lean and stringy but fat and juicy; and a bull was as big as a steer. This was a chance we must not miss. We could load the wagon with several quarters, and when the blood heat passed off we could stop at a water hole, cut the meat into strips, and string it on thongs to dry. It was a long way to the

eastern Transvaal. We must not go empty-handed if we could
help ourselves.

"N'kulu, take M'sabu's old flintlock. I'll take the smooth-
bore. I'll ride while you drive the wagon. We'll get at least
one or maybe two while Kininni and Hagar pack our gear."

"That will be good hunting, bukra."

"Hagar, go with them and help butcher," Trudi ordered.
"That way we will save time."

I thought that Trudi might choose to come with us, too, but
she decided to stay. Her hand crept into mine as I mounted,
and a desire to take her again into my arms, to hold her close,
to tell her of my love, passed powerfully through my brain; I
resisted doing it because it would use up precious seconds—the
herd was walking rather briskly—and because a man must not
give way to erratic impulse. I had already seen to my gun;
N'kulu patted his, lay it in reach, and, as soon as eight of the
oxen had been inspanned, took his proud seat. We left the mis-
erable camp; and, looking back, I was surprised to see how soon
it disappeared from view. The plain was deceiving. It gave the
impression of almost limitless visibility. Sometimes, indeed, we
could see a bustard half a mile away. Actually the grass and the
mean thorn and the little hollows and hills tricked the eyes.

But in only a minute or two I spied again the herd of eland;
and, considering the lay of the land and the early morning
breeze, I planned my campaign. I could not wait for N'kulu to
hitch his wagon and make the stalk beside me. This meant that
only one shot could be fired, which must not be wasted.

So I rode on at a fast trot, the wagon in my dust. When I had
outflanked the herd, I turned in toward them, tied the mare to
a thornbush, then crept through high grass to an ambush behind thickets. In hardly a moment the big beasts came into close
view. They were walking faster than before, perhaps because
they had heard or glimpsed the wagon. They had rather short
but massive spiral horns, white stripes on their withers, and
heavy dewlaps, yet were wonderfully clean-limbed. You could
never mistake them for oxen. They had the dash of the bucks.

The second animal in the file was a barren cow, rather young from the look of her, and perfect for our needs. I let her draw within forty yards, then put the two-ounce ball under her chin. She dropped as though pole-axed while her herd thundered off. When I had bled her, I waited for the wagon to come up.

Its bed contained an inclined plane, and a hoist by which we could lift heavy loads. As N'kulu was getting out the rig, we heard the full-throated boom of a gun. It came from the direction of camp.

"I wonder what M'sabu shot at?" I asked aloud.

N'kulu did not look at me. "Perhaps a rhino came too near, and she wished to frighten him off."

"It *was* the pin-fire rifle that we heard—wasn't it?"

"It must have been, bukra. There is no other gun in camp. Yet it did not sound as sharp as the pin-fire. It sounded like a smooth-bore of heavy gauge."

"Bring the wagon as fast as you can."

I ran and untied my mare and mounted. Without my laying quirt to her even once as we raced toward camp, she ran as fast as her legs would carry her over the rough ground. The way seemed long, because Time had stopped moving—it was like a herd of elephants utterly motionless in the shade—still the view of the camp slowly emerged into my gaze.

I could see nothing good, as yet, or anything evil. Indeed the little man-made speck on the veld, a kind of carving out of the wilderness to lay our bivouac, seemed utterly deserted. I could not see Trudi anywhere, and then I suddenly came aware—largely to my relief but partly, a small, cold part, to my terror—that I did not see her pony. He had been grazing, dragging his halter rope. It stood to reason that she had seen game on the plain and had hastily saddled and bridled him and ridden out of sight. The report of the gun had sounded alien to N'kulu's ears because it had come farther than he thought.

Swiftly the brain works when it is aroused! My horse had bounded only three or four times more when a very strange fact leaped to my attention. Stunning and hard to believe, yet it was undeniable. All the remaining oxen appeared to be lying down.

I rode on into the awful quiet of the camp, then dismounted. I no longer hoped for good—that was past and done—and could hardly believe in the half-bad, in being let off with moderated disaster, so deep was the sense of evil haunting my soul. I saw something black lying by the ashes of the fire. In the next instant I recognized the body of Kininni, and in his breast was a yawning hole, and his blood reddened the grass. I stood still and gazed about me. I knew now why the oxen lay so still—the throat of every one had been cut.

And in the dust, drawn by a stick, were large, rough letters. They were English letters to be read in one glance,

I DID IT ALL ALONE
HARVEY

It took me half a minute or more to find Trudi. She was lying in a little hollow, most of her clothes torn off; and a look close to the look of death was on her bruised and beaten face. But it was not death's look. Any man could tell the difference. She was breathing; I saw her bosom rise and fall; the bubble of blood at her lips swelled and broke; and as I came and knelt beside her, she knew of my coming.

"I'm here. It's Edward. You're safe now. I love you. Don't try to speak. Smile just once—make any sign—to promise me you'll live."

She heard me and her lips curled, but it was a smile of pity.

3

My girl was an Afrikander. She had ridden, and tended cattle, and hunted, all her remembered days. She had survived the hate and cruelty of her father's homestead on the sun-baked veld; she had grown up beautiful and brave instead of ill-favored and afraid. She was not one to yield quickly, or to die without due cause.

From the very first this was my main, and greatest and truest comfort. Kininni was dead, and I could do nothing for him but give him decent burial. His days were over and his sun had set and his story had been told. But life was in Trudi still. I seemed to see it quicken—at least I believed it—with every passing moment. As far as I could tell, she bore no mortal wound. She was in great danger——if I had not known it, Hagar's terror-filled eyes would have told me—and perhaps, just now, she did not care to live; but from this last sickness she would make a swift recovery. Hagar's love and mine would be certain medicine.

So our long fight began.

"Would it be safer to stay here a few days, or to trek?" I asked Hagar. "We can sling a hammock in the wagon for the M'sabu."

"I do not know, bukra."

"Tell me what you think. What would the old women say?"

"I cannot speak for the old women, but I'll say what's in my heart. Either one is bad, but to stay here is the worse. She would not lie down and sleep. Every minute she would watch the grass. Besides—have you forgotten?—she is a Voortrekker. She will want to go—to know that the great wheels turn. And that much sooner—while the Red Jackal sniffs the meat ere he sets his fangs—we may bring her to Heer Doctor."

I thought possibly she might mean the greatest doctor that had ever set foot on the land of Africa, although I believed that he was far across the sea. I had no time to question her now, as she and N'kulu and I made last-minute preparations for the trek. An eland skin, slung on thongs, must serve as a hammock until we could provide a better one. N'kulu made a quick trip after a hindquarter of the carcass, which Hagar would cut up and hang on the cover in the sun and dust while we were en route, saving time thereafter. Something like a tiny piece of luck developed before we left camp. At least it encouraged us a little, and conceivably it would prove important before the end. Trudi's gelding Johan, that I had thought either stolen or dead, returned to the bivouac unharmed. He wore a piece of a halter and apparently had broken away in a nightmare moment which I knew had come to pass, but which remained a kind of blank spot on my brain.

On his back we lashed the body of old Kininni, wrapped in an eland skin, for we would not leave it to the undertakers of the veld, and could give no time for its decent disposal until far and wide of camp. The gelding would follow the wagon and our eight oxen, all we had left to draw the big wheels through mud and sand. So before they began to turn we jettisoned every ounce of non-essential baggage. Then the whip cracked and brute strength surged once more.

I gave thought to doctors now. Those practicing in Capetown, Elizabeth, and Durban could not help me, from being out of reach; of a few scattered among the Boer settlements on the Orange River or in the Transvaal, I could think of none who was not some sort of renegade. But Hagar had spoken of the greatest of all. . . .

"Hagar, did you mean the Heer Doctor who first laid eyes on the Falling River?"

"It is told that he is coming back from across the sea. N'kulu heard of it, as well as I."

"Is it true, N'kulu, or only the talk of the kraals?"

"I heard it first at Zumbo from one of my own tribe," N'kulu answered. "Since then the drums carry the word far. He has already gained Capetown, and will come to the mouth of the Great River by the end of the rains."

"If we could get boats, we could arrive quickly at Sena on the Zambezi, and from thence find our way to him, at whichever of the Delta towns he might put in. Who would provide us with boats and oarsmen?"

"There is only one who could, and, instead of boats and paddlers, it would be his way and according to his custom to provide the hyenas and the jackals with a feast of our bones. I speak of the old Manikusa, king of the Matshangana. Think you, you could buy our passage from him and his son Umzilla? Both of them hate all white people, and their power is absolute from the Manhissa to the Zambezi."

"When we come nigh to their kraals, I'll speak with them."

"Do so, lord. You are a man, and it is your right to speak even to God. But unless grass grows green on the Kalahari, that night the hyenas, the jackals, and perhaps the lions will speak to us."

The hated camp drew out of sight, and soon the desolate plain on which it stood; and the changing scenery gave me a sense of change, perhaps for the better. Trudi lay asleep in her hammock. She was a young woman of great strength, not only of body but of will, and perhaps she had taken no real harm. Perhaps the days would pass, the wonderfully bright and sunny days, the starlit nights would intervene with her sleeping in my arms, the landscape of Africa would pass before our eyes, sometimes sunburned and ugly, sometimes beautiful beyond description, and we would see the great herds of game that wander in the middle distance, and she would be well again. There were bad cards in the deck, some of them black beyond my imagination, but perhaps they would not fall. . . .

Time passed. Every hour that spared her and me from the worst, raised my hopes—seemed to increase our chances—for the better. At present, about noon, she lay deeply asleep. Not much light entered the wagon—we had hung a curtain between the bed and the seat—and mainly it came in darts and flashes, very brilliant, dancing wildly on the walls; yet now and again it picked up the pale gold of her hair; and in the dimness the pallor of her face was marked but not alarming.

Then the brilliant light lingered there a second or two and showed me something puzzling and worrisome. Her face was suddenly drenched with sweat—the cold kind that comes with acute pain or nausea. She uttered a low moan, slept a moment or two more, then came wide awake. For a little while she stared wildly into my eyes. A sense of awful foreboding came upon me. Then her mind turned a little corner, she accepted something which until now she had rebuffed, and she spoke with perfect clarity.

"Stop the wagon and let me out."

"What are you going to do?" So I spoke, not knowing what I said.

"I'm going by myself into the grass. Don't come with me, Edward. If I live, I'll come back to you. If I don't, let me stay here, alone. That's what I want, believe me. I don't want anybody bothering themselves about me. Don't look for me. Forget me as soon as you can. Go back. Go home. Leave me alone."

"You're asking what I can't grant."

"I don't want you to see it, Edward."

"Do you think your not wanting me to see it would stop me from coming with you?"

"I might have known it wouldn't. All right. Then come quickly."

"I'm going to let Hagar come too. It's her right, and she might know—"

"As you please. It hurts so awfully. I wish I could die, but I'll try to live for you."

"Oh, thank you, my beloved."

"For Hagar, too," she corrected herself, with great care. "Only come soon."

The wheels stopped turning. The oxen lowered their heads to graze. I got out of the wagon, and Hagar lifted Trudi down into my arms. Away into the veld we went, the three of us, N'kulu watching with tears streaming down his face. I came to where the grass was young and soft, and there I lay Trudi down. There I crouched, so that my shadow fell upon her face and kept the fierce sun from her eyes.

A little springbuck went leaping away, delicate and beautiful, and I wanted to believe he was a sending of some sort, a sign of good fortune. But a maribou stork, a bird of death, with a beak like a rapier, perched in a nearby tree. I found I could not believe in one without the other.

There, in the wilderness, in the vast silence and solitude, alone except for us two who loved her, Trudi gave birth to a perfectly formed but lifeless man-child, no bigger than my hand.

CHAPTER XV

River's End

I N A SHADY PLACE, pleasing to our human senses because of
its appearance of coolness and moisture, N'kulu and I dug
a hurried but deep grave, deeper than hyenas were known to
burrow, and put there the bodies of old Kininni, who had
drawn a quarter of a billion breaths, and of Trudi's babe, who
had never drawn one. As we dug, both of us wondered over
what we had been told concerning human souls, but we did not
pause for any ceremony, because there was life to save. Then
we put Trudi back in her hammock and resumed the long,
long trek.

The wheels turned early and late, stopping only enough for
the oxen to graze. This they learned to do swiftly, while the
chance offered, for if they dawdled, they went hungry and the
cruel whip cracked the same. To my forever wonder, they stood
up to the grueling labor, until we could hardly believe they
were flesh and bone like us, and not the Movers of Mountains,
sent us in our need. We ourselves took turns eating and sleeping and watching over Trudi. There were moments, or hours,
or whole days and nights that we thought she was mending;
then not only our faces and voices but the look of the very land

seemed to change; the wheels made a different sound; the obstacles in our track fell apart; we laughed at the snorting rhinos and loved the glorious stampedes of the game herds; then all at once the spell would pass, the world turned cold and gray, and the light we could not deny fell upon her face, and we saw it more pale, more wasted than before.

We came nigh the great dry-season kraals of Manikusa, king of the Matshangana, at the head of navigation of the Sanvati, a great north-flowing tributary of the Zambezi. Smoke in the sky showed him already resident there, his boldest outpost. Instead of swinging wide, we made straight for them, and we were only a distant dot on the hillside when a hundred of his warriors, naked, painted, and plumed, with their assagais and great shields, came running to accost us. They gathered about the wagon, yelling and prancing and brandishing their weapons, strangely like red Indians on the Western plains. A score or more surrounded my horse, and the assagai of only one was needed to end my ride. When I paid no attention to them, and N'kulu and Hagar looked at them with calm faces utterly devoid of fear, they thought that some very strong *dowa* was at work; and, remembering the ghosts and demons and the wizardry and the voodoo upon and around them always, squeezing their lives small, they grew quiet, and walked behind us in the dust. So we came to the thorn enclosures and to the beehive houses. Instead of a hundred, there were a thousand of the Matshangana, waiting the merest shift of the wind to murder or welcome us.

"Take me to the king," I said in Afrikaans.

"Take the bukra to Manikusa," N'kulu translated in a Zulu dialect that some of the old men understood.

Some of Manikusa's sons led me to a naked ground outside the largest of the houses. Out came the king, he too an old man, naked except for a lion-skin around his shoulders, and unarmed as I was. He was tall, proud, more royal-looking than any human being I had ever seen, capable of unbelievable cruelty but quite possibly of a great generosity, akin to chivalry and to grace. I remembered that he was the most gifted and powerful son of Gaza, king of the Swazi. The lords of Capetown wished to make treaties with him; the pious Dutch feared him only one degree less than the Devil; the Portuguese considered him the Devil Incarnate.

"O Manikusa, my name is Edward, and I come from beyond the seas," I told him. "With me is my woman, sinking toward death because of a babe born before its time. Furnish me with boats and oarsmen, that I may take her quickly to the great doctor."

When N'kulu had translated, Manikusa asked but one question.

"What great doctor?"

"He who treated the sick at his house at Mabotsa, on the headwaters of the Limpopo, ten days northeast of Kuruman, where the great spring flows. He who led the Bakwena to Kolobeng, for they knew there was never such a man in Africa, black or white, and to lose sight of him was like losing sight of the sun. He who was the first to lay eyes on Lake Ngami, and the first to see the great falls of the Mother River."

"How dare you lie to me, son of a jackal? The doctor has gone to his own place, across the seas."

"I am no liar, Manikusa. At the end of the rains, or very close thereto, he will return. Ask your witch doctors if it is not so."

The wizard called up by the king was exceedingly tall and gaunt and bore the scars of manacles on his wrists and ankles, and of the Kiboka on his back. I thought that in hating Arab slavers—or perhaps a heartless Dutch or English master—he would hate all white people. But instead of a shrill and impassioned reply, he spoke gravely and calmly.

"Manikusa, the white man speaks true. The ship bearing the great doctor has even now passed Capetown—the drums have spoken over the mountains, over the desert, even unto this village. This moon will wane. When once more she returns and waxes full, he will disembark at the Kongone mouth of our river."

"Go to the wagon, look at the M'sabu, and say what had best be done."

He was gone not more than five minutes. When he returned, his eyes glowing in their deep sockets, already conveying to me his answer, I felt a surge of oneness with all human kind that I had experienced only once or twice before in all my days, foreign to my nature, but deeply thrilling.

"Manikusa, you are a great king. You take life, or make life, or spare life at your whim. For you the maize grows green, or the pumpkins ripen, or an old elephant dies and leaves his tusks on the veld. It is in your power to take this life, the life of the young M'sabu—a cloth held tight over her face while you count ten times would leave her dead as a stone—but, Manikusa, can you save her life? The medicine I make is not strong enough. That I know full well. But if you will supply swift boats and swift boatmen, and send her to the great white doctor with all speed, it may be that his medicine might banish Death and let her live. You care not whether she lives, nor do I, but it is a good game. You are an old man now. The Red Jackal will come for you before long. The woman is very beautiful, according to the notions of the white man, and a very great evil had been done her. It would be better sport than killing a lion with spears, to see if by your power she lives or dies. I say to you, send her forth on the great river. Let these, one white man, one Zulu, and a Kaffir woman, go with her. Let them race with the Red Jackal. It may be that, when he comes for you, you will have a joke on him, how he couldn't take the little M'sabu half-dead already. Would that not be good sport?"

"Very good sport, Wise One!"

"It is worth trying, I think, although the odds are long."

"When have I, Manikusa, cared for long odds. Am I a beggar or a king? Bid the boatmen load their craft, and put in it these mad wanderers, with meat and mealies, and set forth!"

The king stalked into his house, every inch a king.

It seemed a fitting ending of the event—but the event did not yet end! The gaunt witch doctor, who seemed to have no other name than Wise One, made a little sign, and all the warriors drew farther back. Then he came up to me, smiling strangely, and addressed me in fluent Afrikaans.

"Not for nothing am I called Wise One," he said.

"So I see."

"What caused the little M'sabu to drop her babe before its time?"

"She met with an accident."

"No, she met with the slaver known as Harvey, whose heart is blacker than my skin. Am I a child? I heard, too late, how he had skirted the lands of the Matshangana, following a single wagon. What wagon could it be? Not one of the Voortrekkers, because it made for the Whispering Veld, where no Dutchmen have gone. Then the drums told that Harvey's followers, five of them, hated and feared only second to their master, had not returned to Zumbo, and their bones had been found not far from the camp of the mad bukra who ever washed the gravels of the rivers. I, even I, made one mistake. I thought that you had lain in ambush and shot them all through the head. But I might have known that only the daughter of Jan Du Piel—or Oom Paul himself—could have killed all so cleanly."

"How did you know the daughter of Jan Du Piel?"

"I saw her at Lydenburg, where I was in bondage, ere Vrouw Du Piel quit her kraal for love of a music-maker, and Jan took his daughter beyond the farthest settlement and became an outlander." Wise One's tone changed slightly. "And at Lydenburg, also I knew Harvey."

"What business is afoot? The men have started to load the boats."

"On Harvey's finger he wears a ring, fashioned in the form of a coiled snake. It is made of yellow gold, and that gold was once worn in the ear of a maiden. When you overtake him—for after you have found the great white doctor, you have another quest—will you take the ring from his finger and bring it to me? Mark that you need not go out of your way. You must return to our kraals to get your wagon and oxen, when your quests are done. The Matshangana will not harm you—I hold them here." Wise One shut his left hand. "And neither old Manikusa or his son Umzilla will seek to reduce your reward, for I hold them here." And the witch doctor closed his right hand.

"What will be my reward? Speak plain."

"All the valley of the watercourse we call M'Kazi, to herd your cattle and build your kraals. If you wish not to dwell near the Matshangana, I will send porters with you, bearing a hundred tusks, each worth fifty Cape dollars at the trading post."

"Now that is a good price, for a little gold ring shaped like a snake. By what god, or what sign, or what *dowa* do you swear faith in the dealing?"

"By the great *dowa* of a little gold ring shaped like a snake."

2

Almost before we knew it our world of sunburned, wind-blown grass became a world of water, deep, blue, clear, flowing like life itself with unhurried, quiet power. Our boat was a long war canoe which would hold sixty warriors. Twenty paddlers manned it, and gave no thought to any tribal enemies on the shore, since, in the middle of the Zambezi, we were often more than a mile out of spear cast; and no boatmen in these parts could race with Manikusa's men. There were many little islands, and usually these were our safe retreats at night.

Sometimes we passed great herds of hippos, numberless in the water as locusts in the swarm; then suddenly the reaches would be blue and empty and we would see no more until, again, they became a pleasant surprise. Often huge crocodiles lay on the sandbanks in the shallows; and sometimes herds of elephants waded and swam far out from the shore; and not one of us knew whether they were on business or pleasure, or could guess at the nature of either. Before sunrise and after sunset there are always a great flight of waterfowl. How such great assemblies gathered I could not guess; the air was full of the whistle of wings as, on stormy days, with the wail of wind; some were beautiful fliers, taught, it seemed, by angels; others belted along with ponderous wingbeats; but none ever seemed in doubt of his destination; they flew neither in haste nor with leisure, but with a steady intent as it seemed the waters flowed.

Often as I sat by Trudi, unable to do anything to help or even to think of anything to comfort either of us, I fell into reverie over the majesty and magnitude of the river. I thought of its countless thousands of insignificant sources, springs, ponds, brush-grown dongas known only to wandering wild things; but the trickles joined to become rivulets, and the rivulets met to make brooks, and the brooks interflowed to form small nameless rivers, and these rivers searched for and found one another over a territory great as all my Southland; and then, as though by the sudden wish of God, a river great as the Rio Grande, perhaps as great as the Oregon, flowed divinely and forever, clean from Lake Dilolo to the Indian Ocean, a distance of more than two thousand miles.

If only the minutest fraction of its prodigious life could pass into Trudi and bring her back to the sun!

We went by Zumbo in the dead of night and saw only a lantern or two glimmering on the shore. When the time came we passed down the Kebrasasa Rapids, a perilous experience at this time of year, but Hagar and N'kulu and I could not work up the least consternation to take our minds off our trouble, and Trudi, dwelling in a dream between two worlds, did not even hear the rushing waters, and Manikusa's men mocked the Red Jackal, Death, that could only run and bark along the bank, since they were obeying Manikusa's orders, and the power of his voodoo was on them.

Then we came to the lower river, with humid days and hot nights and languid waters. This was a soft land, quit by such steppe-dwellers as the giraffe; but the twelve-foot, white-plumed speargrass thronged with buffalo, and now and again elephant backs showed and disappeared; and short date trees and tall coconut trees became a common sight; and green parrots and roseate flamingos lighted up the reed-grown shores.

We were deep in the mangrove forest, only a day's journey from the Kongone mouth of the river, when we came on a fleet of boats manned by some sort of Zulu. They were peaceful, having dealt for three and a half centuries with the Portuguese, and one of them knew a lingua franca spoken by N'kulu. Yes, the great white doctor from across the seas had made port. We ourselves could lay eyes upon him on the morrow. He was not as thin and wasted as when they had seen him at Tete two years before, for he had conquered the Demons of the Fever, and although his hair was more gray, his eyes were such that a king could not look into them without bowing down.

We went on, and the moment that I had dreamed of, longed for, and most dreadfully feared came close to hand. We brought our boat alongside the *Pearl* where she lay at anchor in the river mouth, and a young man hardly thirty, who introduced himself as Dr. Kirk, himself a man of parts, spoke to me and asked how he might serve us. At my suggestion, he swung down into our boat. He glanced only once at Trudi before he ordered her to be carried on board the *Pearl*. Here a rather lightly built man, but obviously fashioned of steel, with the most wonderful countenance I had ever seen, came and spoke to her and held her frail hand in his. That he was the great doctor, known by all races and kinds of men from the Zambezi to Fish River, I had no question.

"We have come a long way," I said. "Help her if you can."

He nodded, pricked her finger, smeared a drop of her blood on a small glass slide, and looked at it through a microscope. Then he wanted to tell me something which he wished Trudi need not hear.

"Speak plainly, will you, Doctor?" she asked, her voice very low and soft, but still clear. "I have the right to hear."

"No one has a better right, but I have no good news for you."

"Then give me the bad news. I'm not afraid."

"I can see that. I wish, when my time comes, I can be as unafraid as you. I don't see how you have lived this long. There is nothing left."

"I lived this long for the sake of my beloved. Yes, and for the river that I wanted to see join with the sea. It was a hard fight but I won it. Now—unless there is something more to do—I want to go ashore."

"There is one thing, Trudi," I said. "I want to ask the doctor —or the captain—to marry us. If you can stay only a little while, I'll have the satisfaction of it—and the triumph—as long as I live."

"I can stay only a few hours. The time has come to outspan. But it is my wish also—and my great pride."

So I sat at the edge of the cot where Trudi lay and took her hand in mine. The doctor went out and returned with the captain of the *Pearl,* a ruddy man by nature, bold, domineering, and with a great self-control, but now he was pale, and his voice shook, and in his eyes was a deep humility in the awareness of powers he could not understand or control. He read from a book. The eyes of Dr. Kirk filled with tears. The gray doctor, the great doctor, passed his hand across his brow, and upon his face were the flar-flung shadows of a thousand great scenes; and in his eyes was a power, come to him God knew whence, before which kings must bow down.

We made our contract, Trudi and I, for as long as it might last. A ghost of one of her broad, slow smiles haunted her wide, full lips. Then the captain ordered the lowering of a dingy, in which N'kulu and I rowed Trudi and Hagar to the nearest land. Chance guided us to a bower of coconut palms, only a little way back from the sand. Here the shade was deep, and birds of many hues lighted on the fronds, and sea birds winged back and forth; and a light-footed animal, no bigger than a terrier, that I took for the faun of a blue buck, came out of the thickets and romped and ran in a stone's toss.

N'kulu cut grass for a couch for Trudi. She lay on it, and we talked of the long miles we had covered together. The time had been short, but the journey long.

"We have seen the Great Falls of the Zambezi," she told me in a low murmur that did not tax her breath.

"Yes, we did."

"We saw the veld one night, without fire to blind our eyes."

"It was wonderful seeing."

"We have seen the herds of wildebeests, passing in countless numbers, and the great elephants and the white rhinoceros."

"All that, and more."

"We traveled far in the bright sunlight, and at night I lay in your arms."

"I forgot what it was to be lonely."

"Don't be lonely any more. I couldn't bear it. Go back to America and find the girl you left there. If she's not free, find some other who'll keep you company, and love you, and—bear you sons and daughters. But don't bring her to Africa. I don't want her riding with you in the wagon and sleeping with you under the stars. I don't want her broiling your meat over a campfire, and making mealies. I don't want you and her to see what we have seen together. This is my country. I don't want her to share it with you. What we have had is ours. I don't want to share it with anyone. I am a Boer woman, an outlander, jealous of the little that I own. I am an Afrikander."

"We will always own it together—no one but us."

"Now I'm going to leave you."

"Not yet."

"Yes, in a few minutes. I can feel a hollowness—an emptiness filling my body. There's no pain. There's not even sorrow any more—I've got rid of that. Do you know where my soul will go?"

"No one in the world can know that."

"I'll tell you. It's going back to the veld. It won't stay there long, perhaps, but it wants to see the grass again—and the silver colors that come after sundown—and the herds of game. It is going to ride. It's going to inspan at dawn and outspan at sundown. It will drive the wagon, and it will cross the little dongas that no one knows and sometimes climb the great scarps. It will long for you, Edward, but it will know it can't have you, for on one side of the River is Life, and on the other side is Death, and it will be on the other side. I loved you at the beginning, and I loved you to the last. Kiss me goodbye."

I raised her in my arms and kissed her pale lips, and, although the sky was blue and the waves glittered, I went a distance with her, down into the Death. I felt its shadow and its chill, and at the same time its great peace.

"Goodbye, Trudi."

"Goodbye, Edward, Mynheer."

She lay back and her breathing began to grow shallow and far apart. I held one of her hands, Hagar the other, and N'kulu stood guard with a rifle in his arms, although there was no conceivable danger. Her fingers tightened once on mine, then she gave a long sighing gasp, and lay still. Her face was strangely childlike, but it was hard to believe that her bright face could be a treasure of Death. Even here in the shade it looked sunlit.

Goodbye, Trudi! Goodbye, my lovely Voortrekker, whose hand so briefly lay in mine. You are across the River from me now; and you are inspanning for your great adventure. Still the Red Jackal barks on the bank in endless and insatiable hunger. Only love can bear tidings from one bank to another. Farewell, Trudi! Roast me some meat and cook me mealies on the great, grassy plain. Think of me sometimes, and remember our great joys.

The Great Falls of the Zambezi. The veld under the moon.

BOOK FIVE

CHAPTER XVI

The Hunters

ONE NIGHT, as the moon set, Hagar, N'kulu, and I had bivouacked on the middle veld, high on the Maputo River.

We had got here after various small events, without following any fixed route. First, I had had sent back to Manikusa the boat and boatmen he had lent to us, and one of the latter bore to Wise One my promise to return, as soon as my ventures permitted. Then we had come by a Portuguese coaster from Zambezi's mouth to Delagoa Bay.

Since we were going in what I felt was the right direction, much faster than by land, we enjoyed the change in surroundings. Then we had hired riding beasts and a pack mule or two for a trek into the hills, partly to pass the time before the next sailing to Capetown, partly to see the country, and mainly to come to a decision in the free spaces and open air of the veld.

On this clear, pale-blue, and beautiful night, we were sitting about a thornwood fire. Our horses were picketed close by, because this was lion country.

"Not far away is a village of the tame Zwazis," I said, after we had all been silent a long time. "If either or both of you wished to go there, the first stage of the long journeys to your native villages, you could ride the horses I have rented for you, and I can pay the owner for them when I return to Delagoa Bay. But it may be that you wish to remain in my service while I undertake a much longer journey. If so, I would be glad to have you."

"To what part of the land, bukra?" N'kulu asked.

"It is in my mind to go first to Capetown, in one of the ships. From thence I do not know where the search may take us, before at last we return to the kraals of the Matshangana."

"The bukra speaks of a search. What search does the bukra mean? Is it the wish of my heart, more dear to me than my life, or is it to seek again for little white crystals in the gravels of the rivers? How can I know? You are white and I am black. You were born to another land, another tongue. Sometimes your heart sems to beat with mine, but sometimes I know nothing of it, it is cold and far away, and as hidden from me as the heart of a rock python asleep by the river."

N'kulu got up, cut a piece of dried meat to chew and quiet him, and resumed his seat.

"His heart may be cold and far away from yours," Hagar said with a little laugh, "but not from mine."

"How can you know, Hagar, when N'kulu, my brother of the trail, is in doubt?" I asked.

"Because a woman gave you birth—and I am a woman. Because a woman fed you at her teat. It is good to be brothers of the trail, but what do they know of each other, compared to a mother and son? It has never entered my head that you would trifle at the river beds with the business undone."

"What is the business, Hagar?"

"N'kulu will tell you. Tell him, N'kulu, in plain words, and speak no more folly, for you are a man, and it is unmeet that you should talk folly, even though the gods have given us women the right to do so, to ease our hearts sometimes."

"Bukra, your business is to find the white man known as Harvey, and let him join his little company, their names being

Mustapha, Sligo, Fritz, Culpepper, and Bernardino, he having been parted with them too long already."

"N'kulu, do you wish to go with me on that hunt, and have a part in the reuniting of him with his band?" I asked.

"I wish to go with you, lord. What part I shall have in the outcome—I do not know. To fight and kill is one thing, the blood being hot. To stalk and kill is another thing; and there are farther things that pass before the eyes of my mind like dreams. I can say no more."

"What do you say, Hagar?"

"I? Is it not a common fault with women to say too much? So I will let the night speak for me. Listen, bukra."

Only to those who listen closely will the African night speak with deep meaning and eloquence. Its plainer sounds are so common that the hearer hardly notices them. These are the barking of jackals, usually sporadic, sometimes chorused in a frenzy of excitement, and the eerie outcries, like human sobbing or devilish laughter, of hyenas. But under and below and beyond all this is intermittent sound, dim and far-off and half-believed, that causes curious prickling sensations at the base of the human skull. Sometimes it is a deep grunt that begins, lasts a while in a rhythm cadence, and then stops. Sometimes it is a noise like that of a saw ripping through a tough board. Sometimes it is a series of deep-throated roars, which, no matter how far away, still all other voices. Sometimes it is a trumpet-like note, clear, true, and strangely beautiful in the vast hush.

Now and then tonight there rose the ear-piercing squeal of a wart hog, just before the ugly beast died an ugly death. The grassy plain sometimes acted as a sounding board, and the terrible neighing scream of a zebra, with a lion on his back, rushed in like a cry for help, and caused our horses to surge and stamp in their pickets. And there were other sounds that I could not explain away. These were not especially alarming, here by the bright fire, but they had hellish accents. The listener falls to wondering what he would do in certain cases. He wonders if he is going to get off lightly, by merely dying, or if some further and awful accounting must be made. For a moment, perhaps, he knows himself for what he is, God's fair-weather friend, the knower of evil learned long ago, from whom the little demons of cult and story had better run and hide.

2

A half-caste Portuguese called Alfonso had told me that Harvey had a woman in Capetown, good to look at, who worked at White's. The latter was a mug and gambling house of considerable pretensions. But if he had known a safer place, there he would have trekked. He was no longer the hunter, but the hunted.

The veld offered him maneuverability and abundant hiding places, and, at times, infinite solitude; but if he passed in view of any human eye, he would be marked down and long remembered. In the crowds of Capetown he could smell his kind again, see without being seen; he might trust his woman to help him; and he would laugh to think of any hunters looking for him here.

We went there, and I got my bearings, and put by for a while the whispering veld. Then I took my diamond to the largest private moneylender in these parts, who accepted without question my tale of having bought it from a Dutch sailor who in turn had brought it back from the East Indies. He had never quite seen its like in fire, paid me a hundred and twenty English pounds, and hurried me out the door lest I regret my bargain.

White's had been named after London's great gambling club. It was large and luxurious, the odd adjective "respectable" being often applied to it. As I came in the door I felt something like nostalgia. Here were the same strained faces, the same bleak haste, the swirling smoke, the dice clicking, the cards falling as in Memphis' rooms, from whence, with only a few delays, setbacks, and circuities, I had come hence.

But I let that be, as we poor whites and the colored say in the Low Country. My eye roved around, and I saw three young women "playing" for the house. This practice has spread from the dens of San Francisco during the gold rush. The girls soon learned to deal faro and even three-card monte, a sharper's game, and it made for heavy spending and a more generally refined and peaceful atmosphere in the gaming rooms. A "mark" playing monte against the house must make a choice of one of three cards to find a red ace. If I were Harvey, I knew which of the three I would choose for my light o' love, and it would not be one of two washed-out Cockney blondes. It would be a foreign-looking girl with blue-black hair and cheekbones as bold as a squaw's.

I watched the cluster of players about her, to try to tell if any one of them knew her well and whose acquaintance might be worth seeking. But they were a dreary lot, staring dumbly after their departing money, while the monotonous cry went on, "Who sees it, who sees it?"; broken by the greedy question, "For how much," when a mark thought surely he could lay finger on the ace.

Among the spectators was a lean, middle-aged man, with the glinting restless eye of a mark, but not as feverish as a chronic sucker. I saw him get out his wallet and sadly put it back: plainly he had been burned not long ago but still yearned toward the fire. The odds would be long that he knew anything about the young woman's affairs with Harvey, but there was no better prospect in sight.

"Do you think that's an honest game?" I asked, with a gesture toward the table.

"I don't see how it could be crooked. It's a contest between the dealer's hand and the player's eye. There are two black aces —both clubs—and one red ace. She picks 'em up, and lets you see her lay 'em down. All you have to do is play the card you think is the red ace. But though you've seen it just as plain, when you turn up the card it's one of the other two—and you've lost your money."

"Have you seen anybody win at it?"

"Yes, the very night I lost my roll. He didn't win any great sum, but he took her for fifty Cape dollars while I was there."

"Yet you lost steadily."

"I'd been working in the sun and had a headache and I think I couldn't see straight. That's why I'm half a mind to try it again."

"What did this fellow look like? An Afrikander or a shill?"

"He was about three inches shorter than me—well built—in his thirties—and had red hair. I reckoned him to be Scotch. But if they knew each other they didn't show it."

"What kind of eyes did he have?"

"Light gray and sharp as a hawk's."

"I may have seen him. Did he wear a ring?"

"Yes, an odd-looking one, gold and shaped like a snake."

Sometimes a rube draws four aces in the first hand of play. The risk of my informant's warning my quarry was too slight to trouble me: I meant to work fast. I thought over what he had said about Harvey's eyes. I too remembered their light color and comprehensive, penetrative gaze. I had been told, and could not doubt, he was an expert marksman.

3

Like most gambling dens, White's was almost deserted from nine in the morning—when the last bitter-enders slunk away to their lairs—until four in the afternoon, when the first *bon vivants* dropped in to slake their thirst and risk a few shillings at play. At five a few stragglers had assembled, ready to watch but not take part in high play; such spectators would stop any desperately beaten dealer from welshing. Five was the hour I picked for a maneuver I considered necessary, not especially difficult, neither anticipated nor disliked. N'kulu and Hagar waited for me in a hut in Kaffirtown.

"What shall I call you, miss?" I said to the white squaw from somewhere east of the Oder.

"Gertrude."

It came to me, with a long-drawn sensation, as of going through smoke and fire, that my Trudi might have been christened Gertrude. Certainly Jan Du Piel would not have given his baby girl, when he had craved a son, and already wishing in his heart her descent into hell, such a sweet, light name as Trudi. My superstitions were awake and clamoring, and I looked in dread of some other connection, eerie and devilish, between this mug-house woman and my Voortrekker; but there was none, and I got my feet again on solid ground.

"Do you know anybody by the name?" she was asking.

"No."

"I thought you might have a sweetheart named that—or even your mother or sister."

This remark was strangely characteristic of harpies and whores throughout the world, and I could not call it hypocrisy. Rather it seemed a need of sentimentality. I felt a brief and passing pity for this Gertrude, who, because of a bad draw in the way of lovers, now was in for trouble.

I did not answer, and she asked if I knew how to play monte.

"I watched you last night. But you've met your match tonight."

She rolled her eyes, but she was not as silly as that. No fool, except a particular kind like me, could deal monte as expertly as she. She had light and rather dainty hands, but which were of course strong, in order to manage her barely visible "hopover."

"How does that happen, chum?" This last—out from England—was a popular address in the colony.

"Because I'm pretty good at shooting running game. That takes good eyesight."

"Well, we'll see."

She quit toying with the cards, her expression changed subtly, and at once three or four loungers who had their eyes on her vital face and form drew nearer. "Watch closely now," she addressed us all, as she passed the red ace and two black aces through the air, then placed them, with quick changing of position, face downward on the table.

"Who sees it?" she called.

Although she had not employed the "hop-over," only rapid movements, the others shook their heads.

"I do," I said.

"For how much?"

"Five Cape dollars."

"I'll see you. See if you won."

I did win, and then intentionally lost the next bet, an equal sum. But I bet a tenner on the next hand, and to her considerable surprise—although she was not yet warmed to the game— found the ace exactly where she had laid it.

She thought she had caught her mark, but not an easy one. Her expression changed and I saw her buckle down. She began to play with considerable brilliance; and by easy riding, not yet throwing any great nervous energy into my play, I lost about as many bets as I won. She could not recover from her surprise that I won any. She did not know whether to blame it on my good eyesight, or on some kind of cramp, soon to pass off, in her hands; now and then I saw her shake her fingers. I let her win three tenners in a row, then, suddenly, jumped to fifty.

I was tired of the play already, tired of the tense faces, the swirling smoke, the brittle quiet, and the strain. I craved to end the game quickly, a dangerous craving usually against a dealer as adroit as Gertrude. But my vision had not slowed down in my long stay on the veld, rather had quickened, and as my attention narrowed and intensified I knew I could pick her up on every play.

"Fifty?" she echoed. "Chum, you must be confident."

"Will you raise me?"

"Not this hand. And I can't play many more. I've got to get my supper. But I'll call you."

"You're mistaken about getting your supper. If you're hungry, it will be brought you. Remember White's war cry: 'Perpetual play and no bets barred.' "

"You talk pretty well. Let's see if you saw it. Where is it?"

"Here."

I saw her flinch as I reached. She had hoped to the last I had been led astray. When I turned over the ace, a fine line of sweat, often the sign of an earthen but yet nobler passion in young women, beaded her brow.

I bet fifty on the next two hands, winning both with no conscious effort. Yet I was pouring out nervous energy at a sickening rate. She was frightened now; I saw a little rim of white under the glistening pale blue of her iris. She began to try to dazzle me by rapid play.

Once more she lost; and by now a little crowd had gathered. I began to await the play with which she hoped to recoup—I could almost vision the cunning darting frightened hunger of her thoughts, reflected in her face by a curious sharpening of her features that made her at once more predatory-looking and more desirable to a man. I was eager for the same play, for I meant it to be the kill.

When again she called "Who sees it?" she threw a languishing look to the spectators. Hoping for some kind of a tip-off from the dealer such as a singsong "cop left," or "cop right," to break the run of losing hands—or at least to ride on my luck, a somewhat dapper lounger, a cheap sport, called "I see it."

"You do, do you, damn you, Frank Webb. Well, place your bet."

"Can't I wait for this gentleman to place his?"

"You sure as hell can't."

"Then I'll place five."

Both looked at me.

"I didn't see it, and I will pass."

"Where is it, Frank?"

The man had changed color. He hesitated several seconds trying to recapture his lost confidence. Then with a sudden motion he picked up a black ace.

"Hell's kite," he swore, a strange swearing on the part of a barfly, which I had read somewhere long ago.

The interlude gave Gertrude the chance she was waiting for. Her hand manipulated one of the thin decks; as she separated them for the deal I noticed that the red ace had been bent a little, as though by accident. It was not a very obvious mark, but meant to be unmistakable to eyes as sharp as mine.

"Light my cigarette, pal," Gertrude said.

I did so without glancing at her hands. It was not necessary to know what they were up to. As I stood back, she dealt quickly.

"Who sees it?" she called.

"I do."

"For how much?"

"I want my supper, so I'll say a hundred."

"Chum, you've taken all my cash but here's ten blue chips, to meet you, and I'll raise you ten more of the same."

"I'll raise you another hundred."

I saw the fever in her eyes to raise still another hundred. She lacked the nerve—from lack of solid assurance that her high-bought knowledge of the human race would surely apply to me —and, anyway, to win her present bet of three hundred Cape dollars would let her break about even on the game. The crowd moved forward one stride as though it had been drilled. Many faces were flushed, one or two had paled from strain, now the men stood still and waited.

"Pick your winning card."

Her eyes bulged as she watched my hand move slowly forward. I felt a twinge of pity for the heart beating so wildly, while mine was steady and cold. Yet when I took the unbent card on the right of the marked card, she did not cry out. A desperate look came into her face, but her only sound was a long, childlike sigh.

I picked up my bills and the thirty blue chips.

"Keep those a little while, will you?" she asked, in low tones. "Mr. White isn't in—meanwhile we'll have a drink—Belle hasn't a game and can take my table. To tell the truth, I need one. I think I'm out of a job."

We moved to the nearest refreshment table. I had pocketed the bills, but stacked the chips in front of me for all to see. Thank heaven, I need not delay the upshot. As soon as the Kaffir waiter took our order, before she could begin to decide how to cut her loss, I told her what it was.

"I want either one of two things," I told her. "The money now, or an I.O.U. that I can show Mr. White if need be." This last was a form of promissory note valid in San Francisco. "However, if you give me the true answer to some questions, I'll tear up the paper."

"I might have known it," she said, bowing her head.

"Do you agree?"

"There's no way out of it for me—if I want to keep my job. Are you a police officer?"

"No, a private citizen."

She took a tab sheet from her pocket, wrote with an India ink, tore off the page, and handed it to me.

"What do you want to know about him?" she asked.

"Where is he living?"

"Somerset Arms. That's a mughouse on the waterfront."

"On what days does he come here, and what time?"

"He's likely to come any day, but he always comes Saturday about sundown. And, chum, I might be speaking of anyone, you know. We haven't mentioned any names." Her spirits had revived a little.

"We're going to mention them now. I mean a red-headed man, known as Harvey, once captain of Harvey's Hustlers. Is that whom you mean?"

"Yes, God damn your soul. What are you going to do to him? Kill him?"

"That's a private matter."

"I knew he was hiding from someone, but I don't know what he's done, and that's Jesus' truth, may I die and go to hell if I lie. Well, I'm going to do that, anyway. The *Dummkopf* trusted me. He would have told me, if I'd let him. He said he didn't trust me—he bragged about it to me, showing what a knowing cove he was—but he did trust me in his heart and on the side. He's the only one of my suitors that does—isn't that the term you toffs use?—and he's the one who's going to get the Judas kiss."

"You speak English quite fluently for an Eastern European."

"My mother was English, and I lived three years in the City of Brotherly Love. These Englishmen seem so much more gentlemanly than our Königsbergers. But that doesn't fool me any more. And the Americans are worse."

"I don't know about that. And there's only one more question."

"What is it?" she asked, her lips a little parted in repulsion.

"After you answer this, I'll leave the joint. If the address you gave me proves right, you'll not see me till tomorrow, otherwise I'll return. Meanwhile you're not to tell him or anyone that I've inquired about him."

"Go on," she said when I paused.

"Think carefully before you answer this one. Has Harvey another hideout in the country? What part does he know best? If he had to slope in a hurry, and wanted to be safe, where would he go?"

"Well, I knew you'd ask that. It was in the cards. If I tell you, will you do something for me?"

"I'll have to decide that later."

"You'll burn in hell longer than he will, no matter what he's done. He did his deviltry hot, while you do yours cold. All right. If he's pressed hard, he'll hit for the Great Karroo. He'd take the old trade route—that was what he said—I don't know what or where it is—that crosses the Hex River. I remember Hex all right. I'll remember it better from now on. Then if he can find a tribe of Bushmen that he knows—he once saved the chief's son from a bone in his throat—they'll keep him safe till doomsday."

I said nothing, and she paused and added, "Maybe doomsday has already come."

"I don't know. Your information seems reliable."

"Reliable is right. I'm a real reliable girl—until I get stuck for a hundred quid."

"What was the favor you wanted to ask?"

"Do you know what it means for a girl like me to mistake a sharper for a sucker and lose a hundred quid?"

"I reckon it's pretty rough."

"Oh, thanks! Well, what I want is, if I've set him up for you proper, and every word is true, will you give me back the paper and half the bills? I can manage the rest."

"Gladly."

"How much is a piece of silver?"

"What in hell do you mean?"

"You know. In the Bible. People were always getting paid off in pieces of silver."

"I suppose it was a shekel. I don't know what it was worth."

"I do. It's worth two marks and about fifty pfennigs—two shillings, sixpence. Thirty of them come to—let's see—almost four quid. That's a lot of money to get for my easy rider." She leaned forward and picked up the blue chips. "Now will you get the hell out, and take your gentlemanly airs with you? They stink up the joint."

She sprang up and ran away.

4

The following day was Saturday, warm, and fair, sure to bring good business to the dens. Men of Harvey's general stamp are even more habit-bound than the more law-abiding; and I thought that the quiet crowd at White's would give him confidence. I put N'kulu dressed like a houseboy on watch shortly after noon, feeling quite confident he would spot the quarry.

The black man reported at five. The red-haired, light-footed, gray-eyed man, compactly built as a topi, had come to the usual bait. Dressed carefully, I followed him, and in one glance found him sitting alone at a table. He saw me the same instant. Undoubtedly he had kept one eye on the door. He turned enough to conceal his face from me, and as soon as he saw his chance he intended to drift out. That suited my plans—our business was incompletable in Capetown—but I wished to talk to him first.

I went straight to his table and sat down.

Actually, I was taking quite a severe risk in doing so. I carried no derringer or knife, and he probably had both. If he had shot me down, he would still be safer from the British crowd than he was from me alive; and that was a boast I made to my own soul, and by the stars that ever shone above me, I believed it to be true. Still I did not believe he would commit such a desperate act at this stage. His general prospects were still too good, he thought. He had counted them over scores of times. The fact remained that, while he had not put away his snake ring—no doubt it was his fetish of good fortune—he had turned it around to hide its intertwined head and tail, so that at a casual glance it appeared an ordinary gold band.

"Hello, Harvey," I said.

He looked at me long.

"Didn't I see you at Zumbo on the Zambezi?" He had a deep, male, dominant voice, apparently unshaken by my sudden appearance. His picked-up Cockney accent did not conceal Scotch overtones, somehow quaint and odd.

"Yes, and I got the message you left for me at our camp by the sweet-water pan in Matshangana country."

By drawing a deep breath, I too spoke calmly.

The impulse rose in him to deny it. Perhaps it could be called an instinct, for stupid denial is often the first answer people of his beginnings make to accusation. He had risen above those beginnings; his name had been known and feared through a country large as western Europe. Instead he struck a pose. This too was characteristic of his kind, but the pose was mitigated and almost dignified by a good deal of self-reverence.

"Well, you don't blame me, do you?"

The question took me by surprise.

"Why didn't you take it out on me, a man, instead of on a woman? She pulled the trigger in my behalf."

To my amazement, Harvey laughed.

"She pulled it five times—every time a bull's-eye. There are only a few people in Africa who could do that—and one of them was Trudi Du Piel—and she was the only one in a hundred miles of there. You couldn't have done it, but she did do it, and out went my Hustlers, every bloody one. Still I didn't kill her. I beat her up a little and took a price from her but I didn't know she was in family way, and if she hadn't been, she'd be alive now. The price was what a man can take from a woman, and a beating is what a man can give a woman. You toffs don't understand that. You treat your women as though they was angels with wings. Well, they ain't. But she was a woman and I was easy on her. As for killing that old Kaffir, I don't count that. And I cut the throats of those oxen for the Devil of it—even at that, I still owe you a score instead of you owing me one. You lost your girl—but I didn't half come out even."

When he began and when he ended, his eyeballs flicked a little in their sockets, but in the middle of his discourse, when his confidence rose high, they held steady upon mine.

"That may be true, but it won't affect the outcome."

He considered this carefully. He sipped his drink, but his hand jerked a little and almost spilled it.

"A man's got to stand up for his pals—that is, if he is a man," he went on. "Don't you agree with me?"

"Heartily, Harvey."

"You're being sarcastic. Wasn't I standing up for mine?"

"Quite so."

"Yes, she was a woman. But sneaking up on her was more dangerous than sneaking up on a leopard. One glimpse of me in the grass—and I wouldn't be here."

"I guess you wouldn't."

"I'd made up my mind to lay for you too, and the rest of your oxen, and the ponies thrown in, but when I noticed—afterward—that she was beginning to swell a little, I guessed the truth about her, and decided to call it square."

"And soon after that the baby died—and then she died."

"I didn't intend that. I meant only to take a man's due. Now what did you mean when you said it wouldn't change the outcome?"

"I mean it's your turn next. And that's the second time I said that. The first time was to Culpepper. He turned on me swinging his rifle, but it was too late."

"I won't be too late," Harvey said quietly. "I accept your challenge, all or nothing. When do you want to start?"

"Right away."

"Are you armed?"

"Try to find out." And that sounded like boys, with chips on their shoulders.

"Not here. When I kill you, I'm not going to give you the satisfaction of being hanged for it. I'll meet you on the veld."

"That suits me very well."

"Will you excuse me for a moment. I've got to go to the privy."

I had used the same excuse, in much coarser language, when I had gone forth to save life at Puerto Miramar. In the present case the life to be saved—so Harvey thought—was Harvey's own.

He left the table, walking slowly at first, then with an irresistible quickening of his gait, and I knew he was on his way to the Great Karroo.

CHAPTER XVII

Hunt's End

THE GREAT KARROO, along with the Little Karroo, comprises about a hundred thousand square miles of desolation. All ready to trek, we beat Harvey to the start, and I felt almost certain he would follow the old wagon tracks for the peace of his soul; and if he found the prints of three horsemen, he would mistake them for Griqua travelers', and not be alarmed.

Its name means the Barren Lands. On one side of a range of *kopjes,* there is hope for the land, grass is short, sunburned, but covers its nakedness, many pans hold sweet water, sometimes there are limpid trickles among the shrubbery of the donga beds; and the trees are tall as the elephants that wander through them. On the other side the grass grows in skimpy patches, there lie wide wastes of barren gravel, only dwarf mimosas mark the dry watercourses at this time of year and there is no other bush but wild pomegranate and the bleak Karroo bush itself. Bands of Bushmen, as lean as the thorn, roam the solitudes, eating unclean things, and the secretary birds seek the venomous adder, and vultures keep watch in the sky, but of all the herds of game that swarm the veld, only the quagga, the African wild ass, is seen in any numbers; and the hyenas look like caricatures of Death, and the jackals and little foxes scuttle close to the ground.

Yet the Great Karroo reminded me of some place I had been and deeply hated, and for a time my brain was blocked, and I could not remember where. Then the truth broke upon me with an eerie presentiment of evil. It seemed an unlimitable continuation of Camp Despair. Put that bleak and hateful heath where my dream had ended down in this howling desert, and it would feel at home.

With our water flasks, our pokes of jerky, and our guns, N'kulu, Hagar, and I took lookouts twenty miles apart, whereby we could watch a corridor more than sixty miles broad. The two blacks left their horses with mine, concealed in dwarf mimosa thicket; thus they could patrol their beat and look for Harvey's horses or their footprints without much danger of being seen. Both had little mirrors that I had taught them to flash, under certain circumstances, in the sun. They were ordered not to fire on Harvey, even if he walked into their waiting sights, except as a last resort to save their own lives.

The watch was only two days long, but it seemed shorter than that, to me, those days were so full of visions. Harvey had not loitered along the way, and on the third day, when my pinfire rifle, stood upright, cast a shadow of exactly its own length, I watched carefully north and south and caught the flash of a mirror on a *kopje* top fifteen miles away. The signal came from N'kulu. I answered it, and passed it to Hagar, about ten miles in the opposite direction. She arrived in an hour and a half, running all the way. Both of us riding, and leading N'kulu's horse, in an hour more we spied his form, like a little, slowly moving upright stick on the empty plain.

"How fresh are the tracks, and how many?" I asked.

"They were made since sunrise, by one horse," the Zulu replied.

We came upon the trail; and then there began what seemed to me a journey into hell. Perhaps I was overtaxed by the long wait, the planning, the yearning, and at the same time undermined by the sense of what was lost, never to be regained; yet I would never be able to believe that the high powers of Africa did not show themselves that day, the nature gods that, whether or not of man's invention, are yet potent to save or to destroy; the nightmare world that lies under our sunlit world; the half-glimpsed, half-dreamed reality that is behind the black magic of voodoo. I gazed upon the land half-dead with thirst, I heard its muffled voices, I could not smell its life, the tang that rises from the shrubbery as it puts forth leaf and stalk, for here every branch and blade of grass had drawn into itself, covering up against dearth, seeking only to stay alive until the blessed shower; but sometimes I smelled the dreadful smell of Death, and the great vultures hopped off from the stripped bones and flapped away in the hot dead air.

Up from their lairs, out from their coverts, came forth and stood the inmates of the land, and I saw them through a haze, and they seemed not creatures of flesh and blood, but embodiments of forces, most of them evil, or of brutality, and all that lies on the other hand of grace. I was given no close view of the fleet, beautiful quaggas—always they sped past in a cloud of dust—but I saw the merciless wild dogs stand with bared fangs, and the hyenas did not flee but capered strangely, as though in glee of our entrance into their weird domain. We would not come out again. If we did, it would be as different people. We would be forever and terribly changed.

Out of a low thorn that looked as if it would not hide a springbuck—a lovely name for a beautiful lithe and playful creature I had seen once in numberless herds—emerged a huge white rhino. He stamped, and flung up dust, and lowered his monstrous head so that his lance stood forth; but I felt no fear of him, we did not even hold our pieces ready, well we knew he would let us pass, perhaps he had no choice. The wild thought came to me that he would like to warn us if he could, for we too were part brute, and the same doom that lay on us hung over him. But we knew good and evil, and he did not. The Serpent had instructed us in the mystery, long ago in a fruitful and verdant garden. Since then we had wandered upon the face of the earth, and now we had come into its waste place, hidden away behind the rocky *kopjes,* the place where Cain had fled, bearing that awful mark. We might yet turn back—but we did not turn back.

The heat of the day increased. The last traces of the sweet and saving water, the baptism from the sky that washed away sin, that breaks in the mother's womb that she may give forth life, faded from our sight. There was nothing of any hope or joy between the burning sky and the brown, sun-baked ground. The rhino might have been one I had seen at Camp Despair, running as though the Devil were in pursuit. Now, out of a mimosa forest that looked too low and mean to hide a hermit buffalo, moved forth an old she-elephant, so wasted by age and famine that her bones stood forth. I knew her now, I thought. She was the same I had seen at Camp Despair, and had come hence to prophesy the soon ending of our lives, or the death of our souls. She stood in our path. She scuffled with her feet and wiped out for a few feet the tracks we were following so grimly, so implacably. It may be she was not the death-elephant, but earth-born like ourselves. Perhaps she had come to tell us something. But we marched on, oblivious to her outstretched trunk and outspread ears; she could not stop us, so she withdrew the way she had come.

A secretary bird flew over us, circled and swooped down. Then in our plain sight, not fifty yards ahead of us on the almost naked ground, there came to pass a battle savage and terrible as those between the archangels and the legions of darkness before the world was made. She thought nothing of killing little adders and yard-long asps, the scratch of whose fangs was death, but now she had swooped down upon a black mamba, the serpent that many tribes of black men worship as a god, fast as a whiplash, malignant as a fiend, venomous beyond any being with the breath of life. The bird screamed, and the snake hissed, and they danced the *danse macabre* in the grass until the grass wore out, and dust rose in a cloud.

"Come," said Hagar, when N'kulu and I would stop and watch, or at least ride wide of this phoenix and this dragon. "We can't wait for a bird to kill a snake."

The fury of their battle intensified until it passed credence, passed the mark of what we had learned to accept as earthly; and chills of horror ran down our backs. But when we were ten paces distant, the bird took wing, leaving the mamba in his death throes, the forward six feet of his twelve sweeping stiffly from side to side in a great arc, close to the ground, while the rear lay paralyzed and dead.

"Look," breathed N'kulu in a hoarse whisper.

My gaze followed his pointing finger. A hundred yards to one side and thirty feet above the sun-blasted earth the secretary bird was flapping wildly in the air, flying in jerks and circles, and as we stared in dread, its wings clapped together and it pitched down, and the thud as it struck the hard ground came weirdly to our ears and harrowed our souls with thoughts we could not grasp and auguries that we dared not heed. Hagar lashed her horse to a run, and it bounded over the writhing snake. But as N'kulu and I turned a little off the path, its half-length that was still alive rose and swung swiftly two feet off the ground, and its fangs barely missed my foot.

2

The heat thickened like smoke. It shimmered on the rocks, and mirages of great wonder rose and hung under the horizon, one of them a brave ship on a cool sea, with every mast and spar, and one was Capetown, spread out for us with all its roofs and towers under Table Mountain. The hills of warrior ants became feverishly animated. Smelling meat and blood, they rushed at us in a black swarm, seeming to move so fast, although we outdistanced them in a few steps, and so the swarms of men must look to the seraphs, fearing our defilement, as they wing through the sky; and the vultures made merry, soaring and climbing and gliding without stirring a feather on the rising currents, but the lizards grew motionless, a delicious trance stealing upon them, and then they lay like dead folk, careless of the insatiable hunger of their desert fellows. The sun looked like a white-hot metal disk in the burning-glass sky. We could not look at it or near it without tears. It scorched all skin exposed to its blast whether black or white.

Suddenly N'kulu laughed aloud.

"Look, bukra!" he cried. "We have got turned around, and come up on the seaward side of the Langkloof, and there are evergreen forests on the slopes. Let us go and rest awhile in the cool, among the dripping ferns, then we will rouse up and follow the bukra's trail with refreshed hearts."

I replied, grimacing and gesturing, "Harvey is no bukra. He's a bushwhacker."

"And that is no forest, only a cheat on the eyeballs," Hagar said with a quiet mien. "Let us make haste."

The sun pitched at last—it was a little lower every time I raised my hand as a shield against its beams and measured its height in the sky. It dropped down, and I thought that the air stirred a little, but there was no cooling of the land or of the baking rocks and the burning sand. The shadows stretched very long. Evening sounds began, such as the yapping of foxes and the sporadic barking of jackals. I knew that night was surely coming when the vultures, hideously hungry, left their vain watch. They went away to some eerie roost guarding an entranceway to hell that lay hot and close by. We ate of our sun-dried unsalted meat that the strong acids of the stomach could dissolve without much help from water, and sipped with a pitiless sparingness at our canteens.

But we could do nothing for our horses, whose wildly rolling eyes and red nostrils already declared their thirst, and who pawed and trembled in their pickets half the night, standing still with their heads dropped through the latter half. We three people fell into short spells of apoplectic sleep. Through our dreams ran the chuckling and sobbing and the long wailings of the hyenas and the strident bark of jackals, rising now and then to a frantic clamor, then dying away, and the whimpering cries of foxes, like infants in the dark. Late rose a moon half-eaten away by the wasting sickness that in due course takes all. The name of that remorseless malady is Time. Her light was weak and wretched, but in this sky bereft of the lightest cooling mist it extinguished the pin-point twinkling stars that somehow promised hope, a distant but final redemption, and which taught the durability of little things, and which made us dream we were not forgot of God; also it dulled the noble shine of the great stars. As she rose up, our visions widened. I could see the mean thorn thirty yards away, and when I looked down could make out plainly my own footprints in the dust.

"Get up and trek," I told my two companions.

"You took so long about it, I thought you were struck dumb," Hagar told me.

Was it not Hagar who as Sarai's handmaid took Sarai's place? "Hagar, you are well named. There is not much difference in your quest now and your quest then. Then it was to make life, now to take life. One little letter different. She looked like you, Hagar, as Abraham called to her, and Sarai railed at her."

N'kulu's black eyes were rimmed with white. I saw it in the moonlight.

We mounted our horses, they not complaining even in their hearts; it was too late now, nothing mattered now; they thought that God Almighty worked His will through our hands, and never dreamed it might be Satan usurping God's place. Their feet rose and fell, but they did not lift their heads until we crossed a small, dry watercourse, where they snorted and nuzzled at a hole late-dug in the sand. The bottom felt faintly damp. But not a drop oozed through the baking ground, and we struck them with the cruel quirts, and they surged forward a few quick paces, ere again they hung their heads and trudged as in a dream.

The sun rose, and its first ray scorched like a hot iron. The time drew on to midmorning, and I felt sure we were pressing the quarry close. If not, we had lost and would almost surely perish in defeat. Then we came on a rocky plain, dotted with thorn clumps, and presently to a thin line of dwarf mimosa marking a watercourse now bone-dry, grave-silent. But farther on, it entered a kind of ravine, a good place to search for a dwindling water hole.

"Do not go there, bukra, until I crawl and look," N'kulu said.

"Harvey's horse's tracks do not lead down to it."

"That is why I bid you swing wide of it. The tracks keep a straight course, but I think they will circle back. Would he miss the chance to find water? And he may be there now."

The trail would pass within a hundred paces of the ravine. I could see it through my Lemiere field glass. Instead of following it, we swung out in the other direction, so we would pass at over three hundred paces; then N'kulu could reconnoiter from the opposite direction, which appeared to give better cover. I admitted the possibility of his proposition, but did not believe it. The scene looked too dead. The silence lay so deep and the heat felt so extreme. I had forgotten how a silence can be shattered by a clap of thunder, and that greater heat than this can be generated in a gun barrel by a trigger touch, and that, without life, death cannot exist.

The thunder roared twice. Our out-swing from the ambush was not wide enough; the great marksman waiting there had been handicapped but not made helpless. My horse dropped under me, dying; N'kulu's horse bounded forward, about ten frantic leaps, then fell in a heap. Silence set in again, broken only by a faint clatter of rocks inaudible except in such silence.

"Run and take him, before he can reload," Hagar muttered, her quirt lifted.

Instead we could only stand and watch as a horse burst out of the brushwood at the other end of the ravine. Wildly rode Harvey, his double-barreled rifle in his hand. No doubt he was disappointed that both N'kulu and I had got quickly to our feet. Not daring to aim at our bodies visible above our mounts, the target being too small, he had hoped to cripple one or both of us, at the same time making sure of immobilizing us. So he might be laughing as he galloped away; at least his heart was singing in his breast. He had escaped, he thought. He would find his tribe of Bushmen and live among them until once more he could return to Gertrude and much else that he had loved. He would begin again, win again.

I thought not. I looked at Hagar, and believed that her thoughts leaped with mine. But I did not speak until we had come down into the ravine, looked at Harvey's carefully laid ambush, and then at a hole he had dug in the bed of the water-course. A cupful of water had oozed into it, but the wells were only faintly damp; perhaps enough had accumulated after a patient wait for Harvey to wet his lips, but his horse had not drunk.

"We're better off," I told my two companions.

Hagar nodded quietly. N'kulu stared.

"How can that be, master?" he asked. "We three can ride Hagar's horse a little way, then he will fall."

"How soon will Harvey's horse fall from burning thirst? No, we will leave Hagar's horse here, and follow him on foot."

"Did you Zulus never know that a man can overtake a horse in the great Thirst?" Hagar asked scornfully. "So can a woman."

So by taking time to dig away some of the earth on the side of the well, we fastened Hagar's horse so he could put his head in it, his lips touching the bottom. Perhaps before night fell again, he could drink. Perhaps there would be only enough water to tantalize him, and if the wild dogs found him they would kill him; but we dared not set him free, lest we have some awful need of him when we passed this way again. I thought upon his innocence, how he had never harmed a living soul from his foaling in some greener land until this bitter hour in the desert, then I tramped on with my companions, and forgot him.

3

The land looked different, now that we gazed upon it from our true height instead of high in the saddle. A dream came upon me, a kind of an invisible mirage, in which I saw myself the brother of the yapping jackal, the wailing hyena, and the howling wild dogs, and even the little green and brown lizards asleep on the stones. Then, along with my sense of having time to spare, of being no longer harried and driven by the whips of hate, I felt a strange assurance of victory that at first I could not completely believe. The truth was, we were winning—or at least our chance of winning had been greatly bettered—by an idea. We traveled unburdened while our quarry was laden down with a thousand pounds of horseflesh. Our flasks of water were ample for such desert-hardened trekkers as Hagar, N'kulu, and me today, tonight, and all day tomorrow, and our course would be changed long before the expiration of that period of grace. Unless he could find his Bushmen in a few hours, Harvey would turn back. Where else could he go?

Before long, Harvey's footprints led us to a deserted kraal of a small tribe of Bushmen. The dry wells were deep-dug, and the kitchen midden contained the bones of foxes, durboas, sour-tasting aardvarks, and other creatures that even Bushmen will not eat except in the bitter drouth. I examined them without haste. Then I spoke, my voice drunken-sounding from concealed exultation, to my two companions.

"There are three *kopjes* about ten miles apart," I said.

"I see them, but where is our quarry?" N'kulu answered.

"He will return before dark. Meanwhile we will each climb one of the hills, I with my field glasses, all with our little mirrors, and keep close watch. Then he who spies him will signal to the others, and we will close in for the kill."

When our brief plans were complete, all three of us made haste. The central hill that I climbed rose about three hundred feet above the plateau, and gave a wide and comprehensive view. At two o'clock in the afternoon, in the extreme heat of the day, I took my post. By four I had seen more clean and handsome creatures than I had ever dreamed roamed these sun-blasted wastes. Several small herds of quaggas had wandered across the distant grass. There were other bucks I could not name, one flock of ostriches, and, close at hand, a family of beautiful sable antelope such as had run with Trudi and me on the day of the windstorm. Perhaps it was a sign that the long hunt was almost over.

Trudi, wherever you are, do not gaze tonight across the River. Do not watch what occurs tonight. In the silence or the music, in the darkness or the pearling light, do not know of it.

A flock of vultures took flight behind a long thorn thicket. They had flushed up from what was likely an unguarded car-cass, probably last night's kill of a leopard or even a black-maned lion sometimes ranging such deserts as this. What had frightened them? Rarely does the killer return to his broken meats—well knowing the uselessness of it—and his time is be-tween sundown and sunrise, not in the blast of the day's heat. Quickly the grisly birds settled back to their bone-picking; and, watching closely, I made out a moving form on the flank of the thicket. Except for man, only a maribou stork looks so tall and lean.

It was Harvey of Harvey's Hustlers, and his course was run. Unable to follow a straight course, he tacked like a ship in a head wind, and sometimes stopped and staggered. I flashed a signal to N'kulu, received his answer, then did the same with Hagar. In a little less than an hour we met at the foot of the hill. In the meantime our quarry had advanced less than a mile.

We sipped at our flasks, then followed at a fast walking pace. Half an hour later we made a wheeling movement that fetched us up behind a mimosa-lined watercourse not more than three furlongs in advance of our prey. Here we lay an ambush, only to have to move it twice because of Harvey's veering to the right and left. But now he was staggering into easy range. I raised my rifle and saw him plainly in the sights. I had only to press the trigger to be rid of him. He could be left in silence in the dead grass, never knowing what hit him, and when the wild dogs gathered, or the birds of death soared down, he would not hear flapping wings or feel the first wary setting of bared fangs.

He would disappear from the sight of men, his evil deeds nullified by the blotter of Death, and I could go from this place and wash my hands in the first water hole we came on, and it might be my soul would be saved.

Instead the desert closed round me, whispering evilly in my ear, and the burning sky was over me with its seeming hate, and I would not heed the pleadings of a lovely ghost that came across a wide deep river and touched my hand.

"Drop your gun, Harvey, or I'll shoot," I called, loudly enough for a delirious man to hear.

The piece fell out of his hand and he came toward us in a staggering run.

"For the love of Jesus Christ," he wailed out of his thirst-thickened lips, "give me a drink of water."

4

The horse we had left in the ravine had lived through that night, managing to drink of the slow-seeping water; and the use we made of him was to carry our still weak but reviving captive. With replenished canteens, we made good time toward the Hex Mountains, arriving on their slopes, the Karroo left behind, before the sun pitched down. Again we saw trees, a carpet of grass as far as the gaze could wander, watercourses with olive-green herbage; and everywhere we looked, gladdening the heart, restoring faith in God and men, roamed herds of game.

The quaggas had come here, out of the waste of the Karroo, for better living. There was no four-legged thing as fleet, unless it was the cheetah, the hunting leopard, who could gain upon him at the start of the race, to lag behind at its end. Where there was deep shade and rank reed, slept and fed and chewed their cud wide-horned Cape buffaloes, the cows vigilant, the bulls lazy but furious in wrath. In the way of freaks of nature—or so we thought, not knowing how natural they felt to themselves—roamed droves of giraffe in ever silence, never giving sound to any joy or pang of the heart, with a sedateness of behavior, a calm trust in God and unfortunately in man, a sweetness that their very grotesqueness caused to catch at the heart. Undignified, squawking and fighting, the ostriches ran in six-foot strides, pell-mell at the slightest danger, and their feet flushed the little larks who were their cousins.

Lonely roamed the white rhinoceroses, their only fellowship being mother and calf, or sometimes two old males, outvying each other in selfishness. But I did not believe they were the origin of the legend of the unicorn. The latter had the body of a thoroughbred horse, was pictured as snow-white, not dirty gray, he was lusty and frolicsome and had strange dealings with women. In among the rocks of the *kopjes* and in the thick of the dongas dwelt creatures of the night.

"Is tonight my night?" Harvey asked, when we had pitched a little camp by a cool spring. Sitting there with his hands tied, his concern over my intentions deeper than any ocean, he still spoke with a trace of bravado.

"Yes," I answered, going on with my chore.

"Well, don't be so damned close-mouthed. Haven't I the right to know? Are you going to shoot me like a man, or hang me like a dog?"

"Neither one."

"I've got a killing coming. I don't deny it, in spite of what the girl did to my good Hustlers. She did it for you, I know. I hadn't ought to have taken it out on a woman. But I tell you, Stony, or whatever your damn name is, if you peg me out on an anthill, you'll burn forever, and I tell you you'll burn forever and ever, world without end."

"I'll not tie you to an anthill. I know something better than that."

His eyes half-shut and his lips trembled like a child's and he said nothing more. I finished the chore I was doing, then gave N'kulu orders as to close care of the captive, then with a picket rope fastened to my saddle strings, the pin-fire rifle in its scabbard, I rode forth in the grass.

In a matter of minutes I came in range of a herd of large roan antelope and had shot a heavy bull. When the horse had dragged the carcass in a long looping course across the grass of the veld, a half-mile in all, I let it lie within four hundred paces of our camp. Then I turned the carcass on its back, the four legs in the air and cut strips of rawhide two feet long and three inches wide on the inner side of the thighs, leaving these attached at one end. The table had not been set for the lions and hyenas, leopards and wild dogs, that would cross and follow that blood trail. Nothing remained but to finish spreading the feast.

As I rode back to camp, I made a fleeting inquiry into my own sanity. I followed it only a little way, then laughed and rubbed my hands that felt hot and dry. As I rode into camp, Harvey's gaze fixed in yearning intensity on my lips when I spoke, on my hands when I moved. His own lips were pale, oddly grimacing at times, and his blunt, brutal hands had become strangely awkward. I noticed the serpent ring which for a while I had forgotten. At my command, N'kulu tied a slip knot in the picket rope and put the loop over Harvey's head.

"Pull it tight if he struggles," I ordered. "It will surely quiet him. We'll loosen it if it quiets him too much."

"I'm not going to struggle, you bastard," Harvey said, and I believed him. "I'm going to take my medicine, and not give you the satisfaction."

"We'll start with you putting out your hands."

"What for?" he asked, holding them forth in their leather bonds.

He turned gray, his eyes glazing, as I removed the ring.

"What do you want of that?" he muttered, when I took the ring.

"I'd better ask what you want of it."

"I took it from the ear of a dead girl who had been false to me. A girl of coffee color, but the comeliest I ever saw. Later a black Bushman came and told me that if I'd give it to him to take to his master, I could leave Africa alive. But if I didn't—"

"Did you beat him for his insolence?"

"Yes."

"You should have believed him. How much money have you in your belt?"

"Five hundred Cape dollars. I've made thousands but couldn't keep 'em."

"Do you mind my taking it? I can use it, and you can't."

"No, I don't mind."

"Don't imagine this will change anything," I said, when I had the bills in my own belt.

"I'm not that big a fool."

I wondered what he did imagine. Now he would soon know the truth. At my nod, N'kulu led Harvey like a haltered animal to the roan carcass, Hagar and I bringing up the rear. When Harvey saw the rawhide strips peeled off and hanging from the thighs he turned his head and looked at me in stunned disbelief.

"You can't," he burst out, his chin palsied.

I did not answer.

"You can't do it!" he went on, his voice rising.

N'kulu gave a light, nervous jerk on the rope, but the cords of Harvey's neck stood out, and he did not feel it.

"You can't do this to a white man," he shouted as loud as he could, the cry ringing over the silent plain.

"I can do it a little better to a white man than I could to a black man."

Suddenly his throat eased, his expression changed, and he spoke to me in a low, desperate, but strong rumble of sound.

"Well, go ahead, God damn you. But He'll damn you without my asking. Maybe I'm damned too—I've done enough to deserve it—but when you're sent to hell, you'll be shut up in solitary. You know what that means? A corner that the rest of us, the decent damned, whisper about, but have never seen. Only God could imagine it, as only the Devil could imagine this. The Devil's got your soul already, just thinking of it. Will you let me off and give me a decent killing?"

"No, I won't let you off. There's your bed for the night. You'll find it soft enough."

"I thought you were a gentleman, but you're not."

It was a grotesque remark to make the Devil hold his sides, but I could not even smile.

"Lay him face-up on the breast and belly of the carrion, and tie his arms and legs with the rawhide," I ordered N'kulu.

"Spare me the task, bukra," the black man answered.

"Do as I tell you."

"No, not if you order me the same death."

Then up spoke the black woman whose face made me think of Gertrude's as she dealt for the kill. "I'll do it, bukra."

"No, I'll do it myself. Hold the rope tight."

"I told you there's no need. I told you I won't struggle, and I will not. But you deserve it more than me."

The conviction ringing in his voice made me look at him and listen.

"How do you count that, Harvey?"

"Because you could do this to a fellow man, and I couldn't. Neither can that black man, and he's a savage. A black woman can do it, but they're not human either, when love for someone turns 'em into fiends. It's the end of me, but it's the end of you, too. You can give up hope. You can run up and down the world and cross all the seas and all the deserts and all the mountains, and you'll never get away from this spot, this hell-hole in the veld. The Devil will be waiting for you here. You'll know it, and when there's nowhere else to turn, you'll come back here and he'll get you. Do you think I'm lying? Do you

think that the vision that's come to me is false? I was born in
Mull off the Scottish coast, across the Firth of Lorn from
Argyll. I was a gilly for English lords who came to hunt the red
deer in the days before I won a whole kingdom, half a continent, to hunt o'er for myself. Oh, the mists that rolled in from
the outer islands across the Pass of Coll! Silver and snow-white
and pale gray, with the sun shining through them, ere the
winds tore 'em to shreds. Oh, the blue of the lochs, and the
green of the young rye! But the grass was never greener than
in the kirkyard, and oft we'd see the Devil, black as the coals of
Linlithgow, waiting there for his own. He's close by now. It's
for you his hand is out, not for me. Fine Southern gentleman
you make out to be, this is your last chance."

"Lie down in your bed, Harvey, and I'll tuck you in for the
night."

He lay down without an instant's struggle, and I fastened the
rawhide strips to his wrists and ankles, and pulled the knots
tight. As I finished the job, I must rub my eyes for better
vision, for the light was failing. The bottom had fallen out of
the sun, and it had dropped behind the rocky hills, and the
shadows no longer crept but leaped and rushed.

"You've still time to cut my throat and save your soul,"
Harvey told me.

I need not answer for some shadow-folk answered for me.
They spoke in my place, as one night they had done for Hagar.
The first voice was only the chattering, snarling chorus of a
band of jackals. Then a hyena gave voice to wild laughter that
ended in a sob. He laughed over the bones left by the lordly
lion, with good meat on them still, but his maw would never
be filled, there was always hunger, there was always pain, and
the end was defeat and death.

"Oh, they'll come tonight," Harvey told me in low tones.
"You've planned it well; the whole cursed lot will come. There
will be jackals and hyenas and leopards and lions, and some
will hang back, but some will come up, and I may live a long
time, maybe for hours, 'specially if they start on my guts in-

stead of my throat. Even at that, I'm glad it's the nighttime and not the day. I won't be here at daybreak, I'll promise you that. I'll be where no fang can touch me, and no man-made law can cop me, and no hate can harm me."

"Yes, I think you will."

"It's hate that's got its hand on me tonight. It's not law, and it's not justice. You don't claim it is?"

"No, I don't dare claim that."

"Then go away and leave me, so it can start, and once it's started, it can get over with."

"I call you, Harvey."

But he did not know what I meant. He thought I was mocking him.

I beckoned to N'kulu and Hagar, and I led the way toward our camp. It seemed a long way in the thickening dusk, and for a hundred steps or more I kept my gaze fixed on it, as though in fear of losing my way, but the real reason was I did not wish to look back. My soul had darkened with the darkening hillside, and I did not want to see the first little jackal stealing upon the carrion—a little flicking shadow, darker than the rest. Then it came to me that although I could hear N'kulu breathing hard, and the faint swish of grass from his footfall, I had heard not a sound from Hagar. I stopped, turned, and saw her coming toward us on a light run.

"Where have you been?" I demanded.

"A task was appointed me, which I have done."

"What was it?"

"Something that the M'sabu commanded me to do."

"What do you mean? M'sabu has been gone many moons."

"Yes, but only across the River. She came to me just now and gave me the order. It was not meet that I could disobey, even though you kill me."

I pushed past her and, at a fast pace, retraced my steps. As I came near the scene, there was a rustle of grass as some little creature, a fox or a jackal, scuttled away. But there rose no other sound. I had never come to a more silent place.

"Harvey?" I called.

There was no answer.

I pushed close. Harvey lay almost as though asleep, but his head had rolled back a little, and his breast and his bed too looked black in this dim light from some clean baptism of Death.

I turned to Hagar and spoke in bitter reproach.

"Woman, I did not bid you take my sin upon your soul."

"M'sabu bade me, bukra. When I said I would, she smiled her wide, slow smile. So there was no evil. That was the sign. She had lingered until now, you held her here by hate, but now she has inspanned and gone her way. It is all right now. Let us, too, go to our own place."

The jackals barked, the hyenas laughed and sobbed, far away a lion roared out his sovereignty of the veld, but there was no evil in any of these, and the night wind felt cool on my fevered face. And now I must follow blindly Hagar and N'kulu, because I had been given the holy baptism of tears.

CHAPTER XVIII

The Park of the Three Lions

THERE WAS nothing any longer to hold Hagar, N'kulu, and me in the Hex Hills. When the morning broke, strange and gray, we did not visit the scene of the atonement, and actually the exact spot might have been hard to find, so clean sweeps the broom of life across the veld to efface the tracks of Death. The bones would likely be scattered or hidden away in dens. The strips of skin I had cut would be devoured with the rest. The skull would be rolled and the dark stain on the yellow grass would be licked off by small, rough, avid tongues. All the feasters had gone now, vanishing as invisibly as they had come; and although after sunrise the vultures might find vestiges worth their lighting down, we did not wait for them to begin their implacable watch. Shaking some dust from our heels, although not all—we could never in this world shake all—we rose from our beds and trekked.

It was a long way back to the kraals of King Manikusa on the Sanyati arm of the great Zambezi. When we made it at last, I thought to find both the aged monarch and his chief witch doctor gathered to their fathers, but Manikusa, although very feeble, still walked in the sunlight in his lion-skin of state, and Wise One looked as lean and timeless as a thorn tree.

"The ponies are both in good flesh," he reported to me. "Of the eight oxen, seven are well and one is dead on the horn of a rhino that broke through our kraal, and we have kept the axles of the wagon in fresh grease made from the fat of the wild hog."

"You have done well," I said.

Then, when I paused, the aching expression on his face, more agony of suspense than I had ever seen on any face unless it were Harvey's, more than I had ever let come on my face even when I waited to be hanged, caused me to speak in haste in the Dutch tongue.

"Don't be afraid. All is well in regard to the ring."

"You have it?" he gasped.

"Yes."

"I will put my hand in yours, making what these buffalo think is *dowa*. Then give me the little gold snake, and by its *dowa* every promise I made you will be kept."

My card-sharpery stood me in good stead, in fishing the ring from my tobacco pouch unseen by that sharp-eyed throng. While he performed his hocus-pocus, I slipped it into his hand. When he felt its shape he could not keep two tears from running out of his wildly bright eyes.

There followed some sort of palaver between Wise One and Prince Umzilla in one of the beehive houses. I had not yet sought audience or had been greeted by the tall, young, royal black, so I did not gaze in that direction. Presently both men came forth, and although Manikusa's son could not speak to me, he gave me a broad smile and a little curved bone from the neck of a lion, famed as a good-luck token.

"The great Umzilla bade me tell you that his tribesmen, and their women and children, and in truth all his kinsmen of the Sun, whether his friends and foes, and the Hottentot, and the Bushmen, and even the pale-faced Chiquaa take you in brotherhood for the sake of the falling dead of the slave dealer Harvey and his band, at your hand and at the hand of the little M'sabu which is now stilled."

"I take them in brotherhood, also," I answered without thinking.

"Also, the great Umzilla has bade me offer you, as a token of his brotherhood, all the valley of the donga we call M'Kazi, twenty miles long by six miles broad, wherein to build your kraals and herd your kine. Moreover, if you do not wish to become an outlander, so far from people of your skin, he bids me appoint a hundred porters, each to bear upon his shoulder a tusk from our great store, none to weigh less than half a hundredweight, for you to sell at the trading post in Bulawayo." As he named this outpost, the white man's farthest thrust into the South African blue, the lid of his left eye drooped a little in some kind of sign.

Even now I could not afford to lose face with Wise One. Not knowing what the sign meant, I appeared not to notice it. In a few minutes he was leading a band of a hundred porters, deep-chested, broad-shouldered young men pleased at the prospect of change and adventure, to the ivories stacked like cordwood behind the kraals. I would not be cheated in the dealing. Wise One himself chose the big, curved pale-yellow tusks, many of which had been borne by an old bull and weighed a hundred pounds.

When my wagon wheels were ready to turn, Wise One waved away the crowd, then spoke in sly glee.

"No doubt Heer Edward will sell his tusks at Bulawayo," he remarked in Afrikaans.

"Perhaps so, but how do you know my name?"

"Has *Bwana* forgotten that he gave it, when he first came seeking boats to go down our river?" *Bwana* meant master in the East Coast argot employed by the Arabs.

"Yes, Wise One, I had forgotten. But you bade the porters take the ivory to any post I desired, so why not Zumbo, somewhat farther, but where the price may be somewhat higher?"

"No, you will take them to Bulawayo. I have seen it in a vision."

"Did you see what made me choose that post, Wise One?"

"Could it not be that you wish to lay eyes on the great Moffat, who has his kraal there?"

The great Moffat was no misnomer. Few greater men had ever come to Africa from Great Britain than Robert Moffat, the Scotch missionary, teacher, traveler, and pioneer.

"That would be a good cause for going there."

"But it comes to me there may be another cause. Only two months ago a tall ship brought a message to the burgomaster at Lourenço Marques, in Delagoa Bay. How did I, an old black medicine man, know of it? Because the message was not his *shauri* (business) but the *shauri* of another, whom the sender asked to be found, and since he was old in the way of Africa, he had the drums send forth the call, and for all drummers friendly to the white men to repeat it, so it would be heard far and wide. Meanwhile the message would be carried by a north-bound trader to the kraal of the great Moffat, since this has come to be a rendezvous for trekkers in the Zambezi country, where the lost one had lately made his way."

"What was the name of the lost one?"

"He had two names. The first of them was Edward. The other I have forgotten."

"Did the drums describe him?"

"He was darker of skin than the English and the Dutch, and had a big nose, and a gun that loaded in the middle, not the end."

"I suppose you didn't hear the name of the sender?" For sometimes this much was told, in advertising mail, so that the addressee could judge its importance.

"All who can understand the drums heard it, but it meant nothing to us black men—except one. I was that one, and I have forgotten it. But I remembered hearing it before."

Wise One laughed and spat.

"I have a curiosity to know in what connection."

"Long ago I was slave of Dutch farmer folk, and the old grandfather had read many books. When an Englishman who came often to our kraals boasted of great journeys his countrymen had made, the grandfather boasted of great Dutchmen who had sailed the seas and found new lands. One of them sailed in a ship whose name was the *Half Moon,* which I knew was lucky. And the sender of the message was his son or daughter, or, more like, his grandson or granddaughter, for the name was the same."

"Hudson?"

"Yes, that is right. I am old and foolish or I would have remembered."

"You are not old by our counting, and if you are foolish, so is a jackal, a hyena, and a fox rolled into one. You were born among savages, but had you been born with a white skin, among the most knowing of peoples, you would have still won to high place."

"I will remember the *bwana* saying so, long after the wind has brushed away his footprints."

"And I will take my ivory to the kraal of the great Moffat."

2

Wagon ruts led across the high veld from Manikusa's kraals to Bulawayo, and our outfit made the journey in twelve days.

There were many beehive huts of the Bechuana natives, but only two structures large enough to be called houses. One was the trading post run, oddly enough, by an English-speaking Cantonese named Shen N'u. It was to him that I went first.

He was pleased by the appearance of my ivory and told me he would pay one Cape dollar a pound.

"Do you think I have as much as five thousand pounds?" I asked.

"I will offer you five thousand Cape dollars for it, before it is weighed," he answered with a toothy grin. "If it does not go considerably more, my grandfather was a turtle."

"I can make good use of the balance, but five thousand Cape dollars is the sum I require for a certain purpose, even if I have to transport it clean to Sofala," so I confided to him, in the way of lonely men fresh out of the Blue.

"Your purpose can now be fulfilled. Will you stand by to see it weighed, or trust the office to the blacks? They are used to weighing corn, or I miss my guess."

"It is in my mind to call on Dr. Moffat, without delay."

Some boys had already run to tell him of my arrival. I found him on a kind of porch attached to his roomy native-style house, the former, he told me proudly in a little while, the work of his own hands. Besides being a good carpenter, he was also a kraal-builder, a blacksmith, a vegetable and flower gardener, and a farmer; and all these craftsmanships had shaped his hands into wonder-works of human flesh, and built something indescribably impressive into his face. I could not doubt that they had helped him perform his still greater labors, the writing of his famous account of his missions and travels, the translation of the Bible and *Pilgrim's Progress* into the Sechwana tongue, and giving savage people a written language of their own. He was still in his early sixties, ruddy, and vigorous, and he spoke with a Scotch accent in a movingly humble way.

"Did you say your name was Edward Stono?" Dr. Moffat asked, belatedly catching at a vague memory.

"Yes, sir."

"Then I have a message for you put by. It arrived some weeks ago—it had been brought on a Portuguese vessel—and it came from America. But perhaps you know about it, and that is the main purpose of your visit here."

"I have three purposes, one being the sale of my ivory to the factor. In the other two, I request your good offices."

"It will take about fifteen minutes to produce the message. My native secretary has filed it, and no one but he can decipher his records, and he is running an errand to the chief's house—" The good doctor looked distressed.

"After being delayed this long, it can certainly wait awhile longer. In fact, I'd like to have it wait until I have settled the third matter—one I had in mind a great deal longer than the news of the message."

"Now that's an odd thing."

"I suppose it is. I'm following my heart in this, and perhaps a gambler's instinct. Have you the latest map of the country lying east of Victoria Falls?"

"I have a rough map, drawn at Dr. Livingstone's directions, and I think it is the latest."

He took me into a plain but comfortable office, on the wall of which hung a better map of the Falls region than I had known existed. After studying it a few minutes, measuring distances with the doctor's forceps, I was able to indicate a minor tributary of the great river some twenty-five days' journey by wagon below the Falls.

"In how many years will this territory be settled?" I asked.

"Much sooner than you think. The Doppers have their eyes on Bechuanaland and Matabeleland, and the English aren't far behind."

"After it's been ceded by native kings—the first step in the settlement—how much could be bought for five thousand Cape dollars—a thousand English pounds?"

The doctor's eyes fixed on mine with a curious intensity. "Why—it's pretty soon to consider such matters—but if history repeats itself—and the land is opened to settlers as other strips have been—I should say between fifty and a hundred thousand acres."

"Well, I want to buy that much as a memorial to my wife." I began to speak rapidly, afraid that Dr. Moffat would think me a fool, and in great haste to tell him the good sense that my mind and soul, working together, had arrived at. "It's hardly enough land for what I hoped, yet it would be a start—"

Just then a Negro, in white cotton shirt and trousers, with intelligence written in his face, appeared at the door.

"Do you want me, sah?"

"Get out the message that came for Mr. Edward Stono."

"Yes, sah."

"Now what were you saying, Edward?" And I knew it was right and kind for him to call me by my first name, and I felt the warmth and sympathy in his voice, and my trouble passed away.

"Doctor, you know how the game has disappeared in the regions settled by the Voortrekkers. They need the meat—and the good sport of hunting—but the time comes, and they can't find any. I had hoped that this tract of land that I want to buy could be marked off, with posts every half-mile or so, and everywhere on it the game left undisturbed. Some of the farmers might not like the notion, but in time they'd see that the animals will breed there and spread to other places where they could hunt. Even fifty thousand acres is eighty sections—a piece ten miles long and eight miles broad. A good many could live there—bucks, buffaloes, even a few lions and leopards and rhinos. The area I've pointed out is especially good game country. She and I saw a good deal, on the night we spent there, separated from our outfit, without any fire. Doctor, if I turned over the money to you, would you take charge of it until the land is opened up, and then do what you can to carry out my dream?"

"Will you give me a free hand? I mean—if I can't get that particular spot—if for some reason it's not available—can I select some other that would be a good preserve for wild animals?"

"Oh, yes—"

The Negro reappeared, an envelope in his hand. Evidently he had known just where to look for it. Dr. Moffat took it and handed it to me. I laid it on the table unopened.

"Do you wish me to leave the room, while you read it?" he asked.

"No, sir. I wish to wait a minute until we finish what we were saying. I don't want anything to interfere with that. Or to tempt me to postpone it—or to let it go."

"I don't think there'd be any danger," the great missionary said, looking into my eyes. "And I'll say now, I'll not only do what you ask, but I think I can do more. I am a close friend of Paul Kruger, of Martin Pretorius, and of Sir George Grey. All three would favor the idea of a game preserve in the new country—to build on from where you began. I think that not eighty square miles but two hundred might be set aside as a sanctuary for the game. In these vast expanses, four hundred could easily be spared and the money you have donated would set a seal of solid fact, of earnest intent, on the whole enterprise."

I turned away to the window, steadied myself, and spoke.

"Four hundred miles would be twenty miles long, twenty miles wide. That was a long day's journey in our wagon."

"Then I'll do it in great joy—the best—the most—I can. Have you any name you'd like to suggest for the sanctuary?"

"Yes, I have. The Park of the Three Lions."

He nodded, and went out of the room. I opened and read the message. When Robert Moffat returned, in about five minutes, I was again standing by the window, looking out at the golden grass and the green and distant hills. It was as though for the last time.

"Edward, I look into your face, and it comes to me you'll never see the Park of the Three Lions," he said, when I turned to him.

"I doubt if I ever will," I answered. "The wheel of my Fate has turned, and I'm going back to America. But many others will see it. And sometimes—in the moonlight—there may be a rider who'll see it without being seen; at least my heart tells me so. And this much I know. Wherever she is, she'll be glad."

BOOK SIX

CHAPTER XIX

The Challenge

AFTER ONE day's trek from Bulawayo, making generally southeast, we pitched beside a rippling donga in highlands thronged with game. "We will feast tonight," I told my two companions, so I went forth on horseback with the rifle, and soon returned with a fat gazelle. Hagar dressed the meat, roasting some on spits, baking marrow bones in the ashes, and saving the white fat for a relish, but there was business to be done before we could fall to.

When the coals were red I brought forth the paper given me by Robert Moffat, and, first in English, then in Afrikaans, read its writing aloud.

Edward Stono
South Africa

> My son, Mate Hudson, has been killed in a boating accident while alone at sea with Clay Hudson. You are the only survivor among my husband's sons who I think might help me in my great need. I call upon you, Edward, and if it is possible for you to answer, pray do so.
>
> Mildred (Mrs. Mason) Hudson

"Does this mean that you wish to return at once to America?" N'kulu asked, after a thoughtful pause.

"It is my purpose to return as quickly as possible, and I wish to know if you both will go there with me."

"What would we do there, bukra? Always we have known one another's minds, and it has caused us three to move together like oxen long inspanned. It would be of benefit if you would tell us who is Mate Hudson, and who is Mildred Hudson."

I explained my relationship with Mate, even to his marrying the maiden to whom I paid court. Still I could not wholly explain Mildred Hudson's calling on me in this affair. "Indeed, I did not know until I read this paper that she knew I was her husband's son. Now I know that she knew all the time."

"It is the way of women to know all the time," Hagar said simply.

"But now that she has called upon me, I find I am not surprised, and instead my heart is warmed and stirred."

Then Hagar rose from her squatting position and spoke with a rush of words.

"The old days are gone, bukra, and if you will give me leave, tomorrow I will begin a journey to my own place."

"You are free to go, riding your horse, with a share of the drying meat," I answered. "But where is your own place, Hagar? Surely not to the farm of Jan Du Piel."

"I will not go there. I go to a kraal in Bechuanaland, not far from Kuruman. It is a long way, but what do I care for that? My father dwells there, still the best spearman in his clan, and there are many young warriors who would vie with one another to buy me, to take to wife."

"I will be sorry to have you go."

"Aye, but it's best, for then you will no longer try to keep M'sabu alive in me."

"I did not know of it, but M'sabu seems nearer to me when you are near."

"It is a cheat on the eyeballs, bukra, such as came to us on the desert. M'sabu has gone. She has crossed the River, and may return to you only in dreams. You need not deny her that. Dream of her as your heart longs to do but only at night, when the stars shine, and you lie asleep. Think of her sometimes in the daylight hours, but do not let those thoughts come between you and living. I tell you she is gone, and you must make your life without her, as I will do. In the way of nature your time to die is a long way off. Meanwhile there are many years in which you must breathe, labor, weep, rejoice, journey, and, if my heart speaks truth, love woman. We both loved M'sabu beyond all telling—you because of a great loneliness and loss—I because she smiled at me, and I combed her yellow hair. Ask no other reason. There may be others, but I needed no more than these. But she has gone away, never to return. Let the strong life surge through your veins again. Seek great goals. Be true to your own—for you are not left alone; no human being need ever be alone. M'sabu loved you, so do as she would have you do."

"What is that, black woman of the veld?"

"Live, O white man from across the sea. Live with all your might and main."

"It may be you are a witch."

"No, I'm only a woman, who loves you for M'sabu's sake."

She touched her forehead and her heart—oddly enough a Mohammedan salutation—then, turning away, she stood where the firelight met the dark—where the high flame revealed her shape and the glossy bronze of her skin, and where, when it sank, the dark rushed in and covered her. It was highly dramatic sign language of farewell. She had told me goodbye; the rest would be aftermath.

"N'kulu!"

The Zulu leaped to his feet. "Bukra!"

"I go across the sea to my own place. Is it your desire to remain here, either as a painted and plumed warrior of your clan, or maybe as the gunbearer to such a one as Heer Piet, or do you desire to join once more with the maroons on the green island, or can it be your wish to follow me still?"

"Bukra, I have seen the sun return twenty and ten years," he answered, after a moment's thought. "Wearing paint and ostrich feathers does not count with me as much as it did when I was half that age. Also, I have fought in better wars than those waged against a neighbor clan for women and cattle. As for finding and following such a one as Heer Piet, I have told you, bukra, of him being half-mad, and so it was great joy to follow him, for I never knew what he would do next; besides that, he was a mighty hunter, and it seemed to me that the grass bowed down for a mile's width when he walked across it, as though from a strong wind. I could search all Africa, and not find another like Heer Piet. As for the maroons, when they run with the dons' slaves in the forest, it is good sport, and my blood sings in my veins, but mostly they stay in one place and plant beans and maize and melons, and that is not a fit life for a Zulu. What does that leave, lord, but that I should follow you?"

"Is it your desire? Is the profit good enough? You are a man, so speak plain."

"By your leave, bukra, I will ask a question. Do you expect to become a rich bukra?"

"I am rich already, by one way of thinking. That is, I have enough, and more than enough, for my next trek and the business it entails. You know that my weight of ivory came to almost half again as much as the sum which I had bonded myself to give the great Moffat, and did give him. With this remainder, I expect to sail to America in the style of a Charleston aristocrat, and take you with me if you care to go, and live in that style while I pursue the undertaking for which I am called home. Thereafter, we shall see."

"Still, you are not rich in the sense of the great planters of Cuba, or even of some of the Voortrekkers, with their farms no pony can cross in a single day, and countless cattle and sheep."

"No, I reckon I'm not."

"Bukra, I doubt if you will ever be. Always you will outspan, only to inspan again. There is ever another mountain you must cross, and another river whose gravel you foolishly wash. There are no diamonds in Africa—Heer Piet found them all—yet you do not believe it even now."

"If I did not have to go home, I would prove your words are wind."

"You will go from one hazard to another. I think it very possible you will die young, not live to ripe old age as did Heer Piet."

"Hazard is unavoidable for a gambler. Indeed it is only another name for gambling."

"Yet if it were not so, I would not follow you again across the great, rolling ocean. You have fed me well, you have shown me many strange sights, you have brought me into danger and forth again, wherein my heart beat like a war drum, and finally you have never treated me else than as a man, a brother with a black skin, and for that, bukra, it is my desire to follow you— no little weak and doubtful desire, but a great desire, filling all my body and soul, speaking forth in my dreams at night. I do not know what life is, but thereby I may live, not a weak life, but one red and fierce and crackling as a grass fire, before which even the lion runs away in fear. Ho! ho! ho!"

With this wild laugh, his head thrown back, and baying at the stars, N'kulu came into my service for as long—so our souls confided—as we both would live.

2

During the journey to America, N'kulu and I reversed a position we had taken on the out-trip. Instead of his teaching me a language, I taught him one. It was not one found in any book, but spoken with great gusto, and I thought charm, by the Negroes of the Low Country, and we called it Gullah. Of course it was not the real Gullah spoken by a people of that name in West Africa; but an incredibly bastardized English. Nevertheless our plantation Negroes made themselves perfectly understood to us and to one another; I had often been homesick for it among alien tongues of Africa; mellow and quaint-sounding, I liked the sound of it.

I had no large purpose in imparting it to my follower. He would have picked it up himself on the Carolina shore, when neither his African lingua franca nor the harsh Afrikander proved any longer useful. However, he would be saved a period of homesickness and a certain amount of loneliness if he could establish immediate understanding with our Low Country Negroes, and his usefulness to me would be increased. He picked up the dialect with astonishing ease. Evidently Gullah lent itself readily to the Negro lips and tongue. Instead of being a trial, being instructor to him made some otherwise long-drawn hours pass pleasantly every day.

Our trig schooner landed us at Baltimore, from where we made our way by coaster to the city of my birth and of my countless dreams. I thought it would be changed. I had been gone so long and so far. Instead, it was my dream come true, forgotten designs taking their places in the tapestry—the busy docks, the Negro stevedores with their chanted Gullah, busy merchants not quite aristocrats but making their dollars felt, small parties of the elect in satin and broadcloth, talking with gaiety but walking in grandeur as they visited the big passenger boats, the varied mingled smells of wet cypress, barnacles, fish, dusty burlap, balsam, and attar of roses; the great folk walking in the Battery, the houses opening on hidden gardens, their fronts locked against the street. The city was more populous than when I left, I thought, busier, and richer. But in the air was a contagion of anxiety, changing all the faces, that I could not explain.

There was no time to loaf, to pick and choose among old threads, to luxuriate in getting home. More than a year had passed since Mildred Hudson had penned her letter to me; this was the breaking spring of the year 1859, and I fell barely short of being twenty-eight years old. So N'lulu had hardly unpacked my bags—I still could not recover from the wonder of

a Zulu warrior happily performing the tasks of a trained valet—
when I sat down, dipped pen, and wrote:

Dear Mrs. Hudson:

     I am sorry it has taken me so long to reply to your mes-
sage, but only just now, after many inevitable delays, have I
gained my home shores. If even yet there is any service I might
do you, I beg that you call on me.

Your obedient servant,
Edward Stono

I went downstairs in search of Julius, a sort of major-domo
around the hotel, a breathing gazette of the births, deaths, be-
trothals, marriages, and larger happenings of the Charleston
aristocracy. The large, impressive-looking Negro, with a dignified countenance and popping bespectacled eyes, had changed
not a whit since I had seen him last.

"Is Mistress Mason Hudson at present in the city?" I asked.

"Dar ain't no place else for her to go, no mo'."

"Where is she living?"

"De big house, frontin' de sea wall, was took over by Mas'
Clay Hudson, when he come back from—where it was he been.
'At was mo' an' t'ree year ago. Since then he done took over
de plantation, Hudson Barony. So Mistress Hudson, she gone
to live wif her daughter-in-law at a house on Queen Street."

Julius promised to deliver my note to Mistress Mildred Hudson at once, and he returned with an answer within the hour.
If I were not pressed for time, would I please call at four in
the afternoon?

I dressed carefully as was my wont. A hired hack took me to
an unpretentious house, as far from a shack as from a mansion,
which eased my worst fears for the well-being of my father, his
wife, and niece-by-marriage; and my hopes climbed a little
more at the signs of the effort made to restore a long-neglected
garden. Of course Mildred Hudson would grow flowers. She
was in some kind of spiritual communion with them that no
priest—only a woman—could understand. An old black woman,

quaintly but tidily dressed, opened the door to me. I wondered what had happened to Nicodemus, who had admitted me to the great hall of Hudson Barony. The family would neither sell him nor turn him out, so it stood to reason that he had died. Why was it that the death of the Negro I hardly knew haunted my imagination more than the death of a white man I hardly knew? Perhaps the former had not had as good a chance in life. Usually he had not been in as good a position to fight back in the days before all fighting summarily ceased.

I noticed the delicate and beautiful furniture, warmly glowing in the late afternoon light. Already there was a good market for such pieces among newly rich Yankees; thank God they had not got their hands on the Hudsons' intimate things, relics of a bygone glory. Let them bustle about their great cities, Boston, New York, and Philadelphia. I would not trade the Battery for the whole lot. I would see them all burned to the ground rather than Middleton Place alone!

When Mistress Hudson entered the room, walking with that proud but graceful step fixed in the bodies of the older women of her generation, I thought she had borne up remarkably well under the loss of her son. At my first glance at her, I found her very little changed from when I had seen her last. Then I noticed that her eyes had faded a great deal in color and brilliance. There was a tension of unremitting grief about her lips.

"I thank you for coming, Mr. Stono," she said.

"I am proud that you sent for me."

"I won't call you Mr. Stono. I'll call you Edward. I am sorry I have not received you heretofore. Will you sit down?"

"Thank you."

"The idea of calling on you was put in my mind by Mate himself, only a few months before he was killed. Then I was troubled only about a business matter. Mate said that if you were here, you would help me. He said you helped him in a serious matter in Augusta."

"What I did for him there, I did mainly at Salley's request.

The fact remained that I owed him an obligation of which she told me."

"I know what it was. It concerned his championing you when I—had—rebuffed you. Now you may think I'm a poor one to ask further help."

"No, it is a very welcome indication of an attitude toward me more cordial—at least less distant—than I could hope for."

"Sometimes right comes out of wrong—I don't know how or why. And, if you please, I'll say no more in that connection."

"Just as you please. May I inquire for Salley and Mr. Mason Hudson?"

"You may inquire for Salley—" Her voice broke strangely.

"What is it, if you please?"

"She will greet you in a few minutes. But plainly you haven't heard—"

"Is your husband living?"

"No, my husband—your father—is dead."

Her eyes filled with tears, mine as though with shadows from another world. I did not know what they were, or from whence they had come, or what was their meaning. I was reminded that I had never had a father, in the usual meaning of that word—the dear, close relationship, the deeply human bond. But the existence of a worthy sire had helped to give place, order, and meaning to my life. I was what Texans call a maverick, neither church nor law having made any provision for my existence; I had half a family, not a whole one; instead of paternal memories as men sometimes have to lean on, I had had lies. Thereby, somehow I had become a gambler, perhaps the reason being I had less to prize than most men, less to lose. But I had been a good gambler. Sometimes I had gamed for someone besides myself.

And I could not yet lay down the deck. This was the clear confiding of my soul, the insistence of my inmost instincts, useless to deny. I would not have been called here, if my prowess had not been needed. There was one more game to play.

"I can hardly believe he's gone," I said at last. "The last time I saw him, he seemed so well—"

"He died of a heart attack only six weeks after we lost Mate."

I waited, and then asked, "Was there latent heart disease?"

"Of course there might have been, but he had never given the least sign of it, and the doctor thought not. In truth, he began to fail almost at the moment the news was brought."

"I wish I dared ask one question. But you said—"

"Ask any question you wish. Whatever it costs is a trifle compared to the cost of what I—we—may ask of you."

"Did my father regret that he had given me birth?"

"I'll answer that the best I can. For the first few years he was greatly worried about it—both for your mother's sake and yours, and in fear he would be found out. I knew it even then, but I didn't relieve his fears as I should have done—I was too bitter. Some bitterness was human and inevitable, but I didn't give enough thought to his love for me—the reality of it—the long and endless proof of it—or remember that we are all flesh and blood with only a leaven of spirit. Later, when he began to give you books, he took an interest in you that was closely akin to pride. And when Salley told him how you had saved Mate, there came a glint in his eyes I'll never forget."

"All that time you knew—and never told him so."

"I couldn't tell him until almost the end."

"I told him something once. I'm glad I did. We both paid a price. But perhaps human life, once given, is beyond price."

"I think it is. And that makes me remember—with a greatly troubled spirit—what Lord Brougham said. But it's not the time for that."

I was fairly certain to what famous utterance she referred, but could not deal with it now.

"Have you forgiven my father—and me?" I asked.

"Could I have called you if I had not? No, I would have called you just the same, so great is our need. But the answer to your question is yes."

"Is there anything more you want to tell me—now?"

"Very little more. Salley will tell you the main part; she can do it better than I. She has felt close to you for many years. She'll call on you as her husband's brother and my son. And I ask that you keep in mind one terrible truth. I told you of my husband's swift collapse after the news of Mate's death. So know and remember this. If your brother Mate did not die by accident—if instead he was done to death—it's the same with your father. I ask that you help us if you can."

She spoke slowly and calmly. At the end she rose and pulled a bell cord. After a dim and distant chime, the old Negress returned to the room.

"Please tell Miss Salley that Mr. Edward is here," Mistress Hudson directed, this wording what I might have dreamed of hearing long ago. Then to me, "Sir, I beg you to excuse me."

Mistress Hudson went out, and a moment later Salley stood again in my plain sight. I did not expect to see her look so young.

In respect to the still-early season, her own dark coloring, and perhaps to the recent close of her period of mourning, she wore a dress of black velvet, simply fashioned, with a bertha of ancient ivory-colored lace. Again I perceived, almost with a sense of shock, the elegance of her black hair, the moving brilliance of her brown eyes, and the impassioning dusk of her skin. Her lips were dark red. I knew secrets of their beauty—they had been imparted to me one night while the moon set. She was light-limbed and free-moving—in that she made me think of Trudi, riding an unimaginably distant veld. She held her head a little back, which emphasized the molding of her facial bones, the effect of which was at once primitive and aristocratic. She smiled strangely into my face.

"Salley, you look almost—not quite—the same."

"Edward, you look almost—not quite—like a different person."

"Can we go outside? The late sunlight will become you well. Most of our meetings have been outside."

"All except one." I wondered by what compulsion she had

reminded me of both our brief victory and long defeat. I saw again the moon toppling westward. "You're my mate, but he's my Mate," she had told me, wishing it did not sound so clever. Since then I had seen the sea of waters and the sea of grass.

She led the way not to the half-restored garden in the front yard but to a walled area, which early settlers had called a "close," behind the house. No spade had been turned there lately, brambles grew wild, but there was a marble bench, fit for a show place, and out of keeping with this modest house. The latter struck me now as being very old. I had not noticed at first its antique roof and sturdy design. Quite possibly it was the residence of a well-off Charles Town burgher, in days before mansions of the Gadsdens, the Rutledges, the Laurens, and the Ravenals rose in glory. I thought it had stood here when the fleets of the Spanish and French attacked in 1706.

"I have so much to ask," she said, "and nothing to give."

"Don't you think that feeling like a gentleman would still appeal to me?"

"I doubt if it counts with you any more. Maybe it's too old a story—maybe the dream is over. The fact remains that you are Mason Hudson's son, Mate Hudson's brother. So are Clay and Arnold Hudson, but Clay is a renegade as far as the Hudsons are concerned, although he's loyal enough to the Ashleys —and Arnold has had no use for us since the money gave out."

"How about the venture in Alabama? Did it fail?"

"No. Last year it did quite well. Our heads are above water."

"You might start at the first."

"Then I'll begin by refreshing your memory as to Clay's antecedents. I told you once, but maybe you've forgotten. His mother, Uncle Mason's first wife, and my father, were brother and sister. Their father was a Sass, but their mother was an Ashley, descended from a black-sheep cousin of the Lord Proprietor for whom the river was named. Clay looks back to him. According to legend, he is very like him. I saw a portrait of him once—and the two great aristocrats could be twin brothers."

"Did your father look like him too?"

"Not at all. He was tall and red like most of the other Sasses. He had enough of the Ashley to be bad, but never evil; it has come to me lately there's quite a difference between the two terms."

"Was your father's sister—Clay's mother—one or the other?"

"She was one or the other—and I think I know which."

"You can tell me the story now."

"It's rather simple. Clay has a very fine fast boat. It's catboat-rigged—so he can sail it alone—but it has the lines and deep keel of a cutter. People say it can outsail even the provost boats, but I doubt it. I don't know all the uses he makes of it, but one of them is fishing. And he persuaded Mate—against my will and protest—to go fishing with him."

She paused, and a very strange glint came upon her eyes.

"Well?"

"She came back with a big cobia, and Mate's dead body."

"He'd been drowned?"

"I'll tell you what Clay said. He was very calm about it—very polite—exceedingly distressed, but quite himself, Clay Hudson, a far-removed nephew of Lord Ashley. He had let Mate fish downwind in a tide rip off the Isle of Palms, holding her up by a line fastening the boom to the taffrail. In a hard gust of wind, the line broke, the boom swung around like a club in a giant's hand and struck Mate in the neck. He went overboard and Clay said he must have swallowed water, for when Clay dived in and got him aboard Mate was dead."

"Were they fishing from an anchorage, or drifting?"

"They were drifting, but Clay said he heaved his anchor the second the accident occurred, then went overboard and swam. He's a very good swimmer. I remember that from his child-hood, when he came to visit us—his uncle, but especially me. However, he had to swim back against the tide and it took a little time and when he got Mate aboard and tried to revive him, it was no use."

I sat and thought awhile.

"What kind of a line was it?"

"I know about that, because he brought it for Uncle Mason to see. It was a weak line. It was frayed in several places. Clay had bought a new one, but they saw the cobia in the rip, and in their fever to make a catch they used the old one."

"How did the fish happen to be aboard? One they had caught before the accident?"

"No. Clay said it was the very one. Mate was using one of Clay's fine lemonwood rods, with a big reel and very strong line. When he went overboard it got stuck under the taffrail. The fish was still on when Clay raised his anchor to sail home, and he hauled it in."

"The story seems to hang together very well."

"Perfectly."

"Yet you doubt it. Do you care to tell me why?"

"I care to answer any questions you ask. Good God, that's the least I can do. In the first place, it isn't like Clay to use a weak line. He always takes very good care of his own skin—and if it broke he might be the one to get belted overboard, with the boat drifting out of his reach. It might even bash his head in or break his neck, risks which my cousin Clay would miss a dozen cobias rather than run."

"What other use did he have for the boat?"

"I don't know."

I could make a guess in this instance, I thought. Still it would not sound very probable, and I kept it to myself.

"Is Clay rich?"

"The report is that he has money coming in from Panama, from large estates. It didn't take much to buy our equity in the house and the plantation; since then he's been paying on them regularly and liberally. I suppose the report is true. He lives very well, without visible means of support."

I had heard him say that none of his family had ever been known to save a dollar, so my suspicions of him having invisible means of support was strengthened. Could Mate have found out what those means were? Somehow I did not believe that this alone could impel Clay Hudson to the risks of murder. The crime—if there was one—was even blacker than that.

"What do you want of me, Salley?" I asked. "I think I know, but my mind would work better if you told me in plain words."

"When I speak for myself, I speak for Aunt Mildred too. I was Mate's wife and she's his mother and the wife of Uncle Mason, who proved to be one of the victims. I want to know the truth. That comes first. Even if it won't do any good to find it out, I still want to know it. Anyway, it will do good. If the story is true—if, just once, Clay Hudson is innocent—something very like a curse, more like an evil spell laid by conjure, will be lifted off my soul. If you can prove he's guilty, I want him hanged. A descendant of the Ashleys hung by the neck—and, believe me, our courts will do it. Mate was greatly loved. Not only our friends, the people we grew up with, but all the people he ever smiled at mourned his death. Edward, can you handle a pistol well?"

I too had received and would never forget Mate's smile, so I answered quickly, "Yes, I can shoot fast and quite true."

"Then if you become convinced of his guilt—and still can't find evidence that would stand in court—I want you to challenge Clay Hudson to a duel and shoot him dead."

"I thought you meant, whether I could defend myself. I couldn't act on any opinion not demonstrable to a court."

Her gaze met mine in deep and latent antagonism. "Whatever your terms are, we'll meet them."

"I have no terms. I'll do what I can. I'm a natural son of Mason Hudson. I believed for a long time that set me free—mistaking the law's and the church's irresponsibility for me, for an irresponsibility on my part to all and everything. It's not so. Since time out of mind bastards have pondered their status, out of which arise their freedoms and their bondage, and Edmund cried, 'Thou, Nature, art my goddess.' But he was no more right than I was. Not having a father to come to, a brother to share with, has wrought deeply and strangely upon my soul. I am intensely lonely and have always been. I leap to any son-ship or brotherliness that comes my way. This is badly put because I can't think it through—I can only say what comes to my lips. Besides all that, I have a duty toward Clay Hudson. If he is what I think, I must see to him. If he deserves it, I must dispose of him."

She was so astonished she could not speak. At last she laid her hand lightly on my arm.

"Edward, do you know Clay Hudson?"

"Yes, I know him well."

"From what you know, do you believe he could murder his half-brother Mate?"

"I'll give you his own words. 'Cain killed Abel, and they were full brothers.' "

"Do you think it's the same story?"

"In a measure the same, but I want evidence of that. Mason Hudson loved Mate. Did he ever love Clay?"

"No. No one could, except his wicked mother."

"He was the strong son, and Mate the weak."

"Mate developed a good deal of strength, after I had married him. He was largely responsible for what success we've had in the black belt of Alabama."

"Clay was the firstborn."

"And the highest born. Don't forget that, because it's immensely important. There was never a nobler strain of blood in all the Low Country—using noble in the sense it is used in feudalistic societies—as this branch of the great house of Ashley, the evil branch. Clay was only a boy when my Aunt Eva died, but he always bitterly resented Uncle Mason marrying and having other children to share his estates. He thought Aunt Mildred's children were interlopers. Probably he didn't care about you because you were outside the pale—"

"I think he did care."

"I tell you again—maybe you don't need telling—that he's not just a bad man, as my father was. He's an evil man, his life dedicated to evil; his heart is malignant. I found that out when I was very young."

"Still there has to be an overt motive, if a jury is to believe he murdered his half-brother."

"There is one."

She spoke quietly and with great dignity.

"I ask you what it was?"

She breathed deeply, and said, "Me."

CHAPTER XX

Sea Meeting

SALLEY DID NOT have to say more. I looked at her, and the vision came to me of Clay Hudson, coveting her from his childhood years; the covetousness enduring and growing and overriding all his lesser lusts, clear to his present early middle age. It did not follow that he believed that by wiping away Mate he could get her for his own. Evil does not always move for a direct reward, only for evil's sake.

As I was thinking this, a look came into Salley's face, touched with both trouble and triumph.

"Do you remember, Edward, before you promised to try to get Mate out of Memphis' and Clara's toils, you asked me where the money you would need was going to come from?"

"I do remember."

"You haven't asked me that today. That, and your clothes—although those have always been good—and your bringing back a servant from Africa indicate it isn't a problem in this case."

"I made no big stake but I have enough."

"I want to tell you something. Before Uncle Mason died, he talked with me about you. The Alabama cotton lands were doing better, and he had a little money that he thought Aunt

Mildred and I could spare. He asked how you would rather be remembered in his will, with a few hundred dollars, his sapphire seal ring, or your choice, up to two hundred volumes, of his books. I ruled out the money. The sapphire is a beauty, as you know, very deep blue, but I didn't think you'd want to wear the Mason arms."

"Not without the bar sinister," I said, grinning. "I hope you picked the books."

"I did. And he made another provision for you, the best of all. He arranged for Judge Lucas to take you into his office to read law. He said you told him you wanted to study law."

"I had a smattering of it in my late boyhood, but I wouldn't have thought he remembered."

Reading law would make a good screen for me as I pursued another inquiry. It must be I was a vengeful man, for I looked forward to it with joy.

2

My joy was an unreasonable joy. It is the kind that gamblers know when the game is going strangely, and the air does not taste like common air, and the shadows do not look and jump like common lacks of light, and the cards stick to a man's fingers as though they were alive, and combinations far beyond mathematical probability may come to pass at any second. I was thrilled through that my half-brother Clay had become my opponent in play not of his choosing. I meant him to remember all he said to me as I had sat in bonds in the barracoon at Puerto Miramar while he had presided in grandeur; and although the odds were top-heavy on his side—any player who had ever figured a percentage could tell that at a glance—still I loved the challenge of taking them on, cutting them down with every wit I possessed and perhaps, ere the cards fell and turned cold on the table, winning.

I might find my way to an old millhouse on an Ogeechee branch and talk to Faro Jack. I might go down to Augusta, and enlist, by such means as I could, the expert services of Clara Day. Meanwhile I honed my wits on a couple of hard facts. They were, to wit, as the saying goes, that if Clay had committed murder, which my soul, sensitized and more of a friend to me than before I took off for Africa, never doubted, why then it was a highly expert job, one to rejoice his strange, solitary, and flagitious soul, and it could never be brought home to him except by the testimony of eyewitnesses, or by a fatal mistake made by Clay himself.

He had got over the fear of having been seen and had probably never doubted the perfection of his play. This was my best card against the appalling high cards that time itself, so rarely the friend of justice, or often its enemy, had dealt him. A year had passed since Clay had sailed into port with his strange cargo, a fine cobia, not as pretty and bright-colored as when first hauled out of the sea, and a man's body with a white face and still-drenched clothes. The thought of that time having passed, every hour adding to Clay's safety and raising his conceit, and an hour added to those hours every time the town clock struck, gave me a fever. So I was hardly ensconced in Judge Lucas' offices, a cubbyhole to myself, a few books scattered about, and the right to witness unimportant documents that did not require the Judge's affidavit, when I sent a message to Salley to visit me in haste.

The day lay dark without being dismal, its clouds lowering but faintly luminous along their seams and joinings, and a light cool April rain lending a wonderful *esprit* to the spring foliage. The greenest livery on the street was the oilskin hood, jacket, and skirt that Salley wore, whereby she walked swinging through the shower while most of the ladies must simper along under parasols. It was not a new style from Paris but a very old one from Colonial days—when Charleston women were even more dashing than now—that she had revived. When she took it off, underneath was a dress of deep green almost the shade of a certain grass called Charleston.

"I want the names of those I can trust and those I must distrust," I told her, when all the doors were closed.

"Jeff Legare," she answered quickly. "He danced with Clara Day—remember?—the night you and she came uninvited to my party. Jeff was almost Mate's only friend. He's shy and awkward, and inept, but absolutely true. He'd run any risk—commit almost any crime—that you ask in Mate's name."

"Who else?"

"You can trust Judge Lucas and almost all of Uncle Mason's old friends, but always ask me before you confide in any of them."

"What about Arnold Hudson?"

"Arnold dropped all pretense of loyalty to the family when we lost our money."

"Butler Mims used to be rather close to Mate."

"I don't think he ever was. He made up to Mate, but he was much closer to Arnold. Now he's closer to Clay than anyone else in Charleston. He might even know the truth of the murder—I'll call it murder, because I feel—I know in my heart—that's what it was. He'll carry any story to Clay that you want to plant. But on second thought—a story got out that you beat him unmercifully at Bailey's livery stable when he was going to horsewhip you for coming—and bringing Clara—to my party. The whole town chuckled over it. He's not a popular character. But if the report is true, he won't be any use to you."

"The story is exaggerated. However, I'm glad he's useless to me. I don't want any truck with him."

"He's nothing, anyway."

She wiped her mouth with her handkerchief and I got the idea that Butler had paid her unwelcome attentions since Mate's death. Maybe he had been trying to serve as an emissary for Clay.

"Now this is just a chance, but by no means impossible—in fact, fairly likely," I went on. "On the Isle of Palms live a good many slaves belonging to the plantation and quite a few free Negroes. The latter are given to fishing in the pass between that island and Dewees Island. They and the other colored watch the comings and goings and doings of the bukras, and what they see they often keep to themselves. It's quite possible that someone on the northern shore, looking out at the tide rip that often forms in the pass, might have seen what happened."

"If so, I can find out," Salley answered with a sudden, dark flush.

"Good for you."

"The minister of the African Methodist Church, Preacher Jessup, used to be one of our slaves. He hasn't heard anything yet, or he would have told us. He may uncover something by careful questioning. The trouble is—well, I can't tell you what it is—but all the slaves of the Low Country seem to have become closed-mouthed lately—lots of my friends have said so— and the free Negroes seem frightened out of their wits."

I felt a tingle throughout my nerves as when a high card falls. It had come to pass that in choosing gambling as a livelihood and means of advancement I had wedded adventure. It was very like marriage; my life was interbound with it; it came to meet me everywhere and would not let me go.

It must be it had changed my soul as a wife changes her husband's soul. I had embraced adventure when I had been denied access to Salley's company, as some sort of substitute, but in a sense I ate my cake and had it too, for she sat with me now in a small, dusty office, dressed as usual with due respect to her own beauty but to charm me the while, and her eyes shone at everything I said and did, and she was giving me intense attention. The great lady who had rebuffed me from attendance at a beach party twelve years ago had implored my aid and presence far beyond the beaches and the sea that beat them. In Cuba I had heard of a slave dealer whom I suspected was my exiled half-brother, Clay Hudson; but no outside force or even concatenation of circumstances had made me seek him out and become so deeply involved with him that one of us might reasonably kill the other before we were done.

In one sense—at least it seemed to me I had had free will—I could have left him out of the gaudy pattern that made up my life. But as a gambler, I had sought him out, challenged him for such satisfactions as he could give my body and soul, narrowly missed destruction at his hands, and now yearned to give him the full dose of his own medicine.

What in God's name could I expect from life, when I kept on making bets for all my goods? With the winnings from the greatest game I had played until then, I had gone to Africa seeking more of the same, instead of buying a neat business, or lodging myself in an office. There I had found Trudi. Any man of pride would have taken a strong stand against that cruel, child-beating fanatic, Jan Du Piel, but only an inveterate runner of risks, a wooer of Fortune, would have taken her away. Then all the luck that a gambler could dream of was poured into my hands—until it ended.

Once more I was involved with Salley and with Clay Hudson. It was no wonder to me that he coveted her; he was enough like me that this was inevitable, once the two came into juxtaposition. It was in his nature to kill Mate; I could have guessed that four years ago, and in that way—more than our wanting the same woman—he had become my great antagonist. By nature I must strive with those who thought themselves gods, and with empty giants who thought themselves godlings, such as Butler Mims. When the glory of having Trudi became less like a lost existence and more like a blissful dream of a bygone night, when Time had healed the proud flesh of my wound, I would again seek Salley's hand in marriage. There is no bridge across the River except remembrance. And I myself, without being other than myself, the bastard son of Marie Aubry, might yet win for myself a daughter of the Sasses and the Ashleys, kin of the Ravenals and the Hudsons, a woman of great beauty and grace and passion, and then as Faro Jack had gone to the Oconee to gamble with bass and bream, I would take my bride to the black belt in Alabama, and play at hazard with drouth and flood and hail and Yankee traders—and perhaps farther than that, and more exciting games!

Just now all the antagonism to my winning, the total enmity, was centered in one man. He was my half-brother. One of us was the Nemesis of the other. I wondered which.

"Salley, have you heard of any slaves coming into the Low Country lately who couldn't speak English?" I asked.

Her eyes widened slightly. "Oddly enough, I have. Cordelia Laurens mentioned that an uncle of hers, who has a plantation near Georgetown, bought a batch of twenty from a rascally trader who claimed to be from Florida."

"What language did they speak? Did she think it was an African tongue?"

"No, they spoke a bastard Spanish."

"Didn't she wonder where they came from?"

"The trader said they came off some tobacco lands developed by Spaniards somewhere near Tampa."

"Have you heard of any other instances? Think hard."

"Jeff Legare said that a Yankee who has drained and cleared an enormous plantation on the Savannah below Augusta had two hundred Portuguese-speaking hands. As a matter of fact"— her hands dropped in her lap—"such people have been showing up all through this part of the South for the last two years. What does it mean, Edward?"

"There's been a heavy importation of contraband."

"Where did it come from?"

"From various countries and islands where Negroes, worth a thousand dollars here, can be bought for a hundred dollars or got for nothing."

"Not Africa."

"No. That's risky. From this side of the water."

"Is that where Clay's money's coming from?"

"I think so."

"He uses his boat to meet the slaver captains?"

"Probably."

"Is that why he killed Mate?"

"I doubt if it had anything to do with it. But that's what our Negroes know that they won't tell. That's why the free Negroes are so frightened."

She paused a moment, then spoke with a twisted mouth.

"What did you mean when you said some of them might have been got for nothing? Did you mean free Negroes that had been kidnaped?"

"Yes, that's an old trick of your cousin Clay's—to deal in them."

"That's as bad as some of the lies Mrs. Stowe told in *Uncle Tom's Cabin*."

"I haven't read it, and I never will. But I'm going fishing, too."

3

I chose the first clear warm day that wind and tide were favorable to fishing. To maintain his reputation as an enthusiastic fisherman, Clay Hudson was almost certain to go today, and when I came to the yacht basin I saw that his trim catboat was absent from its mooring stake. N'kulu, not only speaking but dressing like any sportsman's handy man, took his place in the bow of a handy-rigged smack that a middle-aged free Negro, known as Solomon, kept for hire. I had a lunch basket, a flask, and excellent tackle borrowed from Judge Lucas.

"Where do you think we'd better go?" I asked Solomon.

"Boss, you willin' to pass dis whole tide, and half de flood of de next tide?"

"Yes."

" 'En wit 'is wind blowing whar she be, we can go most any grounds you please."

"Where do you reckon Mas' Clay Hudson went today? He always makes good catches."

Solomon's expression changed slightly and his tone fell. "I reckon he somewhere off de coas' of de Isle of Pam."

"Then let's try it there."

It was a long sail out of the harbor and around the headland;

and I had plenty of time to watch the water and the clouds, the wondrous play of light, the glimpses along the shore, and the sea birds that kept us haphazard company. There were terns and skimmers and oyster-catchers, superb aerialists all, somewhat vain if I were to judge bird conduct by human conduct, elegantly dressed and feeling themselves a cut or two above down-to-business fliers such as coots, cormorants, and pelicans. I saw great fishes leap clear of the waves and wondered at their lives so hidden from us, except for seconds of great glory when they broke through the barrier that confined them—their precincts of water and weeds and old wrecks and uncharted rocks—and looked out upon the world as strange and new as heaven would look to us. And there was nothing to stop the long flow of my thoughts, revisiting old scenes and events, as I wondered why I had done this or that, and if it had been inevitable, and how it would count for me or against me at long last.

Few acts that I could remember possessed as little logic as this excursion to meet Clay Hudson. Otherwise, I would have been certain to run across him in a few days in Charleston, perhaps under conditions where he would have tried to guard his speech and mannerisms, and thus a gambler might fare better with him and learn more. By today's action I was declaring war; would it not be the part of wisdom to try to take him by surprise? Perhaps I was doing only what my heart desired. That was to meet him in an open place, with no witnesses but N'kulu and a Negro fisherman, to startle him deeply, to make his thoughts fly, to intensify his consciousness of me until it could not leave him night or day, perhaps to kindle superstitions until they haunted his every moment, every thought.

Before long I made out his boat, gray-sailed, blue-hulled, hard to see against a green island or amid light and shadow. Solomon pretended he didn't see it. He gazed interestedly on another course.

"Gemman, there's some grounds down de wind from hee I'd like to try our luck," he told me.

"Hold her more into the wind. I see Mr. Hudson, and want to come up alongside and see how he's doing."

"Yessah!"

The long space of water slowly but steadily shortened. I soon saw that Clay was drift-fishing, for black jewfish or possibly bass. When we sailed up within a cable's length, it would have been sea etiquette for him to acknowledge our existence with a wave of his hand, but he did not, and continued to ignore our approach—the sign of a haughty or a rancorous man.

"Bring her up within ten fathoms," I ordered Solomon.

He looked at me half in dismay, half in open-eyed wonder, not lacking in respect.

"Yas, sah!"

He even beat it a little. When he heaved to, fastening his boom to the taffrail, we were no more than forty feet on the catboat's lee. Clay could not help but look at us now—any other conduct would be grotesque—so he and I had come face to face again. But now there were no ropes on my hands and feet. There were no walls or dim lamps or stifling heat. The cool breeze blew; away to the west the land dimmed by distance, to the north and south and east lay the luminous, illimitable spread of sea. In this game I could play my best. The sky was the limit.

Clay's boat was a saucy little craft, fine and yare, but I thought of its uses, and Solomon and N'kulu and I with our plain high-smelling smack were not put to shame. Moreover, we sailed almost as well. But I was in no way in a class with him when it came to appearance, and I marveled that a keen-eyed English ship's officer and Faro Jack had both spoken of a resemblance. His sensuous mouth was beautifully molded. His dark eyes, strikingly set, reminded me a little of Mate's, greatly of Salley's, but were more striking and magnetic than either. His nose had a high and noble hook, the Huguenot nose enhanced by long Norman lineage. Still, although he might be the greatest of Charleston aristocrats, he was not a natural human being. Again I felt it in my bones.

"Any luck, Clay?" I asked.

"May I ask by what qualifications you address me by my first name?" he answered, not stiffly, not witheringly, but in an impersonal tone, adequate to be heard clearly and no more above the smacking of the light waves against the hulls.

"I am Edward Stono, whom you acknowledged as your half-brother. Surely, with all that between us, I needn't stand on formality."

"The light was not good when I saw you last, but I recall you now."

"You meant to have a better look at me in the morning."

He did not reply.

"That appointment failed," I went on, "but we will have plenty of opportunities to view each other in the future."

"I can hardly believe it."

"I take more than a brotherly interest in you, Clay. There are several matters between us that need settling. My most immediate concern is the death of our brother Mate. Is this the scene?"

"Somewhat closer to the land."

"I trust you are now using a stouter line to secure the boom to the taffrail."

"The line is quite adequate, I believe."

He spoke with sudden cheer, almost jollity. He was not one to bluff; I knew that a wave of pleasure had swept through him at my intervention in the affair. I thought of a boast scrawled in the dirt with a stick, "I did it all alone." Although it hardly seemed possible, in one respect the lordly Clay Hudson could be compared to low-lived Harvey of Harvey's Hustlers, and that was vanity. The dazzling inkling came to me that I had hit upon my great antagonist's Achilles' heel.

I made the best answer that I could.

"You didn't tell me what luck you were having."

"Not one strike, as yet."

"It seems to me your luck is going to get worse. The clouds are lowering."

"You think so?"

"I believe you're out of luck. It's all done and over. Do you remember what you told me was waiting for me when the morning came, and it was light enough to see?"

"I remember quite well." He turned and looked me in the face, and his face went white, and in it was a torment of self-fury for the chance he had missed.

"When it's light enough for me to see—not tomorrow, but not many tomorrows away—what you promised me will be waiting for you."

"You amaze me! Now will you be kind enough to leave me to my sport?"

"It won't be from a tree in the forest. It will be another kind of tree, in the jail in Meeting Street—*Hasta la vista?*"

CHAPTER XXI

The Shawl

IN THE NEXT month my gains were trifling, while the truth drew farther, at its implacable unhurried gait, into the shadowy past.

I found out from Jeff Legare where Clay spent a remarkable number of his evenings. He was invited to very few of the social affairs of the old elite; and he declined the invitations of new-rich climbers, who wished to lend distinction to their parties by sounding his exalted name. When he did not sit alone, with a bottle and a book, he usually repaired to a particularly notorious tavern, called the Lighthouse, across the estuary. It was frequented by sodden sailors, small, sharp-toothed swamp rats, a kind of Low Country man known widely as white trash, and occasionally by harbor girls far down on their luck. The first three groups avoided his table, but occasionally one of the latter dared or was invited to sit with him. It did not surprise me that he got in no fights. A drunken roisterer would sooner tangle with a squad of provosts.

At the end of the month came a stunning blow delivered by a few lines of ink on the faintly scented page brought by a middle-aged Negress dressed in faded bombazine.

Dear Edward:—

Our old servant, Preacher Jessup, has kept his ears open and has even questioned an old conjure woman. He is positive that no one living on the Isle of Palms witnessed Mate's death; or if someone did so, the secret will be kept forever. What can we do now, old gambler? Only please don't give up.

Salley

There was something I could do. It was to pack my bag and take the train for Augusta and then catch a stage that let me off two miles from an old millpond branch of the Ogeechee. I hardly toyed with the hope of Faro Jack aiding and abetting me in any definite way, but I thought to see his rugged face and hear his voice and gather a little of his wisdom would lend force to Salley's appeal. I would have obeyed it anyway. Obey was a better word than grant, and answer, from my heart, was the best word of all.

By teachings and preachings I had now and then heard or read, Jack's sins should have overtaken him by now. Surely he was a sinner, having caught many a sucker and skinned many a shark. Instead, few painfully upright lives of pillars of the church had come to such mellow and peaceful autumns. His strapping brownskin girl still kept his cabin tidy, helped him work his garden and cornpatch, care for his pigs and poultry and clean his fish; she washed and mended his clothes; maybe too she ran his little still, but every Southern gentleman worthy of the name would let it go at that. The pond thronged with bass, bream, and catfish; trustful summer ducks darted down among the flooded cypress; po' joes and pond chickens and angelic white cranes lent charm to the scene.

The month was early May, spring was in full flush, ardent-hearted summer hung just around the corner, but a thunder shower brought down cold from the upper skies, so after supper we sat late by a chuckling fire. I told him of the main happenings since I had been away, so it came to pass that I spoke mostly of Trudi, and the wonder in my heart that she had caused, but the tale touched upon the great doctor from England whose face I would never forget, and of the black faces of Hagar, N'kulu, and the chief wizard of the Matshangana. Still I could not avoid speaking of Harvey, and, in the still midnight, of my brother Mate, and my brother Clay. Jack listened with burning eyes.

"I felt sure you would run into Clay Hudson again," the old gambler told me. "It was in the cards."

"Anyway, it happened."

"Have you read *King Lear?* I have, and understood 'most every word, and it's no wonder to me the tale has lived two hundred and fifty years. It's a tale to tear your heart out, and the worst of it is, it's true. I started to say that you and Clay are to each other like Edgar and Edmund, but the shoe's on the other foot, as far as bastardy goes. Edmund tried to kill Edgar, and brought about his father's death, then Edgar and he met. It was a meeting that had to be, and so is this meeting. If one of you don't win before then, the game will go on till the last card falls. It's a dreadful game, with death in the pot for one of you."

Faro Jack was gazing into the red coals, and his low tone held the darkness of prophecy.

"It began when you tried to set yourself up as a gentleman, your father's class instead of your mother's. It was a terrible undertaking, and you're not done with it yet. It was what made you set free your brother's kidnapped Negroes. That was the beginning of the great duel. His murder of Mate, the only one of your father's tribe who accepted you, made it like a marriage in Holy Church, the vows in force as long as you both live. It may be you'll be unable to bring him to justice for this killing. To tell you the bitter truth, I see little hope for it— the time's too long, and he's covered his tracks too well. But in spite of the defeat, and a black one, you can take grim comfort you're not done with him yet. Even if you'd like to quit, you can't. The reason is, he'll wait his chance and strike again. And even though the deck will be stacked against you, he'll have to deal you a hand somewhere, sometime, and then if Luck is with you, you may win."

"Jack, I hope—I feel—I'll win before then—before the summer's end."

"Edward, is it a hunch?"

"I think it is. At least, I'm going to make a great try. I believe I can find a pard."

"I wish it could be me."

"There's nothing you can do. But there may be something she can do—if she will."

"You don't mean Salley?"

"No, she can't go down into that jungle. She couldn't find her way. But Clara could. Where is Clara Day?"

"She's hardly sixty miles from here as the wild ducks fly."

"Savannah?"

"Yes, she went there when Memphis died—you wouldn't believe it, but that cold-hearted shark left her a thousand dollars. She's set up a couple of little rooms, where she deals faro, and has three or four tables for draw and stud and casino, with a percentage for the house. But, mark you, that sets her free. She's got everything to lose, and what would she have to gain? Have you got the right to ask her? Think good, for there are more angles to it than you know."

I did not know what Faro Jack meant by his last expression, but I remembered Mate dancing with her, and before then I recalled him standing in attendance on her, as she climbed a flight of stairs.

"Yes, I've got the right to ask, and she's got the right to accept or refuse."

"That settles it in my mind."

"There's one thing I'd like to settle in my mind. I either heard—or dreamed—or imagined something a long time ago, and it may be important to this case, and it may have concerned some other person than Clay Hudson. When I was a boy off Marsh Street, I knew a good deal I was not supposed to know. I believe I knew the reason that a young aristocrat, Mason

Hudson's son, had to leave Charleston. But if so, I can't recall it. It's on the tip of my memory, but I can't get hold of it. Jack, did you ever know?"

For a few seconds, Jack's face was a study. Then it turned oddly blank and he shook his head.

"I can't say that I ever did. Whatever it was, it's blown over and forgotten."

I could not escape the feeling that, for once in my life, Faro Jack had not given me a straight answer.

2

The Lucky Chance Casino, not far from Savannah's historic theater, was neither elegant nor gaudy and it smelled fresher than most gambling dens, perhaps because a good deal of soap and water was used in its care. When I came in, midway the evening, there was a scattering of rather well-dressed people, persuading me it had a smaller and better custom than the flashier joints nearer the waterfront. There was no play against the house except faro, the fairest game in the lexicon of gambling, the other players making up their own tables. Hence there was much less sharpery, stakes were inclined to be smaller, and the faces that I saw did not look as mirthless and strained.

I doubted if all these mitigations of the evils of gambling went to Clara's credit. By nature predatory, at war with the world, it was not likely she had undergone a change of heart. More likely she was cunning enough to make a smaller profit, longer. However, the modestly furnished and neatly kept rooms reflected her personality; I recalled that she was almost always ladylike. I wondered if she had changed. Deterioration was often rapid and severe in young women of her calling. I had not had a good look at her yet.

With a good deal of anxiety I moved so I could gaze between two bulky people playing faro; and at once my heart warmed. Time had been kind to her; or else the extreme prettiness I had always seen had the durable qualities of beauty. As a little girl she had fought for half a hoecake and she fought with hidden savagery for food and roof and pretty, soft dresses and a few pieces of jewelry and hardest of all for the freedom that was her light and boast; but the scars of battle were not on her. Her large, dark eyes had never acquired a feline glitter. Her mouth looked soft and wistful. Oddly I remembered her going to sleep on my shoulder, on the cold ride back from the ball at Hudson Barony.

Her gaze flitted across mine. Her expression changed only slightly and unreadably; her hand paused briefly, then went on with the deal. I went up to her table and laid and lost a few bets. She spoke to me now, her voice fit to be heard at Saint Cecilia Ball, her words perfectly proper from a dealer to a player. But I thought her pupils had enlarged, giving the effect of greater luminousness. I was glad they had not contracted to bright points. It went to show that she had borne me no grudge in my long absence. Perhaps she still treasured—and sometimes wore—a fairyland gown of crimson velvet.

I drifted away, returning now and then until I could speak to her ear.

"Where, and how soon?"

"I close at midnight on Saturday," she answered. "Knock on the alley door and I'll share my supper with you."

The signs so far were good. Evidently she had no jealous and ever-attentive lover, who could easily play hob with my hopes. Indeed I had harbored no great fears along this line— Clara had never been a one-man woman or a many men's woman either, and I made the blind guess that, except for an occasional truce, she was at war with all men. But my hopes were not high either. How could they be, when I was playing such long chances? Sometimes, when the cards were hot, I had drawn from a whole deck to fill a straight flush broken in the middle; but I had never bet against odds as long as these.

So my thoughts ran, as I waited. There was no magic about Clara; she was not a conjure woman; I had never seen her accomplish a single clever feat. But I had seen her enter, proudly, on my arm, the wide, bright door of Hudson Barony, which took more nerve than one of the unregenerate trespassing the Gate of Heaven; and once in a long time pure courage won the pot. The hands of my pocket watch came simultaneously upright. I went out with the last to leave and waited in the alley until the lamps in the gaming rooms went out and a glimmer came in a dark window of a back room. Then I knocked on the door beside it.

She opened the door, and without a word gestured to a vacant chair. She returned to one by a table, on which a white cloth was but half-spread, and on which sat three half-filled paper bags, drooping and unprepossessing, that no doubt contained our supper, sent out by an eating house. No doubt she had intended to make me a pleasant spread, but fatigue or a sudden heaviness of spirit had sapped her energy. The lamplight flung on her face and she raised her hand as though to shade her eyes. I did not look at her yet but instead glanced about the room.

This was a combined dining room and parlor of tidy, by no means cramped, lodgings. They were furnished in good taste with a few inconspicuous touches of elegance. No doubt they were palatial compared to the shack in the piney woods where she was born.

"So you're back," she remarked at last, without the least accent of surprise or pleasure.

"Yes."

"All the way from South Africa. That seems far as the moon. You crossed the ocean twice—and here you are safe and sound. And Mate—who never went anywhere—he's dead."

I felt a prickling sensation on the back of my neck—a symptom of deep wonder.

"Why speak of him?"

"I always think of him in connection with you. The night you came to Memphis' rooms—the night we went to the ball. Edward, do you remember what he said when I told him his

luck was about to turn? The only luck for him was what everybody got at last. He got it, all right—and so soon."

"Well, what did you think about it? Clara, I want you to
talk plain."

Her eyes slowly widened.

"I don't think I dare talk plain. Vulgar people like me are
always thinking someone's going to steal something—or someone is trying to kill someone—or there's some other devilment
going on. The aristocrats have got more faith in the human
race."

"Something must have happened—you must have heard something other than the newspaper accounts and I want to know
what it is. It may be terribly important."

"It isn't. I'll tell you that. It's only a hunch I had when I
heard he was with Clay Hudson."

"You didn't know Clay Hudson—did you?"

"Yes, I did. Well, I mean I saw him. He talked to me a little
while. I asked him if he knew Mate Hudson, and he said they
were half-brothers. He had come to Memphis' joint to inquire
for you. He said he knew you in Cuba."

"He went to Jack's place, too."

"He was courteous—soft-spoken—with a winning, diffident
manner. Yet he frightened me more than I can tell you. I
thought if he ever got hold of you, you were a goner. And when
he spoke of Mate—and Mate's marriage to the girl you both
loved—there came a sheen on his eyes. . . ."

"I've seen that sheen."

"Well, is there anything to it? I have an awful feeling that
there is, or you wouldn't be here. And then—where will I be?"

She was slightly pale and drawn from fatigue, and I got a
sandwich from one of the bags and had her eat it as I told her
all—the little whole—of what Salley had told me. The homely
human act permitted her to hear the story in true proportion,
and to weigh it well. I related our failure to find a scrap of
evidence that Clay's story was not true. Then I explained that,

unless an actual witness could be found, or Clay in some fashion incriminated himself, defeat of our cause was certain.

"Now comes the bad part," Clara said, when I paused.

"Will you help us?" I asked.

"I won't help you or that beautiful highborn woman you want to marry. I thank you for the dress—it was the most beautiful, the best winning I ever made in my whole life—I've got it still—and I haven't forgotten I told you you could call on me again. But not a business as bad as this. I won't say I won't help Mate, but if it was anybody else than him, I'd tell you no right now, and a big plain no. What do you want me to do? Come out with it. Chances are you can go to the Devil. But I'll listen if you want to tell me. Only tell me fast."

"First, can you close up for three days?"

"I can close up for three weeks, if I wish." A dark pride crept into her tone.

"If you went out with Clay, would he have any suspicion, from what you had said to him in Augusta that you were spying for me?"

"I don't think so. I didn't brag about knowing you well. He took a little interest in me—I thought so, anyway—but I never told him my last name and I doubt if he's thought of me since."

"Still you'd have to come on him in what seemed very commonplace circumstances, and then work fast. Butler Mims, for instance, or Arnold Hudson either, mustn't see you in Charleston in time to warn their good friend, Clay. You'd go to the hotel and stay there until I brought you word that Clay was at his usual hangout, a mughouse known as the Lighthouse. You might have to wait one whole day, or conceivably two whole days, but if you arrive on Sunday, I think that night would be the night. You'd go to the Lighthouse, pick him up, and"—my tone faltered—"lead him on."

"Where to, Edward?" she asked quietly.

"Wherever necessary, to find out all you can about Mate's death."

"You've got a lot of nerve."

"I suppose so. So have you, when you need it."

"Have you and Salley talked this over?"

"No, I haven't mentioned it to her. I spoke of it to Jack."

"Was he for it?"

"He agreed I had the right to ask you, and you to accept or refuse."

"Did you consider paying me?"

"No, only standing your expenses—not even those if you're in funds."

"Well, thanks for that much, anyway."

"Do you want to undertake it? I believe you know already, and there's no point in you delaying your decision."

"Damn you, Edward. Damn Jack, too, and every man but Mate."

"I reckon we've got it coming."

"Excuse me for not leaving out Memphis. The old penny-pincher left me a thousand dollars. What did Mate leave me? I know if you don't."

"No, I don't know."

"He left me—the two times I had any dealings with him—feeling like a lady."

"Well, I once did something—not nearly as hard or as bad as this—in order to feel like a gentleman."

She did not hear me. "Once when I was walking up some stairs—once when he danced with me. He accepted me as a lady. I mean, he didn't ask what I was, no suspicion crossed his mind, I was just one of God's children, a human being he was drawn to. I played him for nearly a thousand dollars. I wonder if he remembers it, where he's gone!"

She rose, poured herself a drink of whiskey, and wiped her mouth.

"If he does remember it, he's forgiven me," she went on. "He'll remember he was human too—the most human being I ever knew. You stay here and I'll take the steamer to Charleston early tomorrow morning. Don't come with me. I don't want you around. If I need you, I'll send for you."

3

Sunday passed freely and rather quickly as I wandered about sight-seeing green and beautiful Savannah. It was no common earth, this city; it had been founded and dedicated by one of the greatest humanitarians that modern times had known. By profession and fierce instinct, I preyed on my fellow humans; the most powerful drive of General Oglethorpe's life had been to serve them. Out of the muck grows the lovely lotus flower. A Bombay Indian I had met in Capetown, by religion not a Hindu but a Buddhist, had told me so. "The jewel is in the lotus," he said, his face alight. Out of the dirt and stink and heartbreak of English debtor prisons had bloomed this flower-festooned city of the New World, with its many pretty parks, and with it the state of Georgia, rightfully calling itself the Empire State, for it was bigger than all England, stretching from the Savannah River to the Chattahoochee, from vast Okefenokee Swamp to the Great Smokies.

But no longer did its leading citizens proudly trace their histories to Fleet and Newgate. In their parlors hung painted coats-of-arms. Their boast was faded deeds of gift bearing the hand and seal of a royal George. Rich and lordly, still they were like me, I thought. In their place I would do the same.

My wait became anxious Wednesday morning, when Clara did not return on the passenger boat from Charleston. In vain I met the packet steamer at midnight, and on Thursday afternoon a little coaster. No young woman of youthful face and pretty, girlish form came down the gangplank. At nightfall I was thoroughly frightened. Why in the name of all my gods had I yielded to Clara's demand that she go alone? Had I not known with whom she was dealing? No, I had only assumed the knowledge, a spine-chilling fact. Fratricide was a strange crime. Clay Hudson was a most strange man.

The next few hours were as weirdly haunted as some I had
spent in Africa. The air, so fresh and cool three nights before,
turned sultry. My friendliest stars were dimmed in smoky haze.
Like almost everyone, I looked to, and half-believed, in certain
omens of good or evil fortune, and only the latter would show
tonight, everywhere I gazed; and more telling than these was
a deepening bleakness of spirit—an experience known to millions of my kind. Had some dreadful thing happened not just
now, not a few hours past, but perhaps as long ago as Sunday
night? What was to prevent Clay Hudson from discovering that
Clara was my spy? Only much good luck and no bad luck!
And I had never been Fortune's darling. My empty hours—my
empty arms—were proof.

At midnight I heard of a packet schooner, with auxiliary en-
gines, just now put into dock. Her home port was Baltimore, a
porter told me, but she often touched at Charleston to load or
unload freight, and she had accommodations for a few passengers. I rushed to a cab and promised the sleepy driver an extra
dollar for a pellmell ride. Presently the old nag's hoofs clattered
on the stone.

I came down on the dank-smelling wharf to find the ship
dark except for watchlights, her gangplank taken in, and her
deck deserted except for shipwatch. At my halloo a youth of
about sixteen leaned over the rail.

"Did anyone get off here?" I asked.

"I reckon they did, but I was for'ard, muggin' up, and I
didn't pay no 'tention."

"Did you have a young lady passenger from Charleston?"

"I heard we did, but she was sick and stayed in her cabin."

"Do you mean seasick?"

"I don't guess so. We had a smooth sail."

"Will you go and see if she's still aboard?"

"Nay, sir. Us seamen don't dast go near the passengers' quarters, and the stewart's gone over town."

I got back into the cab and now we made full-tilt for the
Lucky Chance Casino. A carriage was just leaving—we heard

her rumble of wheels and clatter of horses' hoofs—but the rooms were dark, and likely it was occupied by a late customer seeking a game of chance. Instead of trying to overtake him, I got out. I had heard a faint sound that might be a door opening. A moment later the rear window did not look quite so black. It was either a glimmer of light from within or a trick of my eyes. As I stood still and breathless, it slowly grew.

I paid and dismissed the driver, then knocked on the side door.

"Who is it?" The voice was weary-sounding but unmistakable.

"Edward."

"Wait just a minute."

From where I stood, I could see the lighted window. I watched it, idly expecting to see Clara's shadow thrown on the shade. Instead I saw something that puzzled me in an odd, uncanny way. The yellow glimmer became distinctly less. Clara had turned the lamp low.

A moment later she opened the door, then, leaving me to shut it, retreated rather hurriedly to a chair well away from the table from which the lamp threw murky beams.

"Forgive me for my rude ways," she said, "but I'm fagged out."

She was something more than tired. I had come in from the dark and my pupils were wide and receptive, and I could not fail to see instantly that she had been through an ordeal far more devastating than she wanted me to know. Her cheeks were haggard, her lips pale, her eyes appeared red, her light and shapely hands were shaking. Rather surprisingly on this sultry night, she wore a black lace shawl over her low-collared blouse.

"Let's make this short," she said. "I've got to get to bed."

"Just as you like."

"As short as the Devil, if you please, but he's pretty long—at least his shadow is that he casts across the world. Excuse me for babbling. I'm not drunk. I haven't even had a drink. I'm just a little lightheaded from—let's say lack of brains."

"Was the trip a failure or a success?"

"You'll have to decide that. I know he murdered Mate. Well, I don't know it, he didn't come out and say so, he only dropped the hint, and when enough liquor was down him he made it pretty plain. I've never seen a man hold so much booze. If I hadn't connived with the waiter to bring me tea instead, I'd been under the table in an hour. He was cold as a fish but after a long time he warmed up."

"Well?"

"Well, hell. When the evening was far enough along, he told me something else. I think that on this alone depends the success or failure of my noble efforts. You'll know, I don't. I think it was important because it jarred him—saying it, I mean —and he changed the subject and didn't mention Mate again."

She had been pale when I came in. Now she turned ashy gray and breathless.

"What did he say, Clara?"

"Mate didn't drown between the Isle of Palms and Dewees Island. It was between Dewees Island and Capers Island."

"Clara, that gives me new hope."

"Oh, you're not just saying that!"

"We can start the search again. Why did he lie in the first place? Was he afraid that someone had seen him, and we'd find that someone? If he exists we will find him. We'll comb both islands. I don't know what you've been through—"

"You remember how you used to want to be a gentleman. Whether you've given it up or not, act like one now. I mean this minute. Don't ask me another thing. Put on your hat and make off. Maybe I'll see you again some time. In the sweet by-and-by."

There came a hysterical note in her voice. Not knowing what else to do, I rose at once.

"I'll tell you one more thing that might interest you, though it has no connection with the case," she went on, struggling against tears. "You may not believe it, but it's true. Your old friend Clara Day—once Memphis' shill and now proprietor of the Good Chance Casino—well, she's a lady."

I looked at her and believed her.

"I didn't think I could ever be. I didn't think I could be Sunday night, but for the sake of Mate—and I suppose you— I made it."

She went to the door with me and opened it. A sudden gust of fresh air off the sea blew aside one end of her shawl. For an instant was revealed a narrow crimson welt that ran from under the back of her dress onto the side of her neck.

The door closed behind me. I looked up at the stars, shining now the late wind had blown away the murk, and, suddenly, I remembered something which only lately I had tried in vain to recall. It was a whispered story, told in my boyhood, of why Clay Hudson had had to leave Charleston. Now I asked the stars that he should leave Charleston again, by my sending, and on another, longer road.

CHAPTER XXII

The Verdict

ONE OF the best drops for cobia in any of our waters lay close to the southern shore of Capers Island, where the configuration of the land caused a brisk tide rip with choppy waves. Indeed in all the pass between Capers and Dewees Island it was by far the most likely place for Clay Hudson to have heaved to on that fatal morning. Beyond was "high mash," as the Negroes call it, a wide expanse of marsh grass interwound with tidal creeks, and a favorite resort for mullet-netters and fishermen with hook-and-lines. From the open sea Clay would not be sure of seeing all who had poled bateaux into the wind-blown reed, but if he had brought Mate to cast in the rip, they would have certainly seen him.

After my furtive survey of the ground and long talk with Jeff Legare, it came to pass that N'kulu, known now as Ned Coon by such Gullah-speaking Negroes as had made his acquaintance, went to live in a deserted cabin on a half-tilled plantation, owned by an absentee landlord, on Capers Island. According to public report and the records of white people, he was a free Negro who farmed on shares a few acres of cornland, grazed a couple of cows, and ran a few pigs and chickens. But

375

the colored knew better. There had come into their midst the most powerful conjure man in the island's history. He had magical equipment such as his predecessors, who meddled with roots, cow's horns, and pig's teeth, never dreamed of. One item was a spear with dried blood on it, another the two-toed foot of a bird that had stood as high as a horse, a third, and the most potent, a human head shrunk to the size of a coconut. The most remarkable attribute of his conjure was, it would work only to do good, never to do harm. It would lay ghosts, put a crimp in evil spirits, restore a wavering love, but it would not bring a rival to a lingering death, or blight a woman's beauty, or even drive her to distraction with a toothache. The most astounding thing about the conjuror himself was that he would take a case of "credick" not to be paid for till the crop was made.

That "Ned Coon" would soon know every great and guilty secret of the island, I had no doubt. Was there, among the rest, the witnessing of a murder not committed by a poor white, quick to draw his knife, or a passion-maddened Negro, but by one of the great bukras of the land? The laws of chance ran heavily against it, but I played the lone card for all it was worth. I had no other choice; besides, deep in my heart—more in my daydreams than in my hard-hammered thoughts—I believed that it would win.

"Murder will out." The ancient adage is far from a fact of human life, yet it contains a great deal of human truth. The mark of Cain is a reality, whether or not it is visible to the casual glance; and good men who know of unpunished murder are haunted in their beds. In any case, my ruse had an early and sudden upshot, startling in the extreme. Clay Hudson had not perfectly covered his tracks. It came to me in a great rush of hope—that evil was no more infallible than good. Almost every normal human being longs for that assurance, and suddenly I found it. Whether I had found victory lay in the lap of the gods.

The movement of event that must now whirl on to failure

or fulfillment began with the delivery to me, on a sweltering July day, of a mess of diamond-back terrapin by a free Negro shrimp fisherman dwelling on Dewees Island. "Ned Coon tell me to carry you these," he told me in unrecordable Gullah. He stood holding out the bag in one hand, his hat in the other, never dreaming he was bringing me a summons of unestimable moment. A moment later, he had gone.

The mists of moonlight found Jeff and me in his knockabout, making for the southern shore of Dewees Island, he knowing every fathom of the course. We found our way to a beach cottage, no more than a shack, Jeff's retreat from a world to which he had never become acclimated; and here, in the hushed night, came N'kulu, in the company of a lank black man, about forty, with curiously delicate features and an air of distinction and purposefulness.

"I've seen you, several times, fishing in the creeks," Jeff said to him when he saw him in the lanternlight. "Your name is Phineas."

" 'At right, suh," the Negro answered in an oddly deep voice.

"Ned Coon, you've brought him here to tell us something," I said, speaking Gullah, not the strange-sounding Afrikaans that might frighten Phineas.

"Yas, suh. Somp'n 'at he told me. He told me so his soul could res'. He'd already made 'fession to de Lawd, but I told him he had to make it 'fore de law, or he couldn't git right in his heart."

"Phineas, will you sit down while you tell it?" Jeff asked, waving his hand to a bench.

"No, sah. I'll stan' up. After 'at, I'll sit down for a minute 'cause it'll be harder wuk than sawin' pine knots."

"I'll stan' up wif you, Phineas," N'kulu said.

"You can start then."

"Bukra, I couldn't tol' it at all if Ned Coon hadn't tol' me I 'bliged to tell it. He said if I kept it secret any mo', Old Debbil take my soul. And I reckon he would. Nothin' been the same wi' me and Molly, she my woman, since I seen what I seen. De owl and de bat, dey come and dey come. De buzzard, he shadow it flick-flick over de cabin. We hear de sound of laughin' down in de swamp—de Debbil laughin' at me, 'cause I 'fraid to tell of de Debbil's work I seen wif my own eyes. To tell de truf, I mighty 'fraid right now. I know Mas' Clay gwine kill me, soon or late, unless somebody stop him. Wo'se an 'at, he send me off on one of 'em ships 'at come in night and hide behind de island, den I go back into slavery way off somewha' in de sugar-cane field; and once a man free, like me, he rather die than be slave agin."

"Phineas, you'll be safer after you've told us than when you kept it secret," I said. "If Mas' Clay knew you'd seen what he did, but hadn't told anyone, he would kill you sure to shut your mouth forever, but after you've told it, what would be the use?"

"He'll kill me jus' the same, if he kin, for the Debbil of it."

"We'll guard you all we can."

" 'At all I ask. My mammy tol' me, when I come to manhood, 'Phineas, you's a black man, but be a man right on.' Mo' 'n a year ago now, de moon was in de las' qua'ta after de full moon o' early April. I'd caught some shrimp in my net, and about half-tide, I got my bateau to pole out to Fishduck Creek, to try 'n catch a mess o' spot-tails. 'Fo I pushed off, I waved to Joe Wadley, to fin' out if he want to come wif me. No use yellin' at him, 'cause Joe, he deaf and dumb."

"Can Joe talk at all?"

"He can talk good on his fingers, and I learn enough to talk to him a little. He used to belong to ol' Miss Wilcox, and she taught him 'at, and to spell good. He mighty glad to go. But as we was gettin' into de creek, Joe look over the high mash, and he seen Mas' Clay's boat comin' into de pass. Right away he sign to me to go back. All de colored mighty scared of Mas' Clay, but Joe he wo'se o' all."

"Did you see who was with him?"

"Yas, sah. Dey was a young bukra wif him and I thought it was Mas' Mate. Afta I'd took Joe back where he could git in a little skiff he keep moor on a sandbar and went out agin' alone, I took ova de high mash, and 'at time I catch a good look, and it's Mas' Mate for sho'."

"How far was Mas' Clay's boat?"

"Why, it wa'nt mo' 'n a quata-mile."

There would be no trouble about a Low Country jury believing that a colored man could identify a bukra at a quarter mile. A beady-eyed tern wasn't in it with him for long-range and accurate vision across a seascape.

"Do you think Mas' Clay saw you?"

"Not then, he didn't. He might of got a look at de boat befo' Joe went back. We passed a piece of low mash where de boat might show. And he didn't see me after 'at, but I seen him."

"Tell us what you saw."

"I didn't put out no bait. I foun' a place where I could jes' see over de mash, and I frowed out my anchor and jes' waited. I wanted to see what he gwine do. Somepin tol' me he hadn't come all 'at way, clean to de rip by Caper Island, jes' to catch cobia. Pity quick he heaved to, fast de boom to de taffrail, rig up Mas' Mate, and let him fish in de rip behind de boat. And in jes' a little while, Mas' Mate he got a strike. I could see de pole bend, and Mas' Mate brace himself. And 'en I seen somethin' Mas' Clay do behind Mas' Mate's back. And fo' God in Heaven I seen it plain."

We waited while Phineas caught his breath.

"He whop out his sheaf knife, and in one whack he cut de line fastenin' de boom to de taffrail."

"You saw the boom swing round?"

"It was almost too fast to see, but I seen it hit Mas' Mate and knock him overside. I see de big splash. And den I see what was de wo'se of all. Mas' Clay he jes take de tiller and let de boat drift wi' de tide, stayin' close to Mas' Mate, but not comin' up on him. He didn't heave his iron, and go swimmin' after him. He jes' waited and waited, givin' him time to drown."

There came visions into Phineas' round black eyes. He saw again the high marsh, waving in the wind, the expanse of blue water, the drifting boat, the small murderous figure at the helm.

"After awhile, he wait long enough, and I reckon he was afraid de body would sink, but they wan't much danger in de rip. So he got close to de body and heave his iron and slip overside. I t'ought maybe de good Lawd make him drown, but in a minute or two he come a-swimmin', and I seen him come up on de lee side and crawl aboard still hangin' onto Mas' Mate. He wait awhile longer, jes' to make sure, 'fore he drag him aboard. And den he light one of his little cheroots and smoke it. I didn't see de match and I couldn't see de smoke, but I see his hand go back and fort' to his mouf, and I knew what he was doin'. And he stan' there like he own de whole ocean."

"What did you do?"

"Bukra, I kept on a-watchin'. I was mighty scared, but de Lawd tell me, in my ear, to watch close, 'cause I was His witness to what Mas' Clay Hudson did to his brot'er, Mate Hudson. I was de only witness in all dat mighty sweep of water and mash.

"By and by, Mas' Clay take Mas' Mate's pole dat stuck under de taffrail, and boat de big fish. Then he took the line he done cut, and he put it against the housing and pound de ends wif' de ax, and den he pounded it two or t're places along both de pieces. I knew what he doin', as well as though he told me. He making de line look old and worn, so he can say it broke in a gus' a wind. Den he take his knife and he do somethin' wif it wif de ax, and I t'ink he dull the edge of it 'cause it must be razor-sharp to cut de line in one hack. Den slow and steady he fasten a new line to de boom, fix it to de taffrail, and take up his anchor. Den he go sailin' back to town."

Thus, suddenly, the story ended. Gray-faced, Phineas looked at Jeff and me with imploring eyes. A sheen was on N'kulu's eyes. I could imagine him once more as a plumed and painted warrior of the Zulu.

"Sit down, Phineas," Jeff said kindly. Then he turned to me, and I saw that he was fighting devastating sorrow, the outcome of profound disappointment. I was saved from it only by the curious kind of optimism which is the greatest and perhaps the

only reward of a gambler's habit of mind. Not even four aces
will always win. A pair of deuces will not always lose. Fortune
is never quite as good, or ever quite as bad, as the cards show.

"Tha' we is," Jeff said in Gullah, "but wha' is we?"

"Nowhere," I answered, "yet."

"Explain it to me, Edward. You've read enough law to throw
a little light. The judge would believe the story, so would the
jury, any man who heard it would believe it. Surely society
won't countenance cold, calculated murder—" He paused.

"The story could never get to court in its present form. The
farthest it would get is a magistrate's hearing, after someone
had sworn out a warrant for Clay's arrest. There isn't a scrap
of corroborative evidence—he has only to say the Negro had a
grudge, and no magistrate would hold him for trial. Still, you
never can tell—" Then my heart got rid of its cold cramp, and
I turned to Phineas again.

"Phineas, it was more than a year since all that happened."

"Yas, sah."

"When you repeat that story, before a law man in Charleston, leave out about Joe Wadley going back. He may have gone
back, but for the present you've forgotten. Tell it as though he
was with you all that time—that he too saw the line cut, and
Mas' Mate knocked overside, and Mas' Clay leaving him there
to drown. Say 'we seen,' not 'I seen.' Can you do that?"

"I reckon I kin, but wouldn't I get in trouble wid de law?"

"You can remember later, if you have to. And if you don't
do it, Mas' Clay will get away like a fish off your hook, and he'll
never have to answer for what you know he did."

Phineas sat twisting his gaunt hands. "Mas' Edward?" he
called at last.

"Yes."

"I never seen you 'fo tonight, but I seen Mas' Jeff a heap o'
times. I don't know your name, but all us colored know de
name Legare. I want to ask him straight out."

"Very well."

"Mas' Jeff, if I go to de jailhouse for not tellin' de truf, I'd be mighty shamed, me bein' free and all. But if you say for me to do what Mas' Edward tell me, I will."

"Edward, can you keep him out of jail for perjury?" Jeff asked me.

"Yes, sir. At the most he'll be reprimanded for a slip of memory."

"Will it do any good? I don't see how it can, because Joe Wadley would certainly be questioned sooner or later."

"It may do good. I've seen a pair of deuces win over a full house. In poker there's such a thing as bluff—in fact, the game used to be called that—and I'm not sure it won't work on Clay Hudson. I want to try it. I want to bring the bastard science of the gaming dens into a magistrate's court. When everything is said and done, that's the only science that I know. If I succeed, it will be the greatest hand of poker I've ever played. If I don't, I'll take my medicine whatever it is."

"I'll take it with you, old man." Jeff turned to the wide-eyed Negro. "Do just what Mas' Edward says."

2

In Charleston there existed an ancient and honorable society for the help of the afflicted, white and Negro. From its secretary I received a list of all deaf mutes residing in the city, and the names of their nearest of kin. Many of the people on the latter list could talk on their fingers, as the saying goes, but there was not one that I knew well, or had any reason to believe would risk an official reprimand or perhaps a more serious penalty for a flagrant piece of subterfuge in a magistrate's hearing. Actually there might be several who would do so. It had warmed my heart to discover that the death of Mate had neither been forgotten, nor, among the many who had suspected the truth, forgiven. Some who take lightly the solemnities of court and who live by their own half-humorous code, would do it for the Devil of it, trusting to get out with a whole skin. I knew the adventurousness of human kind.

Clara Day would undertake it, if she knew sign language, and if I asked her to. But I was glad that, since she was not competent, I need not call on her again. Thinking of her, my mind jumped to another of her sex, and in that respect at least, somewhat like her, even if before the world she cut an entirely different figure. This was Miss Arabella Wilcox, one of the *grandes dames* of Charleston, who dwelt with a staff of servants in a time-honored mansion facing the sea wall. She was one of the directors of the aid society. She had spent a great part of her life—having never married—teaching deaf mutes to communicate and the lame to walk and the blind to make their way as well as possible through a lightless world. One of the beneficiaries of her humanitarianism was Joe Wadley, Phineas' friend, now living on Capers Island.

She was said to be high-tempered, rather imperious, impatient of restraint, and an implacable enemy of the Devil and all his works. It happened, one of those little flukes of chance that sometimes prove mighty factors in an enterprise, she was a distant and affectionate cousin of Mildred Hudson. But she gave no sign of any of this when, having written me a formal note in answer to my request for an audience, she received me in her ancient mossy garden. Her greeting was courteous, but I could not call it warm. How could I expect it to be when I was a notorious gambler, not long returned from Africa, now on an unknown mission?

A hoary-headed butler brought out mint juleps, expertly made. The hospitality mitigated the effect of her severe dress and somewhat distant manner; and I was able to plunge into Phineas' story. Still this green garth with its cool stone cloistered from the world seemed the wrong scene for a wicked tale of fratricide; and I feared Arabella Wilcox would not believe it with all her heart and soul, and even if she did, she would stay calm.

I had misjudged her. Her stillness changed to that of profound emotion.

"I knew that Clay Hudson would kill before he was through,"

she said. "Somehow I didn't think his victim would be Mate—I thought it would be Salley, for refusing his love. That would have been an act of supreme egoism on his part. They both had Ashley blood, so she was the only woman worthy of him, his own woman. Killing Mate was not nearly as grand a gesture. Actually it was little more than vicious spite."

"I'm glad to hear you say that—for a particular reason."

"Since you've mentioned it—what is it?"

"The more common a murderer he is, the more likely he will provide the rope to be hanged with."

"He is a common murderer. Believe that, and have confidence in yourself, as well as faith in your cause. I wish I could help you."

"I'm going to give you the chance—the chance to help me play a chance to win. And it's no piddling chance. It's a good, solid chance. As a gambler, I feel sure that it's worth running. And I believe we have no other."

So I told her what I wanted her to do. As I talked, I watched her face, especially her brilliant and beautiful eyes, and not once did I see her flinch. She had only a few questions. . . .

"Would I have to do it again when he's brought to trial?"

"No, Miss Arabella. He'll either convict himself at the hearing before the magistrate, or he'll never be tried."

"You'll give him every opportunity to convict himself?"

"Either through vanity—or through panic."

"I too think it's a runnable chance. I used to play a pretty good hand at macao and whist. Also, I've won more bets on horses than my rightful share."

"Will you do it? If you're caught at it, Mr. Meadows will give you a severe reprimand." Mr. Meadows, usually called Judge, was the magistrate who held hearings on arrests for capital crimes.

"No, he won't. I'd tell him I'm old, and can't interpret as well as I used to, and I misunderstood."

"He may believe that—even though he looks at your eyes and hands—but I wouldn't."

"I think you're of a mind to pay me a compliment, and I'd like to hear it."

"I'm practiced at appraising manual dexterity and power of vision. You have very beautiful and fluent hands, and I doubt if your eyes miss much. I thank my lucky stars I am to have such an able partner."

3

Ned Coon, as he was known, and Preacher Jessup, unfalteringly faithful to the family that had set him free, arranged a watch over all waters adjacent to Charleston into which a seagoing vessel could run and lay in hiding. There were not many such waters; most of the island coasts were too thickly inhabited to be clear for smugglers.

Before dawn of an early August morning there came a brief, sharp rattle on my windowpane. I went out into the dark and found a young Negro, who gave his name as Ben, and said that he lived on the southwestern end of "Jim" Island. Was he free or slave? He was slave, but Ol' Mas' was visiting on Edisto, and the straw boss Mas' Parker, had let him off to run the errand Preacher Jessup had done asked him to, if the 'casion came. A ship had slipped into the inlet at the previous sundown. She flew no flag and her name had been painted out and her hands were swarthy and heavily mustached and spoke in a foreign tongue. As a final indication of her business, the bright-skin boy named 'Manual, who was known to work for Mas' Clay Hudson, had gone aboard the ship, then taken off for Charleston on horseback.

"Horseback?" I asked wonderingly. "The ship must have found a berth close to shore."

"Yas, sah, she lying in Stono Creek, so near de land you could t'row a stone."

It was a good augury, I thought.

The sun was not up before I had gotten word to Phineas and to deaf-and-dumb Joe Wadley, stored away for safekeeping at Judge Lucas' plantation; and they were with me, at the door of the magistrate's temporary quarters near the bay, when the official arrived at eight o'clock to begin his daily duties.

"Judge Meadows, I wish to swear out a warrant for the arrest of Mr. Clay Hudson," I said, when he had taken his chair.

"For what crime, Mr. Stono?"

"The murder of his half-brother, Mate Hudson."

Judge Meadows was a quiet man. He was hardly ever known to raise his voice, and his expression was habitually calm.

"It is customary for the person making such a serious charge to give the magistrate his reason for so doing."

"Phineas, give his honor a very brief account of what you saw off Capers Island. You need not, I believe, go into detail; I think you will be called upon to do that when Judge Meadows holds a hearing on the case, to determine whether Mas' Hudson is to be held for trial."

I thought that the multisyllable words I had used might confuse Phineas. They did not in the least; like most Negroes he knew the legal processes regarding arrest; and he answered to the point.

"Jedge, we seen him cut a line so de boom of de boat would swing round and hit Mas' Mate in the neck and knock him overboard. Then we seen him let him drown."

Meadows eyed him gravely, then turned to me.

"You would not have brought the man here, unless you believed his story," he said. "Moreover, there is general feeling that all the facts of Mr. Mate Hudson's death have never come to light. I will accept your oath and issue a warrant for Mr. Clay Hudson's arrest, and hold a hearing on the case as soon as he is brought into custody."

That should be very soon. Time was moving fast, but I did not think it moved against us; Clay Hudson made a practice of rising late and having breakfast in his garden, and the tide to help him on his way to Stono Creek had not yet started to flow. I asked the magistrate if it would be proper for me to accompany Sheriff Bowman when he served the warrant.

Meadows looked at me curiously. "Certainly, if you wish to

do so," he answered. "The thought occurs to me that you have been the prime mover in opening up the case."

"It is for this that I returned from Africa."

"I may tell you in confidence that the widow of the victim approached Sheriff Bowman many weeks ago. At that time he was unable to give her any encouragement. According to a report as to why the elder Hudson remembered you in his will, you were something more to Mate Hudson than a friend."

"That is correct."

"This will jar the city to its foundations."

I could believe that; I could know, too, that, whether or not my great gamble won, Clay Hudson would be finished in Charleston. However safe he remained from the retribution of the law, Phineas' simple story would put him forever beyond the pale. Maybe I would have to be content with this half a loaf. It might be I would not attempt the *coup de grâce;* for it needed the most careful timing and a run of high cards between now and the fateful moment when I was either to nod to Arabella Wilcox, or shake my head. As for me, I had nothing to do but look, listen, divine the position of the cards, and make that one decision.

I felt a lightening of heart as Sheriff Bowman, his deputy Dan Manville, and I were shown in what was once the garden of the Hudson mansion facing the Promenade. A frightened Cuban servant brought us there, and although Clay Hudson was never more grand as he looked up from his breakfast table at us lowborn visitors, I saw his brows knit and there came a swift change of light, indicating some terrific inward tension, in his dark eyes.

"Could not your business wait till I finished breakfast?" he asked coldly, addressing Sheriff Bowman.

"No, sir, it could not."

"I don't think it's that important."

"You may think differently, when you know what it is. I hold a warrant, made out by the magistrate, for your arrest for murder. We've come to serve that warrant."

"May I ask who 'we' are? I see your deputy, whose presence is no doubt lawful. But you will need a good excuse for permitting the intrusion of the third person."

"If you mean Mr. Stono, he swore out the warrant, and Judge Meadows said he had every right to see it served."

"Every right, and with sterling pleasure," I said quickly. "You once told me, Clay, that I was at the end of my rope—but it didn't prove to be true. Now I can tell you the same thing— and this time it's a sure thing. When you took your brother's life, you should have looked carefully into the high marsh that overlooked the scene—provided, of course, you had any care for your own life. It was not easy to encourage the two witnesses to tell their stories. They held you in quite justifiable fear. They are over it now. Their safety has been guaranteed. You yourself can listen to their accounts at the magistrate's hearing in a very short time, then you can judge the truth of what I say. Your time has run out. Sheriff Bowman, I suggest you clap handcuffs on this murderer, and haul him to the courthouse."

"Mr. Stono, I don't think we need do that. The testimony of the two Negroes won't become official until the hearing. Meanwhile we'll treat him like a gentleman—until he shows himself unworthy of it. Will you come now, Mr. Hudson?"

"As soon as I speak to my servant as to his duties."

He pulled a bell cord and the Cuban re-entered the room. Clay spoke softly to him in Spanish in an even tone, but I was listening with all my ears, and three times I heard him use the word *batel,* meaning a small vessel. Nor was Diego's mien as perfect as his master's. His swarthy face became quite pale.

"I am ready now, officer," Clay said, gracefully rising. As he did so, he gave me a view of his perfectly formed, sensuous lips curled in a faint smile. I did not know what it meant. I thought it might be in some strange victory or farewell. But I saw the beauty of molding of his face, its signs of ancient lineage and exalted race, and, once more, its resemblance to Mate's. I wondered if Cain's face had resembled Abel's.

I had seen the steam of evil coming up almost like swirling

smoke in the gambling dens. Wondering at the root of the evil in Clay, the root that had flowered fratricide, I could not explain it by the bad strain of the Ashleys, for Salley too was of that strain. It came to me as a kind of inkling that it had some distant but powerful connection with Africa. Before I could seize it or make sense of it, the vision faded.

At eleven o'clock, Sheriff Bowman brought his prisoner into the temporary courtroom of the magistrate, Judge Meadows. With him was not Butler Mims, as I expected, but another lawyer I used to know, Matthew Whitlow. Had Butler refused to take the case? I hoped so fervently, because of the effect of such a refusal on Clay and hence on my play; and, after all, it would be quite like Butler to flee what he thought was a sinking ship. Still he may have been merely unavailable at the moment, and intended to come to Clay's rescue at the trial. Meanwhile the blunt-nosed, porcine-eyed shyster was an opponent not to be despised.

"We meet again, Edward," he told me, holding out his thick hand. "And you've come up in the world, to be swearing out warrants for Mr. Clay Hudson. But this time you've bit off more than you can chew."

Still his eyes wobbled as he spoke, and he plainly feared he was treading on thin ice.

Sitting quietly on a bench to one side were Phineas and Joe Wadley. Not far off, neatly and quietly dressed, the epitome of Charleston's Old Guard, sat Miss Arabella Wilcox; and I saw Clay's slight but perceptible recoil as he caught sight of her. The county solicitor was present, so was the deputy sheriff, a clerk with his pad and pencil, and a newspaper reporter, but except for Jeff Legare there was no audience, for this was only a preliminary hearing, not a trial. I looked in vain for Salley and Mildred Hudson. I did not know why they had failed to appear—it stood to reason Miss Wilcox had told them of the event—and perhaps it was simply a matter of good taste. So wild was my gamble, so great the chance of its failure, that I was glad of their absence.

But I rejoiced at the living eyes and purposeful demeanor of Miss Wilcox. I wished I were gentle-born.

The benches were hard, the heat extreme, the fly-specked windows let in sparse light from a breezy but gray day. I went to one of them for a quick view of the harbor hardly a hundred yards distant, and what I saw gave a sudden and sharp lift to my spirits. Fast to the dock, with its sail ready to spread, lay Clay's boat. His Cuban servant had brought it there—for what contingency? When Miss Wilcox gave me a questioning glance, I smiled into her eyes.

"I have called this hearing not to try to determine the guilt or innocence of the person charged," the magistrate began when the room had grown still. "But only to determine if there is enough evidence to hold him for trial. I will first hear from the free Negro, Phineas. Phineas, step forward and face my chair."

The tall, gaunt Negro did so, and at Meadows' request, he began to speak. He told his story as simply as before, employing the Gullah dialect, and it was as though he was telling us what was just now before his eyes. We, his hearers, saw him standing there, with a wonderful dignity in his face that could be nothing but the sense of his own great mission and a solemn pride in his having mastered fear; and we saw the judge at his bench, only a plainly-dressed magistrate sitting before a paper-strewn table, listening with profound gravity; and we caught glimpses of one another, the sheriff and his deputy and the clerk sitting in their shirt-sleeves, the latter writing rapidly, all with deeply attentive expressions and sweat-damp faces, while Matthew Whitlow wore his customary black coat and string tie; and the prisoner and Jeff dressed as I was, in cutaway coats, jeweled stocks, bright waistcoats, and tight trousers in the style of the upper crust; and on the prisoner's face at first was a haughty smile. And we saw the big but shabby room that was now a court of law, and the dirty windows, and the light beyond pouring through gray clouds reflected by the sea.

But as we saw all this, we saw the pictures painted by Phineas' simple words. The owl and the bat, they came and they came. The buzzard's shadow flick and flick over the cabin. From down in the swamp rose the sound of the Devil's laughter. So he was obliged to tell, this time before the Law, of Mas' Clay's boat heaving to in the tide rip, and of its two small figures busied, one at the helm and the other with fishing gear. A knife flashed. The boom swung around. And we too watched that awful waiting, until Clay heaved his anchor and at last slipped overboard, and we too watched him swimming back with something in his arms. But although he came aboard himself he did not at once bring his burden. He left it in the water a good while longer. ... And then a fly's buzzing sounded loud in the hushed room, and the flesh of Meadows' jaws looked drawn and hard as flint.

Matthew Whitlow half-rose from his bench, then sat down again. His client's smile had turned to a grimace.

"Did anyone go with you that day?" Judge Meadows asked.

"Yas, sah."

"Who was it?"

"Joe Wadley, who deef and dumb. He go wi' me a heap o' times."

"Miss Arabella Wilcox, I have asked you to be present at this hearing because you know the sign language employed by deaf mutes, and in fact taught it to our next witness, Joe Wadley. Ask him to tell his story, which you are to interpret aloud."

As she rose to take the seat Judge Meadows indicated, her gaze brushed mine. I gave her a slight nod. In grace and ladyship she sat down, and her right hand began to ply, its fingers in rapid, constant changes of position, before Joe Wadley's eyes. When her small white hand dropped in her lap, Joe raised his big black but fluent hand. As its fingers flew Arabella Wilcox's voice came forth into the silent room, pronouncing words at intervals of several seconds, giving the effect of reading very slowly.

"I am ... Joe ... Wadley. ... I live on ... Capers ... Island. ... On that day ... I went ... with ... Phineas ... fishing ... in Fishduck ... Creek. ... I looked ... over ... the ... high

". . . mash . . . and I . . . seen . . . Mas' Mate . . . and Mas' . . . Clay. . . . Pretty . . . soon . . . "

The tale went on, its main facts as Phineas had related them, but with added detail. The black hand never rested, its flying fingers never stilled. But now a change came in the scene—a change of mood—that I had never dreamed. Joe's eyes became lighted by an intense fury. Twice he gestured toward Clay, then he pointed at him with his left hand, the leveled forefinger accusing beyond any indictment I had ever heard in a courtroom.

The air in the silent room appeared to crackle. I knew there would be an explosion, but what form it would take was still a formless vision in my brain. Then with a hoarse cry Clay Hudson leaped to his feet.

"Yes, I did it," he howled, as he ran to the door. There he stopped, whirled, and fixed his mad-dog eyes on mine. "I drowned my baby brother who usurped my rightful place. But you'll never have it, you lowborn bastard aping a gentleman!" Then, still howling as he ran, "The curse of Agoon on you all!"

Agoon was the West Indian conjure god—but I did not think of that now. I acted on impulse and, for the first and probably the last time, in concert with Matthew Whitlow. The sheriff and his deputy had now collected their wits and sprang up to pursue the fugitive, but in the rush of excited men to the door I managed to collide with the fat, puffing Bowman while the shyster lawyer, with a last and feeless loyalty to his client, tripped up lean, swift Dan Manville. Thus the two officers were the last to make an exit except for my partner and me.

We came close together in the now deserted room.

"What did you ask Joe, with such wonderful results?" I said to her in low tones.

"I asked him to tell the court how Mas' Clay Hudson tore down his fish trap off Capers Island," the lady answered.

Excited by the race, she too hurried from the room. I made for the window that overlooked the bay, and in a matter of seconds saw the end of the first part. Running like a youth, Clay gained the dock and, not even pressed close by his pursuers, leaped aboard the boat and raised his sail. The brisk seaward breeze filled it instantly—I could imagine its flamelike crackle —and a widening streak of blue water began to show beyond the piling. He was an expert sailor; I had never seen a boat get under way as quickly and cleanly.

He was fully fifty feet from the dock when Dan Manville made his belated appearance. He did not even reach for his pistol— he was only a deputy and a poor white and the idea could not cross his mind—but for a few seconds he stood poised on the brink as though inclined to dive in and swim after the runaway. Luckily for him—for Clay would have certainly struck at him with an oar—his dignity or some other consideration restrained him. In the few seconds before Sheriff Bowman and Judge Meadows appeared on the scene, the smartly sailing craft began running before the wind, well out of reach.

Still I refused to believe that the highborn yachtsman could outrun the provosts soon to give chase; or, if he did, he could get aboard a friendly vessel in time to clear the port. Actually I had never considered this. My first doubts rose when the patrol boat took such a deal of precious time to get under way. It appeared there was a confusion of authority or a failure in its delegation, whereby a superior officer had to be rounded up to sign the order. Cursing did no good; when finally she put to sea, bearing Dan Manville, Jeff, a dozen bluecoats and me, Clay Hudson's cutter looked like a toy boat far and away down the harbor, and Clay himself like a tiny stick in its stern.

The officer of the bluecoats looked long through a glass, then handed it to me. I got a good focus and then an unforgettable view of my opponent. He never deigned us a backward glance. He stood with what I thought or dreamed was grace; his hand appeared to lay lightly on the tiller but truly it was strong as steel and there was death in it yet for those who impugned his right to reign or blocked his course. But I still did not know the keystone of the evil in his soul. I could see its flower but not its root; by what black mass and miscreancy it possessed him, I could not dream.

Nor did I dream it was my last clear view of Clay Hudson.

"There's a squall making up off James," the officer said, taking back his glass. "He's changing his course to make for it, and if he gets inside it, we've lost him."

"Cap'n, he's sailing mighty close to the outlying buttresses of Fort Sumpter," one of the crew replied.

These were wave-washed and a hazard to strange shipping, but Clay was supposed to know them like the palm of his hand. How he had misjudged his course only the Devil knew. The man's voice had hardly died away when the deep keel struck; with the naked eye, we saw the craft's brief check, her quick list as he reeled on, and then her sudden flounder in the choppy waves. The thought came to me, with something like a wish, that Clay would go down with her; but life was too strong in him to yield up till the last ditch.

"There he goes, swimming for James Island," the officer cried, holding the glass steady. "His black head shows plain in the chop."

"He'll never make it," I answered.

"I don't know about that. He's an easy swimmer, or I miss my guess. If he's screened by the squall, he can land anywhere on that beach, cross the creek to Morris, and rendezvous with the smuggler that's probably got her glass on him now."

For about five minutes not one of my shipmates said a word, and there was no sound but the sail's hum and the slap of little waves against our hull. Then I heard my own voice rise in a wondering tone.

"Cap'n, there's some sort of commotion in the water where he's swimming or so it seems to me."

"I'm under the same impression. See what you make of it."

The officer handed me the glass. I could make nothing of it but splashings, no more revealing than the odd fact that quite a few gulls were flying in that direction. He looked at me with a white face and spoke again.

"Now, if Mr. Hudson had been hurt in the wreck and bleeding a little . . ." His words died away. The sailors looked at one another, with round, awed eyes.

I started to speak, for I remembered a like commotion, overside from the *Sally Tucker*, out from Puerto Miramar, when Clay Hudson, then known as Cap'n Walker, had saved transport and burial expenses for six sick Negroes. A similar pack might have gathered about Clay. I could dream it was the same pack, for such bands range the ocean, and Fate might have liked to round out one of her strange tales. But perhaps Clay had met with only a big school of barracudas, not one of which would weigh over fifty pounds, but all of wolfish appetite and with teeth like rapiers.

I did not speak, because I was looking for a black dot in the turmoiled water.

"Can you see anything of him?" the officer asked, handing me the glass.

After a long scrutiny, I handed it back.

"No, sir, I can't."

"Well, we'll sail up that way for a close look. But I'll tell you right now we might as well put back in port."

I wondered to what port Clay Hudson had gone, or what infinite open sea.

Aftermath

M Y HAND is wearied of the pen; and since the pattern of my life can never change—ever it will be the climbing of jagged and beautiful mountains, with many defeats and falls— I am in haste to lay it down. But there came to pass one event, with preliminary incident, so intimately bound with these previous events, at least as their epilogue, that it should be chronicled with them.

After Clay's arrest and disappearance, my standing in Charleston changed rapidly and markedly. The real reason was the remembered grace and charm of Mate Hudson; plainly a great number of people had liked him, had deplored his death, had suspected a situation akin to the truth; and these gave me my full due and more for bringing it to light. My ill-fame as a gambler did not reduce in the least the flood of human warmth poured out to me. Lonely as the last catamount in the swamps of the Santee, I had never dreamed of such a thing and, although I felt sure it would not last long, I reveled in it. And not only the rank and file extended their hands to me; I suddenly began to receive signs of esteem and even fellowship from the quality. And in this development, the bar sinister did not militate against me. An open secret now, with many of high position it counted in my favor. The blanket on whose wrong side I was born at least was no common rag.

Indeed, my dream of being accepted as a gentleman of the Low Country bid fair to come true.

Meanwhile a minor public honor came my way. The sudden death of a Charleston member of the lower house of the state legislature had caused a vacancy that could be filled permanently only by election; meanwhile it was customary for the Governor to appoint a member pro tem. On Judge Lucas' recommendation, the dignitary consented to give me the little plum, for the few weeks of its term. I was expected to take no more than a figurehead's part in state affairs, and otherwise follow my leader; but I could make a maiden speech in regard to the Convention for Secession soon to form; and later, when I came to practice law, the appointment would look well on my record. There was very little to gain but apparently nothing to lose, and since Judge Lucas had gone to some effort to get me the accolade, I accepted it gladly.

The fact that Butler Mims was an outstanding member of the body, with the reputation for political acumen, had entered into my decision, but I did not know in what way. It stood to reason that it would have made me lean toward the other side.

2

Any concern with Butler Mims was a harking back to the past. So were my brief and rare dealings with Salley and Mildred Hudson; they appeared to have no bearing on the future, or hold no promise for it. When, in her small, neat parlor, Mistress Hudson tried to thank me for what I had done in memory of her son, she broke into tears; and a moment passed before she was again her quiet, gracious, reserved self, telling me that I must take the will of thanksgiving for the deed.

Salley sent me, without a word, a beautiful pair of dueling pistols that Mate had inherited from a Hudson forefather.

Mounted in silver, and beautifully engraved, they were flint-locks of obsolete model, but I knew that Mate had treasured them, and I thought the gift was a noble one, and perhaps of more appropriateness than I could readily bring to mind.

I saw her, graced by candlelight, at a small supper given by Judge Lucas in honor of the Governor. She did not stay long, and the few minutes that I talked to her tête à tête I spoke mainly of Africa, its grassy plains, its rocky *kopjes*, and lean mimosa forest, and principally its swarming herds of game.

But she took the opportunity to congratulate me warmly on accepting the passing honor of my appointment.

"Every man of ambition should take part in public life," she told me, "and since I'm going up to Columbia shortly—for a long visit with my school friend, Helen Bettis—I expect to go to the capital to hear your maiden speech."

"It's a mere formality—letting me make it is the customary gesture on the part of house leaders."

"All the more reason for you to make a good one."

"For an immediate Convention for Secession?"

"If that's what you want—if you think it's best for the South. What's the use of waiting until next year? It seems to me the die is cast."

She left me then, and a few minutes later waved me goodbye. I did not see her again until Miss Bettis entertained for her at a garden party at her ancient family seat overlooking the Con-garee River. Many of the guests were public figures; the Min-ute Men had marched by torchlight only the night before; most of the talk revolved about the great political issue of the day, whether South Carolina should secede at once, leading the movement in the South, or wait for concerted action with other Southern states. Still, when I asked Salley to walk with me, she slipped her hand in mine, the sound of voices quickly died away, and the trouble that lay so heavy on the South seemed forgotten and gone.

"It reminds me of Miss Abigail Cumming's garden in Augusta, when I was a dreamer," I told my companion when we had found a rustic seat.

"I remember it was about this time of year," Salley replied. "The roses and honeysuckle were all gone, but a few red japonica were beginning to show. I wore orange, I remember. It went so well with the autumn foliage."

"Today you wear garnet. You don't know—but you do know, of course—how wonderfully it sets off your olive skin and brown hair, and your dark-red lips. Your beauty has waxed since then. Even then, cub that I was, I never doubted it. It was always one of the verities of my life."

"From that I would almost think you are still a dreamer."

"Not of impossible dreams. I won't submit to their persuasions. Even unlikely dreams have rough going with me now."

"I'm sorry to hear it. And I don't see why, considering how many are coming true. You're a guest of the Bettises. In another year you'll be practicing law in Charleston—you've already received a temporary appointment to a state office. Once you called yourself a captain of the deck. People hardly mention that any more—it was just part of the wild oats you sowed. Victory is in your hands."

"Well, we'll talk straight. It's necessary, sooner or later. You and I had a closer bond in that garden six years ago than we have now."

Her expression changed subtly. "I don't know if that's true. Certainly I don't know why—unless we were both so young."

"I had hopes of having you then. Of winning your hand in marriage—and that's the way I said it to myself. Now I look in my heart—and I can't find any."

"You said to talk straight, and I will. I look everywhere for Mate, and I can't find him. He's in my heart but nowhere else. Certainly he's not in you."

"No, you would hardly imagine two men more different."

"Yet you were very fond of each other—and you did more for him than anyone else alive. You think I've forgotten that. You may think I'm ungrateful—"

"No, but those very acts you speak of—services, you might call them—serve only to set us more apart."

"That doesn't seem possible."

"Yet, it's true, and I know why. Every one of them reminds you of what he was—and what I am. Practicing law—making a little speech—getting invited to parties—can those things change me? You know what I am. If I'm no longer a captain of the deck, I'm still a creature of the night. You might be able to love a man like me, but you won't marry a man like me. I'm going to say something that sounds crude, but it's plain, and you'll understand, and to my great regret it's true. Before Clay Hudson ran from the courtroom, he called me what I am. Before I left Clara Day one night, she told me too. I'm not a gentleman, and can never become one. I might fool others, but I don't fool you. I'm not of your social station. The marriage would be a *misalliance*."

Her eyes became round and glistening. "Edward, I swear to you I hadn't thought that—"

"You don't need to think it. You've seen me operate, and that's enough. Well, you didn't see me when I pulled Mate out of Memphis' coils, but he no doubt told you about it. I used my skill as a gambler—the tactics of the underworld. You did see me bring Clara to Hudson Barony, and frighten you into postponing your engagement to Mate. And you've found out by now the methods I used to break Clay. Trickery—deceit—the practice of a gambler—the ways of the underworld."

She leaned toward me, and it seemed I had only to open my arms for her to come into them.

"Well, I can't eat my cake and have it too—"

"A marriage of compromise would not suit me."

"Then what does it mean, Edward? What can it mean, but that there isn't any hope for you and me?"

"All the king's horses—and all the king's men . . . It was Clara who said that. Still, I won't marry someone like Clara. It's a dilemma that can't be resolved."

"Then will you take me back to my friends?"

3

The day came that I was to make my maiden speech in the South Carolina House of Representatives. It was to be the preliminary to a full-dress debate whether the assembly would pass on the Senate's bill setting the date of the Convention of Secession for January 8, or to pass a new bill putting it forward to December 6. I favored the later date, and under the direction of Mr. Lesesne of Charleston, one of the most moderate of the leaders, I prepared to say as much, giving substantial reasons; but this was the only meat in a ten-minute address; the rest was to be a tribute to the state as was invariably made in maiden speeches by new members. It was well gotten up and would surely be well received.

I felt no twinge of stage fright. In fact I was unable to attach any real importance to the event. The fact remained that almost all members answered present to the roll call, and several men from the upper house—friends of Judge Lucas with whom I was soon expected to practice law—dropped in to hear me. The visitors' seats and public benches were largely occupied, almost altogether because of the debate to come. I looked in vain for Salley.

The speaker had announced the order of business and had begun a brief speech introducing me when he was vastly surprised to see a member get up from his chair and raise his hand. The interrupter was a large man whom I knew well—whom I had known most of my remembered days—and suddenly there came to me an inkling vivid and swift as lightning that this seemingly trivial occasion would prove one of the most momentous episodes in both my past and future days.

"The gentleman from Charleston, Mr. Butler Mims, has attracted the attention of the chair," the speaker intoned. "Sir, you have the floor."

"Mr. Speaker, you have told us that the newly appointed member, Mr. Stono, intends to give us his views on setting a time for a Convention of Secession," Butler said in his resonant voice. "I wish at this point to request that he leave that subject to senior members, and instead give us his views on an even more crucial matter, which we must know before we can take any of his utterances in this chamber at face value."

"I'm not sure that I understand you."

"Pray let me explain. At this great time of crisis, all who are not with us are against us. It has come to my knowledge that Mr. Stono has before now acted as a liberator of slaves in the neighboring island of Cuba. I am not speaking of his own slaves —in fact he has never owned any. Those that he freed belonged to another, and regardless of the way the owner got possession of them it strikes me as very strange that a South Carolinian would by trickery permit them to escape into the Cuban forest. All I wish to ask Mr. Stono is, does he believe in the institution of slavery? If he avers that he does, I have no more to say. But if he does not, then I feel that this house should know that we have an abolitionist in our midst."

"This is a very serious challenge. Mr. Stono, do you wish to answer it?"

"Sir, I've always answered every challenge put to me by Mr. Butler Mims."

But I hardly knew what I was saying. I gazed at the still attentive throng, and felt a sense of moving Fate, perhaps of irretrievable disaster. And my heart was suddenly so full.

"All of us will be glad to hear that Mr. Mims is mistaken," the speaker said quietly after a slight pause. "If he is not—but we will wait and hear."

"Mr. Mims has made one great mistake of fact. The four hundred Negroes whom I helped to escape in Cuba were not properly slaves, but free Negroes that had been seized in Haiti to be sold in Cuba."

"Then they were slaves right on," someone growled.

"The gentleman from Charleston, Mr. Stono, has the floor," the speaker reproved him.

"Mr. Speaker, this has never been put up to me before. I have

never put it to myself. If my words come haltingly, I beg that
you and the gentlemen excuse it. Strangely, the words that rush
into my mind were spoken by Lord Brougham nearly half a
century ago, his famous description of slavery. He called it,
'that wild and guilty fantasy that man can hold property in
man.' "

To my surprise, someone applauded loudly. I looked, and it
was an elderly, stout man with a very red face, and he was clapping with the full sweep of his arms, like flapping wings. A
nearly empty bottle was somewhere about. I knew he had not
understood a word I had said.

"Most of the civilized world has come to that opinion," I
went on. "Nearly twenty years ago Great Britain set free every
slave in her vast dominion. It has been ten years, now, since
any human being in France or her colonies wore the chain of
slavery. Last year the Portuguese government decreed freedom
for her slaves, after a period of tutelage. It's been thirty years
since slavery was abolished in Mexico and for over forty years
every Argentine has been born free. In what nations is the institution of slavery growing and thriving still? In Brazil—in
Cuba—and in the Southern states of America."

"I've heard enough," came a deep voice from the assembly.
A brawny man, who looked as though he might have come from
the Piedmont, hurled up from his chair, and started for the
door. Instantly men were getting up all over the hall; without
deigning me a glance they fell in behind the leader—ten—fifteen—twenty and more marched out with a heavy clump of feet.
They seemed to walk in step. If I had tried to speak, I could
not have made myself heard; the only other sound was the frantic clapping of the fat, red-faced man. The rest of the members
were waiting a moment more, some looking me in the face in
rage or cold contempt, others gazing at the floor as though in
embarrassment.

I should sit down now, I thought. It would be the gentlemanly act, now that all my pretensions to gentlemanliness had

gone by the boards. But by the same token there was nothing more to lose, and my heart was on fire.

"Mr. Stono, you have not yet made a direct answer to the member's question," the speaker said in an icy voice.

"I will do so, if I may have the floor for a few minutes more. I submit that if the South would free her slaves, even if this body would declare against slavery, the word would go forth through the world and in our quarrel with the North—over tariffs, over representations, over the right of secession itself—our weak hand would become a gigantic hand. As long as we uphold slavery, we fight on the wrong side, and on the losing side. It is not that we are an ignorant and gross people. All of us know the difference—"

But hardly anyone could hear me now, so loud was the clump and scrape of feet as man after man, band after band, made for the door. Among them were the most fiery secessionists, followers of Robert Rhett, and moderates from the upper Piedmont. And now the spectators began to leave, many of them booing and yelling. But the clerk with a face of flint continued to write in his record. A newspaper correspondent who had been feverishly taking notes threw his notebook to the floor. The fat man with the red face had dropped his head on his breast and fallen to sleep.

Then the speaker rose, and headed for a door behind the rostrum. The clerk laid down his pen and closed his book. I raised my voice in a shout.

"That wild and guilty fantasy that man can hold property in man."

Then suddenly the nightmare-like scene was over. I looked for Butler Mims, but he had gone; and the sleeper and I were left alone in the empty, echoing hall. I think I smiled at myself and at Fate—and my own and everyone's subjection to Fate, regardless of his handsome dreams—and smiled too that I was a pretty good gambler, who would back his hand.

Gathering up my notes, I started up the long corridor to the doorway. As I did so, I saw a girlish figure emerge from some recess in the entranceway and appear to stand waiting.

I did not know what was coming. I dared not guess. My soul seemed rising out of my body in some great ascendancy, almost transfiguration, but I called it back and bade it not be a fool. As I came up to Salley, her eyes glistened with tears but she gave me a dim and lovely smile.

"A pretty kettle of fish," she said in low tones. Yet I heard her plain.

"I'm sorry to throw you down."

"I don't know that you have. Like our old friend Butler, I've got a question to ask. Edward, South Carolina is going to secede from the Union. What will you do then?"

"That's an easy one. I'll go with my state, of course."

"Then will come war. I can almost hear the marching and the cannon. Where will you be?"

"Somewhere in the ranks. I'll find a place there all right—among other po' whites from the South. I won't even have to change my name. Some captain from the mountains will be glad to enlist me, when he sees how I handle a gun."

"The South will lose. Uncle Mason said so, before he died."

"It won't be the first time I've lost all. And the war won't last forever."

"You won't have lost all, if you count me."

"I don't know what you mean."

"It ought to be plain enough. If you want me, I'll be waiting for you. I'll do better than that. I'll take you before you go."

"Don't say it unless you mean it. You refused me when I was winning—and now I've thrown away my dream of becoming a gentleman."

"It wasn't a dream, Edward. That's the wonderful part of it. You were one all the time. Neither of us had the sense to know it. And if you don't believe me—what I said just now—try me—"

She opened her hands a little. When I held out my arms she ran into them with a childlike cry. We stood in the empty hall, a lonely and forsaken place, but neither of us would be alone

again. Her kiss told me so, and her rush of words. I forgot my
lonely oneness; it had ceased to exist.

I did not know what life meant—an allotted time, to aspire,
to love, to strive—but it was no dim lamp in the dark of non-
existence, no trifling boon.

THE POLITICS OF
PROVINCIALISM

The Democratic Party in Transition,
1918–1932

THE
POLITICS

OF
PROVINCIALISM

The Democratic Party in Transition,

1918–1932

DAVID BURNER

Alfred A. Knopf   New York   1968

THIS IS A BORZOI BOOK
PUBLISHED BY ALFRED A. KNOPF, INC.

FIRST EDITION

To

SANDY and DIANE

ACKNOWLEDGMENTS

I am indebted for criticisms to Professors Richard Hofstadter, Walter Metzger, and William Leuchtenburg, all of Columbia University. Professor Hofstadter, critical yet patient and encouraging, was a model doctoral adviser; the rich content of one single-spaced, seven-page letter from Professor Metzger kept me working for the better part of a year; and Professor Leuchtenburg's help was invaluable in matters of bibliography and style. For criticism and favors I am obliged to Robert Burner, Robert Cross, Alden Vaughan, Marvin Weinbaum, Jordan Schwarz, David Ellis, Lowell Dyson, and to many helpful students and librarians; and I owe a special debt for the typing and editorial assistance of Marian Wilson. As Gilder Fellow at Columbia I was able to devote the year 1962–3 to research, and Oakland University later awarded me travel grants. I am especially pleased to thank Thomas West of Catholic University, whose keen sense of literary architecture and style has its imprint on every page of this book; the work has profited in every way from his generous help.

Stony Brook, New York   D . B .
June 1967

CONTENTS

PREFACE   *xi*

CHAPTER

I   *Rural Traditions and Urban Encroachments*   *3*

II   *The Wilson Coalition*   *28*

III   *The Divisive Themes*   *74*

IV   *The Election of 1924*   *103*

V   *Franklin D. Roosevelt and Party Organization in the Twenties*   *142*

VI   *The Congressional Democrats*   *158*

VII   *The Brown Derby Campaign*   *179*

VIII   *The Composition of the 1928 Vote*   *217*

EPILOGUE: *Franklin D. Roosevelt and the Depression*   *244*

APPENDIX: *Homogeneous Election Districts Used in Voting Samples for Chapter VIII*   *253*

BIBLIOGRAPHY   *256*

INDEX   *follows 293*

PREFACE

In the years of Republican ascendancy from 1920 to 1932, the national Democratic party transformed itself from an institution largely rural in its orientation and leadership to one that embodied the aspirations of the American city dweller—and most notably, the urbanite of immigrant stock. Ever since the elections of 1894 and 1896, the party had looked to the country for its largest vote; even in the Wilson era the strength of the party in rural areas exceeded its strength in the cities. But in the congressional elections of the 1920's, the urban representation in the House began to take on a solidly Democratic cast; and since the cities were growing steadily, rapidly surpassing the countryside in population, the urban congressional victories signified that the city Democracy was destined to electoral predominance within the party. The nomination of Alfred E. Smith as presidential candidate in 1928 demonstrated the power that the city could wield in national Democratic politics.

Strife and bitterness accompanied the passage of Democratic power from country to city. The rural Democrats fought a strong rearguard action upon the grounds of nativism, prohibition, and Protestantism; often their efforts were directed less against the Republicans than against the urban Democratic faction. The conflict centered in the national conventions and in the presidential elections, where country Democrats, even when they did not cross political lines, gave only lukewarm support to their party. Each of the losing candidates in the twenties—James M. Cox, John W. Davis, and Alfred E. Smith—was in some way associated with the city or its political machines and therefore possessed little real appeal for the rural South and West. Yet in each of these presidential elections—if in that of 1924 the Democrats be credited with the La Follette supporters who voted for Democratic congressional candidates—the party gained additional urban strength. Had the city and country been able to cooperate by naming candidates acceptable to the whole party, the Democrats could have provided the Republicans with a more formidable opposition during the twenties. But a national coalition could not easily be constructed in a party so deeply split over emotionally charged issues.

The most prominent Democratic figures of the decade were not pawns in a greater battle between conflicting social factions, for their own persons and ideals represented too vitally the issues at stake. Informal, slangy, cigar-smoking, Governor Smith of New York was the personification of the city, its natives as well as its immigrants. The qualities of his speech, his gait and bearing, betokened an upbringing and way of life as yet new to American presidential politics. William Gibbs McAdoo, born in Georgia and raised in Tennessee, defended rural society against the encroachments of the city; he advanced prohibition and accepted support from the Klan. But McAdoo was also a New York businessman—he had secured financial backing for the first Hudson River tunnels; in his person the manner and outlook of the countryside found only partial expression. The champion of the country was the aging William Jennings Bryan, after whom McAdoo attempted to pattern his own political career. Bryan, the spokesman of fundamentalist religion and prohibition, remained until his death an influential figure in the Democratic party.

The programs of the Democratic leaders reflected their divergent loyalties. Bryan believed in the innate superiority of rural to urban America, and in the style as in much of the content of his reform he was an agrarian; Smith, who went so far as to exhibit a personal misunderstanding of the hinterland and a distaste for its ways, proposed reforms that were directed chiefly toward the urban population. Substantially more radical than the multitudes he enraptured, Bryan championed a galaxy of far-reaching reforms as emphatically in the twenties as at any other period in his life. The progressivism of Al Smith was somewhat more narrowly circumscribed; it limited its attention mostly to the kinds of change that would promote efficiency in government or lift some economic or legal burden from his working-class supporters. In the late twenties, as the city eclipsed the country in the Democratic party and as the immigrants began to vote in larger numbers, the evangelical reformism of Bryan and his followers among the small, unorganized farmers gave way to the self-interest of urban political pressure groups, both ethnic and economic.

It was to a large extent the Great Depression, against which the two factions of the Democracy could make common cause, that restored the party to health. But the restoration also demanded an individual who could somehow bridge the gap between the mores of city and country, and mold the party's program to a more encompassing and inspiring form. Franklin Delano Roosevelt of upstate New York was ideally suited to this task. Throughout the twenties he had maintained ties both with Tammany Hall and with the South and West; and one day, his craftsmanship as a mediator of divergent views and personalities would prove itself amidst the administrative and party tensions of the New Deal.

THE POLITICS OF
PROVINCIALISM

The Democratic Party in Transition,

1918–1932

CHAPTER I

Rural Traditions
and Urban Encroachments

In the decade following World War I, as the American city made continuing encroachments upon the countryside and an earlier, village way of life, the traditional and the younger Americas came into something approaching total conflict. One faction, the rural and nativist, had been long familiar to America in the politics of William Jennings Bryan; the other, the urban and immigrant represented by Al Smith, the Irish Catholic Governor of New York, was testing its power in national politics. The Democratic party was the arena of their confrontation.

At the 1924 Democratic Convention in New York City the two factions clashed openly and in full ceremony. In Madison Square Garden the prohibitionist collided with the cockney and the liberal, Protestant glowered at Catholic, the East Side jeered the Nebraska spread, and Smith battled William Gibbs McAdoo to a 100-ballot stalemate. The tensions, indeed the very chaos of that scene belied the notion, sometimes expressed by observers then and since, that during the decade of Republican ascendancy the Democratic party was torpid. And when in the years of the Great Depression the party regained some measure of internal harmony, its objectives redefined, and its center of gravity now clearly shifted to the city, it was able to demonstrate both the strength of its parts and the political effectiveness of their new arrangement.

Ultimately the conflict of the 1920's was one of values: those "Protestant" virtues and comfortable if narrow tastes to which nineteenth-century village America had adhered, set against the standards—scarcely less moralistic perhaps, and at times scarcely less provincial—of the modern American city and the enthusiasms of its communal enclaves: Roman ritual, Jewish scholarship, the disciplines of celibacy, and the pleasures of the saloon. And of course, there was the fact of urban cosmopolitanism, the sophistication and enlightened curiosity that might give their character to one city dweller even while his neighbor held to the secure institutions of the Old Country. The mere existence of a cosmopolitan outlook could awaken fears and hostilities on the part of a receding and beleaguered small-town culture.

A number of specific themes and issues defined the larger conflict. Anti-Catholicism—a phenomenon possessing its own independent existence as well as a connection with other attitudes—has a well-chronicled history older than that of the nation itself. Another question of long standing was that of prohibition. Since the late 1840's it had helped to separate the immigrants of that day, the Irish and the Germans, from many old-stock Americans; but the victory of the prohibitionists was incomplete until the ratification of the Eighteenth Amendment in 1920, and that victory was soon to vanish in new strife over the issue. The movement for immigration restriction originated fairly early in the nineteenth century, and as the population expanded, the arguments for restriction, both social and economic, assumed force and an increasing ability to generate ill feeling. In the 1920's Congress debated with passionate intensity bills curtailing immigration.

Other events contributed specifically to rural-urban confrontation in that decade: the assembly-line automobile, the radio, and the movies. Each provided a physical, cultural invasion of the country by the city; country folk could see and hear the city as it moved out upon them. Add to this World War I, with its aggressions, its raucous patriotism, its concern over hyphenism; and even the census report of 1920 that declared the cities to have outdistanced the country in population. While the census declaration was arbitrary in many ways, it must have had its imaginative effect on the American consciousness. An analogous report in 1890 had announced the end of the frontier, and it had some part in prompting Frederick Jackson Turner to his frontier thesis that helped to shape the American imagination. So too the census of 1920 could have brought the American city to a new awareness of political and social strength, and the American hinterland to a heightened state of fear and militance.[1]

But why in the twenties did the urban-rural antagonisms center within the Democratic party? There was at least one ephemeral reason: only the Democrats needed to suffer the

[1] Census reports must be read and evaluated with care; semantic ambiguities particularly complicate the reports that locate the changing areas of rural and urban America. To census officials in 1920, for example, "rural" referred to farms and towns of fewer than 2,500. A small town of 5,000, or even a small city of 25,000, located in the middle of a farming area and dependent on farming for its economic well-being, might in fact possess a rural character unrevealed in the reports. Nor were dwellers in the large cities necessarily untouched by country ways. Even in New York and Chicago there were men and women residing who had come too recently from the country to be truly urban in outlook. And nationality groups recently arrived on American shores often adhered to some of the mores of the European village. While the ghettos of New York and other big cities presented the ethnic variety and the viewpoint of a new American urbanism, that urbanism itself reproduced many of the institutions of County Cork or the southern Italian plains —above all, the church of the European peasant. And urban provinciality itself sometimes fully rivaled in its narrowness the vision of upstate New York or the Middle West and South.

While the census reports of 1920 were perhaps premature in calling America urban, those of 1930 most assuredly were not. The Census Bureau did not hold to a consistent standard in its definition of rural and urban; but if the discrepancies be leveled and a single reasonable measure imposed, we will find 14,365,512 more urban dwellers recorded in 1930 than in the previous report. See United States Bureau of the Census, *Fifteenth Census of the United States: 1930. Population*, I, 7–8.

divisions of the presidential nominating process. In 1924 and 1928 the choice for the incumbent Republicans was predetermined, and even in 1920 the Republican candidate, once nominated, attracted a diversity within the political and social spectra. More basically, however, the composition of the two parties was such as to assure that the Democratic would be the party of deeper social and ethnic conflict. The Republican cause was that of the middling elements in American civilization, in country and city alike, and appealed to a wide range of incomes and occupations, while for decades the Democracy had attracted the extremes—the most aggressively Jeffersonian or populist of the farmers, particularly in the South, and the most powerful of the urban immigrant machines. And the city immigrant was of necessity the symbolic urbanite; alienated in varying degrees from American society as a whole, he had to take his identity as an American exclusively from his immediate surroundings.

We might fix on two moments in the history of the Democratic party—the age of Jefferson and the time of Jackson. During these periods, the party adopted a distinctly rural or frontier countenance and established certain traditions and assumptions about itself upon which the country faction of a later era could draw. Yet the Democrats were by no means the uniquely rural party. In the early and middle nineteenth century, no national political organization, whether Democratic, Whig, or antislavery, could have survived even temporarily without drawing massive rural support. The Civil War and Reconstruction won for the Democrats the agricultural South, but settled the Republican party upon sections of middle and western America. In the early twentieth century, it was the politics of William Jennings Bryan that shaped the rural Democracy.

Bryan's earliest appeal to the countryside was as an economic reformer. In 1896 he adopted a free-silver program that had its passionate adherents among the agrarians, and very few among the city dwellers. Of the fifty most populous counties in the nation, forty-five gave pluralities to McKinley in the November election; of the remaining five that went for Bryan, four were in the traditionally Democratic South. The combined population of the twenty-three McKinley states was 44.8 per cent urban—if an urban community be defined as one having a population of 2,500 or more—while the twenty-two that went for Bryan were 21.4 per cent urban. A comparison with the previous presidential election is telling: the Democratic plurality of 162,000 in the eighty-five principal cities in 1892 was replaced in 1896 by a Republican plurality of 464,000. Outside the most urban areas the 1896 election told another story. Bryan improved on Cleveland's record in the agrarian states and carried 1,551 of the nation's 2,738 counties. With Populist help he also increased the Democratic vote in thirty of the nation's forty-five states.[2]

Thereafter Bryan turned to a more general kind of reform. His program was to embody policies of urban as well as rural progressivism, yet its expression and its energy were of the character of middle-border protest. By 1912 he had proposed a graduated income tax and government ownership of the railroads; he fought against the abuse of the labor injunction; he pioneered in proposing a bank deposit guarantee similar to that

[2] For a view of the 1896 election returns in a long-range context, see Tables I and II. McKinley's success in the cities and Bryan's in the country do not constitute *prima facie* evidence of urban-rural tension in the elections. V. O. Key, Jr., sees a more distinct sectional antagonism in the returns: "A Theory of Critical Elections," *Journal of Politics*, XVII (February 1955), 15–16. On the emphasis given to free silver in the campaign, see Paul W. Glad: *McKinley, Bryan, and the People* (Philadelphia, 1964), pp. 137–8, 164–5, 167, 173–5, 179–84, 206. All national, state, city, and county tallies—hereafter not footnoted—for the years 1916 and before are to be found in Edgar Eugene Robinson: *The Presidential Vote, 1896–1932* (Stanford, 1934); those for 1920 through 1940 are in Richard M. Scammon: *America at the Polls: A Handbook of American Presidential Election Statistics, 1920–1964* (Pittsburgh, 1965). United States Bureau of the Census, *Tenth Census: Population*, I, 9–57.

forced upon Franklin Roosevelt in 1933. Impelled by a Jacksonian faith, he championed sundry democratic reforms: initiative, referendum, and recall; direct primaries; a single-term presidency; woman suffrage; and the movement against the lame-duck Congress. If these programs appear shallow next to those of the New Deal, they were radical compared to those of the preceding generation. William Allen White later observed that Bryan had "stood for as much of the idea of socialism as the American mind will confess to." If Bryan reformism did not compete successfully against Republican progressivism in most of the Central and Western states, it did win for the party in 1900 and 1908 a larger proportionate vote there than the Democrats had been winning before 1896. This support, coupled with that of the South, and set against the success of the Republican progressives and conservatives among at least the non-immigrant urban classes, gave the national Democratic vote a strongly rural complexion.[3]

Of itself, the popular support that Bryan won in these elections may not have had a more than temporary influence upon the party, which was always too heterogeneous to sustain a Bryan stereotype. In 1912, however, he helped secure the Democratic nomination for his fellow progressive, Woodrow Wilson, and thereupon agrarian progressivism became an even stronger force within the Democracy. Upon his victory, Wilson felt obligated—despite some qualms—to choose the Nebraskan as his Secretary of State, and Bryan gave unstinting support in working for a version of Wilson's reform program more far-reaching even than that which Wilson himself had set forth during the campaign. But the growing respect between the two leaders ended abruptly in 1915. Wilson's harsh note to Germany

[3] President Theodore Roosevelt had incorporated into his politics and even, in part, into law a reform program similar to Bryan's, as George Mowry points out in his *Theodore Roosevelt and the Progressive Movement* (Madison, Wisc., 1946), p. 35. White is quoted in Paul W. Glad: *The Trumpet Soundeth: William Jennings Bryan and His Democracy, 1896–1912* (Lincoln, Neb., 1960), p. 158.

on submarine warfare clashed with the neutralist conscience of his Secretary.[4]

Yet in spite of their failure to agree on handling the German problem, these two progressive Democrats pursued common policies—from interference in Latin American affairs to regulation of big business—and thereby gave a measure of coherence to the Democratic party program. Wilson was attentive to agricultural protest, though sometimes at variance with its leaders, and was disposed to share the rural and small-town aversion to the city. Both Wilson and Bryan worked more diligently than any other statesmen of their time for an international organization to settle world problems peaceably. The issue of prohibition was one of the few on which the two were far apart.

In at least one major respect their characters were as similar as their politics. For better or worse, each man brought a strong sense of Christian morality directly into American politics. Both profoundly believed that for every problem there was a "moral" course of action. And each man could stand intractably behind his commitments. Bryan, for instance, refused to abandon free silver, even after 1900 when that program had lost its initial popularity and he could have campaigned more effectively on a policy of anti-imperialism alone.[5] As distinctive in its stubborn courage as in its political folly was Wilson's intransigence on the League of Nations.

Similar in moral rigor and in their legislative programs, the two men also drew overlapping political support. It is true that some urban political leaders, such as Roger Sullivan of Chicago, had played an important role in nominating Wilson in 1912, whereas Bryan had identified certain urban bosses with large corporate interests. But Sullivan had supported Wilson in part to prevent a possible stalemate which would result in Bryan's nomination. In rhetorical thrusts at Wall Street and Tammany,

[4] *New Republic*, II (March 13, 1915), 139–40; Arthur S. Link: *Wilson: The New Freedom* (Princeton, 1956), pp. 206–7, 213, 222.
[5] Glad: *The Trumpet Soundeth*, pp. 59–60.

as well as in his snubbing of Boss Charles Murphy of New York in the 1912 campaign, Wilson showed the same independence of urban machines that had characterized his tenure as governor of New Jersey. In the 1912 convention, Bryan's attachment to Wilson had developed largely because of Murphy's opposition to the Princetonian. And in both 1912 and 1916, Wilson drew even more support from the countryside than had Bryan. In 1916 twenty-three states of the South and Far West voted for Wilson, and the biggest cities did not figure greatly in the electoral victory. Wilson did improve on Bryan's vote in the eastern cities, but he also carried almost all of the wheat states, and thereby outdid Bryan in his home territory. At the same time, patronage dealt out by Postmaster General Burleson maintained rapport between Wilson and the urban machines, which, with the aid of Burleson and presidential aide Joe Tumulty, were actually strengthened at the expense of some urban progressives. But if in some measure Wilson may have harmonized the city and the country wings of the party, most fundamentally he "emerged as the present heir of the great populist-Bryan tradition."[6]

The Wilson coalition of 1916 was based upon agrarian and peace sentiment, as well as upon Wilson's impressive record of reform, and was strongest in its rural component. Had the election been decided in the nation's ten major cities, Charles Evans Hughes would clearly have won. And the nation's industrial states, with the exception of New Hampshire, Ohio, Washington, and California, went entirely to Hughes. The voters in the South and West, who formed the backbone of the rural Wilson

[6] Arthur S. Link: *Wilson: The Road to the White House* (Princeton, 1947), pp. 353-4, 403-4, 433, 465, 495, 527; *Wilson: The New Freedom*, p. 160; and "Woodrow Wilson and the Democratic Party," *Review of Politics*, XVIII (April 1956), 146, 150 ff.; John Blum: *Woodrow Wilson* (Boston, 1956), p. 114, and *Joe Tumulty and the Wilson Era* (Boston, 1951), pp. 152-3; Glad: *The Trumpet Soundeth*, p. 172; Mortimer Smith: *William J. Gaynor, Mayor of New York* (Chicago, 1951), p. 145; Seward Livermore: *Politics Is Adjourned: Woodrow Wilson and the War Congress, 1916-1918* (Middletown, Conn., 1964), p. 240.

coalition of 1916, cast their ballots for the incumbent presidential candidate as the statesman who "kept us out of war"; in their quest for peace they looked also to Bryan, who campaigned for Wilson throughout the West and South, as they looked to him in matters of social reform.

By the 1920's, then, the Democratic party had laid for itself in the hinterland a solid progressive foundation, and progressive in the manner of Bryan. Somewhere in the process, moreover, the country Democracy was acquiring more and more clearly a tone that had always been present in the progressive movement itself—a tone of moralism, the style of the Jeremiad.

The aims of the rural faction became larger than the economic and political; it sought no less than the rescue of traditional American virtue, and that virtue it identified with the countryside, which must now resist the moral corruption of the cities—their political machines, their saloons, their strange religious faiths—even as it must also resist their financial perfidy. Bryan led the way. Of the election of 1916 he exulted to a meeting of prohibitionists—he had enlisted in the cause by about 1909—that the party had "won without the aid of the cities, and . . . received the support of nearly all the prohibition states . . ."; in *The Commoner* he wrote that the election was a victory for "the West and South without the aid or consent of the East. The scepter has passed from New York, and this is sufficient glory for one year."[7] This was to be the moral tone of Bryan's heir apparent of the early twenties, William Gibbs McAdoo, who deferred to the Bible Belt and, like Bryan, became a strong prohibitionist. To be sure, "the impassioned criticism of the social order, which Bryan had brought to the Democratic party . . . was not for McAdoo," as Herbert Agar has noted. The enterprising McAdoo frequently indulged in Populist rhetoric, but he lacked a strong emotional or intellectual commitment to populist

[7] On Bryan's symbolic importance in the 1916 convention, see Arthur S. Link: *Wilson: Campaigns for Progressivism and Peace* (Princeton, 1965), pp. 44–5, 47, and *The New York Times*, June 16, 1916, p. 1, which called Bryan "the outstanding figure of the convention." Bryan is quoted in *The Commoner*, XVI (November 1916), 1.

reform. McAdoo, moreover, was not so conspicuously country-
bred as Bryan; he had lived in New York City for many years,
and he numbered Bernard Baruch of that city among his important supporters. Nevertheless, his utterances were replete
with condemnations of the city as the home of Wall Street and
with praise of the country as the hope of America.[8]

The later career of Bryan indicated the continuity of the progressive with the moralist phase of the country faction. He
never relinquished his commitment either to progressive reform
or to the Democratic party. When in 1920 the Prohibitionists,
meeting in Lincoln, Nebraska, tendered their nomination to
Bryan, the honor was insufficient to lure him from the Democratic organization. Staying within the party was for Bryan a
simple matter of loyalty and faith. In another setback to the
prohibition forces, Bryan swallowed hard in 1920 and voted
for the wet Democratic candidate James Cox.[9]

And in contrast to the stereotype of the aging Nebraskan, the
seedy figure with the palm-leaf fan, furnished by H. L.

[8] According to Arthur Schlesinger, Jr., the "facile and plastic" McAdoo
made himself over in the image of Bryan. *The Crisis of the Old Order,
1919–1932* (Boston, 1957), p. 94. William Watts Ball of North Carolina,
among others, preferred Bryan to McAdoo, whom he called "mercenary"
and "shoddy." Ball to [?] Watson, August 28, 1924, Ball Papers. Not
until the 1924 convention did Bryan, who apparently relished the role
of an elder statesman, work for McAdoo's nomination. But he supported
the efforts of Robert Woolley to take control of the party away from
National Chairman George White and the urban faction in 1921. It was
evidently the candidacy of Smith, which Bryan had termed "impossible,"
that forced the older Democrat to give some support to McAdoo's camp.
Post to Bryan, February 8, 1921, Bryan to Post, February 28, 1921, and
March 1, 1921, Post Papers; Woolley, unpublished memoir, Chap. xxx,
Woolley Papers; J. J. Alexander to Thomas B. Love, May 10, 1924, Love
Papers; *The New York Times*, October 13, 1923, p. 1; December 31, 1923,
p. 7; May 11, 1924, p. 1; July 8, 1924, p. 1; Agar: *Pursuit of Happiness*
(Cambridge, Mass., 1938), p. 340; New York *World*, June 23, 1924, pp.
1, 23.
[9] *The Commoner*, XX (May 6, 1920), 1; *New Republic*, XXI (January
28, 1920), 258; Lawrence Levine: *Defender of the Faith: William
Jennings Bryan; The Last Decade, 1915–1925* (New York, 1965), pp.
170–4.

Mencken, the more generous and more accurate portrait by Lawrence Levine shows Bryan in his last years working to rekindle reform within the party. In 1919 he stood by his peace principles when he gave strong endorsements to the League, though he did severely criticize the President for failing to compromise on the issue of Article X of the League Covenant. He also remained consistent in his concern for economic progressivism. Before the presidential election of 1920 the Commoner lauded the achievements of Wilson's first term, which he considered a fruition of his own work, but he charged Wilson with the responsibility for the demise of progressive Democracy after 1916. In 1920 he also urged the Nebraska Constitutional Convention "to authorize the state, the counties, and the cities to take over and operate any industry they please. . . . The right of the community is superior to the right of any individual." The next year he came out with a bold new program of twenty-two miscellaneous progressive planks, which included proposals for a department of education in the President's cabinet, government ownership of certain monopolies, and an excess-profits tax. In 1923 Bryan was still enunciating a simple radicalism directed especially, but not wholly, to the needs of the farmer; he also called for an alliance with progressive Republicans to secure legislative goals. Claude Bowers, among others, praised Bryan's lifelong efforts in behalf of reform: "Almost everything we've got today in the way of reforms originated with Bryan. . . . And yet everybody thinks of him now because of his prohibition views and on account of that evolution trial."[1]

At one point in the twenties Bryan remarked: "I don't think there is a busier man than I am. I have got to keep the Demo-

[1] Bowers: Oral History Memoir, Columbia University, 1954; see also William Gibbs McAdoo: *Crowded Years* (Boston, 1931), p. 337. On Bryan's political influence in the twenties, see Levine: *Defender of the Faith*, pp. 186–8 and *passim*; *The New York Times*, February 17, 1921, p. 3; March 18, 1923, VIII, 1; April 2, 1923, pp. 1, 6; and William E. Dodd: *Woodrow Wilson and His Work* (New York, 1922), p. 431. *Review of Reviews*, CXII (July 1920), 42; *The Commoner*, XX (February 1920), 8–9; Bryan to Henry T. Rainey, January 2, 1924, Rainey Papers.

cratic party straight, and I have got to see that Prohibition is enforced, and I have got to see that religion is defended." William Allen White exaggerated when he said that Bryan dominated the platform committee of the Democratic National Convention of 1924, but even in New York his presence was imposing. The New York *Herald-Tribune* called Bryan's July 2 speech to the convention his "greatest flight of oratory in years." Many of the country delegates at the old Madison Square Garden clung to him as a symbol of righteousness in the face of the jeering Irishmen and Italians with whom Tammany had packed the galleries. But in New York, Bryan saw with grief that his was an embattled America. When he addressed the delegates, applause greeted his remark that this would probably be his last convention. "I may change my mind," he threatened, but his life was in fact nearing a close.[2]

The following summer he appeared at the Scopes trial in Dayton, Tennessee. Bryan's belief in reform had always been sustained by his faith in a beneficent God, and in the era of Republican normalcy he had turned increasingly to the Protestant churches, which he had always viewed as agencies of reform. Even in his gesture at Dayton—the culmination of the events through which, philosophically and practically, he severed himself from the rising urban Democracy—his loyalty to the fundamentalist faith was in part a loyalty to his own special religious-moral brand of social reform, as well as to what Walter Lippmann called his "dogma of majority rule." In a passage from a lecture on the evils of Darwinism that he did not live to deliver, Bryan said of the evolution theory that "by paralyzing the hope of reform, it discourages those who labor for the improvement of man's condition. . . . Evolution chills

[2] White: *Politics: The Citizen's Business* (New York, 1924), p. 69; *Christian Register*, III (July 10, 1924), 104; W. J. Dwyer to Breckinridge Long [1925?], Long Papers; *The New York Times*, July 2, 1924, p. 5; *Official Report of the Proceedings of the Democratic National Convention . . . [of] . . . 1924* (Indianapolis, 1925), p. 327; Paxton Hibben: *The Peerless Leader: William Jennings Bryan* (New York, 1929), p. 379.

the enthusiasm [for social reform] by substituting aeons for years." But this observation did not interest his followers, who had turned to simpler moralist concerns and a mood of pure moral antagonism to the city.[3]

The alliance between the Democratic party and the major immigrant groups had its origin in the early national period, when the Jeffersonians opposed the anti-Jacobin and anti-Irish Alien and Sedition Acts. New Americans found their way into the local organizations of the Democratic-Republicans and then the Democrats, and in their turn attracted later comers. As the Democrats stood by their immigrant supporters against the Protestant nativism of the late 1840's and early 1850's, the party drew even larger numbers; and an appeal for the votes of the economically deprived also strengthened the party among the immigrants. Most of the recruiting was among the Irish, partly because they were by far the most numerous of the immigrants during the first half of the nineteenth century, partly because they were almost solidly Roman Catholic and therefore the most unified in their opposition to nativism, while the Germans—after the Irish the largest group—were divided in religion and more often settled in rural areas away from the influence of Democratic political machines.

The traditions of Ireland and the experiences of three generations of American Irish help to explain the Irish role in the Democratic party. Under English domination, where common-law institutions reinforced the relationship between the ruled and the ruling people, the Irish learned to bargain at the local level for the favors of the central government. In their Church and in their anti-English secret societies the Irish learned loyalty

[3] William Allen White wrote that "the passing of Bryan has changed the whole aspect of the Democratic party. He was the one living force that held his party in check against the new order." New York *Herald-Tribune*, June 25, 1928, p. 3. Lippmann: *Men of Destiny* (New York, 1927), p. 45; *American Review of Reviews*, LXXII (September 1925), 312–13.

and discipline; and in the early-nineteenth-century Catholic
Association movement, which in several ways functioned as a
political party, they strengthened their feeling for political
power. Once in America, the Irish used the Democratic party as
a secular extension of their identity. Shunning union with a
middle class that had ordained a Protestant America, they introduced to the party their national and Catholic traditions of discipline, hierarchy, and communal solidarity. Pluralism was discouraged by the parochial school system and by the social and
religious influences of parish priests who distrusted Protestant
reformers. It was opportune that the Irish settled in the American cities, where their cultural traditions would be well adapted
to political life.[4]

Before the Civil War, some important urban Democratic
machines—notably Tammany Hall—were acquiring an Irish
stamp.[5] Even by mid-century, the city was pressing the immigrant communities into compact political units representing a
considerable part of the urban populations among which they
lived. Cities provided, therefore, a means of effective and self-

[4] Edward M. Levine: *The Irish and Irish Politicians* (Notre Dame, Ind.,
1966), pp. 4–10, 30, 35–51, 65–9, 83, 87, 98–101, 116, 125–9; Nathan Glazer
and Daniel P. Moynihan: *Beyond the Melting Pot: The Negroes, Puerto
Ricans, Italians, and Irish of New York* (Cambridge, Mass., 1964), pp. 221–
38.
[5] On the Democracy's longstanding attraction for the Irish, see Oscar
Handlin: "The Immigrant in American Politics," in David F. Bowers,
ed.: *Foreign Influence in American Life* (Princeton, 1944), pp. 88–90,
and Carl Wittke: *The Irish in America* (Baton Rouge, 1956), pp. 105–
13; on the Irish in New York State, Florence E. Gibson: *The Attitudes
of the New York Irish Toward State and National Affairs, 1848–1892*
(New York, 1951), pp. 14, 56, 88–90, 103, 451, and Lee Benson: *The
Concept of Jacksonian Democracy: New York as a Test Case* (Princeton, 1961), pp. 171–3, 321–3; on the Boston Irish, J. Joseph Huthmacher:
Massachusetts People and Politics, 1919–1933 (Cambridge, Mass., 1959), p.
14 and *passim*; on the Irish in Chicago, Harold F. Gosnell: *Machine Politics: Chicago Model* (Chicago, 1937), pp. 45, 64–6, 101–2. On federalist
antipathy for the Irish, see Wilfred E. Binkley: *American Political
Parties: Their Natural History* (3rd rev. edn.; New York, 1958), pp.
79–80.

conscious political expression denied to the rural immigrant settlements.

In the decades that followed the Civil War, the Irish seized not only the Democratic city machines but many of the cities themselves—New York, Brooklyn, Jersey City, Boston, and San Francisco. But after about 1885 the current of migration began to shift: the preponderance would now be from the South and East of Europe rather than the North and West. On whom would the newer Americans bestow their political allegiance?

At first the Irish, instead of cultivating these potential allies, guarded their own command of urban politics as tenaciously as they maintained control within the American Catholic Church. In several cities the Republicans tried to win the votes of new immigrants—with some lasting success in such cases as the New Haven Italians and the Boston Jews. But the Republicans had inherited some of the nativism as well as the propertied identity of the Federalist-Whig tradition, and by the 1890's the nativist American Protective Association and the Republican party were closely linked in several states. In time, moreover, the Irish warmed to the other white ethnic elements; in Chicago by the 1920's Irish Democrats even learned to address meetings in Italian. Between the newer immigrants and the Irish there was enough similarity of interests—in economic status (despite the edge Irish-Americans had over the more recent comers), often in religion, in the very fact of immigrant background and estrangement from old-stock American society—to overcome mutual antagonisms and pull most of the southern and eastern Europeans into the Irish machines. In considerable measure, Democrats captured the new immigrant as well as the old.[6]

[6] Of the Chicago Italians, for example, Giovanni E. Schiavo wrote in 1928 that "brought up in a corrupt political environment, under the influence of Irish politicians, the Italian has not yet evolved a political conscience of his own. He is still following in the footsteps of the Irish. His methods, his ambitions, his ideals, his goals are the same as those of the Irish." *The Italians in Chicago* (Chicago, 1928), p. 104. On the ties of Republican state parties to the APA, see Wittke: *The Irish*

Between 1894 and the 1920's the Democratic party itself could not be called the party of the cities. Some cities with a predominantly native-born population were traditionally Whig and then Republican; some others were ruled by immigrant Republican machines. As Carl Degler has shown, moreover, there was a period in the late nineteenth century and into the twentieth when the Republican party, uninhibited by Jeffersonian precepts against "energetic" government and therefore free to innovate, was able to appeal widely to city voters as the party of industrial growth and economic experiment.[7] From the Homestead Act to the Dingley Tariff, the income tax to the Blair Education Bill, the Republican party stood for a social and economic nationalism that would appeal to a range of classes at the same time that it spoke the shibboleths of free enterprise and laissez faire. Theodore Roosevelt and other progressives of the early twentieth century called for a strong national government and worked to establish an urban-rural harmony of interests. Doubtless some urban immigrants at the time were won by this image; perhaps ethnic conflict repelled a few of them from the Irish and into the Republican organizations. But the Irishmen, possessing their traditional and highly effective Democratic machines, held their loyalty to the Democracy with only some temporary defection in a few special elections such as 1920, and with a few political deviants like the Republican organizations that captured the Irish of Philadelphia and Rochester. They provided the Democrats with a faithful city immigrant-stock constituency larger than any single bloc the Republicans could

in America, p. 124; on Republican anti-Catholicism after the Civil War, Robert D. Cross: *The Emergence of Liberal Catholicism in America* (Cambridge, Mass., 1958), p. 24; on Irish domination of the Catholic Church, Wittke: *The Irish in America*, pp. 91–5, and Oscar Handlin: *Boston's Immigrants* (rev. edn.; Cambridge, Mass., 1959), pp. 165–7. Robert E. Lane: *Political Life* (New Haven, 1958), p. 241; Oscar Handlin: *The American People in the Twentieth Century* (Cambridge, Mass., 1954), p. 216; Gosnell: *Machine Politics*, p. 24.
[7] Carl N. Degler: "The Nineteenth Century," in William H. Nelson, ed.: *Theory and Practice in American Politics* (Chicago, 1964), pp. 25–42.

usually hope to muster, a constituency broadened more and more by the absorption of new ethnic elements. And in the twenties the immigrants, totally lacking in blood connection with the American hinterland, and thrust by the rural nativist movement into a position of counterattack, were at the forefront of national urban politics. Increasingly they were introducing into the Democratic party a character absent from the Republican: a city gesture, a cockney edge. The Irish continued in their leadership of the city machines. Meanwhile, their new immigrant allies were coming to a full involvement in politics, and at some point in the twenties, as Tables I and II show, the Democrats won the cities.

For the immigrants who came here around the turn of the century, American politics had been a strange business. The new arrival from Italy or the east of Europe was indrawn; he reverenced family, church, and, suffusing all else, his own nationality. He was, in the words of Robert Lane, "pitifully conservative." "Political apathy," declares Lane, "is a function of peasant . . . origin with its associated views of government as part of a natural order beyond control." Even for the Irish, the Catholic Church had at first discouraged political participation, viewing itself as a sanctuary from the harshness of life in the urban ghetto. The segregation of its flock heightened the innate conservatism of the communicants, but the Catholic hierarchy soon found itself unwilling and unable to support the nominal separation of church and state. Church-related issues and pressures on the clergy were as intensive for the Catholic as for the Protestant churches; and the policy of sheltering immigrants from political life was gradually abandoned.[8]

After living in America for a time, the immigrants began to see that his economic and social status could be raised by shaping his activities to political means and ends. The urban machines

[8] Lane: *Political Life*, pp. 244, 251; Handlin: "The Immigrant and American Politics," pp. 90–2. On the attitude of the Catholic Church, see Cross: *The Emergence of Liberal Catholicism*, p. 25, as well as Lane, *passim*.

TABLE I

Urban Presidential Vote: Per Cent Democratic, 1876–1940*

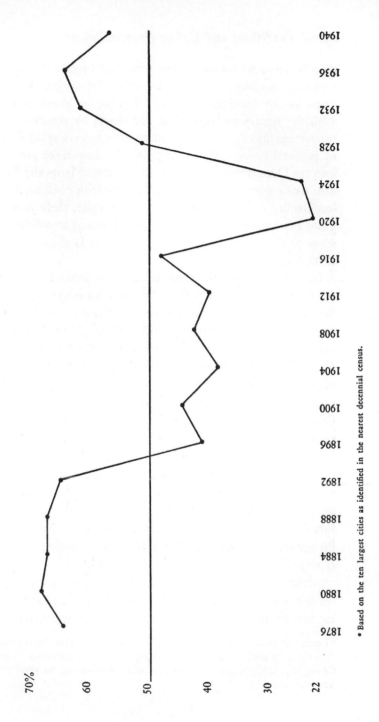

* Based on the ten largest cities as identified in the nearest decennial census.

TABLE II

Urban Congressional Representation: Per Cent Democratic, 1876–1940*

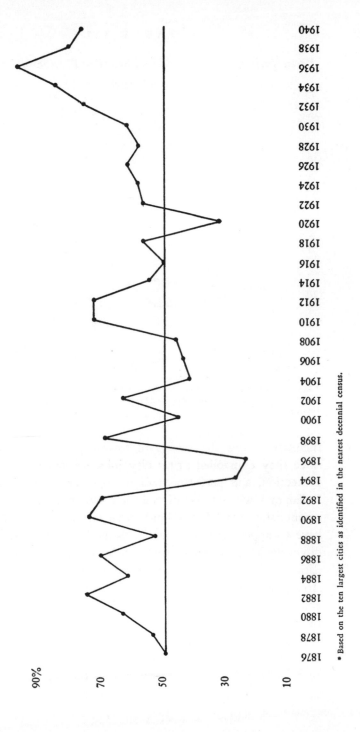

* Based on the ten largest cities as identified in the nearest decennial census.

TABLE III

Participation of Ethnic and Old Stock in Presidential Elections, 1896–1940*

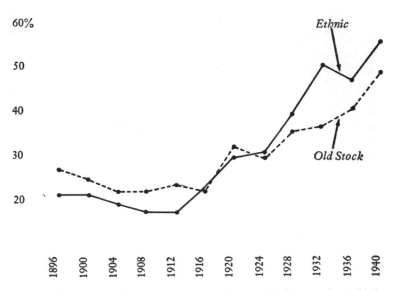

* Based on those cities identified as ethnic and old stock by Carl Degler: "American Political Parties and the Rise of the City: An Interpretation," *Journal of American History*, LI (June 1964), 55–6.

themselves drew the immigrant toward political participation, since they controlled many city jobs, offered police and fire protection, and performed other important functions. If the Italian or Jew was to be offered some patronage or perhaps even a minor slot or two for his kind on the city ticket, then he would have to appear regularly at the polls. Immigrant nationalism, directing itself to issues promoted by the foreign language or nationality press, sharpened political sensitivities, and these were strengthened further as second-generation Americans gained in education and in understanding of political matters. Unions, by requiring naturalization, also brought the new American into politics. Immigrant participation—which is charted in Table III—rose markedly during the foreign-policy debate of 1916 and continued its increase during the 1920's. In 1924 the immigrants of at least one big city, Chicago, were voting as heavily as native whites. The years of neutrality, of the great war, and of that war's unsettling aftermath had awakened the immigrant-stock citizen to the importance of the government as his agent in international relations; and in the twenties, national events touched him directly as immigrant, or as Catholic, or as representative of the ways and aspirations of the city. The movement for immigration restriction sustained his interest in events in Washington, as did the fight to repeal prohibition. The "new immigrant" communities of the postwar era, moreover, were just a bit further up the social and economic scale—certainly a little more firmly rooted—than they had been in their earliest years; and along with improvement in status and opportunity came a quickened energy, an increase in knowledge of political affairs, and a heightened sense of the distance the immigrant had yet to span in the attainment of equality. Apathy once had measured the paucity of his expectations; heightened political participation now represented his new hopes and ambitions. The Great Depression brought the immigrant even more heavily into politics. In later generations, as the immigrant became better assimilated and more economically successful, his political concern, except in relation to European wars, would wane.[9]

Despite the enormous influx of eastern Europeans, the Irish influence remained stronger than that of the newer groups far into the twentieth century, at least in New York, Boston, Chicago, and San Francisco. As late as the administrations of Franklin Roosevelt and Harry Truman, immigrant-stock executive appointees were overwhelmingly Catholic Irish—"a vivid testimonial," according to Samuel Lubell, "of the extent to which the Irish have dominated the Democratic party."[1] Yet until the 1920's the Irish produced no leader who might claim national eminence. A few Irish Democrats, such as Joe Tumulty, had served their party with distinction. But the first national

[9] Lane: *Political Life*, pp. 244–51; Harold F. Gosnell: *Getting Out the Vote* (Chicago, 1927), p. 87.
[1] *The Future of American Politics* (rev. edn.; New York, 1956), p. 83.

figure of the Irish Democracy, though his ancestry was in fact mixed, was Governor Alfred E. Smith of New York. Smith became the spokesman of urban Democracy because he was a machine man—the less so as his career progressed, but his feel for machine politics never left him. As the machine had fixed most of the immigrants to the Democratic party, Smith, as a product of Boss Charles Murphy's Tammany Hall, was their logical representative. The other ethnic and racial minorities easily identified with Al Smith, who radiated warmth and genial impulsiveness. Hitherto, immigrants of different nationalities had often quarreled more strenuously among themselves than against the nativists; but Smith's affability, his stand on prohibition, and the urban-rural tensions of the day molded the city immigrant Democracy into a force of unprecedented cohesion.

The career of Al Smith in the New York Assembly represents in microcosm the politics of the ghetto in its combination of pragmatic reform and pragmatic service to the machine. Smith entered the Assembly in 1904, and in 1911 became Democratic majority leader and chairman of the Ways and Means Committee. He introduced several reform measures designed to eradicate various social injustices and business malpractices—measures representative of the kind of bread-and-butter progressivism that the immigrant condition generates. Among his important accomplishments were the reorganization of the lower criminal courts in New York and a law restraining the issue of fraudulent stock. His factory inspection tours after the tragic Triangle Shirtwaist Factory fire of 1911 led to some important labor legislation, such as that limiting the work of women and children; and in 1914 he supported a far-reaching conservation program. But Smith was often forced to subordinate his own progressive instincts to the will of Charles Murphy, who supported reform only when it seemed likely to pass anyway or was dictated by political expediency. As governor of New York, Charles Evans Hughes introduced a spate of reform measures to the legislature. To embarrass the governor, Tammany joined with the Old Guard Republicans to defeat much of Hughes's program, and Smith was instrumental in carrying out Murphy's orders to demolish the governor's proposals. Smith forced the Assembly Democrats to vote against strengthening the public service commissions—which were a threat to patronage—and against state regulation of the telephone and telegraph. As one student of Smith's Assembly career puts it: "He had achieved notoriety for using his extensive legislative talents against the popular reforms Governor Hughes had sought to institute." Under pressure from Murphy, Smith also pushed through the "West Side grab," an overly generous franchise for a right of way to the grateful New York Central Railroad in New York City. He also wrote the notorious Levy election law that strengthened Tammany's hold on the city. It is only necessary to read the reports of the Citizens' Union of New York during some of his Assembly years to see unquestioned evidence of Smith's frequent readiness to subordinate principles of good government to political aggrandizement.[2]

When Charles Murphy died in 1924, Al Smith eulogized that he had "made of his life a lesson and an example to the youth of the country." Unhappily, it was an example vastly inferior to that of Smith himself. Murphy won a measure of respectability by keeping his hands off the courts and out of the public till, and his religious background apparently cut off prostitution as a source of income; but he was resourceful at profiting from city franchises and private contracts. J. Joseph Huthmacher, in an effort to show the urban lineage of progressivism, refers to him as "that rather obscure progressive figure." And Murphy does deserve credit, whatever his motives, for committing his well-disciplined following to a variety of substantial reforms. But he has been lauded for supporting some reforms, such as workmen's compensation, that had passed almost unanimously, and for others, like the direct primary, that he earlier opposed.

[2] Revealing on the contradictions of Smith's career in the Assembly is a 1964 St. John's University doctoral dissertation by Louis D. Silveri: "The Political Education of Alfred E. Smith: The Assembly Years, 1904–1915"; the quotation is from p. 156. Citizens' Union: *Report of the Commission on Legislation, 1909* (New York, 1910), pp. 17–19.

Murphy acquiesced in that primary which he and Smith had fought so bitterly, but acquiesced only after a Democratic debacle at the polls followed the ruthless impeachment of Governor Sulzer. If Murphy gave his blessing to some reforms, he stood in the way of many more. It would be a misreading of his character, and of Smith's background, to ignore the comments on Murphy made by certain contemporaries. Uninterested in reform, he was "arrogant and selfish," according to the New York *Evening Post;* he was more interested in "money and power," insisted the writer of a Tammany exposé. *The New York Times* said Murphy "was the exemplar and beneficiary of a system which . . . condemns New York City to suffer from . . . the lowest moral standards in public office." "Mr. Murphy and his machine," noted the *New Republic*, "were successful only by making a mockery of the processes of political democracy"; in the city government of 1924, according to *The Nation*, "there is endless graft. . . . The system [Murphy] headed was the same corrupt one which has for generations degraded New York. . . ." The liberal journals were surely closer to the mark than the loyal governor on the occasion of Murphy's death.[3]

As the more constructive activities of Smith's legislative career indicate, he did not merely stagnate under the aegis of Murphy's organization. And in 1915 he emerged a statesman through his widely acclaimed understanding of governmental affairs at the New York State Constitutional Convention. In 1918 he became governor of New York in a rise that testified to the growing

[3] Miss Nancy Weiss, in a forthcoming book on Murphy, presents a balanced portrait of that political figure, whom she credits with bringing Tammany a measure of respectability that helped to make possible the presidential candidacy of Governor Smith. New York *Tribune*, June 17, 1903, p. 1; Huthmacher: "Charles Evans Hughes and Charles Francis Murphy: The Metamorphosis of Progressivism," *New York History*, XLVI (June 1965), 25–40; New York *Evening Post*, January 5, 1919, p. 2; Morris Werner: *Tammany Hall* (New York, 1928), p. 322; *The New York Times*, April 26, 1924, p. 24; *New Republic*, XXXVII (April 19, 1924), 323; XXXVIII (May 7, 1924), 269; LVIII (May 5, 1929), 320; *The Nation*, CXVIII (May 21, 1924), 574; CXXXI (August 27, 1930), 214

power of the immigrant urban supporters as well as to his popularity among an even wider public; his political career up to that time was one of genuine, if only partial, growth in stature from his early position as loyal Tammany henchman. His outlook as governor—even after he became independent of Tammany—would remain conservative in several basic ways. Yet there is no question but that the endeavors in which he excelled, such as administrative reform and labor legislation, entitle him to the highest rank among New York governors and the reputation of a farsighted progressive. In his inaugural address in 1919 he asked that cities be given the right to regulate their own utilities, and he urged state intervention to relieve the postwar housing shortage; during the next year he vetoed a number of laws passed by a legislature in the grip of the Red Scare; and he gave Belle Moskowitz a free hand in choosing members of a Reconstruction Commission to reorganize the state's administrative structure. Before his term was out, the *New Republic* called him "one of the ablest governors New York has ever had."[4]

Before the twenties, the career of Alfred E. Smith struck a nice balance between his instinct for pragmatic reform and his adherence to the machine. Indeed, a harmony existed between certain kinds of reform and the urban machine: a harmony of spirit, technique, and often of economic objective. And although by 1928 Governor Smith had drifted from both of these positions, he remained the fit representative of the plebeian city electorate in its clash with the rural and nativist. The emotional South, where Bryan had moved in the early twenties, and the belligerent ruralism of parts of the West were to be found in the same political party with another emotional quantity, the urban Irish. But the immediate ground for political conflict was prepared in the latter days of the Wilson era, when a progressive Democratic coalition disintegrated, and the elements that had composed it began to regroup into mutually antagonistic factions.

[4] *The New York Times,* January 2, 1919, p. 4; *The Nation,* CVIII (January 11, 1919), 38; *New Republic,* XXIV (November 3, 1920), 226.

CHAPTER II

The Wilson Coalition

In 1912 the Progressive movement, advanced in earlier days by the flamboyant energy and skill of Theodore Roosevelt and the workmanlike experimentation of Robert La Follette, was delivered into the sober keeping of President Woodrow Wilson. By 1916, progressives could look with satisfaction on the manner in which the Chief Executive and his party were forwarding the cause of reform. In that year, President Wilson—winner of only a plurality of the popular vote in 1912—was able to forge a coalition of voters strong enough to win him a second term; and the condition of the Democratic party, like that of the Progressive movement whose life the party had helped to sustain, seemed comparatively sound and its future promising.

The winning coalition assembled elements harmonious enough for 1916, though by no means permanently compatible. Since more voters than usual crossed party lines to give the minority party a victory, the contest belonged to what political scientists have labeled "deviating" elections. Wilson's reform legislation attracted a spectrum of progressive voters ranging from middle-class Americans, who would be content with a few restraints upon the activity of finance and industry, to socialists bent on the eventual destruction of American capitalism. The President captured not only the loyal Democratic followers of William Jennings Bryan, but also some of Theodore Roosevelt's Progressive adherents who saw Wilson enact, one by one, the important elements in the Bull Moose platform of 1912. Among Wilson's supporters, in fact, were a number of businessmen who had believed in the viability of the New Nationalism preached by the Roosevelt progressives; for Wilson had in effect begun to accept the distinction between good and bad trusts, and he had dulled the cutting edge of the new regulatory agencies, the Federal Trade Commission and the Tariff Commission, with his conservative appointees. However they might deplore the Adamson Act and Child Labor Act, businessmen could appreciate the continuing economic prosperity (as could all elements in the coalition), the conservative tariff plank in the 1916 platform, and the stability that Wilson had brought to the currency system. Particularly appreciated in the banking world was the Kern Act of 1916, which eased restrictions on interlocking directorates. Probably the Republican party continued to attract a majority of men from the business world, but Wilsonianism made significant inroads.[1]

Farmers occupied a vital place in the Wilson coalition. They warmed to the antimonopoly measures and agricultural education programs of Wilson's government, its regulation of railroad rates and promotion of good roads, its generous loans to agriculture coupled with the advancement of credit against ware-

[1] For a view of the election that emphasizes long-range trends, see the important work of political scientists: Angus Campbell *et al.: The American Voter* (New York, 1960), p. 533. The Republican rift of 1910 had not yet healed in 1916; indeed, the issues of the war had renewed the feuding among Republican leaders. Arthur S. Link: *Wilson: Confusions and Crises, 1915–1916* (Princeton, 1964), pp. 319–21. John Garraty: *Right-Hand Man: The Life of George W. Perkins* (New York, 1960), p. 356; *New Republic*, VIII (September 2, 1916), 103–4; *The Commoner*, XVI (October 1916), 1–2; 14–15; George H. Mayer: *The Republican Party, 1854–1964* (New York, 1964), p. 342; Robert H. Wiebe: *Businessmen and Reform* (Cambridge, Mass., 1962), pp. 152–4.

house stocks. These reforms came into law not through Wilson's own initiative—indeed, he had at first blocked the rural credits bill, and apparently he signed the Federal Farm Loan Act of 1916 mainly for reasons of political expediency—yet they were products of his administration.[2]

By 1915 and 1916, labor as well as agriculture found that it could look to Wilson. To be sure, the labor legislation of Wilson's early days in office had been disappointing; but the approach of a presidential election, the threat of strikes that might endanger the administration's preparedness program, and the reports of Frank P. Walsh's United States Commission on Industrial Relations and its successor, the Committee on Industrial Relations, together impelled the administration toward a stronger labor policy. The new labor program included the controversial Adamson law, making the eight-hour day mandatory on interstate carriers, a measure for which Wilson's support was essential; the Keating-Owen Child Labor Act, which epitomized the best impulses of the Progressive Era; the Kern-McGillicuddy law, which provided workmen's compensation for federal employees; and the La Follette Seamen's Act, which Wilson supported after coming to know the desperate labor conditions in the merchant marine. Labor might also take satisfaction from the appointment to the bench of Louis D. Brandeis over the staunch opposition of Senate conservatives—a nomination that was of the greatest significance in the face of labor's gloomy experiences before the Supreme Court. Equally gratifying was the dedicated service of the President's Secretary of Labor William B. Wilson, formerly an official of the United Mine Workers.[3]

[2] *Wallace's Farmer,* XIV (June 24, 1916), 1190; William Allen White to Franklin D. Roosevelt, April 6, 1916, White Papers; Arthur S. Link: *Wilson: The New Freedom* (Princeton, 1956), pp. 262-3.

[3] Marc Karson: *American Labor Unions and Politics, 1900-1918* (Carbondale, Ill., 1958), pp. 77, 80, 82-4, 88-9; Richard J. Fenno, Jr.: *The President's Cabinet* (New York, 1959), pp. 73-4; John S. Smith: "Organized Labor and Government in the Wilson Era," unpublished doctoral dissertation, Catholic University, 1962; *American Federa-*

At least as important as progressivism in winning converts to Wilson was peace. With the bellicose Teddy Roosevelt once more backing the Republican party, to which he could impart a measure of his own chauvinism, the Democrats identified their party with the cause of peace and credited their President with keeping us out of war—both in Mexico and in Europe. Wilson had tempered his preparedness program when in April 1916 he appointed as Secretary of War the pacifist-inclined Newton D. Baker. And in the passage of the 1916 Jones Act for governing the Philippines, Wilson also pleased the anti-imperialists. The peace program attracted not only native-born isolationists, pacifists, and agrarian socialists, but also immigrant groups whose ancestral homelands would profit by continued American nonintervention in the European conflict. Among them were the Irish, some Germans and Austrians, and Scandinavians who desired to emulate the neutral stance of their native countries. Admittedly, Wilson must have alienated many immigrants with his charges of hyphenism and his inaction on behalf of Catholics in Mexico, and others were piqued by what they interpreted as Wilson's partiality toward the British. The German press in particular denounced Wilson, and Hughes became known as the German-American candidate. Yet many Germans thought Wilson would not fight if re-elected and that Hughes eventually would. Hughes, moreover, lost votes by his approval of Theodore Roosevelt's speeches. As Carl Wittke observed: "The slogan, 'He kept us out of war,' probably was as irresistible to many German-Americans as it was to millions of other voters, particularly in the Middle and Far West."[4]

---

tionist, XXIII (July 1916), 541, and (November 1916), 1068; see also AFL Executive Council Minutes, July 24, 1916, and July 29, 1916, AFL Papers.

[4] Wilson also attracted immigrants through his veto, in 1915, of a bill that would require a literacy test for entrance into the United States. Among the Irish, strong Democratic traditions and Wilson's labor record strengthened resistance to Hughes. For some statistics on Irish and German voting in 1916, see the relevant tables in Chapter VIII. Wittke: *German-Americans and the World War* (Columbus, 1936), pp. 98, 100-1,

To the union of progressives and isolationists was added the South, long loyal to the Democratic party and strongly influential in the Wilson Administration. The alliance that carried Wilson into his second term was preponderantly rural in composition, an alliance of South and West; he failed to carry the industrial states of Massachusetts, Rhode Island, Connecticut, New York, New Jersey, Pennsylvania, Michigan, and Illinois. Urban progressivism and labor gave the alliance vitality and a distinctive character, but the electoral strength, with few exceptions, came entirely from states as rural as the Presbyterian manse occupied by Wilson's father.[5]

Yet only four years after its making, the Wilson coalition lay in ruins. Warren Harding and normalcy[6] won the election of 1920 by an almost two-to-one margin, collecting 60.3 per cent of the total vote against 34.1 per cent for the Democratic candidate, James M. Cox. The party had lost the power to unite a diversity of classes and interests; and even when some of these would return to their Democratic allegiance, they would do so

111, 282; Link: *Wilson, Confusions and Crises,* pp. 278–9; Louis L. Gerson: *The Hyphenate in Recent American Politics and Diplomacy* (Lawrence, Kan., 1964), p. 68; Mayer: *The Republican Party,* p. 346; *The New York Times,* November 12, 1916, p. 6; *The Public,* XIX (November 17, 1916), 1092; William M. Leary, Jr., "Woodrow Wilson, Irish Americans and the Election of 1916," *Journal of American History,* LIV (June 1967), 57–72.
[5] Senator Gilbert Hitchcock of Nevada rated peace first and progressivism second as reasons for what he described as "a transfer of political power from the East to the West . . . and from the crowded industrial centers to the small cities and farms." Chicago *News,* November 11, 1916, p. 2. In 1916 the presidential vote in the ten largest cities taken together was Republican. The Democrats had virtually conceded the East in 1916, and the labor vote contributed significantly to their victory only in Washington, and in states never yet carried by the Democrats in a two-party contest—New Hampshire, Ohio, and California. John Blum: *Woodrow Wilson* (Boston, 1956), pp. 81, 125; *The New York Times,* November 12, 1916, pp. 1, 6, 7; Arthur S. Link: *Woodrow Wilson and the Progressive Era, 1910–1917* (New York, 1954), pp. 249 ff.; Karson: *American Labor Unions,* pp. 88–9.
[6] Warren Harding did not coin the word "normalcy." For at least two nineteenth-century usages, see *The Oxford English Dictionary* (Oxford, 1933), VII, 208.

not as participants in an articulate progressive movement sustained by a national organization and leadership, but as self-consciously antagonistic factions.

To some extent, it is true, the appearance of precipitous decline was unreal, for the defeat of 1920 came at the end of a period in which the Democrats had enjoyed a success disproportionate to their basic political resources. It is in the congressional elections of the Wilsonian era that is seen most clearly the transience of Democratic victory. In 1910 a serious rift among Republican leaders threw the House to the Democrats, and in 1912 the further cleavage of the opposition into separate candidates, Progressive and regular, stabilized the Democratic lead. But once the Republican split began to close, the party was quickly restored to its normal congressional strength. In 1914— with some Progressive candidates still in the field—the Republicans increased their representation by sixty-six seats, in 1916 by an additional sixteen. The year 1918 was by no means an unusually successful year for the Republicans, though it was a turning point in the sense that they won control of both houses of Congress. In the face of a more united opposition party, the Democratic presidential victory of 1916 was itself a near miracle. It testified to the success of Wilson and his program and the powerful effect of the European war upon the electorate; it signified an approval of particular measures and personalities, rather than an assertion of a durable and persistent Democratic power. It is therefore reasonable to surmise that the victories of the Wilson coalition may have constituted in part an interruption rather than a basic shift in party alignments, touching upon particular issues rather than fundamental party loyalties.

Nevertheless, the four years from 1916 to 1920 were portentous for the Democratic party, for its relative political power was to become even smaller than it had been during the period of Republican ascendancy that preceded the Wilsonian era. One group after another deserted the Democracy until it was left with only a meager corps of supporters.

The debacle of 1920 was foreshadowed in the congressional election of 1918 when control of the House of Representatives slipped to the Republicans. In eight states of the interior—Indiana, Ohio, Illinois, Kentucky, Missouri, Kansas, Nebraska, and Colorado—the Republican party carried twenty-three districts that in 1916 had gone Democratic. The ebbing of Democratic strength in these states made a serious and permanent breach in the Wilson coalition. But of itself the election spelled no massive repudiation of Wilson or the Democratic party; in fact, the Democrats won a substantial majority of the popular congressional vote. In the Northeast, South, and Far West, they did surprisingly well, gaining one more seat than they lost. The vote is noteworthy, however, because it represents the first serious breach in the Wilsonian alliance.[7]

What caused the defection in the agricultural interior? Some of it may have been no more than the return of traditionally Republican voters to an allegiance they had only temporarily left either for Republican or Wilsonian progressivism, or for a Wilson peace that had not been forthcoming; some of it may have been isolationism—whatever isolationism could have been active even in the spirited days of Belleau Wood and the Argonne. But mid-American isolationism flourished in the cities as well as the country, while the rural areas alone abandoned the Democratic party in 1918. A different explanation for the behavior of the Central States can be measured statistically. The

[7] These figures were obtained by a comparison of the first *Congressional Directory* of the Sixty-fifth Congress (1st Sess., April 1917) with the first of the Sixty-sixth Congress (1st Sess., July 1919); no April issue was published in 1919. At its initiation, the Sixty-fifth Congress had 215 Republicans, 215 Democrats, and 5 Independents. The net Republican gain of 22 from the Democrats gives the count of the new House: 237 Republicans, 193 Democrats, 4 Independents, and 1 contested seat in Wisconsin. In the Senate the Democrats also performed badly in the American mid-continent: winning a lone seat in Massachusetts, they lost in Colorado, Illinois, Kansas, and Missouri, as well as in Delaware and New Hampshire. On the popular vote, see C. G. Hoag: "Analysis of the Official Returns of the Congressional Elections of 1918," *The Public*, XXI (May 25, 1919), 545.

Democrats could conceivably have retained control of the House of Representatives, had they not committed a series of errors in agricultural policy. Their biggest mistake was to favor the cotton growers of the South over the wheat farmers of the interior.[8]

Much of the resentment in the wheat states in 1918 was directed against the Lever Act of August 1917, which allowed the Food Administration to fix the cost of wheat as low as $2.00 a bushel. The price of $2.20 fixed by the government should have been high enough to stimulate production and low enough to discourage inflation. But the farmers were not satisfied. The price of $2.20 was a precipitous drop from the $3.40 reached in the spring of 1917; and even the average market price that had prevailed in the five preceding months was almost $2.60. The Allies had purchased heavily in wheat futures and, by demanding delivery that spring, temporarily pushed prices upward. Worse still for the wheat farmers, the crop of 1917, like that of 1916, was small owing to drought and freezing. They also protested against a new system of wheat grading put into effect

[8] The wheat issue in the campaign is explored by Livermore in *Politics Is Adjourned*, pp. 170–6, 192–5. This chapter gives quantitative support to his argument but differs with his assumption that the election of 1918 was in every sense a "political upset" (p. 2). Of course, the Democrats did lose their tenuous control of the House and Senate—admittedly spelling trouble for Wilson's League—but the nature of the returns did not indicate any sudden nationwide dissatisfaction with the Democratic party. Even the net Republican gain over 1916 of twenty-two seats from the Democrats was not especially significant, since the average off-year loss by the party in power in this century has been forty-two seats. It is when the election results of 1918 are measured against Wilson's famous appeal for a vote of confidence that the Republican showing appears to be a crucial triumph in the revival of Republican strength. See also Josephus Daniels' manuscript diary, December 10, 1918, and Senator Thomas P. Gore: "The Wheat Farmer's Dilemma," *Forum*, LX (September 1918), 257–66. Ray A. Billington: "The Origins of Middle Western Isolationism," *Political Science Quarterly*, LX (March 1945), 44–64; William G. Carleton: "Isolationism and the Middle West," *Mississippi Valley Historical Review*, XXXIII (December 1946), 380–2; Selig Adler: *The Isolationist Impulse: Its Twentieth-Century Reaction* (New York, 1957).

in 1917 under the Grain Standards Act, a system that would benefit millers and grain buyers more than the farmers themselves. Even in 1918, though acreage had been vastly increased, the yield—still hampered by droughts—reached only the prewar average. On June 7, 1918, Wilson vetoed a bill to raise the ceiling on wheat to $2.40 a bushel. Just a few months before, he had encouraged farmers to sow wheat on land normally devoted to other crops; and those farmers who followed the President regarded his veto as an economic betrayal. It was put to them that it was a patriotic duty to submit to low prices in a time of inflation, but, so it seemed, the principle was inconsistent in its application.[9]

For while the administration was hampering the wheat farmer, southern Democrats were keeping raw cotton off the list of price-controlled items. This unequal treatment of the two sections antagonized the wheat areas; and, as wartime cotton prices spiraled upward—increasing substantially more than the controlled wheat prices—old sectional jealousies revived. During the campaign the Republicans seized upon the failure of the Democrats to heed the farm protest. And in the final results, the Republicans gained in the wheat areas in strikingly close proportion, district by district, to the extent of wheat acreage.

In ten states that led in the production of wheat, the Democrats were victorious in not one of the congressional districts the Republicans had carried in 1916, while the Republicans won twenty-one that had gone Democratic in the previous election. The Republicans gained in Indiana (4), Kansas (4), Missouri (3), Washington (1), Nebraska (3), Ohio (5), and Illinois (1). Some of these districts contained a substantial number of

[9] For the administration's injunction to farmers, see the New York *Herald-Tribune*, February 19, 1918, p. 4. Secretary of Agriculture Houston wrote to Herbert Hoover of the Food Administration, complaining that the minimum price had turned out to be the maximum price as well, and the Assistant Secretary at about the same time admitted that "wheat is perhaps but little if any more profitable than at prices prevailing two or three years ago." Agriculture File 234–403, National Archives. See also File 234–142. United States Department of Agriculture, *Monthly Crop Report*, IV (May 1918), 53; George Akerson to John G. Brown, October 19, 1928, Hoover Papers.

TABLE IV

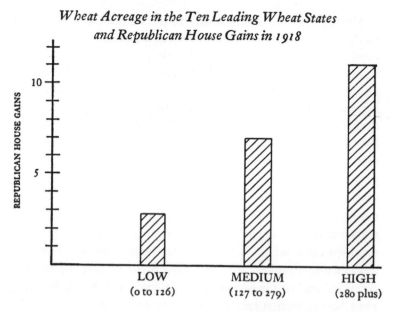

Wheat Acreage in the Ten Leading Wheat States and Republican House Gains in 1918

REPUBLICAN HOUSE GAINS

10

5

| LOW | MEDIUM | HIGH |
| (0 to 126) | (127 to 279) | (280 plus) |

WHEAT ACREAGE (000 omitted)

German-Americans, who might be expected to oppose the Democrats; but in most of the areas, including those in Missouri, the German vote could not have been the determining factor. There are ninety-six congressional districts in these seven states. Table IV, which represents Republican House gains from the region, is based upon an arrangement of these districts into three groups of high, medium, and low wheat acreage, each group containing thirty-two districts. The Republicans won eleven seats in districts of highest acreage; seven in the middle districts; and three in the areas of lowest wheat acreage. Only in Ohio were any of these seats formerly occupied by one-term Democratic congressmen, whose tenure might have been contingent on short-lived conditions.[1]

[1] Wheat areas in other parts of the country also replaced their Democratic congressmen with Republicans; these include the seventh district in California, the first in Maryland, the third in Colorado, the twentieth in Pennsylvania, the second in Michigan, and the eighth in Kentucky. Years later, in a letter to Josephus Daniels, Vance McCormick, Democratic National Chairman in 1916, confirmed the importance of the farm is-

Although the error most costly to the Democrats in 1918 was the rigid wheat ceiling, the administration also antagonized rural interests in other ways. Its wartime purchase, at slightly less than the market price, of virtually the entire wool supply introduced further uncertainty into an already precarious market and, together with anticipated cutbacks in government orders after the Armistice, contributed to a serious wool depression lasting from October 1918 to March 1919. The government's policy favored operators of large farms over the small wool growers located far from Washington, and it penalized them further by needlessly holding up crop payments. In several congressional districts with high wool production, Democratic seats were lost. The government was generous in its loans to the southern cattlemen of Texas and Oklahoma even as it withheld assistance from middle-western herd owners—and the Republicans pointed to the sectional discrimination. Finally, the Railroad Administration raised the cost of shipping grain beyond the point for which a slight rise in the price ceiling could compensate, while a shortage in cars lengthened time in transit, and a rule that the burden of proving negligence should fall to the shipper made it more difficult to prosecute claims for lost goods.[2]

---

sue. March 24, 1941, McCormick Papers. Shifts were determined by a comparison between the last *Congressional Directory* of the Sixty-fifth Congress (1st Sess., April 1919) and the first of the Sixthy-sixth Congress (1st Sess., July 1919). County figures on wheat acreage are found in the United States Bureau of the Census, *Fourteenth Census: Agriculture*, V, V$_1$, V$_{11}$, VI$_{111}$. Maps of the congressional districts, indicating what counties they include, are found in most issues of the *Congressional Directory*. Frank M. Surface: *The Grain Trade During the World War* (New York, 1928), pp. 24, 28, 59–60, 68, 76, 121.

2 Wool districts lost include the twenty-third in Pennsylvania, the first in New Mexico, and the fifth in Washington (also one of the low-acreage wheat districts represented in Table IV). Agriculture File WIB–17D–A2, Box 34 and Boxes 19–33, National Archives; Katharine Snodgrass: "Price Fluctuations in the Woolen Industry," *Annals of the American Academy*, LXXXIX (May 1920), 55–60, esp. 57–8. Corroborative evidence that the cattle loan policy of the administration, whether or not by design, was in practice partial to the South may be found in the Federal Farm Loan Board, *Second Annual Report*, November 30, 1918, p. 19.

Together, the Wilson Administration's agricultural policies heightened western jealousies toward the South's dominant position in the Democratic party. And that southern ascendancy was startlingly apparent. President Wilson, born in Virginia and raised in Georgia, often identified himself with his native section. His first cabinet consisted of five representatives from the South and only four from the rest of the nation. Racial segregation was applied with increased rigor to workers in some federal agencies. In Congress, where many important committees were chaired by men from south of the Mason-Dixon line, the extent of southern control was greater even than in the executive. From the North came complaints over favoritism to the South in distribution of patronage, as well as over the crucial matter of agricultural price-fixing. As John W. Burke, the Treasurer of the United States, wrote to Joe Tumulty: "During the campaign in the last election the argument we had to meet everywhere was 'the South is in the saddle; it has the legislative [*sic*] and the executive.' "[3]

The Republican gain of 1918 was the outcome of a campaign waged in a spirit of sectionalism over particular and ephemeral issues. Of course, some more basic grievances against Wilson had accumulated during the war—high taxes and government-imposed economic planning had been particularly irritating. But the normal disillusionment that ensues at the end of a war had not had time to develop. Most interest groups had as much

---

District 6, Missouri, number of National Farm Loan Associations: 112; number of loans, 1,577; total amount loaned, $3,855,230. District 10, Texas, number of National Farm Loan Associations: 288; number of loans, 5,250; total amount loaned, $13,568,461. McAdoo to W. P. G. Harding, October 25, 1918, McAdoo Papers.

[3] John W. Burke to Joe Tumulty, November 17, 1919, Wilson Papers; Senator Thomas Walsh to W. M. Johnston, November 12, 1918, T. J. Walsh Papers; *Current Opinion*, LXV (December 1918), 350–2; Chicago *Daily Tribune*, October 22, 1918, p. 1; October 31, 1918, p. 1; *Literary Digest*, LIX (November 16, 1918), 14–15; *The New York Times*, November 7, 1918, p. 20; Arthur S. Link: *Wilson: The Road to the White House* (Princeton, 1947), pp. 2 ff.; J. Leonard Bates: *The Origins of Teapot Dome* (Urbana, Ill., 1963), pp. 152, 156.

reason to be satisfied in 1918 as in 1916. During the war, the federal government had increased its activities in behalf of labor, strengthening the good relations of the prewar era; the Republicans, wrote Senator Borah of Idaho in October 1918, have through their inaction "handed the labor vote of this country practically en masse to the president."[4] The war may have set the stage for the quickening reaction against Wilson in 1919 and 1920; after all, our part in the conflict could be taken as a betrayal of the peace slogan of 1916. But it was the uncertainty of peace, the failure to withdraw once victory had been won, that apparently brought home to the voter of 1920 the message of that betrayal; hence the elections of 1918 preceded the period of most intense isolationist reaction.

Since in considerable measure the Democrats lost upon sectional issues, the election probably cannot be viewed as a clear repudiation of Wilson's plea for a vote of confidence—which *The New York Times* thought had won votes for his party—and in no sense was it a national repudiation of Wilson. Outside of the wheat districts, the 1918 House returns show not Democratic weakness but persisting strength, which was probably nourished by wartime prosperity. They indicate a continuing trust in Wilson and demonstrate a nation's gratitude for the recent defeat of Germany.[5] Finally, they signify that while by 1918 a wedge had already been driven into the Wilson coalition, it is the period between 1918 and 1920 that must be examined most carefully to explain the Democratic defeat of 1920. It was in these divisive times after the war that grievances against the Wilson Administration most rapidly accumulated, and the

---

[4] Borah to Shad Hodges, October 10, 1918, Borah Papers.
[5] Vice President Marshall remarked that "the war is a Democratic asset." Homer Cummings, Democratic National Chairman, asked rhetorically if the voters wanted General Pershing to stop his brilliant advances, and James W. Gerard, former ambassador to Germany and a good Democrat, announced that the Kaiser would be encouraged if the electorate repudiated Wilson. *The New York Times*, October 28, 1918, p. 1; November 1, 1918, p. 14; November 4, 1918, p. 6.

cohesive force of Wilsonianism—cohesive both for the Democracy and for the nation as a whole—dissolved.

The tensions of 1919, to which the Wilson Administration fell
victim, were to a great extent the product of America's involvement in the great conflict. Institutions and customs that once
maintained the social equilibrium had been altered or destroyed,
in part by the governmental controls of wartime, in part by the
emotional and social disturbances of war itself. Workers, having
become accustomed to a measure of war prosperity and to collective bargaining enforced by the War Labor Board, anxiously
sought to preserve their gains as the government prepared to
withdraw from the economy; but labor faced employers even
more resolute in wishing to restore the days of open contract,
and applying in their struggle against collective bargaining the
rhetoric of the "American Plan." Farmers cried for various
forms of aid from a Congress deaf to their pleas, and as price
supports came near to ending, pleaded with a cabinet equally
unmindful of their plight. In northern cities Negroes attempted
to hold on to their wartime jobs as soldiers returned home
looking for work. Negroes themselves came back from the
trenches, bringing with them an aggressive edge their fathers
had never possessed. Forced up by the war, the cost of living
played on the anxieties of the population. Following the success of the Russian Revolution and its spread to Central Europe,
an aggressive Attorney General, A. Mitchell Palmer, aroused by
frightened citizens, clashed with liberals of all shades in his ill-
defined attempt to suppress revolutionary plots. Debate on the
League of Nations separated idealist from realist, and realist
from isolationist. Vainly, the progressives worked to resist the
course of reaction.

The atmosphere of conflict was thickened by a state of mind
for which the war itself had in large part prepared the condition. Social unrest characterizes any postwar period. Wars impose upon a people a discipline beyond their normal capacities; in
turn, their hopes for the postwar era expand indefinitely,

only to be followed by disillusionment and frustration. Our participation in World War I, moreover, was too brief to expend the reserve of fighting spirit manufactured by the Committee on Public Information. That wartime propaganda agency had planned a symphony in creed and emotion that was to reach its crescendo by the middle of 1919. Though the war ended sooner than had been expected, the emotion lingered on, no longer fixed and steadied by the pursuit of victory, and some of it turned to a distorted patriotism, to suspicion, to antiradicalism. In its dual temper of anger and of tiredness, the time was unfavorable to the maintenance of progressivism.

An economic dislocation brought on by the return of peace contributed to the unsettled political conditions of 1919 and 1920. But the extent and nature of the dislocation must be identified carefully, for on the surface conditions appeared quite good. Demobilization of the armed forces created some brief hardship early in 1919, but no lasting unemployment problem; nor did the mass revocation of military orders induce an immediate deflation. For according to Paul Samuelson: *"Economically,* the first World War lasted until 1920." The economy was kept active: money was spent on demobilization itself, consumer savings and dismissal pay for veterans were soon in circulation as pantry shelves were restocked and as servicemen returned, business contracts were settled, the military deficit had to be financed, and the Treasury desired to postpone any contraction until after the floating of a last major war loan and further loans to European countries. These monetary policies sparked a revival in automobile production, housebuilding, and numerous related industries which eased the readjustment for the nine million who had been engaged in defense work and the four million soldiers returned to peacetime life.

Industrial production declined a maximum of ten per cent by the middle of 1919, but in the last six months of the year it reached a new high point. Such figures do not record the vast shifting of jobs and resulting hardships that must have occurred in 1919. Yet a need for credit in that year that might have stimulated the economy for the duration was not met, and when government spending and industrial expansion both halted in 1920, unemployment rose sharply. As the hard times closed in upon them, workingmen and farmers condemned an administration whose earlier sympathy for the common man seemed to have vanished.[6]

As a prelude to the privations of unemployment, a steady rise in the cost of living, particularly in food prices, had angered and perplexed consumers. Despite the wartime controls on prices of certain items, the cost of living almost doubled between 1914 and 1920, and in New York City it rose twenty-eight per cent between 1919 and 1920 alone. The people, according to a correspondent of Mark Sullivan, are "more interested in the price of beefsteak and a pair of shoes" than in Wilson's League of Nations. The Wilson Administration had proposed that an industrial board in the Commerce Department be allowed to set maximum prices, but George Peek, lacking authority to keep steel prices down, resigned as its head in May 1919; and Congress had denied further funds to Herbert Hoover's Food Administration, forcing it out of existence in June. By the late spring of 1920 the index of living costs began to fall but the high prices of the preceding years, though worldwide in origin, had done political damage to the administration—but so too would a system of price and wage controls. Added irritants were the scarcities that persisted after the war as labor unions struck and the economy pursued its uneven course. The inadequate supply of coal, for example, caused widespread anxiety that reached its worst proportions just before election day. Viewing the high cost of living as the nation's greatest postwar problem, the Federal Reserve Board acted against the inflation of 1919 and early 1920 by raising the rediscount rate, curtailing credit, and dis-

[6] Samuelson and Everett E. Hagen: *After the War* (Washington, D.C.: National Labor Relations Board; 1943), p. 21; George H. Soule: *Prosperity Decade* (New York, 1947), pp. 83-4.

couraging expansion. A major depression began in 1920, soon enough to contribute to the defeat of the administration in the fall.[7]

Labor presented the Wilson Administration with a particularly vexing and embarrassing problem, for it appeared responsible in considerable part for the nation's social unrest and economic trouble. In several of the strikes organized to retain and extend wartime gains, the Justice Department seemed quick to side with management. In September, Wilson asked laborers not to strike for higher wages, since strikes would raise even further the high cost of living, and he denounced the Boston police strike as a "crime against civilization." When the bituminous coal miners went out on strike in November, Attorney General Palmer obtained two federal court injunctions against the strikers that aroused labor's ire. Following the example of some businessmen, he styled the strikers radicals and their conduct a rehearsal for Communist revolution. Palmer typified a middle class once friendly to labor but now convinced it had become dangerous. Wilson estranged the Railway Brotherhoods by refusing to support the Plumb Plan, which would have given to the workers a role in controlling the country's railroads. And to assuage the hard feelings between capital and labor he called the National Industrial Conference to meet in October. But the AFL withdrew on the grounds that representatives of employers refused—in the face of the steel strike then in effect —to affirm the principle of unrestricted collective bargaining that had widely established itself during the war. In the eyes of fair-minded observers, the conference appeared to reveal only the stubbornness of management.[8]

[7] For cost of living figures, see *The New York Times*, May 3, 1920, p. 1; Samuelson: *After the War*, pp. 13, 31; and the consumer price indexes of the United States Department of Labor (revised in 1962). John A. Peters to Mark Sullivan, 1920 [?], Sullivan Papers; Frederic L. Paxson: *Postwar Years: Normalcy, 1918–1923* (Berkeley, 1948), p. 45; Houston; *Eight Years with Wilson's Cabinet, 1913–1920* (New York, 1926), II, 105 ff.

[8] Editorial reaction of the country's newspapers to the strikes of 1919 is contained in the *Literary Digest*, LXIII (October 25, 1919),

The President and his Secretary of Labor William B. Wilson were apparently preoccupied with the public interest and public mood; but in the end, despite even the generous arbitration of Secretary Wilson in the coal strike and the President's efforts on behalf of the steel workers, labor's dissatisfaction with the economic and political status quo increased as rapidly as the public's dissatisfaction with labor. In early 1920 the Esch-Cummins Act came dangerously close to requiring compulsory government arbitration of labor disputes—a thing that in an era of conservative federal administration would hold little promise for the workers—and the antistrike provision of the act also offended labor. Samuel Gompers blamed this act and the "unrest in the country" on Congress, but the image of the Wilson Administration as a progressive friend of labor was destroyed.[9]

Farmers found themselves in their familiar dilemma of squaring the higher cost of living with declining market prices for their crops. Although the 1918 congressional elections had marked the departure of many farmers from the Democratic party, the Department of Agriculture made little effort to forestall further desertions. For a time the postwar agricultural market prospered as foreign demand sustained the expanded wartime production, but foreign buying declined once credit was withdrawn under the War Finance Corporation, and almost all crops suffered sharply falling prices shortly before the 1920 election. And even though farm mortgages had more than doubled since 1914, Secretary of Agriculture David Houston—a southerner viewed with considerable suspicion by western farmers—along with his successor Edwin T. Meredith, awaited indifferently the end of price supports. To heighten the troubles

---

11, and (November 22, 1919), 11–14. Franklin K. Lane to Woodrow Wilson, October 19, 1919, Serial VI, File 5085, Wilson Papers; Gompers to Lee Seamster, March 29, 1920, Gompers Papers; William B. Wilson to James Duncan, April 22, 1920, William B. Wilson Papers.

[9] David Brody: *Labor in Crisis: The Steel Strike of 1919* (Philadelphia, 1965), pp. 102–11. Gompers is quoted in the *American Federationist*, XXVII (July 1920), 656–7.

of the Wilson Administration among the farmers, the new Esch-Cummins law, passed in January 1920, permitted the railroads to raise their rates by thirty-five to forty per cent, and the Federal Reserve Board gave no effective help to agriculture. Farm prices fell by one third in the year before the election, while the prices of farm supplies remained steady.[1]

Closely joined to the unsteadiness of the postwar economy was an injurious psychological mood. "There is a strange poison in the air," observed Wilson's son-in-law, William Gibbs McAdoo, in 1920.[2] There was indeed. The poison had gathered during the war, and even with the coming of peace and the elimination of the immediate center of infection it was working its way throughout the social body and mind.

The duty of spreading a patriotic war spirit had fallen to the highly efficient Committee on Public Information. The unit owed much of its effectiveness to its chairman George Creel, a Denver progressive who shrewdly worked upon chauvinistic feelings already present in American society and brought to a new intensity a national mood that blended aggression and sincere idealism, patriotic dedication and xenophobia. The success of the Creel Committee, as measured by sales of war bonds and subscriptions to Liberty Loans, went beyond expectations. Liberals in government failed to foresee, however, that wartime propaganda and repression might have harmful aftereffects in a time of peace, that the psychological gratifications of war would be hard to surrender.

In Bolshevism, symbol alike of anarchy and of treacherous retreat from wartime alliance, the aroused American temper found in postwar days a new object to stand surrogate for the defeated Hun. Stories of Bolshevik cruelty replaced those of

1 United States Department of Labor, *Statistical Abstract, 1920* (Washington, D.C., 1921), p. 464; Arthur S. Link: "The Federal Reserve Policy and the Agricultural Depression of 1920–1921," *Agricultural History,* XX (July 1946), 166–75; Benedict Crowell and Robert Forrest Wilson: *Demobilization: Our Industrial and Military Demobilization After the Armistice, 1918–1920* (New Haven, 1921), pp. 126–44.
2 McAdoo to Jouett Shouse, September 17, 1920, McAdoo Papers.

German atrocities, and it was rumored that Germans had instigated the Russian upheaval. Indeed, Bolshevism was the enemy in Siberia, where in February 1919, American troops suffered considerable casualties. And when the international ambitions of the Bolsheviks became publicized, organizations such as the American Vigilantes International sprang up to combat them, and the newly formed American Legion went on the alert. At the same time Lenin's revolution stirred the Socialists of America to new hope and expression. The massive labor agitation of 1919 added to the fear of insurrection from the left.

During the war the Creel Committee had asked citizens to report those who spread pessimistic stories about the fighting or cried for peace. In response the American Protective League arose; made up of business and professional men, it acquired a semiofficial status during the war as an arm of the Bureau of Investigation. The League publication *The Spyglass* directed its postwar attention to the Communist menace. The first of many antisocialist riots instigated by veterans occurred in New York just a few weeks after the war had ended. Soldiers seeking employment in large cities frequently turned violently upon Socialist agitators. The formation of the Comintern the following March further heightened anxiety. Soon various representatives of public sentiment were calling on the Justice Department directly to act against all radicals as well as to keep wartime political prisoners in jail. And at the head of the department was a man with both an aggressive temper and presidential ambitions.

Although Attorney General Palmer at first displayed a judicious attitude, in keeping with his earlier career as a moderate, political opportunism and a lifelong distrust of foreigners and their ways eventually warped his sober judgment. The explosion of a bomb in front of his house spurred him to fanaticism. Red propaganda, he reportedly claimed, gave him "the creeps," and he maintained that the Reds were not going to "get him." But his notorious actions occurred only after alarmist reports from J. Edgar Hoover, newly appointed head of the antiradical division in the Bureau of Investigation, convinced him that the country faced a revolution.[3]

Ignoring fundamental canons of human and civil rights, Palmer, late in 1919 and after, caused the unlawful imprisonment of hundreds of aliens suspected of revolutionary sentiment. Even while opposing immigration restriction, he attempted summarily to deport as many foreign-born radicals as he could. Anthony Caminetti, Commissioner of Immigration in the Department of Labor, temporarily prevailed on his superiors to condone many deportations. The policy itself was not new, but its massive implementation was. The activity of the Justice Department would have its brief effect upon the composition of the Democratic party, since it deepened the estrangement from the party of immigrant voters and of some libertarians and labor unionists who saw the deportations as a potentially dangerous weapon in the hands of employers; but in intensifying the social and political reaction, the Red Scare may have done even greater damage to the Democracy. For Wilsonian reform had been the mainstay of Democratic presidential politics since 1912; and in the new political climate of America, much of the popular reform impulse withered and died.[4]

[3] In April 1919, Palmer told Governor Cox of Ohio that current charges of pro-Germanism in the Cincinnati schools "consisted chiefly of gossip" and "hearsay." As late as June 1919, Palmer argued that more repression would play into the hands of the radicals; in July he told Wilson he thought the sedition sentence of Eugene Debs "too long"; in October he opposed restrictions on immigration; and even in November he thought some of the Senate bills "too drastic." Palmer to Cox, April 30, 1919; see also Palmer to John Lord O'Brien, April 27, 1919, and file 100–374, Justice Files, National Archives; Palmer to Wilson, July 30, 1919, Wilson Papers; *The Nation*, CVIII (June 14, 1919), 927; Palmer to John S. Starkweather, November 17, 1919, and Palmer to Senator Lawrence C. Phipps, November 19, 1919; Stanley Coben: *A. Mitchell Palmer: Politician* (New York, 1963), pp. 155–6, 185–6, 198–9, 203, 205, 207, 212; Donald Johnson: *The Challenge to American Freedoms: World War I and the Rise of the American Civil Liberties Union* (Lexington, Ky., 1963), pp. 119–75.

[4] Stanley Coben has contributed a new interpretation of the Red Scare. He sees it as a complicated social-psychological movement in response to a national disequilibrium induced by radicalism, major strikes, federal controls, the high cost of living, and an unsteady economy. Coben

The "deportations delirium" itself ended abruptly early in the election year of 1920. Palmer's predictions of social unrest failed to materialize, labor agitation decreased, and he encountered the opposition of aroused liberals. Even George Creel, no insignificant spokesman for full-blooded Americanism, worked with the American Civil Liberties Union to free imprisoned radicals. Finally, Palmer met his match in Acting Secretary of Labor Louis Post, whom the Attorney General called "a Bolshevik himself." The authority to deport radicals lay only with the Secretary of Labor, and Post—convinced by an IWW brief concerning encroachment on the rights of radicals—refused to act on about eighty per cent of the approximately 2,700 cases sent to him by the Justice Department. To remove the obstacle, an angry House Judiciary Committee started impeachment hearings against Post; but despite his seventy-one years, the Acting Secretary stymied the committee with a storehouse of irrefutable and damning facts about the deportation cases. Curious citizens who came to scoff at Post remained to applaud when he reprimanded the committee members for abusing the Bill of Rights.[5]

---

finds the term "revitalization movement," as it is formulated by one anthropologist, to be applicable to the Red Scare; the phrase describes a mass attempt to verify accustomed ways of thinking and to destroy foreign influences. "A Study in Nativism: The American Red Scare of 1919-20," *Political Science Quarterly*, LXXI (March 1964), 52-75; Anthony F. C. Wallace: "Revitalization Movements," *American Anthropologist*, LVIII (April 1956), 264-81.

[5] According to the Detroit *News* of April 23, 1920, the President, perhaps through fear of angering organized labor, sided with Post against Palmer— a corroboration of Wilson's alleged caution to the Attorney General not to let the country "see Red." William Preston, Jr.: *Aliens and Dissenters: Federal Suppression of Radicals, 1903-1933* (Cambridge, Mass., 1963), pp. 224-5; Frederic C. Howe: *The Confessions of a Reformer* (New York, 1925), p. 327; Howe to W. B. Wilson, October 9, 1919, William B. Wilson Papers, Pennsylvania Historical Society; *The New York Times*, May 9, 1920, p. 12; Labor Department File 167-255A, National Archives; United States Department of Labor, *Annual Report of the Commission on Immigration, 1920* (Washington, D.C., 1921), pp. 32-4; *Annual Report . . . , 1921* (Washington, D.C., 1922), pp. 14-15; Post: *The Deportations Delirium of Nineteen-Twenty* (Chicago, 1923).

In its larger significance, the Post-Palmer skirmish was symptomatic of emerging political disorder within the Democratic party. The conflict was one of many in an administration that had lost its power to discipline itself or its party, and to unite and stimulate Congress to act on pressing national problems. This near abandonment of party discipline, especially on the part of Wilson, who alone was in a position effectively to govern the Democratic administration, goes far in explaining the disaster that struck the party in 1920.

During the first months of peace, Wilson's schedule made it impossible for him to provide the domestic leadership so sorely needed by his party and his country. He spent the month after the congressional elections of 1918 preparing for the Paris peace conference. On December 2 he left for Paris, and, except for a ten-day trip home in the late winter to sign bills and attend to unavoidable domestic duties, his work kept him abroad until July 8, a period of about seven months. On the winter journey home, he met his cabinet, talked to a fairly complacent conference of governors and mayors about unemployment, and had dinner with members of the Senate Foreign Relations Committee; but a ten-day whirlwind of activity could not replace constant presidential concern and leadership. While President Wilson was abroad, his Secretary of State wrote: "The Democrats in Congress, without his personal leadership, simply went to pieces."[6]

In the weeks to come, the fight over the League of Nations consumed much of Wilson's time, and he continued to give little attention to domestic and party affairs. "There is no real note of leadership coming out of the White House," complained *The Nation* in August. Although weakened by a severe attack of influenza, on September 3, 1919, Wilson began a tour to generate support for his League. On September 25, he had a physical breakdown in Pueblo, Colorado, and shortly afterward suffered a paralyzing cerebral hemorrhage. Since that affliction often leaves some of the bodily and mental functions unim-

[6] Lansing Private Memoranda, December 14, 1919.

paired, and a few of Wilson's visitors during the last year and a half of his presidency found him apparently hale, their testimony has occasionally been taken as evidence that his illness did not seriously damage his capacities. But the opposite was the case. The cerebral thrombosis—its symptoms resemble those of a ruptured blood vessel or stroke—prevented him from performing effectively the complex activity of a President; he was rarely able to work more than an hour or two a day or to sustain more than a few minutes of dictation. In the middle of 1920, Dr. Cary T. Grayson, Wilson's physician, spoke of the President's gradual mental deterioration. Had illness not struck him down, Wilson might have continued as the strong party leader he had described in his *Congressional Government;* as it was, his party floundered for lack of direction, all the more so because earlier he had accustomed it to the vigorous leadership of a prime minister. "Thanks to Mr. Wilson's domination of his party," observed *The Nation,* "[few Democratic leaders] retain any special capacity for independent thought or constructive statesmanship."[7]

The President's absence forced an unaccustomed degree of independence on even the least active cabinet members, whom he had regarded primarily as administrators rather than as members of an important political body. Secretary of the Treasury McAdoo, the most competent executive, had already resigned. Secretary of the Interior Franklin K. Lane, on leaving the cabinet in 1920, complained that government officials would not make decisions and shrank from responsibility. But inexperienced though they were at independent leadership, the more ambitious secretaries jumped at the opportunity to direct government policy. The most flagrant exercise of autonomous power was by Attorney General Palmer, who issued his famous

[7] *The Nation,* CVII (November 9, 1918), 545; CIX (August 2, 1919), 133. On Wilson's illness, see John Garraty: *Woodrow Wilson* (New York, 1956), p. 182; Arthur Walworth: *Woodrow Wilson,* I: *World Prophet* (New York, 1958), p. 400; and the bibliographical note in John Blum: *Joe Tumulty and the Wilson Era* (Boston, 1951), p. 312 (see also, pp. 214, 216).

injunction against the United Mine Workers less than two months after Wilson's collapse. Palmer's actions in the Red Scare severely divided Wilson's advisers: Tumulty, Lansing, and Burleson supported him in opposition to William B. Wilson, Lane, and Daniels. Secretary of State Robert Lansing acquired Wilson's enmity by calling cabinet meetings without the President's consent; according to Josephus Daniels and others, Lansing wanted Vice President Thomas Marshall to take over the government.

The new executive leadership frequently took on a conservative character. Fundamental decisions on economic policy lay chiefly with Carter Glass and David F. Houston, successors to McAdoo in the Treasury; and both Houston and Glass wanted the ailing postwar economy to mend itself. Lincoln Colcord of *The Nation* diagnosed the situation in an article entitled "The Administration Adrift":

> So with the President out of commission, it has been Carter Glass and Mr. Burleson, and Mr. Houston, all Bourbon southerners, who have dominated the Administration and formulated its policies during this critical time. . . . There seems to be little doubt that the leaders of the Bourbon Democracy have utilized the full power and prestige of the Presidency to work their own ends.[8]

Wilson's loss of political flexibility and leadership is revealed in his handling of executive appointments and patronage, which had been used so skillfully by subordinates during his first term.

[8] Between the end of the war and the election of 1920 six of the nine cabinet officers had to be replaced. Wilson's conception of party leadership is discussed in Link: *Wilson: The New Freedom*, pp. 145–7. David Houston, among others, recalls encroachments by Congress on executive domain after Wilson's illness. *Eight Years with Wilson's Cabinet*, II, pp. 71–90; Houston to Woodrow Wilson, April 15, 1920, Houston Papers, Library of Congress. On Wilson's declining role as party leader, see George Creel: *The War, the World, and Wilson* (New York, 1920), p. 134. Richard F. Fenno, Jr.: *The President's Cabinet* (New York, 1959), pp. 119–20. Colcord is quoted in *The Nation*, CIX (November 15, 1919), 635–6; Lane in *The New York Times*, March 1, 1920, p. 1.

Several cabinet members privately resented many of Wilson's new appointments, which were motivated by a strange mixture of nonpartisanship and spite. On February 19, 1919, McAdoo, now out of the government, wrote to Carter Glass about the "universal complaints" being directed against Wilson's willingness to appoint "irregular party men" who were often prominent Republicans. On December 13, McAdoo was again corresponding with Glass on the problem, insisting now that Wilson's cavalier handling of patronage had "enormously weakened the Democratic Party." The appointment of a former Bull Mooser, Bainbridge Colby, as Secretary of State early in 1920, further irritated loyal Democrats. No less politically injudicious was the attitude of Postmaster General Burleson, who dispensed more patronage than the rest of the cabinet added together. When Wilson, heeding a recommendation of the Civil Service Reform League, exercised his wartime power by ordering postmasters to take competitive examinations, Burleson, a faithful subordinate with a gift for antagonizing, executed the order with impartiality unbecoming a party man. Formerly a stabilizing influence in the Administration, the Post Office chief became in later days a source of party turmoil. In 1919, Robert Woolley of the Interstate Commerce Commission told Colonel House that Burleson "must resign—or be forced to—if there is to be a shred of the Democratic Party left to go into the campaign of 1920."[9]

[9] Complaints about the distribution of patronage are a characteristic of American politics in any era; it was Wilson's absence from active political duty that gave patronage its special importance. Some of the recriminations that plagued Wilson's second term are collected in Raymond Hanks: "The Democratic Party in 1920: The Rupture of the Wilsonian Synthesis," unpublished doctoral dissertation, University of Chicago, 1960. McAdoo's letters to Glass are in the McAdoo Papers; Woolley's letter to House, dated June 17, 1919, is in the Ray Stannard Baker Papers. On Burleson's willingness to go outside the party for good postmasters, see the Thomas B. Love Papers, "1920 Campaign," Folder 1. *The Nation*, discussing conflicts in the cabinet, denounced Burleson as the "least fit" member of that body, CX (January 3, 1920), 844. See also Fenno, *The President's Cabinet*, pp. 222–3.

Another indication of the President's declining role as leader was his failure to offer a progressive postwar domestic program. "Can anyone," asked Walter Lippmann late in 1919, "name a single reform initiated or carried through since the Armistice?" Wilson did send three messages to Congress, but they scarcely mention proposed reforms. No program of reconstruction was broached for fear it would cause anti-administration sentiment. Conservationists in particular were discouraged; but for a liberal filibuster, a "giveaway" water-power act would have passed early in 1919. Even such significant and progressive legislation as was passed had for the most part been initiated in prewar days, whereas other measures, such as the Transportation Act of 1920, which labor vigorously opposed, were steps backward from the radical nationalization of wartime. In referring to the railroad act, the *New Republic* condemned "the unfortunate legislation of 1920. . . . It was the fitting product of a mediocre, spineless and leaderless Congress"; the General Leasing Act of 1920 failed to prevent the outrageous scandals of Teapot Dome. A decade later the same journal observed: "Wilson through the force of his own personality carried his party into a position of progressivism which was not native to it, and from which it promptly backslid as soon as his individual authority was removed. By 1920, there was little evidence left in the party of the spirit which in 1913 was busy inaugurating the Federal Reserve Board and so many other measures of reform." In its last years the Wilson Administration had little to offer progressive Americans, and its repressive measures repelled the liberals.[1]

The one issue that might have rallied liberal support was the League of Nations, and yet in fact the League added to Democratic disharmony, as well as to the strength of the Republican

---

[1] The Merchant Marine Act of 1920 was one of the most notable achievements of the session, but, like the Water Power and General Leasing Acts, it too was an inheritance from the prewar era. *New Republic*, XX (November 12, 1919), 315; XXVI (March 23, 1921), 92-9; LVIII (May 8, 1929), 320; Bates: *Origins of Teapot Dome*, pp. 165, 179-80, 200, 211; Philip Taft: *The AF of L in the Time of Gompers* (New York, 1957), p. 469.

attack. It was indeed on foreign policy more than on any other question in the postwar era that the Progressive movement fragmented, dividing into what have been labeled its internationalist, realist, and isolationist parts. For a time the League was able to ride the crest of an internationalism expounded by Wilson in his cherished wish to "make the world safe for democracy"; it was promoted to a degree by the same spirit of wartime idealism that also unleashed the more chauvinistic impulses of the day. Evidence of the League's initial strength was ubiquitous. Newspapers supported it overwhelmingly, and even thirty-two state legislatures endorsed some kind of international organization. But the League—still little more than a pleasant notion in most people's minds—was pushed into the background by the immediacy of domestic problems, and a shift in the sentiment of the people was soon to come.[2]

The President's conduct at Versailles did its part to trigger the reaction against the League. Republicans were the first to be estranged. Already, in his appeal in 1918 for a Democratic Congress to further his policies, Wilson had invited a partisan response from the Republican party; and by failing to take influential Republicans with him to Paris, or to keep the Senate leaders informed of the treaty-making progress, he further widened the breach. And it is ironic that his failure to provide a few favors to Republicans in a matter where political diplomacy would have done some good came at a moment when administrative patronage was being distributed with a bipartisanship destructive of party unity. Wilson's highhanded indifference to the advice and feelings of the Republicans—his apparent assumption, at Versailles and thereafter, that it was the duty of the Senate Republicans, as it was the duty of the Democrats, to provide a rubber stamp for a Wilson treaty—lost him a good deal of the support that he might otherwise have commanded. Of course, if

[2] William Allen White later wrote of a "height of aspiration" lasting from the Armistice to early 1919. But "perhaps there was no reality to that day," he said, "but only an emotional fiz [*sic*]. . . ." White to W. D. Guthrie, July 10, 1923, White Papers.

Wilson had triumphed in peace as he had in war, the Republican cause would have been less hopeful. But he did not. The Republicans, by fastening their argument upon Article X of the League Covenant—a controversial statement guaranteeing the integrity of national boundaries—and by representing the provision as a binding commitment that would involve American soldiers in an unending series of wars and police actions, brought many of their listeners to a new idea of the League as an instrument not for peace but for bloody international adventure. And Wilson stiffened the opposition when he assailed the anti-League senators as "bungalow minds" whose heads were "knots tied to keep their bodies from unravelling."[3]

A more surprising effect of Wilson's performance at Versailles was the desertion of many ardent liberals who could have been expected to rekindle the idealism of 1917 and 1918. Unprepared for the conflict between ideals and self-interest, they abandoned the Treaty of Versailles after becoming convinced that at the conference, and in his earlier defense pacts with England and France, the President had betrayed his own principles. And by tying the League to the treaty, he invited greater opposition than he would otherwise have encountered. For example, the *New Republic* observed in 1920 that the Fourteen Points really belonged to the liberals of the world, not to Wilson, who had negotiated them so badly. Those liberals who had been suspicious of Wilson from the first had their fears con-

---

[3] It is possible, of course, that the President could on no account have secured Republican cooperation. However tactful he might have been, a handful of powerful isolationist Republican senators would have threatened the Chairman of the Senate Foreign Relations Committee with a party bolt in 1920. And despite Henry Cabot Lodge's own milder sentiments, Lodge might have backed the isolationists, if only to prevent a revolt within his party similar to the Bull Moose rebellion of recent and searing memory.

On May 10, 1919, Colonel House wrote in his diary that Wilson "has built up a fire there [in the Republican Congress] which is now beginning to scorch him and it will become worse and worse as his term wanes. It was all so useless and it has hampered him in the exercise of his public work."

firmed; for those who trusted him, the disillusionment was deep. The protests of some of Wilson's own advisers increased the ranks of men who wanted no part of a League tied to a punitive and "reactionary" peace treaty—one that perpetuated existing injustices and so could only lead to another war. Mounting evidence of Allied perfidy in bringing on the war also disillusioned the liberals. *The Nation* imaginatively charged that the international banking interests, operating through Elihu Root, were pushing the League. Domestic events strengthened their belief that the President had relinquished his role as a reform leader. As they saw it, the shambles at Versailles was matched by the repression of the Palmer raids.[4]

For those who continued to support a League, Harding's own rather disingenuous use of the issue was one reason for the failure to recognize that the organization stood in peril. At one point Harding—who in the Senate had voted for the League with reservations—proposed scrapping it, but later he left the door ajar to "an association of nations"; he thereby muddied the issue and helped to prevent the election from becoming the referendum on the League that Wilson had asked for in his message at the Jackson Day dinner. The confusion among proponents of world power as to Harding's real intention was illustrated when on October 14, 1920, a Committee of Thirty-One, made up preponderantly of Republican internationalists such as Herbert Hoover, Charles Evans Hughes, and former President Taft, sincerely pledged themselves and their party to a League; in fact, it was because of the Committee's position that the *New Republic* claimed to anticipate a Republican League in the event of Democratic failure.[5]

The Republicans were hostile, the liberals cool or confused, and the old-stock Americans were increasingly alarmed over foreign entanglement. The Democrats could ill afford to draw into the League debate still another and steadily expanding

[4] *New Republic*, XXIV (September 9, 1920), 18; *The Nation*, CIX (July 5, 1919), 3.
[5] XXIV (September 16, 1920), 35.

force in American politics: the organized immigrant, perhaps more intractably hostile to Versailles than was any native American faction apart from the irreconcilables. The most staunchly Democratic of all the immigrant groups, the Irish, saw the League as an instrument of oppression in the hands of the British. Yet in his January plea that the election of 1920 be a "solemn referendum" on the League, Wilson laid the party open to the animosity of the national minorities.[6] Political bosses, such as Charles Murphy of New York, Thomas Taggart of Indiana, and George Brennan of Illinois, pleaded against the idea. They saw that to make the League a central issue in the campaign would shatter Democratic foreign blocs in Boston, New York, Chicago, and other large cities heavily populated by immigrants or Americans of immigrant extraction for whom the Treaty of Versailles represented a slighting, a betrayal, or an oppression of the old countries. For once the chauvinism of the immigrant was joined to the chauvinism of the native isolationist.

The Democratic party was left with almost no one to defend the League but an ailing President hampered by the constitutional requirement that he share with the Senate his jurisdiction over foreign policy. Long before the presidential campaign of 1920 and Harding's additional blows against the League, the continuing and fruitless debates in and out of the Senate—along with Wilson's infuriating proprietary attitude toward the League—were wearying voters whose wartime idealism paled with each passing day. A growing weariness first arose among Republicans, immigrants, and disillusioned liberals, and among Communists who thought of the League as a rival to their own international movement; and gradually the skepticism came to permeate the mind of the whole nation. The press, antagonized by Wilson's censorship policies as well as his handling of the news from the Versailles Conference, was in a mood to promote

[6] At the Jefferson Day dinner Wilson's "solemn referendum" message was read, while Bryan, in what was one more open split among Democrats, spoke for conditional ratification. Homer Cummings wrote: "The President *must* compromise [on the League] or he will wreck his party." Personal memorandum, January 28, 1920.

the change in sentiment. Many Democrats, anxious to have a winning issue in the 1920 election, had at first resisted compromising on the League. It was the fate of the Democratic party to become a political scapegoat in the League struggle wherein the issues were unclear and distorted. One correspondent wrote to Franklin Roosevelt: "I fear . . . that the Wilson League of Nations is about the most effective millstone that any party, bent on suicide, has tied about its neck to date."[7]

The presidential campaign would be an ordeal for any Democratic candidate who should attempt to face up to the burdens of the League and of intraparty disorder; yet three leading Democrats actively sought their party's nomination. Among James Cox, William Gibbs McAdoo, and A. Mitchell Palmer, the Attorney General was by far the weakest candidate. Palmer timed his campaign badly, incurring ridicule when his grave predictions about a May Day Communist insurrection proved baseless. Another obvious handicap was that in his home state, traditionally Republican Pennsylvania, he had performed badly in earlier races. Worse still, his performance during the Red Scare and his treatment of the unions during the coal strike alienated both liberals and labor leaders, who made him a symbol of the reaction and betrayal that appeared to characterize the Wilson Administration during its second term. In the early Michigan primary, where he campaigned actively, the Attorney General ran some distance behind Herbert Hoover, Governor Edward Edwards of New Jersey, McAdoo, and William Jennings Bryan, all of whom had tried to stay off the ballot. His name did crop up at the convention, where he inspired extraordinary enthusiasm among some delegates and was favored by some urban bosses; but he had little following as a second-choice possibility and was inconceivable as a consensus candidate.[8]

[7] Barbara Leahy to Roosevelt, June 9, 1920, Roosevelt Papers.
[8] On Palmer's bid to win the presidential nomination, see Coben: *A. Mitchell Palmer*, pp. 246–67. Wilson himself, ten days before the convention, reportedly told Carter Glass that Palmer would be a "weak" candidate. Robert K. Murray: *Red Scare* (Minneapolis, 1955), p. 260.

The name of William Gibbs McAdoo recalled, far more than Palmer's, the liberal achievements of Wilson's first term. Although McAdoo's progressivism was never predictable, people correctly identified him with the reforms of those early years as well as with the pro-labor Railroad Administration he later came to head. McAdoo was the most distinctly Wilsonian candidate—many of his supporters had held administration posts; and throughout the war McAdoo had worked closely with such loyal Wilsonians as Josephus Daniels and Carter Glass. Yet in an attempt to dissociate himself from an already faltering administration and to present himself as an unencumbered presidential candidate, McAdoo had quit his government posts at the end of 1918, catching the spirit of the times when he said he was leaving to make some money. According to Newton Baker, Wilson resented the loss of his able cabinet member on the eve of his European trip. Like other administration men, McAdoo lost touch with Wilson during the League dispute, when the Chief Executive was withdrawing more and more into his own moral and psychological realm. And McAdoo's standing with Wilson was not improved when in April of 1919, in conversation with the President, he announced that his own reservations about the League coincided with those of Elihu Root. McAdoo's correspondence and planning throughout 1919 and 1920 indicate that he was waiting for some paternal word and that in truth he was staking his hopes for 1920 upon the President's recommendation; but Wilson never endorsed him.[9]

[9] Colonel House wrote in his diary: "McAdoo remarked that he and the other Cabinet Members were nothing but clerks. This is not true of McAdoo, and that is why the President gets along less well with him." House manuscript diary, September 24, 1918. According to Josephus Daniels, Wilson declared to Burleson that McAdoo was not fit for the presidency. *The Wilson Era: Years of War and After, 1917–1923* (Chapel Hill, N.C., 1946), p. 553. McAdoo apparently "nettled" Wilson in cabinet meetings with his "emphatic manner and language." Fenno: *The President's Cabinet*, p. 122. McAdoo suggested to Tumulty that Democrats as well as Republicans should offer amendments to the Covenant. McAdoo to Tumulty, March 27, 1919. On Wilson's resenting the loss of McAdoo in 1918, see also Charles S. Hamlin's manuscript diary, February 5, 1924.

If McAdoo had persisted in his efforts to win the nomination, he would probably have been successful.[1] He turned aside because he thought the Democratic party had by 1920 temporarily lost its standing with the electorate, and because Wilson, who apparently favored his own renomination, would not give McAdoo the support that the former Secretary of the Treasury thought he would need in the campaign. In failing to endorse any of the candidates, the President signaled his own burdensome availability;[2] and probably more than coincidence accounts for the circumstance that McAdoo's decision to withdraw came just after the publication in the New York *World* of an article by Louis Siebold, based on an interview with Wilson and portraying the President as a healthy man and a logical candidate.[3] Inordinately ambitious and too canny to risk his political future on an imperfectly staged campaign, McAdoo was forced to hold back until 1924; meanwhile, he sent a bronze medal bearing a likeness of himself, together with a list of his accomplishments, to all his convention supporters.

[1] Although unpopular with urban bosses with whom he had not fully cooperated on patronage matters, McAdoo's popularity with many voters was certain. He ran first, Cox fifth, in the *Literary Digest* poll prior to the convention, LXV (June 12, 1920), 20; see also Mark Sullivan in *Collier's*, LXV (June 19, 1920), 9, 18. Josephus Daniels noted in his diary on January 29, 1920, that "McAdoo seems our strongest man." E. David Cronon, ed.: *The Cabinet Diaries of Josephus Daniels, 1913–1921* (Lincoln, Neb., 1963), p. 488. For reference to a "McAdoo Menace" letter prepared by leading Republicans, see David H. Stratton: "Splattered with Oil: William G. McAdoo and the 1924 Presidential Nomination," *Southwestern Social Science Quarterly*, XLIV (June 1963), 62.

[2] Nothing in Wilson's own Anglophile constitutional theory precluded his running for a third term; continuity of leadership was, in fact, central to that theory. Whatever his inclinations, his illness had severed his party support. Kurt Wimer: "Woodrow Wilson and a Third Term," *Pennsylvania History*, XXIX (April 1962), 193–211; Wesley Bagby: "Woodrow Wilson, a Third Term, and the Solemn Referendum," *American Historical Review*, LX (April 1955), 567–75; and Cronon, ed.: *Cabinet Diaries*, p. 497.

[3] Burleson told House that McAdoo wanted a positive expression from Wilson before the convention that the President was not a candidate— and got none. House Diary, June 3, 1921; *The New York Times*, June 19, 1920, p. 21. The Siebold interview is in the New York *World*, June 18, 1920, pp. 1–2.

James Cox, serving an unusual third term as governor of Ohio, found his way into politics as a newspaper publisher. His recommendation in April 1919 that the teaching of German be prohibited in all of Ohio's elementary schools (the measure was adopted, but only one other state, Nebraska, saw fit to impose a similar restriction) and his keen interest in movie censorship marred his earlier constructive record, as other policies had damaged that of Cox's fellow progressive, Wilson. More important in the eyes of the electorate was the matter of Cox's divorce in 1911 and remarriage in 1917—there were children by each wife. Before the Democratic convention, Mark Sullivan was calling the divorce an insurmountable obstacle to Cox's nomination.[4]

In contrast to the other major candidates, Cox was not identified with the Wilson Administration, and he was not a prohibitionist; he had run as an avowed "wet" in the 1918 gubernatorial election. These two negative virtues intrigued city bosses, particularly Charles Murphy of New York, whose hostility to Wilson dated back to the President's days as governor of New Jersey. In May of 1920, Murphy and his counterparts from other large cities attended a "stop McAdoo" meeting in French Lick Springs, Indiana, which outlined strategy that later secured the nomination of Cox. Edmond H. Moore, Cox's manager, arranged with Palmer's forces to oppose McAdoo jointly. In further pursuance of the policy sketched at French Lick Springs, Moore persuaded many of the Palmer and McAdoo delegates to name Cox as their second choices; the wisdom of this tactic revealed itself during the balloting at the convention, for Palmer and McAdoo, who might have pooled their strength in the interest of some other veteran of the Wilson Administrations, came close to possessing between them the two-thirds vote needed for nomination. When Palmer withdrew, his votes were divided

[4] Bagby: *The Road to Normalcy*, p. 154; Wittke: *German-Americans*, p. 181. Palmer wrote Cox in April 1919 that there was no need for restrictive legislation against radicals. April 30, 1919, Justice File 167-200, National Archives. Mark Sullivan to Henry Watterson, April 14, 1920, Watterson Papers.

among several candidates, though they might logically have gone to the other Wilsonian. Pennsylvania, perhaps, was showing its gratitude to Ohio, which had opposed a resolution to drop from each successive ballot the nominee with the lowest strength.[5]

With aid from the Murphy-Taggart-Brennan alliance of machine bosses, Cox finally won the nomination on the forty-fourth ballot. Even at the outset the mood of the delegates had been sober, since they believed with virtual unanimity that no Democrat could win in November; the length of the balloting brought the convention to a still further dispiriting anticlimax.

Ironically, it was Cox's running mate who had the brighter future. Franklin Roosevelt was chosen for the magic of his surname and for the geographical and political balance he would bring to the ticket. Although he had served as Assistant Secretary of the Navy, he had become *persona non grata* with Wilson, owing in part to his tactless remark in 1919 that "any man with common sense could save ten per cent of our government expenses." He continued in the 1920 campaign to denounce government waste and inefficiency. Roosevelt was a much less dominating figure in 1920 than he was to become in the thirties. In personality he thought it expedient to cast himself in the role of the Bull Moose Roosevelt; he cultivated the exclamation "Bully!" along with the politics of the Square Deal. And the papers quoted him as saying: "The Volstead Act—ridiculous!" Yet in 400 formal speeches delivered between August and November, Roosevelt projected his own young, attractive, and friendly personality before the public. Although his argument for the League of Nations was marred by excessive sarcasm, a Republican wired Senator Burt New that "Roosevelt is making friends."[6]

[5] *The New York Times*, May 9, 1920, pp. 1–2; James M. Cox: *Journey Through My Years* (New York, 1946), p. 226.
[6] In a post-election meeting with Cox, Roosevelt predicted, prophetically enough, that the Democrats would not elect a President until a fairly serious depression had occurred. Arthur Schlesinger, Jr.: *The Crisis of the Old Order, 1919–1933* (Boston, 1957), p. 366. The slight against Wilson

The convention adopted a perfunctory and defensive platform that happened to be the longest in the party's history up
to 1920. The first and most significant plank was an endorsement
of the League of Nations linked with an evasive statement about
a willingness to accept "interpretive" amendments; and both
Cox and Roosevelt, who later conferred with the President on
the League, gave the issue chief emphasis during the campaign.
The Wilson men who controlled the platform committee also
paid homage to the struggle for arbitration in industrial disputes
and for abolition of child labor. But even at that, the Democratic
platform was hardly more forward looking than the Republican,
which through the efforts of William Allen White and other
progressives contained a call for the recognition of the Soviet
government, American participation in the World Court, and
acknowledgment of labor's right to bargain collectively. In
rejecting an extreme dry plank, a gesture that again was quite
in keeping with Wilsonianism, the Democratic platform offended Bryan and the prohibitionists. Foreshadowing the in-
ternecine strife that was to plague the party in the twenties,
Bryan called the wet plank "a plagarisn [sic] from the Brewer's
Blue Book." In *The Commoner* he wrote that "The nomination of Governor Cox signalizes the surrender of the Democratic Party into the hands of the reactionaries." Bryan finally
cast a reluctant vote for Cox.[7]

---

was contained in an address at the Harvard Union, February 26, 1919;
quoted in Frank Freidel: *Franklin D. Roosevelt: The Ordeal* (Boston,
1954), p. 35. See also Cronon, ed.: *Cabinet Diaries*, pp. 490, 497–8. Grady J.
Gravlee: "A Rhetorical Study of Franklin D. Roosevelt's 1920 Campaign,"
unpublished doctoral dissertation, Louisiana State University, 1963.

[7] "If . . . Bryan," wrote George White, "made a speech in behalf of the
Governor during the campaign, I did not hear of it and I am sure he
positively declined to endorse Governor Cox's candidacy." White to W. B.
Fields, February 5, 1921, George White Papers. Alfred Lief, however,
remembered one speech that Bryan gave on behalf of Cox. *Democracy's
Norris* (New York, 1939), p. 222. J. Harvey McCarthy to Bryan, Novem-
ber 8, 1920, in George White Papers; William Jennings Bryan to Pat
Harrison, 1920, Bryan Papers; *The Commoner*, XX (July 1920), 13;
Lawrence Levine: *Defender of the Faith: William Jennings Bryan; The
Last Decade, 1915–1925* (New York, 1965), pp. 172–4.

Bound to the disastrous issue of the League, and pitted against a popular political mood that forecast almost certain defeat, Cox and Roosevelt faced another more immediate and practical problem: a party organization that had been nearly dormant since the 1918 congressional elections. Here, as within the administration itself, the Democracy revealed its growing incapacity to order itself or to define its purposes; and again much of the trouble might be traced to the President who was neglecting the affairs of his own party. McAdoo had earlier detected the weakened condition of the party machinery. Worrying, perhaps, over his own possible candidacy, he wrote to Daniel Roper on January 28, 1919, that he was "quite concerned over the organization of the National Committee. We have been drifting for a long time. There is neither direction nor energy . . . in our organization, and unless these are infused into it and promptly, we shall go into the 1920 campaign with a terrible handicap." Even in the midst of that campaign Joe Tumulty telegraphed Cox in exasperation:

> The campaign so far as the National Organization is concerned, is an utter and tragic failure. There is no executive or campaign committee; no plan of campaign; no contact be-between the National Organization and the various state organizations. . . . No bureau of the National Committee is functioning. They have not merely ceased to function, they have never functioned at all. A condition of demoralization and chaos, which is as difficult to understand as to describe, exists.

Claude Bowers, hard at work on his *Party Battles of the Jackson Period*, in 1921 summed up the situation by comparing the Democratic party organization of his own day with that of Jackson's time. "The Wilson period," wrote the lifelong Democrat Bowers to McAdoo, "had not behind it the fighting, sleepless organization, nor has it the brilliant propogandists [*sic*] like Kendall and Blair. . . . The organization men of those days worked ceaselessly, day by day, year by year. . . ." Bowers com-

plained of "the miserably weak publicity that has been sent out
—occasionally—between races or drinks—from our National
Committee."[8]

Cox did little to improve the efficiency of the national organization. In order to resolve intraparty bickering, he appointed the neutral and ineffectual George White of Ohio to the
post of Democratic National Chairman. Of White, one Ohioan
wrote: "His indolence in the campaign of 1920 was commented
on by [Senator] Pat Harrison and everyone around headquarters. . . ." White was notably tardy in the formation of a
finance committee, with the result that the party even had difficulty in maintaining its offices in Chicago, and in Montana the
presidential campaign train nearly stopped for lack of funds. In
1920 the Republicans raised a campaign fund more than three
times as great as that of the Democrats, whereas in 1916 Wilson's
campaign had been almost as well financed as Hughes's. In contrast to the Democrats, the Republicans surpassed even their
memorable performances of Mark Hanna's day. Will Hays was
magnificent in his efforts to revivify his party. He had conferences with almost all Republican congressmen, and gathered
from each of them lengthy press releases to send to friendly
papers. He hired expert salaried fund raisers. To obtain full
cooperation from state organizations, he set up a system of partially matching grants for the national campaign. In addition,
Hays cultivated the various ethnic voters, scrupulously noting
in his records the disposition of Thrace and Macedonia and the
landlocked condition of Magyar territory; and he excelled at
mitigating factionalism within his own party. Finally, Hays was
not overly scrupulous about the propaganda he spread, which
identified anarchism and Bolshevism with the Democrats. With
good cause, a post-election correspondent of Roosevelt complained of "the poison scattered by Mr. Hays."[9]

8 Bowers to McAdoo, January 18, 1921, and McAdoo to Roper, McAdoo
Papers; Tumulty to Cox, September 23, 1920, Tumulty Papers; Blum's
Tumulty, p. 167.
9 On White's performance see Homer Cummings' personal memorandum,
October 5, 1920; Daniel C. Roper: *Fifty Years of Public Life* (Durham,

Cox himself waged a tireless campaign, yet it was as ineffective as it was energetic. He charged the Republicans with accepting improper campaign contributions, but when challenged was unable to prove his accusation. His changing stands suggested to the minds of some columnists the confusions of Warren Harding; the Syracuse *Herald* said that the candidates were "as alike as two peas." After a meeting with the President, Cox decided to support the Wilson League and attacked its hyphenated opponents; but later in the campaign—too late to regain immigrant support—he made known his desire for clarifying amendments and proposed a reservation to the crucial Article X. In further incongruity to the dour Wilson, he wore a loud checkered overcoat and sporting hat as he pleaded for the League. He made three "wet" speeches in the campaign and then he appeared to run dry. He also shifted his stand on exclusion of Orientals. Moderate on the issue at first, he later adhered to the party's platform, which called the white racist sentiments of the West Coast "a true expression of the judgment of our people." The *New Republic* dismissed Cox: "If [he] has done anything or said anything . . . to earn the confidence of liberals, beyond repeating the tamest platitudes of Victorian progressives, we have not run across any report of it."[1]

N.C., 1941), p. 210; Bagby: *The Road to Normalcy*, pp. 129–30. According to Blum, Moore hampered the party organization even more than did White. See Blum's *Tumulty*, p. 249. On Hays see his "The Republican Position," *Forum*, LX (August 1918), 129–36, and W. D. Jamieson to McAdoo, September 21, 1919, McAdoo Papers; Robert G. Tucker to Hays, October 4, 1920, Hays Papers; W. H. Thompson to Roosevelt, November 13, 1920, Roosevelt Papers; Mayer: *The Republican Party*, p. 369.

[1] Ed Moore had been antagonized by Cox's overtures to Wilson. Moore wrote to George White in 1923: "You know what I said to you about Cox when, after we nominated him, he ran out on us and went to Canossa to make his peace with Wilson." August 13, 1923, White Papers. New York *World*, September 12, 1920, p. 12; Arthur Mullen: *Western Democrat* (New York, 1940), p. 185; Garraty: *Henry Cabot Lodge* (New York, 1953), p. 399; Cronon, ed.: *Cabinet Diaries*, p. 562; Andrew Sinclair: *The Available Man: The Life Behind the Masks of Warren Gamaliel Harding* (New York, 1965), p. 166; *New Republic*, XXIV (September 22, 1920), 83; (October 13, 1920), 153–4.

Over the fortunes of Cox hung the long and dark shadow of Woodrow Wilson. The real Republican quarry was always the incumbent President, not the Ohio governor. On the general issue of a League the people may have been undecided or indifferent, but toward the Wilson League considerable numbers were by 1920 unquestionably hostile, as they had become estranged from the austere and unbending President himself. It was Wilson who must bear final blame, if blame can be ascribed to a man in his physical and mental condition, for injudicious appointments that divided the cabinet and to that extent weakened the party. It was Wilson, the progressive friend of the farmer and the laborer, who had presided over an administration that managed in its last years to alienate from the Democracy substantial segments of labor and agriculture. In its toleration of men like Palmer and Burleson, moreover, the Wilson Administration helped to sustain the illiberal mood that served as a principal agent of its own rule. Secretary of the Interior Franklin K. Lane remarked just before the election: "Wilson is as unpopular as he once was popular . . . [he] bears down his party to defeat." And defeat came.[2]

For Cox's poor showing in November, cautious analysts offered "the backwash of war" as a general explanation. But the election involved one noticeable variable: the large numbers of

[2] According to Thomas Bailey, "The crippled Wilson, not the dynamic Cox, was running in 1920." *Woodrow Wilson and the Great Betrayal* (New York, 1945), p. 342. The Des Moines *Register* noted that Cox plaintively shouted to an audience: "Wilson's not running this year, Cox is running." October 8, 1920, p. 1. H. L. Mencken observed in the Baltimore *Sun* that "the heaviest burden that the Democratic party has to carry in this campaign is the burden of Dr. Wilson's unpopularity. He is disliked for a hundred and one different reasons. . . . It is months since I last encountered a genuine Wilson man." September 13, 1920, in Malcolm Moos, ed.: *A Carnival of Buncombe* (Baltimore, 1956), p. 21. In 1919, before the President's illness, an effort of indeterminate momentum to impeach Wilson on twenty-three counts had originated in St. Louis; see the pamphlet signed by John C. Meyers in the Dodd Papers, September 1921 to April 1922, S–Z. Franklin K. Lane to Benjamin I. Wheeler, October 28, 1920, *The Letters of Franklin K. Lane,* eds. Anne W. Lane and Louise H. Wall (Boston, 1922), p. 359.

women who cast their first votes in 1920. And some commentators suggested that the Republicans owed their great
pluralities to the newly adopted Nineteenth Amendment. It was
true enough that southern states and southern Democrats in
Congress had notoriously opposed passage of woman suffrage.
The view that in 1920 women were especially predisposed to
Republicanism arose in part from a frequently cited statistical
study by Stuart A. Rice and Malcolm M. Willey, which was
based on election returns in Illinois. In that state records of voting by sex were kept in 1920—records that reveal greater Republican support among women than among men. But in concluding
that women were in 1920 the more strongly Republican of the
sexes, Rice and Willey failed to take into account the special
circumstances created by the state's large immigrant-stock population, which was rather evenly distributed among the counties.
Even in 1920, Chicago's immigrants gave more support to the
Democratic party in proportion to their numbers than did the
rest of the city's population. Yet America's women of immigrant stock showed greater hesitancy to make use of their new
privilege than did their more emancipated native American
sisters,[3] and as a result their sentiment, which might have somewhat weakened the Republican lead among Illinois women, went
to a large extent unregistered, while the sentiment of their hus-
bands and brothers, which diluted the Republican lead among
the state's male voters, was counted. But it is certain that in
Illinois, and probably in much of the nation, the female vote if
not the female sentiment was more heavily Republican than the

[3] That immigrant-stock women lagged behind women of native extraction
in the exercise of the vote may be demonstrated with particular clarity in
Boston. In the twenty-six wards of that city, registration was obtained by
sex; and it can be seen that immigrant districts were typically districts of
lowest female registration. The only native American areas that had a
correspondingly low registration of women voters were the Negro and
lower-class native wards, where social restrictions on women also existed.
In the Negro sections, perhaps, the Democrats rather than the Republicans
were the gainers. Bureau of Elections, Boston, *Boston City Document
Number Ten* (Boston, 1921).

male, and was therefore of some benefit to the victorious party.[4]

Though the overwhelming Democratic defeat was the expression of a whole national mood, a number of important groups did register at the polls their special hopes and frustrations. Perhaps the most interesting feature of the 1920 election was the voting behavior of the immigrants clustered in the eastern cities. Table V, which is based on five assembly districts with the highest immigrant or native-born populations in each of three cities, reveals the striking rate at which voters of foreign stock fell away from the Democratic party. In New York, for example, the vote for Cox among immigrants dropped off 29.4 per cent from Wilson's total, compared to the nationwide shift of 15.2 per cent. The Socialists of New York benefited more than the Republicans from the shift.[5]

The Democratic losses of 1920, unlike those of 1918, were not merely sectional: the weakened party received less than its normal minority vote in every part of the nation. The passage of the Esch-Cummins Act, as well as the negative labor record of the second Wilson Administration, cooled labor toward the Democrats; in the Northeast, labor leaders and particularly

[4] Rice and Willey: "A Sex Cleavage in the Presidential Election of 1920," *The Journal of the American Statistical Association*, XIX (December 1928), 519–20. Foreign white stock comprised 60 per cent of Chicago's population and 40 per cent of the downstate total. United States Bureau of the Census, *Abstract of the Fourteenth Census of the United States*, 1920, pp. 18, 50, 372, 378. Two Illinois counties (Union and Greene) where the female vote for Cox eclipsed that for Harding were among the handful of counties with an insignificant population of foreign white stock. Charles E. Merriam and Harold F. Gosnell: *Nonvoting: Causes and Methods of Control* (Chicago, 1924), pp. 28–32; Harold F. Gosnell: *Getting Out the Vote* (Chicago, 1927), pp. 83–4; Andrew Sinclair: *The Better Half: The Emancipation of the American Woman* (New York, 1965), *passim;* Doris Stevens: *Jailed for Freedom* (New York, 1920), pp. 327–8; United States Bureau of the Census, *Fourteenth Census, Population,* III, 457–8.

[5] Chapter VIII contains a more comprehensive commentary on ethnic voting in 1920. *The New York Times*, November 9, 1916, p. 4; November 4, 1920, p. 4; Chicago *Daily Tribune*, November 9, 1916, p. 4; November 4, 1920, p. 3; Boston *Municipal Register, 1917,* p. 293; *1921,* p. 271; United States Bureau of the Census, *Fourteenth Census, Population, passim.*

The Presidential Vote in New York, Boston, and Chicago—
Immigrant and Native

	Immigrant Districts		Native-Born		Citywide	
	1916	1920	1916	1920	1916	1920
New York City	D49.3	D19.9	D42.4	D23.7	D52.9	D27.3
	R45.2	R50.0	R57.6	R69.8	R47.1	R60.0
	S 5.5	S28.6		S 4.5		
Chicago*	D60.4	D36.2	D37.7	D22.0	D47.5	D26.3
	R39.6	R63.8	R62.3	R78.0	R52.5	R73.7
Boston*	D71.7	D45.8	D51.2	D33.0	D60.1	D40.3
	R28.3	R54.2	R48.8	R67.0	R39.9	R59.7

* Two-party vote.

railroad men had been disappointed in the selection of Cox over their candidate, McAdoo; and southern support for prohibition must have further injured the Democratic cause among urban workingmen. Though Samuel Gompers' interest in the League had led him to endorse Cox, the AFL in 1920 was more anti-Republican than pro-Democratic. Daniel Tobin of the Teamsters Union was one of the few important labor leaders to back Cox enthusiastically; and some labor groups were so angered at Palmer and Burleson that they refused to endorse the Democratic candidate at all. Business groups remembered that the redistributive tax policies of war had been forced on the country by southern congressmen, who had also promoted government control of the railroads and utilities. The wheat districts in the central states, as in 1918, opposed the party they had in considerable extent supported in 1916, and falling prices for corn and wool also made their mark on the farm vote. In the face of agricultural deflation, Cox himself suggested that more land be reclaimed for agricultural use. The Democracy suffered most in the Far West, where the Wilson popularity of 1916 dissolved in antipathy toward Versailles and its favored treatment of Japan. Key Pittman, Cox's campaign manager in the Far West, thought the fight there was hopeless and let it go almost by default. Even in the South Democrats did badly, losing Tennessee and many prohibition areas for the first time since the Civil War.[6]

The Wilson coalition has been called unstable because it appeared in the middle of a long period of Republican ascendancy. And it is true enough, as the authors of *The American Voter* have shown, that voter preference, as a latent disposition, survives occasional apostasies—and ever since 1894 the Republicans had been the majority party. But a resumption of normal voting patterns only partly explains the sharp reaction against Wilson. To account for this unusual two-to-one loss, the particular mental climate of postwar America deserves special emphasis. The Wilson coalition, even apart from its inherent instability, was a victim to the reversal in political feeling that often develops in postwar times, and that is reflected in the defeat of Clemenceau and of Australia's Hughes, the eclipse of Lloyd George after his khaki victory of 1918—all men of Wilson's time—and, of course, Churchill's downfall in 1945 and the Republican victory in the American elections of 1946.

[6] In the one third of the wheat districts that had the highest acreage, the vote cast for the Democratic presidential candidate was 21 per cent less of the total than it had been in 1916, whereas the loss was 13 per cent in each of the remaining districts. United States Department of Agriculture, *Yearbook of Agriculture, 1928* (Washington, D.C., 1929), pp. 686, 714, 959. *American Federationist*, XXVII (July 1920), 656–7; (August 1920), 737–8; Arvil E. Harris: "Organized Labor in Party Politics, 1906–1932," unpublished doctoral dissertation, State University of Iowa, 1937, p. 310. John Higham in *Strangers in the Land* (New Brunswick, N.J., 1955), p. 265, says that "in California anti-Japanese hysteria, quiescent during the war, broke out again in the latter part of 1919 and rose to unprecedented heights during the election of 1920"; see also Roger Daniels: *The Politics of Prejudice: The Anti-Japanese Movement in California and the Struggle for Japanese Exclusion* (Berkeley, 1962), pp. 79–105. Will Hays considered all the western states to be the battleground of the 1920 campaign. *The New York Times*, June 15, 1920, pp. 1–2. Pittman's view is recorded in Fred Israel: *Nevada's Key Pittman* (Lincoln, Neb., 1963), p. 45; see also Cronon, ed.: *Cabinet Diaries* [October 7, 1920], p. 561–2.

The collapse of Wilsonianism represented the collapse of a philosophy—the "fusion of the peace cause with the idea of progressive democracy," as Arthur Link has called it—in interaction with the decay of a political structure. The philosophy fell victim to the war. Our entry into the conflict not only mocked the idealism of peace but more significantly forced a replacement of economic progressivism by a program of mobilization, and then after 1918 worked its harm upon progressivism in the issues and the very atmosphere it left behind: disillusion, the Red Scare, the League. With no political philosophy to give it direction, the structure of leadership had to disintegrate also. In the necessarily harsh decision-making of war it lost its progressive bearings and its political acumen—witness the clumsy handling of the agricultural problem in 1918. Later it almost ceased to exist when Wilson, abandoned to the League question and broken in health, became incapable of imposing order upon Congress, his party, and his own cabinet. Even in the techniques of patronage the administration grew inept.

The result was the disaster of 1920. Possibly that defeat had little directly to do with the character of the Democratic party in the years that followed. Some of the elements that turned against the Democratic party, like the wheat farmers, were merely moving back to Republican convictions they had never basically abandoned; the immigrants, on the other hand, would soon resume their loyalty to the national Democratic party. The importance of the election as a prelude to the twenties is its demonstration that the party no longer possessed, as it briefly had in Wilsonianism, a principle of cohesion. In 1920 it could not hold the groups and interests it had brought together in 1916, and for more than a decade it would be unable to unify to any significant political end the factions that it loosely incorporated.

CHAPTER III

The Divisive Themes

In Norfolk, Virginia, Spartanburg, South Carolina, and Snow-doun, Alabama, Ku Klux Klansmen in 1924 marched in spectacular parades. As was customary, the marchers usually draped themselves in white sheets symbolic of Christian purity and bore aloft hundreds of American flags; but the parades culminated in unique and lurid naturalization ceremonies, with all the trappings of Christian baptism, for thousands of sometimes reluctant aliens. The incidents dramatized a tension between native American and foreigner that ought to be as closely identified with the decade of the twenties as hedonism or Babbittry. Ethnic conflict pitting old stock against a new had existed throughout much of America's past.[1] But the coming of the "new immi-

[1] According to Walter Dean Burnham, "Profound antagonisms in culture and political style between the cosmopolitan, immigrant, wet, largely non-Protestant components of American urban populations and the parochial, dry, Anglo-Saxon Protestant inhabitants of rural areas can be traced back at least to the 1840s." And Lee Benson observed of New York State in the 1830's: "Immigrant Irish Catholics and native puritanical Protestants viewed each other as negative reference groups whose values, beliefs, attitudes, and ways of life clashed fiercely." Burnham: "The Changing Shape

grant"—less kin to older Americans than had been the earlier immigrants from the north of Europe, and far more alien in manner and tradition—raised that conflict to an almost unprecedented intensity. For while John Higham has demonstrated that much more than the new immigration contributed to a heightening of nativist feeling, it cannot be doubted that the recent arrivals gave rise to the fear that unassimilable elements were being injected into the tissue of American culture. Jews from Russia and the Balkans sometimes brought with them dangerous political ideas, as well as an exotic religion. Roman Catholic immigrants from southern Europe swelled the congregations of that suspect faith. And the World War had strengthened the notion that degenerating influences came from outside America and from alien sources within.[2]

In justification of their attitudes, nativist Americans advanced theories about the innate inferiority of the recent immigrant. Professor William MacDougall, a Harvard social psychologist, gave some of the theories of Anglo-Saxon supremacy academic backing; Madison Grant put them into more popular form in *The Passing of the Great Race;* and the historical writer Kenneth

---

of the American Political Universe," *American Political Science Review,* LIX (March 1965), 26; Benson: *The Concept of Jacksonian Democracy: New York as a Test Case* (Princeton, 1961), p. 322. *The Searchlight,* V (July 12, 1924), 1, 7.

[2] The president of the Clarksville, Tennessee, Kiwanis Club, spoke for his own organization—and for much of the nation at large: "In the last thirty years the tide of immigration has undergone a decided and alarming change. Prior to that time the overwhelming majority of entrants were of a racial stock akin to our own and therefore easily assimilable. . . . In latter years the inflow has been of a distinctly different and inferior character, Italians, southern Slovenes, Magyars, and natives of the Mid-Littoral, the latter admittedly the very antithesis of the Anglo-Saxon. These people have not the same ideals and aspirations of the Northern peoples. Among them the most revolting diseases are far more prevalent. Their ethical standards are entirely at variance with our own. They are unable to appreciate our conceptions of political liberty. Their ideas of right and wrong are so diametrically opposed to our own that no reconciliation between them is possible." F. J. Runyon to Senator Kenneth McKellar of Tennessee, March 19, 1924, McKellar Papers. Higham: *Strangers in the Land* (New Brunswick, N.J., 1955).

Roberts marketed them in the *Saturday Evening Post*. Most extensively of all, the Ku Klux Klan spread the idea that the newest arrivals would weaken the character of American society. Protesting the "Mississippi of foreign elements" that made our cities into "Sodoms and Gomorrahs," Hiram Evans of the Klan spurred the fight for restrictive legislation designed to restore the balance of peoples that had held in nineteenth-century America. The restriction movement was, however, far more broadly based than the Klan. "What a spectre is presented to the country," wrote a correspondent of Senator Kenneth Mc-Kellar, the Tennessee Democrat: "A foreign bloc, representing the Jewish, Italian, Russian, and Polish provinces of New York, Massachusetts, and other sections . . . defying the American Congress on the Immigration bill. . . . What would 'Old Hickory' . . . have said and done?" Replying that he was in "entire accord" with his constituent's indignation, McKellar, like most other senators from the South and West, pledged himself "heartily in favor of the strictest kind of immigration laws." A handful of urban congressmen opposed such legislation.[3]

For the computing of immigration quotas that would maintain within the nation already existent proportions of ethnic stock, Governor Smith of New York favored using the census of 1920 as the base line; while Hiram Evans preferred that of 1890, when the new immigrants had as yet only begun to swell their numbers.[4] Before the end of 1924, and partly in response to

[3] See, for example, MacDougall's books, *Ethics and Some Modern World Problems* (New York, 1924), pp. 21, 49–50, 73 ff., and *Is America Safe for Democracy?* (New York, 1921). On his influence upon nativist thinking, see *Christian Register*, CIV (July 10, 1924), 657. Demand for Grant's book (New York, 1916) carried it through several printings in the 1920's, and Grant himself contributed political leadership in the South and West for racist goals. Some of Roberts' essays are collected in *Why Europe Leaves Home* (New York, 1922); see also Gino Speranza: *Race or Nation* (Indianapolis, 1925), and Lothrop Stoddard's *Rising Tide of Color* (New York, 1920). Hiram Evans: "The Ku Klux Klan," *The Landmark*, VI (April 1924), 240; Legrand W. Jones to McKellar, March 19, 1924, McKellar to Jones, March 26, 1924, and McKellar to F. J. Runyon, March 22, 1924, McKellar Papers.
[4] *The New York Times*, August 23, 1928, pp. 2, 3.

postwar immigration that threatened to acquire unprecedented proportions, Congress passed new and lower quotas based on national origins as listed in the 1890 census, and so solved the problem to Evans' satisfaction. But while the 1924 law, which was to take effect fully by the end of the decade, may have calmed a few hysterical nativists, the belief continued to be widespread that a large alien population resided within America and that it must be carefully watched and controlled.

The city was the embodiment of all that was "foreign" to American life. To the more apprehensive rural followers of Bryan and McAdoo, New York City, the birthplace of Al Smith and the scene of the convulsive Democratic Convention of 1924, seemed a fusion of Babel and the Cities of the Plain. What place could there be in American culture for a metropolis where in 1920 fully three quarters of the white stock were themselves foreign born or the children of foreign-born parents?[5] And in the thinking of nativists, immigration was of a piece with the other ills of the great city. New York was the home of Wall Street, a name anathema to men who had once heeded Populist leaders. The city, moreover, housed a number of cultural attractions that rural manhood deemed snobbish and effete. The legitimate theater, until recently an affront to the American conscience, made its home in New York along with opera sung in a foreign language. Then there was the ease with which liquor could be bought in Manhattan during the days of prohibition; for this the ruralists blamed Tammany Hall, itself a further symbol of the corrupt city. Diversions encouraged by Tammany, and sanctioned in laws signed by Governor Al Smith, included Sunday baseball and professional boxing. Books and magazines, some of them less than wholesome, were pub-

[5] It may be that the Protestants among the older city immigrants developed a nativism as strong as that of the ruralists, but the dialogue on the issue was between the city and country. Walter Laidlaw, ed.: *Statistical Sources for Demographic Studies of Greater New York, 1920* (New York, 1922), p. xxix; for more comprehensive data on the foreign-born population, see Laidlaw's *Population of the City of New York, 1890–1930* (New York, 1932), pp. 245–315.

lished in the city. New York stood also for the forces of rationalism and modernism—Harry Emerson Fosdick spoke from the pulpit of the Riverside Church—against which the rural fundamentalist pitted his faith. In the country the agrarian myth survived. Orators might still invoke the words of the young Thomas Jefferson: "Those who labour in the earth are the chosen people of God . . . , whose breasts he has made His peculiar deposit for substantial and genuine virtue. . . . The mobs of the great cities add just so much to the support of pure government, as sores do to the strength of the human body."[6]

The cities, moreover, were formidable in their growth, overtaking the countryside at a moment when it was actually suffering an absolute loss in population.[7] And the twenties were a time of considerable rural poverty and urban prosperity, a time that might tempt the city mind to a condescending superiority and the country mind to jealousy. With the rise in agrarian poverty and the loss of ambitious farm youths to the urban factories went a decline in rural morale.

More than ever before the city and country stood at odds during the 1920's, and by 1924 the tension had clearly entered politics. Urban immigrants had voted with some group solidarity in the elections of 1916 and 1920; and by the early twenties the

[6] In the papers of a prominent southern Methodist clergyman, there appears an unsigned etymological note: "The name 'Manhattan' had its origin from the drunken bout which the Indians called 'Man-na-hatta-nink'—the Delaware Indian name for a place of general drunkenness." July 1928, Warren A. Candler Papers. During the 1928 presidential campaign a broadside of Governor Smith dictating to a Negro woman bore the caption: "We don't care a cuss about what he does in New York, but we don't propose to sit silent and let him jam New York ideas down our throats. The picture is a New York idea. . . ." Special Collections, Columbia University Library. New York World, May 10, 1924, p. 1; Thomas Jefferson: Notes on Virginia, William H. Peden, ed. (Chapel Hill, N.C., 1955), pp. 164–5. See also Morton and Lucia White: The Intellectual Versus the City: From Thomas Jefferson to Frank Lloyd Wright (Cambridge, Mass., 1962), pp. 12–20.

[7] In 1910 there were 44 metropolitan areas with a population of more than 100,000; in 1920 the figure climbed to 56; and by 1930 it had shot up to 99. Warren S. Thompson: Population: The Growth of Metropolitan Districts in the United States: 1900–1940 (Washington, D.C., 1947), pp. 6–7.

Ku Klux Klan and other xenophobic groups were making their strongest bid. Since the conception of a melting pot seemed fallacious, some native Americans feared a distant future in which the control of political affairs might pass completely from their hands into those of solidly ranked immigrant voters, as had already occurred in Boston and other large cities. Eventually, the Roman Catholic Church might even become the state church of America; prominent Catholic priests had hinted ominously of such things. The high birthrate among the Catholic new-comers made more credible the fear that the Church might come to dominate American politics, first seizing one of the parties, and finally the nation. Those with greater knowledge of the situation saw a milder but more immediate ill. Mark Sullivan, himself no nativist, spoke for some intelligent native Americans when he protested that "the mere existence of a considerable number of foreigners who act together in politics is a present vivid obstacle to political action in the free and spontaneous interest of the nation as a whole. . . ."[8] To a considerable extent, then, urban-rural conflict was at its deepest level a reflection of the cleavage between the native-stock American and the immigrant—a cleavage constantly more distinct than the divi-sion between city and country, or between an urban East and a rural West and South.

That the forces of urbanism eventually brought new vigor to the Democratic party seems to be beyond question; they helped create for it, by the thirties, a powerful new identity, and they contributed their legions of voters to its electoral army. But it is a possibility, incapable of definite proof but worthy of sug-gestion, that even the factional strife of the twenties was doing its part in revitalizing the Democracy. Struggles between rural and urban Democrats over the divisive issues of the Ku Klux Klan, Roman Catholicism, and prohibition increased the self-consciousness and aggressiveness of both factions even as it

[8] John A. Ryan and Moorhouse F. X. Millar: *The State and the Church* (New York, 1922), pp. 33–5; *World's Work*, XLVII (February 1924), 441.

weakened the whole party; and in the increased militance of its camps lay a source of future strength for the entire party. Even the losers, the drys and the Klansmen, created in men like Hugo Black of Alabama powerful leaders who would long outlast the decade. The strength of faction was still more impressive in city areas, where the Democratic contingent among urban congressmen was on the increase and where Senator David I. Walsh of Massachusetts came into increasing prominence as a spokesman for a rapidly industrializing section. And once the personalities who symbolized conflict within the party—William Jennings Bryan, William Gibbs McAdoo, and Alfred E. Smith—had passed from national politics the social issues they represented lost much of their political meaning and the stage was set for a rapprochement between city and country Democrats.[9]

The organized expression of ethnic hatred in America was the Ku Klux Klan, which was revived in Atlanta, Georgia, in 1915 while the racist movie *Birth of a Nation* was showing at a local theater. Colonel William J. Simmons had organized the new Klan, but the leadership fell in 1920 to Edward Y. Clarke and Mrs. Elizabeth Tyler, whose Southern Publicity Association had hitherto been engaged in promoting the Red Cross. About 1922 Hiram Evans, a Dallas dentist, took over from Clarke and helped to bring the Klan into national politics. In the early twenties, the frustrations of a serious depression, a fresh wave of immigration, the dramatized relationship of a few Italians and Sicilians to crime syndicates, and the incentive that a

[9] Black's reliance on Klan support is discussed in Daniel M. Berman: "Hugo Black, Southerner. II. The Negro," *American University Law Review*, X (1961), 35–42. Black renounced the Klan in the thirties. Like other politicians, he had been forced to choose between accepting the organization's support or risking political failure. Many reports also exist of Harry Truman's alleged reliance on Klan support; see, for instance, Norman F. Weaver: "The Knights of the Ku Klux Klan in Wisconsin, Indiana, Ohio, and Michigan," unpublished doctoral dissertation, University of Wisconsin, 1954, p. 82. Walsh's career and his popularity in immigrant areas are described in J. Joseph Huthmacher: *Massachusetts People and Politics, 1919–1933* (Cambridge, Mass., 1959), *passim*.

large initiation fee offered to Klan organizers all combined to swell the Klan's following.

The Klan of the twenties resembled its predecessor of Reconstruction in its attitudes toward the Negro. The industrial demands of World War I had enabled many Negroes to secure jobs that earlier would have been out of their reach, and to move into new areas where their presence was unwelcome. Their more favorable economic and social status antagonized unemployed white veterans, and on such embittered feelings the Klan thrived.[1] Hiram Evans proposed sterilization of undesirable elements within the Negro race; but he also considered African resettlement, and in 1922 met with Marcus Garvey, the Negro nationalist, to discuss the policy. The new Klan, however, was not a direct ideological descendant of the earlier movement, which had contented itself with simple white supremacy; the twentieth-century organization, partly commercial in its nature, drew its members from a broader spectrum and could more definitely trace its ancestry and its attitudes to nativist groups. The immigrant, particularly the Catholic, took his place alongside the Negro as a target of the nativists, victim of a hostility that proceeded only in part from economic frustrations similar to those that helped turn the white man against the colored.[2] Klan strength coincided with areas in which nativism had ap-

[1] But coincidentally with the rise of the Klan, the conscience of the South was tightening against at least the worst form of Negrophobia. During the years of the Klan's most rapid growth, the number of lynchings in the South fell off markedly. Lynching figures are taken from Jessie P. Guzman *et al.*, eds.: *The Negro Yearbook, 1952* (New York, 1952), p. 278; identical government figures are available for the years since 1919 in *Crime of Lynching*, United States Senate: Committee on the Judiciary, *Hearings* (Washington, D.C., 1948), p. 30.

1910	67	1915	51	1920	53	1925	17
1911	60	1916	50	1921	59	1926	23
1912	61	1917	36	1922	51	1927	16
1913	51	1918	60	1923	29	1928	10
1914	51	1919	76	1924	16	1929	7

[2] On the Klan's anti-Catholicism, see John Mecklin: *The Ku Klux Klan: A Study of the American Mind* (New York, 1924), pp. 28, 38.

peared in the past, notably the Middle West and South. In the Middle West, where the anti-Catholic American Protective Association had shown its colors in the 1890's, Klansmen were endorsed by former members of the APA. In the South a narrow denominationalism contributed to a bitter and vigorous anti-Romanism directed against the recent immigrants. The appearance of new centers of nativist and, later, Klan sentiment could be explained by population shifts. Oregon and Washington, for example, were originally settled by immigrants from the Mississippi Valley who belonged to the old American stock from which earlier nativism had drawn its support. California had its peculiar problem of Oriental immigration.

The conduct and reputation of the Ku Klux Klan that followed World War II have somewhat distorted our view of the earlier organization. "The Klan," H. L. Mencken affirmed, albeit scornfully, "was just what it pretended to be—an order devoted to the ideals most Americans held sacred."[3] Whatever abnormality existed was among certain leaders and in the culture that produced it; most Klansmen were probably more devoted to group fraternalism than to nativism and violence. The organization probably appealed most to the lower middle classes rather than to the poorest, who could ill afford the ten dollar initiation fee and the high costs of regalia. Though perhaps among the native born in more influential or fast-growing cities, the Klan played a crucial role within that segment of the rural Protestant community whose religious and moral spokesman was William Jennings Bryan and whose political concern in the twenties was prohibition. Bryan himself deplored the Klan and never was a member. But to win the support of Bryan's rural America, the order offered itself as an arm of the Protestant churches and patriotic organizations, for which it already possessed an affinity; and upon religion and patriotism the Klan built its mystique.

The Klan's famous symbol was the burning cross. The chap-

[3] William Manchester: *H. L. Mencken: Disturber of the Peace* (New York, 1950), p. 146.

lain, or Kludd, was an important official; he opened each Klavern meeting with a prayer, perhaps reminding an assembled gathering, as did one Klan "prayer book," that "the living Christ is a Klansman's only criterion of character." Before an altar, a central piece of Klan equipment, the Kludd delivered the Kloxology. Religious songs became Klan songs: "There's a Church in the Valley by the Wildwood" became "There's a Cross that Is Burning in the Wildwood"; "Onward Christian Soldiers" was metamorphosed into "Onward Valiant Klansmen." Christian burial ceremonies were occasionally graced by flowers spelling "KKK" spread over the grave. And deeply ingrained in Klan consciousness was an aggressive patriotism. A Grand Dragon noted that "one of our great duties in disseminating the principles of Klancraft is to forever and ever preach the gospel of patriotism, never allowing a national or state event in which our flag is being commemorated to pass by without making special effort [to create] . . . love and respect in the hearts of all men for our starry banner." At an initiation ceremony, a Klokard (clerk or lecturer) erected a flag-draped altar, and stood a second American flag to its left. A Klan Khoral Klub sometimes would sing "The Star Spangled Banner." The most effective of all Klan songs were familiar tunes that combined religious with patriotic appeal. And in its devotion to the United States and to Old Glory, the Klan is especially to be distinguished from the southern organization of post-Confederate days.[4]

The politics of Klansmanship in its heroic days and after were frequently intertwined with the politics of the major parties. The influence of the Klan was swelled by politicians who joined as they would any fraternal organization that might deliver votes, and by others who would use it in the service of their personal ambition. And in adhering to the Klan, such men made it all the stronger, all the more desirable to political hopefuls. Its power, like that of other clubs, was therefore self-generating;

[4] *The Knights of the Ku Klux Klan of the Realm of Oklahoma vs. the State of Kansas, ex. rel.,* p. 183; Emerson Loucks: *The Ku Klux Klan in Pennsylvania* (New York, 1936), pp. 121–2.

it was capable of drawing members especially at the local level where its intimate, grass-roots character made support of it a necessity to neighborhood politicians, especially where the organization trimmed its program to local needs. Significantly enough, the Klan promoted opposition to reapportionment of the rurally dominated state legislatures, especially in swiftly urbanizing states like Illinois and Indiana. In Texas, Arkansas, Wisconsin, West Virginia, and other states, elections were sometimes held within the Klaverns prior to regular party primaries; and directions were often given to support various bills in the state legislatures. The Indiana "Military Machine" was designed to bring out every available Klan vote on election day.[5] Though it was strongest in local politics, the order was frequently credited with aiding in the election of senators and governors, who would sometimes respond to the pressures of the organization. Late in 1923 the *New Republic* pointed out that the Klan virtually dominated the politics of Oklahoma, Arkansas, Indiana, and Texas, and enjoyed a degree of political influence in Ohio, Oregon, Maine, Connecticut, New Jersey, and elsewhere. The year 1924 was to represent the high point of the Klan's political influence.[6]

As a rule, the Klan attached itself to the dominant political party. Consequently, its deepest infiltration of the Democratic party was in the South. From Oklahoma and Texas to Virginia, Klan power in the South's party of tradition was formidable. Throughout the rest of the country, however, the Klan allied itself primarily with the Republicans and made overtures to the Democracy in most cases only when it desired to widen its already considerable influence. Democratic politicians sometimes welcomed the Klan's support, as they would any bloc of potential voters, and the Klan sometimes even controlled the

[5] Charles C. Alexander: "Secrecy Bids for Power: The Ku Klux Klan in Texas Politics in the 1920's," *Mid-America*, XLVI (January 1964), 9–10; *The New York Times*, August 1, 1922, p. 21; W. D. Harry to William Allen White, September 23, 1924, White Papers; Weaver: "The Knights of the Ku Klux Klan," p. 195.

[6] *New Republic*, XXXVI (November 21, 1923), 321.

Democratic factions. In Missouri the Klan was used as an outright Democratic weapon to intimidate Negroes who had recently moved northward out of the black belt. But outside the South the Klan usually assumed a Republican coloration; and at times it encountered organized Democratic opposition.[7]

In Indiana, for instance, one Democrat boasted that while in 1924 "the Klan simply swallowed the G.O.P.," his party was meeting the issue squarely. Although the Klan was reported to be in control of "a very large majority of the Democratic organizations," the state Democratic party, under the influence of the Indiana boss Tom Taggart, denounced the Klan—but Governor Vic Donahey then did not endorse the platform. Similar disavowals of Klan support were adopted at Democratic state conventions in Connecticut, New Mexico, Ohio, and Kansas—states where the Klan was supporting the Republicans. All of the Klan "victories" reported by *The New York Times* in its 1924 election analysis were Republican successes; this circumstance was testimony that in the two or three years prior to 1924 Klan membership rolls had been growing much faster outside than inside the South.[8]

Before the 1924 presidential election the Klan constituted a potentially powerful bloc; conservative estimates of its active strength in 1924 range in the neighborhood of only two million, but a greater number of members had been enrolled at one time or another. Since the order was made up almost wholly of male citizens, the ranks who might vote the Klan's way must have been further swelled by dutiful wives. Even

[7] In Texas, Oklahoma, and Georgia the Klan occasionally supported Republicans; and in Oregon, Ohio, and Iowa it sometimes backed Democrats. David Chalmers: *Hooded Americanism* (New York, 1965), p. 81.

[8] William H. Rickens to Senator Samuel M. Ralston, May 19, 1924. In Ralston's telegram to Taggart announcing withdrawal as a presidential candidate at the 1924 convention, the Senator complained that he was being tied to the Klan. June 1, 1924, Ralston Papers. Meredith Nicholson to Robert Bridges, 1924, Nicholson Papers; Edgar I. Fuller, *The Visible of the Invisible Empire* (Denver, 1925), p. 125; *Literary Digest*, LXXXI (May 24, 1924), 14; *The New York Times*, November 6, 1924, pp. 1, 3; Chalmers: *Hooded Americanism*, pp. 145, 267.

where the Klan did not function, many people favored its principles, and in areas where it was strong, those who hesitated to
join might sympathize with its point of view and perhaps follow
its lead. While members of the Klan belonged to opposing political parties, a candidate designated by the Klan could often be
assured of both Democratic and Republican votes. In 1922 the
chairman of the congressional committee that had investigated the order was defeated in part by Klan opposition, as were
two Jewish congressmen in Indiana and Texas. Hiram Evans
of Dallas, who worked assiduously to bring the Klan into politics, claimed that the "Klan vote" was always higher than its
membership.[9] The power of the Klan was to be reckoned with
at national political conventions, and in no small part because
it was of unknown potency.

The Klan's political activities reflected the ambitions of its
leaders. Evans and Edward Y. Clarke tried sundry schemes to
acquire political power. In 1920 Clarke revealed to Georgia
Republicans a plan to "discredit" the Democratic party by
linking it to the Roman Catholic Church; later in the year he
had a "very satisfactory" conference with Will Hays, saying
that Hays had "grasped the possibilities in our plan." In 1923
a document stolen from the Klan's Atlanta headquarters revealed plans for a takeover of the national government. According to an ex-official of the Klan, Evans was brought to the
White House in the same year by the sculptor Gutzon Borglum,
who introduced the Klan leader to President Harding; letters in
the Borglum papers from Evans and to Coolidge prove that such
a meeting was indeed arranged. A few weeks after Evans' alleged meeting with the Chief Executive, the order transferred
its headquarters from Atlanta, Georgia, to Washington, D.C.
As the 1924 election approached, the Klan wooed the Democrats
as well. In the spring of 1923 Evans approached Williams Gibbs
McAdoo at French Lick Springs, Indiana; purportedly he persuaded McAdoo to be the Klan candidate for President, though

[9] Stanley Frost: "The Masked Politics of the Klan," *World's Work*, LV
(February 1928), 404.

more accurately Evans had simply chosen to support him. During the coming months the Klan worked against McAdoo's opponents, Smith of New York and Senator Oscar Underwood of Alabama; and Evans spoke glibly of electing McAdoo to put "a Klansman in the White House."[1]

The politics of the Klan naturally centered around religious as well as ethnic issues. Senator Tom Heflin of Alabama eulogized the Klan: "God had raised up this great patriotic organization to unmask popery." Colonel Simmons, in an effort to maintain his waning influence over the Klan he had founded, turned more and more to the berating of Catholics.[2] And Clarke in 1920 set out to use anti-Catholicism as a drawing card to brothers in other fraternal organizations, particularly the Masons with their well-known tradition of anti-Romanism. Senator Tom Watson of Georgia, who before the war had suggested the

[1] Benjamin H. Avin: "The Ku Klux Klan, 1915–1925: A Study in Religious Intolerance," unpublished doctoral dissertation, Georgetown University, 1952, pp. 270–1, 296–7; Borglum to Harding and Evans to Borglum, both early 1923, Borglum Papers. Clarke was said to have boasted that he would be "the most powerful man in the world through the Klan." Francis R. Welch to Calvin Coolidge, Justice Department File 198589–591, National Archives. Fuller: *The Visible of the Invisible Empire*, pp. 51, 62; Marion Monteval: *The Klan Inside Out* (Claremore, Okla., 1924), pp. 139, 140–1; Rice: *The Ku Klux Klan in American Politics*, pp. 98–9. The Grand Titan of Waco, Texas, quoted Evans as saying: "Mr. McAdoo is our man." Grand Titan to M. E. Foster, April 14, 1924, Underwood Papers. In a 1938 senatorial campaign a Klan membership card was used to discredit McAdoo, but it was undoubtedly a forgery. See Chapter IV on McAdoo's relationship with the Klan.

[2] John Mecklin, a sociologist, wrote that "a canvass of the motives for joining the Klan indicates that anti-Catholicism takes precedence over all others." Mecklin: *The Ku Klux Klan*, p. 38. See also Charles P. Sweeney: "The Great Bigotry Merger," *The Nation*, CXV (July 5, 1922), 9, and Breckinridge Long manuscript diary, March 6, 1924. Although the Catholic threat was more immediate, since it was carried in the person of Al Smith, the Jews also came in for an occasional attack. The extravagant Bishop Alma White warned of a Roman Catholic–Hebrew alliance; White even interpreted the sinking of the *Titanic* as representing the wrath of God toward immigrants and Catholics. *Heroes of the Fiery Cross* (Zarephath, N.J., 1928), pp. 27 ff. Henry D. Lindsey to Arthur M. Hyde, October 18, 1922, Hyde Papers.

formation of a new Klan, campaigned in that year on the issue of popery. In a recrudescence of Know-Nothingism, the Klan helped to circulate stories about the American political aspirations of the Pope. Once again it was rumored that the Holy Father wanted to set up a new empire in the Mississippi Valley, although Governor Sidney J. Catts of Florida insisted that the Vatican had the Sunshine State in mind. In the nation's capital some Protestants worried that two cannons at Georgetown University were pointed toward the White House and that various Catholic institutions, as seen on a map published in *The Fundamentalist*, appeared to surround the important government buildings—"the great fortress-like strongholds of the papal government on strategical and commanding heights." In the filagree of the dollar bill was seen a rosary, cross, and head of the Virgin Mary placed there by a wily Jesuit; and Senator Heflin objected violently when cardinal-red drapes were hung in Coolidge's reception rooms. The conception of a Catholic conspiracy was everywhere: a correspondent of Franklin Roosevelt suggested that as a reasonable precaution all nuns be fingerprinted; a Klan paper complained that Catholic women had been sent by the hierarchy to infest the women's clubs of Texas "to prepare for the final takeover"; land overlooking West Point, it was pointed out, had been purchased by the Catholics in preparation for civil war.[3]

When Al Smith became a serious presidential candidate, the New Yorker—who summed up in his person and background

---

[3] Other tales that survive expose the ignorance of the Klansmen. Men who could take seriously a Kligraff or a Kludd would find little difficulty in believing, as did Reverend Doctor C. Lewis Fowler, editor of the *American Standard*, that Harding died from hypnotic telepathic thought waves generated in the minds of Jesuit adepts. Sweeney: "The Great Bigotry Merger," p. 10; W. O. Whitney to Franklin Roosevelt, October 15, 1928, Roosevelt Papers; *The Fundamentalist*, April 13, 1928, p. 2; *The Protestant*, March 24, 1928, p. 4; *American Standard*, August 1, 1924, p. 1; Joe Tumulty to Elbert R. Zaring, January 5, 1924, copy in Senator James D. Phelan Papers; Morton Harrison: "Gentlemen from Indiana," *Atlantic Monthly*, CXLI (May 1928), 679–80. Heflin is quoted in Alma White's *The Ku Klux Klan in Prophecy* (Zarephath, N.J., 1925), p. 17.

much that the Klan feared—became the focus of attack. Governor Smith outraged the Klan in 1923 and again two years later when he signed bills that practically outlawed the organization in New York State. The *Literary Digest* believed that Smith had thereby signed his political death warrant so far as his aspirations for the presidency were concerned.[4] Smith had committed additional crimes against Klan mentality when he signed a bill in 1922 making New York the first state to repeal its prohibition-enforcement law, a predetermined step in nationwide wet strategy.

At the Democratic National Convention in 1924 the Klan exerted strength sufficient to prevent the delegates from censuring their organization by name. In New York as elsewhere, boasted Hiram Evans, the "delegates were afraid of what we might do." At that convention the Klan also fulfilled its purpose regarding the presidential candidacy of Governor Smith: to help prevent the nomination of the New Yorker in that year and to instill enough anti-Catholicism in the mind of the average voter to diminish Smith's chances of ever winning the presidency.[5]

Why the Klan lost its vitality after 1924 and suffered a sharp decline in its membership remains something of a mystery, but it can be seen that around 1925 a number of forces were converging against the order. The confidence shaken by the war and the ensuing depression had returned with the prosperity of the middle and later twenties; it was thin soil for the sustenance of extremism. Disclosures of rampant local terrorism and widespread corruption injured the Klan. In 1924 America was shocked to hear that in Indiana Grand Dragon David Stephenson had sexually assaulted an ex-schoolteacher, driving her to poison and death. Other eminent Klansmen, including Simmons and Evans, became involved in financial scandals, and the Klan

[4] LXXVII (June 9, 1923), 12.
[5] Rice: *The Ku Klux Klan in American Politics*, p. 84. The Klan's political fortunes in 1924 are drawn in *The New York Times*, November 6, 1924, pp. 1, 3.

was blamed for acts of individual extremists. The Klan, it began to appear, had little to offer the American who sought a fortified ground of respectability from which to challenge the morals and respectability of others. In addition, the rhetorical defeat of Bryan at the Scopes trial and his ensuing death in 1925 weakened the rural fundamentalist crusade against the city and the foreigner. The congressional quota system of 1924, sharply limiting immigration from southern and eastern Europe, accomplished an important part of the Klan program and removed a portion of its *raison d'être*. Finally, despite its authoritarian structure, the Klan membership was extremely heterogeneous: particularly after its leaders entered politics, arguments flared between progressives and conservatives, Democrats and Republicans. As leaders quarreled over issues and candidates, the discipline of the order ran afoul of existing political alignments.[6]

The Klan's passing freed the Democratic party of a contentious issue, but it did not signal the passing of intolerance. The mental stereotypes that gave rise to the Klan had far antedated its birth; at its decline, words like "Pope," "Catholic," and "foreigner"—their sinister implications sharpened through the work of the Klan—kept their explosive power to draw forth fear or hatred. One Klansman who withdrew from the order stated that "there was nothing wrong with the Klan principles. But the members—they weren't big enough for the order."[7] The Klan's demise was primarily an organizational failure and not a result of external attacks; and the same feelings that made the Klan flourish in 1924 continued to exist during the 1928 presidential campaign.[8]

[6] Toxologists noted that tooth marks on Stephenson's victim were alone sufficient to have induced death; it was a strange way to preserve the purity of American womanhood that was frequently stated as a Klan goal. *New Republic*, LII (November 16, 1927), 330–2; Monteval: *The Klan Inside Out*, pp. 66 ff.; Carl Degler: "A Century of the Klan," *Journal of Southern History*, XXXI (November 1965), 435–43.

[7] Quoted in Loucks: *The Ku Klux Klan in Pennsylvania*, p. 163.

[8] For interesting defenses of the Klan, see Charles S. Joiner to John W. Davis, November 17, 1924, Davis Papers, and W. D. Wilson to Franklin

The fortunes of the Klan were closely related to the course of religious fundamentalism, which also declined after 1925. The administrative personnel of the two movements were often shared. Some individuals appear to have acquired in the Klan their initial training for work in the fundamentalist movement, particularly in the evangelical churches; others made the transition from fundamentalism to nativism. During the years 1922 to 1928, twenty-six of the thirty-nine anti-Catholic lecturers regularly employed by the Klan were Protestant ministers of the fundamentalist type, and in these same years sixteen Protestant ministers served as Klan officials, not to speak of the thousands of Protestant clergymen who joined the Klan. The National Catholic Bureau of Information compiled a list of sixty-seven ministers preaching pro-Klan sermons or entertaining Klansmen in their homes. The most prominent Klansmen served in the fundamentalist crusade. Colonel Simmons himself had once held a probationary Methodist pulpit, although it had been withdrawn on moral grounds, and Edward Clarke with Mrs. Tyler joined the fundamentalists in the mid-twenties—and the Anti-Saloon League still later in the decade—after leaving the Klan. In many parts of the country, church buildings served as meeting places for the Klan; everywhere ministers were offered free membership, and Klan donations to churches were commonplace. H. L. Mencken, Charles Merz, Virginius Dabney, and others reported on the denominational ties of the Klan or the aid it gave to passing anti-evolution laws.[9]

Roosevelt, December 12, 1924, Roosevelt Papers. For examples of non-Protestant groups that patterned themselves on the Klan, see Weaver: "The Knights of the Ku Klux Klan," pp. 246 ff., and *The New York Times*, September 7, 1923, p. 17; September 16, 1923, I, pt. 2, p. 5; March 22, 1924, p. 12; November 2, 1924, p. 1; November 5, 1924, p. 20.

[9] Michael Williams: *Shadow of the Pope* (New York, 1932), p. 317; Virginius Dabney: *Liberalism in the South* (Chapel Hill, N.C., 1932), p. 282; and *Below the Potomac* (New York, 1942), pp. 248–9; Robert M. Miller: "A Note on the Relationship Between the Protestant Churches and the Revival of the Ku Klux Klan," *Journal of Southern History*, XXII (August 1956), 355–68; J. Fletcher Moore to Bishop Warren A. Candler, July 20, 1928, Candler Papers; Charles C. Alexander: *The Ku Klux*

In many areas of belief and attitude, as well as in personnel, fundamentalism and the Klan occupied common ground. The strongest bond was undoubtedly prohibition, but anti-Catholicism also characterized both movements. Fundamentalist periodicals appearing during the election years bear ample evidence of the fact; while many of these journals scrupulously avoided any commentary on politics, a significant number urged the defeat of Smith on religious grounds.[1] Patriotism, too, was as much a part of the fundamentalist crusade as of the Klan movement. America was, so it seemed, the native home of Christianity; and in the ceremonies of many nativist churches the flag was used to excess.

The nativist and fundamentalist groups together were in partial alliance with the prohibitionist movement—the latter a program of the Protestant churches, particularly though not exclusively the evangelist sects. The chief prohibitionist organization, the Anti-Saloon League, sometimes held meetings in churches—as did the Klan—and disseminated its propaganda through church organizations; and it operated at election time in somewhat the same manner as the Klan. The Klan, moreover, made Protestant prohibition the main tenet of its social program, and constituted itself a police agency for the enforcement of the measure: when drinkers flagrantly defied the law in Klan territory, they risked retaliation from the vigilant night riders. Finally, the drys and the fundamentalists drew upon a similar

---

Klan in the Southwest (Lexington, Ky., 1965), p. 87; Norman F. Furniss: *The Fundamentalist Controversy, 1918–1931* (New Haven, 1954), pp. 62–6; Charles Merz: "The Methodist Lobby," *New Republic*, XLVIII (October 13, 1926), 213–15; H. L. Mencken: *Prejudices: Third Series* (New York, 1922), p. 34.

[1] John Roach Straton, a leading figure in the clerical campaign of 1928 against Smith, had long been editor of *The Fundamentalist*, perhaps the movement's principal periodical. See also the publications of the Rail Splitter Press, of which the editor, William Lloyd Clark, was rabidly anti-Catholic; and *Bob Schuler's Magazine, The Allied Protestant American, Gopher, The United Protestant Advocate, The Protestant Herald*, and *The Protestant Standard. The Baptist Fundamentalist of Texas; Christian Standard*, LXIII (October 27, 1928), 13; *The Protestant; Bible Beliefs*.

rhetoric, constant in its references to battle and wars: a rhetoric that revealed the aggressive instinct that sustained their causes.[2]

It is evident above all that the Klan, the Anti-Saloon League, and the fundamentalist churches held in common a suspicion of the foreigner and his ways—so much so that one may speak of a nativist "mind" often inclusive of fundamentalism and pro-hibitionism. Advocates of a dry America had reason to fear an immigration from lands where wine and beer flowed like water. "Most of the bootleggers . . . appear to be foreigners," Henry Pratt Fairchild assured his readers in 1926. The New York University sociologist continued: "It can not be purely by chance that a map of 'wetness' in the United States is almost a replica of a map showing the distribution of the foreign born." "I made a list of nearly 500 . . . men recently arrested for violat-ing Prohib. [*sic*]," wrote Billy Sunday. "It reads like a page of directories from Italy, Greece—sprinkling of Irish." And citi-zens of an older American lineage who feared the corrupting encroachments of the metropolis and its immigrant peoples could hope that prohibition might constitute a barrier against the urban manner.[3]

Yet each of the three reform groups, the Klan, the Anti-Saloon League, and the fundamentalists, could work along separate lines and draw support from overlapping but distinct segments of the population. It was therefore possible to be an

[2] In "Prohibition as a Political Issue," *Journal of Politics*, XXIII (August 1961), 507–25, Charles D. Farris demonstrates the existence of a funda-mentalist-dry correlation. *Christian Century*, XLV (January 26, 1928), 103–4; XLV (March 15, 1928), 348–9; see also H. L. Mencken's comment of May 28, 1928, in Malcolm Moos, ed.: *A Carnival of Buncombe* (Balti-more, 1956), p. 156; *The New York Times*, October 7, 1928, p. 1; Norman H. Dohn: "The History of the Anti-Saloon League," unpublished doctoral dissertation, The Ohio State University, 1959, p. 164. "This battle is not a rosewater conflict," observed the Anti-Saloon League *Yearbook* of 1911: "It is war—continuing relentless war." (Westerville, Ohio), p. 4. Furniss: *The Fundamentalist Controversy*, pp. 36, 42.

[3] Fairchild: *The Melting-Pot Mistake* (Boston, 1926), p. 215; William G. McLoughlin, Jr.: *Billy Sunday Was His Real Name* (Chicago, 1955), p. 275.

ardent prohibitionist but to look on the Klan with disgust. Bryan was an idol of the Klansmen. When he died the order fired tall crosses in Dayton and Toledo, Ohio, announcing in one case that "In memory of William Jennings Bryan, the greatest Klansman of our time, this cross is burned; he stood at Armageddon and battled for the Lord." But Bryan was not a Klansman; and before the 1924 election he backed up the Democratic candidate's condemnation of the Klan by name. As a matter of fact, he also aided the Klan when at the 1924 Democratic Convention he pleaded with the delegates to refrain from censuring it by name; yet in the same speech he showed at least a degree of disapproval of the order.[4]

By the third decade of the century, then, a complex of political, social, and moral attitudes had established itself, compounded of nativism, fundamentalism, prohibitionism, and a conviction that the American character resided in the farm and hinterland town. But of the four, it was the cause of prohibition that most broadly realized itself in political action and a legislative program; it drew to its standard Americans of evangelical and of nativist persuasion alike, and possessed a power of symbolism over the minds of diverse social groups, both of advocates and opponents. It was also a strongly coercive reform, aimed at bringing under some kind of control the urban and immigrant population; in fact, the very name of the Anti-Saloon League illustrated the drift of the movement. Founded in 1893, at the start of a great depression, the League singled out not alcohol but an institution—and an institution chiefly urban; the League identified the drinker with a culture, and depended on reverse cultural loyalties for its own sustenance. The "anti" in its title bespoke its basic intolerance of cultural differences. To understand the special nature of the prohibition movement, one must

4 Bryan's objection to prohibition was a broad one; to him liquor was a sign of moral laxity, materialism, and skepticism—which, aided by modern science, were turning the city dwellers into pagans. *The New York Times,* August 30, 1924, p. 1; *Official Report of the Democratic National Convention* ... [of] ... *1924* (Indianapolis, 1925), pp. 303-9.

see that "Prohibition is part of our religion," as the leading dry Wayne Williams put it. The Anti-Saloon League was staffed principally by clergymen; its main source of revenue was contributions solicited through the Protestant churches; and its history was such that one scholar refers to it as "the grown-up child of the Methodist Church." "For thirty-two years," boasted the League's house organ, the *American Issue,* "the League has been controlled and supported by the Church. . . . The Church must meet the challenge of the . . . wets." "The saloon," declared Billy Sunday, "is an infidel. It has no faith in God . . . no religion. It could close every church in the land." Al Smith, on the other hand, condemned the efforts of the Anti-Saloon League "to make God-fearing men and women believe that the Eighteenth Amendment and the Volstead Act are dogmas of religion."[5]

Prohibition was a thoroughly and angrily political question: the *New Republic* called it "the one issue which arouses real excitement . . . the grand old perennial." The Anti-Saloon League provided energy and leadership for the prohibitionist forces; the wets found political expression in the Association Against the Prohibition Amendment. Like the Klan, both organizations helped to weaken still further the existing party system. Founded in 1920 and drawing much of its financial support from the brewers, the AAPA set out to tear away from the prohibitionist organization its veil of Christian sanctity. This task, though difficult, was not impossible, for some of the most

[5] Purley Baker of the Anti-Saloon League despaired that "it has been at the point where the urban population outnumbers the rural people that wrecked Republics have gone down. . . . The peril of this Republic likewise is now clearly seen to be in her cities." Quoted in Andrew Sinclair: *Prohibition: The Era of Excess* (Boston, 1962), p. 9. Richard Hofstadter describes the churches as competing with the saloons in "the business of consolation." Introduction to Sinclair: *Prohibition,* p. vii. Sunday is quoted on p. 63 of Sinclair; Smith in *The New York Times,* October 30, 1928, p. 3. The Anti-Saloon League paid Sunday $1200 for speaking against liquor, and he also received money from the Klan. *Time,* VI (August 10, 1925), 5; XII (November 12, 1928), 8. Gusfield: *Symbolic Crusade* (Urbana, Ill., 1963), pp. 6–11; James H. Timberlake: *Prohibition and the Progressive Movement, 1900–1920* (Cambridge, Mass., 1963), pp. 168–9.

prominent clergymen serving in the dry groups appeared unfit to wear the cloth. W. C. Shupp, Superintendent of the Missouri Anti-Saloon League, secured alcohol withdrawal permits for a drug firm in which he and his son held interests; William H. Anderson, the stormy petrel of the dry lobbyists, was convicted of forgery in embezzling League funds; and Bishop James Cannon, Jr., gambled his money on the stock market. The growing national audience of metropolitan newspapers was introduced to the peccadilloes of these and other League officials, and while they were perhaps not unusual in so large an organization, by the end of the decade the Anti-Saloon League could scarcely declare itself "born of God" or proclaim itself "the Protestant Church in Action Against the Saloon." Furthermore, the more fundamentalist churches had been discredited in the Scopes trial and the decline of the status of "old-time" religion. And when the Anti-Saloon League entered the presidential campaign against Smith in 1928, it invited a close identification in the public mind with anti-Catholicism; as Andrew Sinclair puts it: "The foulness of the religious campaign against Smith seemed part and parcel of the virulence of the dry campaign against him"; and while many Americans were quite willing to cast their vote against Rome, there must have been at least a considerable number of Protestants who were repelled by the conduct of Smith's more violent opponents. So despite the formidable support upon which the League might call, the advocates of repeal of prohibition were never at a loss for ammunition.[6]

But during the twenties the League remained an effective political pressure group, holding sway over diverse groups of people. In none of the congresses elected during the decade were

[6] Anderson said the wets were "a lot of unwashed, wild-eyed foreigners in New York City who have no comprehension of the spirit of America." Carter Glass to Wayne Wheeler, November 1, 1930, Glass Papers; Sinclair: *Prohibition*, p. 304; Anderson: *The Church in Action Against the Saloon* (Westerville, Ohio, 1910), *passim; New Republic*, XLVIII (October 27, 1926), 25. On corruption in the League see Peter H. Odegard: *Pressure Politics* (New York, 1928), pp. 219–43.

the wets heavily represented. In 1922 the AAPA approved 249 candidates, thereby furnishing the Anti-Saloon League and its expert lobbyists with an official list of candidates to oppose: under fire from the League, some office seekers repudiated their AAPA endorsement. Similar tactics backfired in 1924 when late in the campaign the Association listed 262 House candidates as "unsatisfactory"; of these 219 were elected, and only two of the thirteen new senators were acceptable to the organization. In 1926 the results were even worse for the wets, and the Congress elected in 1928 was the dryest of all, with only seventy-five wets in the House and fifteen in the Senate. Not until 1930, when the AAPA worked very closely with the candidates, did considerable wet strength materialize; in the elections of that year 166 wet candidates for the House and twenty-two for the Senate were successful.[7]

The major political battleground for prohibition during the twenties was the Democratic party. There the opposing forces were personified in the party leaders Bryan and Smith: the one totally committed to the crusade that looked forward to a "millennial Kansas afloat on a nirvana of pure water"; the other a child of the saloon, offspring and faithful representative of a social milieu in which that institution held an honored place. The division was apparent in the Democratic Convention of 1920, where Wayne Wheeler, a Republican, and James Cannon, Jr., a Democrat, worked to prevent the party from adopting Bryan's strongly worded prohibition plank—a plank that would set aside the more sensible dry policy of evaluating individual candidates rather than the party to which they belonged. In 1924 Bryan once more added to the prevailing disharmony by

[7] Wayne Wheeler's biographer speaks of the wets's "usual and asinine mistakes in the [1922] campaign." Of Wheeler, he wrote: "[He] had a code of honor which prevented him hitting below the belt, unless it was absolutely necessary for the sake of the prohibition movement." Justin Steuart: *Wayne Wheeler, Dry Boss* (New York, 1928), pp. 194-6, 233. Dayton Heckman: "Prohibition Passes: The Story of the Association Against the Prohibition Amendment," unpublished doctoral dissertation, Ohio State University, 1939, *passim.*

again introducing the prohibition issue. After Bryan's death Bishop Cannon became the leader of the Democratic drys, and Cannon blended his prohibitionist beliefs with anti-Catholicism. At the convention of 1928, the prohibitionists, now bereft of their leaders Bryan and McAdoo, lost the party to the wet forces; even in collaboration with the anti-Catholic and Klan elements, the drys were unable to persuade the necessary one third of the delegates to veto the selection of Al Smith. During the presidential campaign the urban leaders of the party willingly made it a propaganda agency for the AAPA. Important Democrats such as John J. Raskob and Jouett Shouse were closely identified with the group, and in 1930 the Senate lobby committee included the half-million-dollar 1928 campaign expenditure of the AAPA with the "committees and organizations receiving and expending money in behalf of the Democratic party."[8]

Hoover's defeat of Smith was of course claimed as a triumph by the drys, but on the presidential level the victory was of one party over another, while the drys had been accustomed to dominating both parties. In 1929 the Jones law, stiffening penalties against first violators of the Volstead Act, encountered the lowest wet vote recorded so far in both houses of Congress, yet the vote itself registered a slight but discernible change that was related to the new urban strength of the Democratic party. Although the wet tabulation in the House was thirty-eight votes shorter than had been the anti-prohibitionist tally on the Eighteenth Amendment, the losses were comparatively steeper in the West and South than in the North, so that the northern states

[8] Even in 1928 the position of any outspoken wet was recognized to be precarious; Thomas B. Love could argue forcefully against nominating Smith, "a man who cannot be elected because . . . the saloons are closed and the women are voting." Love to W. P. Smith, November 24, 1922, Love Papers. In 1928 Pierre S. DuPont gave $50,000 to the Democratic National Committee, $32,000 to the AAPA; John J. Raskob, $110,000 and $17,000; Arthur Curtiss James, $25,000 and $12,000; R. T. Crane, $10,000 and $12,500. The whole roster of AAPA members gave less than $100,000 to the Republicans. *Senate Lobby Investigations, 1930* (Washington, D.C., 1931), pp. 4032 ff. Sinclair: *Prohibition,* pp. 269–306.

with higher immigrant populations now provided two-thirds rather than one-half of the wet vote. Similarly, in the Senate the North provided eight out of twenty votes in 1917, but ten out of eighteen in 1929.[9]

Prohibition was a battle the country would soon lose to the city. Walter Lippmann called it "a test of strength between social orders. When the Eighteenth Amendment goes down, the cities will be dominant politically and socially as they now are economically." At one time the prohibition movement had received support from all classes—both urban and rural; by the twenties it was rural and fundamentalist. Throughout the decade the possibility of reversing a constitutional amendment seemed inconceivable; yet the ineffectuality of the Eighteenth Amendment became increasingly obvious. Only the expense, the quality of the intoxicant, and the ease of obtaining it were affected. Gradually, it came to be apparent that prohibition had been the work of organized pressure groups accomplished under the special conditions of the war, and a reaction set in so quickly as to suggest that perhaps it had never commanded the support of the unorganized majority. It was no surprise that among working-class immigrants repeal sentiment was strong. In 1922 only ninety-three of the immigrant workers at the Edison plant in New Jersey cast their secret ballots for strict enforcement, whereas 978 favored light wines and beer and 966 voted for outright repeal. But the dry forces should have been more disturbed by certain published surveys of attitudes on prohibition—surveys that perforce revealed the views of a middle-class America prosperous enough to subscribe to the telephone service of that day. In such a national poll conducted in 1922, while 306,000 people voted for strict enforcement, groups of 326,000 and 164,000 chose between wet alternatives. By the end of the decade, various polls showed that only the South remained deeply committed to prohibition.[1]

[9] *The New York Times,* March 1, 1929, p. 16; Sinclair: *Prohibition,* p. 353.
[1] The poll of telephone subscribers is reported in the *Literary Digest,* LXXIV (September 9, 1922), 11, 14; that of the Edison workers is also in

As time passed, the Eighteenth Amendment became more and more an object of contempt. By 1926 there was plentiful evidence of a reaction against the drys. The wet Senator James Reed, a Missouri Democrat, was appointed to an important Senate judiciary subcommittee that commandeered the embarrassing files of the Anti-Saloon League and released them later to the newspapers; it was found, for example, that in a certain Illinois senate campaign, the League had supported a candidate of questionable integrity against the wet George Brennan. Also in 1926 the wet strategy of repealing state enforcement laws, hitherto successful only in New York and Illinois, won a victory in Montana, where a "baby Volstead" law was repealed by referendum. At least in retrospect, 1926 appeared to one Catholic social critic, John A. Ryan, as the year in which prohibition, proven impracticable, ceased to be in the public interest and therefore lost its "binding force" upon the national conscience. Finally, that year's referendum in New York showed upstate areas to be wet by two to one and the city by seven to one.[2]

By 1928 the defeat of prohibition seemed a distinct possibility; and to that end a group of industrial leaders who sought a lowering of income taxes through the restoration of the tax on alcohol turned their financial support to the Association Against the Prohibition Amendment. Led by Pierre S. DuPont, who once had supported the dry cause, the industrialists swelled the budget of the Association and freed it of its dependence on the brewery interests; in 1928 Fred Pabst, Colonel Jacob Ruppert, and the Schaefer and Kreuger brewing companies together contributed only $7,750 to the AAPA, while the DuPonts and Edward S.

---

the *Digest*, LXXIV (July 29, 1922), 5. By 1926 only two states, Kansas and South Carolina, had prohibition majorities in a nationwide poll. LXXXIX (April 3, 1926), 7–8. The *Digest* polls, according to Claude Robinson, were biased toward the wets: more men than women participated and drys frequently disdained to vote, but invariably similar results appeared in polls conducted by the Hearst syndicate, the New York *Daily News*, and the Chicago *Tribune*. *Straw Votes* (New York, 1932), pp. 145–71. Lippmann: *Men of Destiny* (New York, 1928), pp. 31–2.
[2] Ryan: *Social Doctrine in Action* (New York, 1941), pp. 182–5; *The New York Times*, November 3, 1920, pp. 1, 12.

Harkness gave $108,580. And to the growing unity and financial vigor of the wet forces, Protestant prohibition could not respond by tightening its own organization. For Protestantism carries with it an inherent tendency to splinter, as the controversy then raging between fundamentalism and modernism demonstrated. The *Christian Century* maintained that national prohibition was "in danger of becoming just another aspect of the squabbles of religious sectarianism which divide and thwart the church forces of the nation." The end was not far off; repeal came in 1933.[3]

By 1930 the social movements and strains that had fractured the Democratic party were on the wane. The Klan was dead, and fundamentalism was in precipitous decline. But the final slackening of rural-urban tension came with the failure of prohibition. And in retrospect, the failure seems destined. The hedonism of the decade alone could have defeated the measure. How could drinking be undesirable when movies and books made it a part of adventurous living? And if sex itself was no longer taboo, it appeared ridiculous that liquor should be. At the same time the automobile, the movie house, and the radio, conveying city manners and jokes against prohibition, were bringing the country and the city face to face; they penetrated the isolation of rural America upon which the prohibitionist relied. Prohibition received its greatest setback in the Great Depression, which made urgent the need for an increase in government revenues and the creation of jobs; in the quibblings of the Wickersham Report of 1930 which showed that drinking was common and that it was spreading among women; and in the capitulation of wealthy drys, including S. S. Kresge, William Randolph Hearst, and John D. Rockefeller, the Anti-Saloon League's chief supporter who, in a letter of Nicholas Murray

[3] Fletcher Dobyns: *The Amazing Story of Repeal* (Chicago, 1940), pp. 9, 19–26; *Christian Century*, XLV (January 26, 1928), 103. Key Pittman (a chronic drinker himself) wrote in 1923 that the drys were in a "pathetic condition." Pittman to John E. Robbins, February 23, 1928, Pittman Papers.

Butler of Columbia, advocated repeal to "restore law and stop drinking."[4]

Constantly throughout the decade the conflict over religion, prohibition, and ethnic stock—and the more general clash of city and hinterland that at once gave added force to the specific issues and received much of its identity from them—touched upon politics; it deepened political faction, and was sustained in political quarrel. It was a political event, the National Democratic Convention of 1924, that set the conflict into definite form, assigning the participants and fixing the points of dispute.

[4] Even William Gibbs McAdoo had switched to repeal by 1931. Henry W. Lee: *How Dry We Were: Prohibition Revisited* (New York, 1963), p. 11. *The New York Times,* June 1, 1932, p. 1.

CHAPTER IV

The Election of 1924

The crumbling of the Wilson coalition, and its final defeat in
the election of 1920, left the Democratic party with no sure
policies or directions. But the next presidential election year,
1924, was destined even in the very fact of intraparty strife to
mark the beginnings of a fresh process of self-discovery for the
Democracy; and the congressional elections that took place midway between the two presidential contests gave some indication
of the new political era upon which the party was entering. In
1922 the big cities, which had remained predominantly Republican in their congressional representation for a period of twenty-
eight years, threw their support to the Democratic party. In a
few isolated congressional elections prior to 1922, of course, the
cities had gone to the Democrats; but after that date, they would
never again waver from their Democratic attachments. The
urban Democracy was swiftly gaining its strength.

The election of 1922 is significant both in the Democratic
showing and in the number of the party's urban successes. Because President Harding, in his overwhelming victory of 1920,
had carried many areas never before won by his party, the

Republican Congress occupied a vulnerable position in 1922. Factionalism, Harding's ineffectiveness as a party leader, and the resignation of Will Hays as National Chairman also contributed to Republican weakness; moreover, the party out of power usually picks up seats in an off-term election, and the depression of 1920 to 1922—the worst since the 1890's—had generated dissatisfaction with the politics of normalcy. But the tide of change in 1922 surprised Republicans and Democrats alike. At first it looked as though the Democrats had won the House of Representatives, although in the final count the Republicans retained control by a slim margin. The Democrats gained seventy-eight seats—within a dozen of a majority. In no other off-year election, the only kind with which that of 1922 may properly be compared, did the party out of power enjoy a comparable increase. The only larger House reversal in American history came in 1932 when Franklin Roosevelt carried with him several dozen congressional candidates who had no real expectations of victory.[1]

The character of the new Democratic contingent in the House is of special interest. Since not one House seat changed from Democratic to Republican, Table VI deals exclusively with previously Republican areas captured by Democrats. The chart reveals at least three trends. First, states of the character of Missouri and Indiana showed merely a resurgence of traditional Democratic strength. Second, in certain districts of the West, discontent reminiscent of populism, though now more narrowly centered on agricultural problems, may have sent some radical Democrats to Congress. Third and most important, the big cities —chiefly but not solely in the East where over forty per cent of

[1] On Wednesday, November 8, *The New York Times* ran a banner headline: DEMOCRATS APPEAR TO HAVE WON HOUSE. William Gibbs McAdoo did not recognize the evolution of Democratic strength in the cities; better aware of the condition of the party in the country at large, he wrote to a fellow Democrat: "We must not assume that the victory means that the people have turned Democratic and will remain so. The fact is that the victory is more anti-Republican than pro-Democratic." McAdoo to Thomas B. Love, November 25, 1922; see also Robert W. Woolley to Love, December 2, 1922, Love Papers.

TABLE VI

Democratic Congressional Gains in 1922*

States	Number of New Democratic Seats
Connecticut	1
Delaware	1
Illinois	4
Indiana	4
Kansas	1
Maryland	2
Massachusetts	1
Michigan	1
Missouri	8
Montana	1
Nebraska	3
Nevada	1
New Hampshire	1
New Jersey	5
New York	13
Ohio	6
Oklahoma	4
Oregon	1
Pennsylvania	7
Rhode Island	1
Tennessee	3
Virginia	2
Washington	1
West Virginia	4

* *Congressional Directory.* Sixty-seventh Congress, 3rd Session; Sixty-eighth Congress, 1st Session.

the shifts occurred—moved strongly toward the Democratic party. Compared with earlier contests, the 1922 elections amounted to a breakthrough for the party in the city. Particularly the new immigrants trooped into the Democracy as never before; twelve of the thirteen new Democratic congressmen in New York came from districts with high percentages of recently arrived foreigners. And not all of these districts had been Democratic prior to the desertion of immigrants from Wilson's party in 1920. In urban areas, particularly in the Northeast and Middle West—Boston, Providence, New York, Jersey City, Harrisburg, Cleveland, Cincinnati, Detroit, Chicago—the party prospered in 1922. More important, throughout the decade urban areas such as these continued to send a heavy preponderance of Democrats to Congress; and from 1928 to 1952 the large urban areas would give a majority of their vote to the Democratic presidential candidate.

The 1922 shifts occurred within an outmoded congressional map that the House had refused to revise according to the census of 1920. These city victories, therefore, not only strengthened immediately the urban voice in the party; they implied the probability of still further change in the structure of the Democracy once congressional representation should be rearranged to reflect demographic reality. Throughout the twenties, in fact, the 1911 distribution remained. Ironically, incumbent Democrats often feared a shift of district lines as much as their opponents, for in the North predominantly Republican state legislatures could be expected to draw up the new district lines. But the failure to remap the districts cheated the Democrats in the growing cities that could have profited from redistribution. When a new plan finally went into effect in 1932, Los Angeles and Detroit alone gained together a total of ten seats.[2]

2 *New Republic*, XLVII (May 26, 1926), 11–13; *Time*, VII (April 19, 1926), 7–8; *The Commonweal*, VIII (August 8, 1928), 345–6; *The New York Times*, January 4, 1923, p. 18; January 28, 1928, p. 7; March 3, 1928, p. 2; *Congressional Record, House*, October 14, 1921, pp. 6307–49.

⊣

As the 1924 election approached, the shadow of scandal lengthened before the Harding Administration—and with its lengthen-
ing the hopes of partisan Democrats expanded. Late in 1923
Thomas J. Walsh, Montana Democrat and chairman of a Senate
investigating committee, began to uncover the spectacular dealings of Teapot Dome and Elk Hills; encouraged also by their
surprisingly vigorous performance in the 1922 congressional
elections, many Democrats counted on public repudiation of
the discredited regime.[3]

But a series of developments shook Democratic confidence.
The death of the unfortunate President gave the Republicans a
mute scapegoat for the "Harding" scandals. Correspondingly,
the narrow rectitude of the new President, Calvin Coolidge,
helped to dissociate scandal and Republicanism. Moreover,
further disclosures revealed that the corrupt interests had been
bipartisan in seeking political favors. Edward L. Doheny, whose
name grew to be synonymous with that of Teapot Dome,
ranked high in the Democratic party of California. Besides contributing heavily to party campaigns, he had served as vice
chairman of the Democratic State Committee, and in 1920 he
had even been advanced seriously as a candidate for the vice
presidency. And there existed between Doheny and other leading Democrats certain business connections that were to prove
embarrassing to the party. In his oil operations, Doheny employed as counsel such members of Wilson's cabinet as Thomas
W. Gregory, Lindley Garrison, Franklin K. Lane, and William
Gibbs McAdoo; Lane and McAdoo had been paid $25,000 a
year for part-time services. Even Senator Walsh, who did most

[3] In mid-1923 Bernard Baruch wrote to Senator Key Pittman: "We have
the next election in the hollow of our hand." May 14, 1923, Pittman
Papers. The *Kiplinger Washington Letter* of April 12, 1924, predicted:
"We think the Republican Party will not be kept in power," and as late as
a month before the convention, the *New Republic* believed that "the outlook for the Democratic Party is more cheerful than that for the Republicans," XXXIX (May 28, 1924), 5.

to expose the indiscretions of the Harding Administration, confessed to a long acquaintance with Doheny.[4]

In January 1924, further evidence of McAdoo's relationship with Doheny discomfited many Democrats who were advancing Wilson's son-in-law as the party's chief contender for the presidential nomination. After McAdoo's resignation from the government in 1918, Joe Tumulty had sent him a warning to avoid association with the already tainted Doheny. Yet in 1919 the former Secretary of the Treasury took on the oil man as a client for an unusually large intitial fee of $100,000, as well as an annual retainer. Not the least perplexing part of the deal involved a $1 million bonus for McAdoo if the Mexican government reached a satisfactory agreement with Washington on oil lands Doheny held south of the Texas border. The bonus was never paid and McAdoo insisted later that it was a casual figure of speech mentioned in jest. At the time, however, he had telegraphed the New York *World* that he would have received "an additional fee of $900,000 if my firm had succeeded in getting a satisfactory settlement"; since the Doheny companies had "several hundred million dollars of property at stake, our services, had they been effective, would have been rightly compensated by the additional fee." In fact, the lawyer received only $50,000

---

[4] Senator George W. Norris, Republican of Nebraska, added his charge that corruption had also been widespread during the wartime Wilson Administration. And it was later revealed that Governor Smith had in 1920 appointed Harry F. Sinclair, another of the corrupt businessmen, to an unsalaried post on the New York State Racing Commission, and that Sinclair had contributed substantially to Smith's campaign. Even in 1928 Senator Arthur Robinson of Indiana, a Republican, assailed the Democratic party and especially members of Wilson's cabinet for having been involved in the oil scandals. Norris to B. F. Eberhart, March 8, 1924, Norris Papers; *The Nation*, CXXVI (March 28, 1928), 334; Joe Tumulty to Smith, March 24, 1928, Tumulty Papers; *America*, XXXIX (April 14, 1928), 1. The involvement of Democrats in the oil scandals has been demonstrated by J. Leonard Bates in "The Teapot Dome Scandal and the Election of 1924," *American Historical Review*, LX (January 1955), 303–22; see also Burl Noggle: *Teapot Dome: Oil and Politics in the 1920's* (Baton Rouge, La., 1962), pp. 152–76, 191, and *The New York Times*, February 9, 1924, p. 1; February 24, 1924, p. 1.

more from Doheny. It also was charged that on matters of interest to his client, Republic Iron and Steel, from whom he received $150,000, McAdoo neglected the regular channels that propriety dictated he use and consulted directly with his own appointees in the capital to obtain a fat refund.[5]

McAdoo's connection with Doheny appeared seriously to lessen his desirability as a presidential candidate. In February Colonel House urged him to withdraw from the race, as did Josephus Daniels, Thomas B. Love, and two important fillers of Democratic coffers, Bernard Baruch and Thomas L. Chadbourne. Some advisers hoped that McAdoo's chances would improve after a formal withdrawal. William Jennings Bryan, who never doubted McAdoo's honesty, thought that the Doheny affair had damaged the lawyer's chances "seriously, if not fatally." Senator Thomas Walsh, who earlier had called McAdoo the greatest Secretary of the Treasury since Hamilton, informed him with customary curtness: "You are no longer

[5] On McAdoo's excellent chances prior to the oil scandals, see Robert Woolley to Senator Carter Glass of Virginia, August 8, 1923, Glass Papers; Gutzon Borglum to Senator Jim Watson, August 8, 1923, Borglum Papers; and for Mississippi Senator Pat Harrison's like view, Frank Robinson to David Ladd Rockwell, November 22, 1923, Thomas B. Love Papers. On the particularly strong commitment of labor to McAdoo, see Love to McAdoo, November 29, 1922, and J. Louis England to Love, October 26, 1923, Love Papers. In 1921 Doheny gave the Democratic party $25,000; in 1920 he had donated money to both parties. Louise Overacker: *Money in Elections* (New York, 1932), p. 153. Tumulty to McAdoo, November 21, 1919, F. Ray Groves to McAdoo, April 30, 1920, and memorandum of April 12, 1930, McAdoo Papers; William Dodd to John Spencer Bassett, Dodd Papers; McAdoo to Bryan, 1924, copy in Underwood Papers; Wilbur Marsh to George White, White Papers; David H. Stratton: "Splattered with Oil: William Gibbs McAdoo and the 1924 Presidential Nomination," *Southwestern Social Science Quarterly*, XLIV (June 1963), 62–75; Morris R. Werner and John Starr: *Teapot Dome* (New York, 1959), pp. 145–6; *The Nation*, CXVIII (March 5, 1924), 244, and (June 25, 1924), 741; *The New York Times*, February 24, 1924, p. 2 (quoting the New York *World*); February 25, 1924, p. 1; February 26, 1924, p. 1; New York *Herald-Tribune*, April 1, 1924, p. 1; New York *World*, June 4, 1924, p. 1; June 6, 1924, p. 10; July 6, 1924, p. 1; W. A. Watkins to George White, February 7, 1921, White Papers; A. J. Findley to John W. Davis, June 7, 1924, Davis Papers.

available as a candidate." Finally, *The New York Times*, itself convinced that McAdoo had acted in bad taste and against the spirit of the law, reported the widspread opinion that McAdoo had "been eliminated as a formidable contender for the Democratic nomination."[6]

McAdoo was unpopular for reasons other than his close association with Doheny. Even in 1918, *The Nation* was saying that "his election to the White House would be an unqualified misfortune." McAdoo, the liberal journal then believed, had wanted to go to war with Mexico *and* Germany, and he was held responsible for segregating clerks in the Treasury Department. Walter Lippmann wrote in 1920 that McAdoo "is not fundamentally moved by the simple moralities," and that his "honest" liberalism catered only to popular feeling. Liberal critics, thinking him to be a demagogue, found instance in his stand for quick payment of the veterans' bonus.

Much of the dissatisfaction with McAdoo on the part of reformers and urban Democrats sprang from his acceptance of Klan backing. James Cox indignantly wrote that "there was not only tacit consent to the Klan's support, but it was apparent that he and his major supporters were conniving with the Klan." Friends insisted that McAdoo's silence on the matter hid a distaste that the political facts of life kept him from expressing, and

[6] For an inside account of the controversy, see the manuscript diary of Breckinridge Long, February 6 to 24, 1924; McAdoo's floor manager at the June convention, Long wrote in his diary on February 13: "As it stands today we are beat." See also the manuscript diary of Colonel Edward House, February 9 and March, 1924. "Is it McAdieu?" asked William Hard in *The Nation*, CXVIII (April 30, 1924) 505–6. Of course, his eastern opponents promoted the view that McAdoo's chances were nil; the *Kiplinger Washington Letter* suggested that the West was not necessarily in agreement. March 1, 1924. Josephus Daniels to John Burke, March 15, 1924, Daniels Papers; Senator Kenneth McKellar to Hugh Humphreys, March 8, 1924, McKellar Papers; William Jennings Bryan to Daniel Cruice [?], n.d., Box 54, Bryan Papers; Thomas Walsh to McAdoo, February 13 and April 3, 1924, Walsh Papers; Daniel C. Roper: *Fifty Years of Public Life* (Durham, N.C., 1941), p. 218; Carter Field: *Bernard Baruch* (New York, 1944), pp. 204–5; *The New York Times*, February 2, 1924, p. 5; February 29, 1924, p. 26.

especially after the Doheny scandal when he desperately needed support. But McAdoo could not command the support of unsatisfied liberal spokesmen for *The Nation* and the *New Republic*, who supported the candidacy of the Wisconsin Progressive Robert La Follette. A further blow to McAdoo was the death on February 3, 1924, of Woodrow Wilson, who ironically had outlived his successor in the White House. Father-in-law to the candidate, Wilson might have given McAdoo welcome endorsement now that the League had receded as an issue.[7]

These handicaps did not deter McAdoo from campaigning vigorously and effectively in presidential primaries. He won easily against minor candidates whose success might have denied him key delegations in the South and West. Oscar W. Underwood of Alabama was no match for McAdoo. Opposed to prohibition and the Klan, the Alabamian failed to identify himself with the kind of progressivism that would have won him some compensating support. Nor was Underwood a real southerner; he had been born in Massachusetts and his father had served as a colonel in the Union army. "He is a New York candidate living in the South," said William Jennings Bryan. McAdoo defeated Underwood in Georgia and even split the Alabama delegation. Whatever appeal Underwood had outside the South the emerging candidacy of Al Smith erased. Henry Ford—"a man who

[7] Thomas B. Love of Texas—though at one time of a contrary opinion—advised McAdoo not to issue even a mild disclaimer of the Klan. Arthur F. Mullen: *Western Democrat* (New York, 1940), p. 242. To Bernard Baruch and others, McAdoo construed his remarks against prejudice at a 1923 college commencement as a disavowal of the Klan. McAdoo to Thomas Chadbourne, March 22, 1924, copy in Baruch Papers. William E. Dodd of the University of Chicago wrote to his father that Wilson had been "counting on" his daughter being in the White House. April 30, 1924, Dodd Papers. *The New York Times*, however, reported a rumor that Wilson had written to Cox, hoping he would again be the candidate in 1924. May 26, 1924, p. 1. *The Nation*, CVII (November 30, 1918), 640; Lippmann: "Two Leading Democratic Candidates," *New Republic*, XXIII (June 2, 1920), 10–11; James M. Cox: *Journey Through My Years* (New York, 1946), p. 324. David Chalmers agrees with Cox that McAdoo's "representatives solicited the Klan votes." *Hooded Americanism* (New York, 1965), p. 204.

praised the old ways while pushing on the new machines"—once seemed to be a genuine threat to McAdoo. Ford did not interfere when his name was entered in the Nebraska primary of October 1923, but no trace of evidence indicates an interest in becoming President. He announced for Coolidge in December and declared himself unavailable as a candidate.[8] In their immediate effects the heated primary contests drew the financial support of the millionaires Thomas Chadbourne and Bernard Baruch (who was indebted partly to McAdoo for his appointment as head of the War Industries Board); and they firmed the resolve of Governor Smith to make a serious try for the nomination, which he had originally sought primarily to block McAdoo on behalf of the eastern bosses. The contests also hardened the antagonisms between the candidates, and cut deeper the divisions within the electorate. In doing this, they undoubtedly retrieved lost ground for McAdoo and broadened his previously shrinking base of support, drawing to him rural, Klan, and dry elements awakened by the invigorated candidacy of Smith. The primaries therefore played their part in crystallizing the split within the party that would rend the Democracy at the forthcoming convention. City immigrants and McAdoo progressives had earlier joined to fight the Mellon tax plans in Congress, since both groups represented people of small means; deeper social animosities dissolved their alliance, and the urban-rural division rapidly supplanted all others.[9]

[8] A Ku Klux Klan newspaper opposed Ford because he had given a Lincoln car to a Catholic archbishop; it flatly rejected Smith as a Catholic from "Jew York"; and it called Underwood the "Jew, jug, and Jesuit candidate." *The New York Times,* October 13, 1923, p. 1; November 4, 1923, pp. 1, 3; December 19, 1923, p. 1. In a 1923 *Literary Digest* poll for the Democratic presidential nomination, Ford ran second to McAdoo. LXXVII (June 30, 1923), 6. Ford drew support from farmers and laborers, as well as from pacifists, prohibitionists, and anti-Semites. McAdoo and his supporters were keenly aware of the Ford movement. McAdoo to Love, June 2, 1923; George Fort Milton to David Ladd Rockwell, December 10, 1923, Love Papers.

[9] Senator Kenneth McKellar of Tennessee wrote to his sister Nellie: "I see McAdoo carried Georgia by such an overwhelming majority that it is likely to reinstate him in the running." March 22, 1924, McKellar Papers.

More directly, the contest between McAdoo and Smith thrust upon the Democratic National Convention a dilemma of a kind no politician would wish to confront. To reject McAdoo and nominate Smith would solidify anti-Catholic feeling and rob the party of millions of otherwise certain votes in the South and elsewhere. To reject Smith and nominate McAdoo would antagonize American Catholics, who constituted some sixteen per cent of the population and most of whom could normally be counted upon by the Democrats. Either selection would affect significantly the future of the party. Now in the ostensibly neutral hands of Cordell Hull, the Democratic National Chairman from Tennessee, party machinery was expected to shift to the victor in the convention, and a respectable showing in the fall election would insure the victor's continued supremacy in Democratic politics.

Despite the strong showing by McAdoo in the primaries, an argument could be made for the political wisdom of a Smith ticket. In the congressional elections of 1922, the biggest gains had come in New York, New Jersey, and other urban areas where Roman Catholicism prevailed. The new strength of the party, these elections seemed to indicate, lay not in the tradi-

---

The *New Republic* pointed out that Smith's drive for the presidency would send many hitherto complacent or indifferent Protestants scurrying into the arms of the Klan. XXVII (March 19, 1924), 87–8. Frank P. Walsh, a New York lawyer, wrote: "If his [Smith's] religion is a bar, of course it is all right with me to bust up the Democratic Party on such an issue." Walsh to Edward N. Nockels, April 12, 1924, F. P. Walsh Papers. For a close account of McAdoo's activities in this period, see Lee Allen: "The Mc-Adoo Campaign for the Presidential Nomination in 1924," *Journal of Southern History*, XXIX (May 1963), 211–28. In another article, Allen shows that McAdoo's Klan-supported victory in the Texas primary "materially aided in [his comeback] following the February crisis." "The Democratic Presidential Primary Election of 1924 in Texas," *Southwestern Historical Quarterly*, LXI (April 1958), 486–9. Baruch to McAdoo, February 27, 1924 and February 28, 1924; and Baruch to David Ladd Rockwell, April 16, 1924, Baruch Papers; Daniel Roper to Thomas B. Love, May 14, 1924, Love Papers; William E. Dodd to Claude Bowers, July 20, 1924, Dodd Papers; Claude Bowers to Samuel Ralston, August 21, 1924, Ralston Papers.

tionalist countryside of Bryan and McAdoo, but in the tenement areas of the city and the regions of rapid industrialization. And, as Franklin Roosevelt wrote to Josephus Daniels, Smith's followers came from states with the big electoral votes that often swing a presidential election—Massachusetts, New York, and Illinois. Yet the strain of anti-Catholicism in America was a threat of proportions that could not easily be reckoned.

The selection of New York as a site for the 1924 convention was based in part on the recent success of the party in that city, where in 1922 thirteen Republican congressmen had lost their incumbencies. New York had not been chosen for a convention since 1868. Wealthy New Yorkers, who had outbid other cities, declared their purpose "to convince the rest of the country that the town was not the red-light menace generally conceived by the sticks." And, though dry organizations opposed the choice of New York, it had won McAdoo's grudging consent in the fall of 1923, before the oil scandals made Smith a serious threat to him. McAdoo's own adopted state, California, had played host to the Democrats in 1920.[1]

From the start, this "little religious war" of a convention was a cartoon stereotype of the issues and animosities it represented. William Jennings Bryan came from Florida in a Palm Beach suit and carried a fan that a columnist described as one of those presented at county fairs by the local furniture store. McAdoo followed shortly afterwards; upon alighting from his train he promptly damned the city in his best populist rhetoric. "This imperial city . . . the city of privilege," he called New York, "the seat of that invisible power represented by the allied forces of finance and industry which, reaching into the remotest corners of the land, touches the lives of the people everywhere." The city—his home for thirty years—was "reactionary, sinister, unscrupulous, mercenary, and sordid . . . wanting in national ideals, devoid of conscience . . . rooted in corruption, directed by greed and dominated by selfishness." As McAdoo's

---

[1] Henry F. Pringle: *Alfred E. Smith* (New York, 1927), p. 293; O'Keane: *Walsh*, p. 150; *The New York Times*, June 8, 1923, p. 3.

followers arrived, they were treated with a calculated rudeness. To each visiting state delegation a block of the city was dedicated. Texans were aghast to find theirs the block containing St. Patrick's Cathedral. Governor Smith, meanwhile, came down from Albany and stationed himself in a local hotel where he fretfully smoked cigars with Edmond Moore, who had directed Cox's campaign in 1920.[2]

The convention opened at "Tex" Rickard's old Madison Square Garden on June 24. The building itself, shortly to be demolished, had housed Bryan on August 21, 1896, for a speech on the economics of free silver, and it had also been the scene of other Democratic gatherings. It was a red-brick affair with a checkered and fantastic history: in one of its ten-story towers the architect, Stanford White, had been murdered in 1906. It had recently played host to the Barnum and Bailey Circus, the six-day bicycle races, and a number of bizarre athletic events. The tone of the Democratic Convention that followed varied little from that of the Garden's usual fare. At the outset, corpulent Mrs. Josephine Dorman, dressed in red, white, and blue, was carried through the throng on the shoulders of two cowboys wearing sombreros and tortoise-shell glasses, while she screamed "McAdoo!" until her face turned red. Thus, appropriately, began "the snarling, cursing, tedious, tenuous, suicidal, homicidal rough-house in New York," as Arthur Krock termed it, with which a nation listening in to a convention by radio for the first time was entertained and embittered.[3]

To make matters worse, the country delegates displayed an exaggerated sensitivity, especially on the liquor question. When

[2] McAdoo is quoted in the New York *Evening World,* June 23, 1924, pp. 1, 23. He also promised to "remove the influence of invisible Government from the Treasury and Federal Reserve System," repeal the tariff, lower freight rates for farmers and develop foreign markets to absorb their surplus, and protect natural resources, especially water power. Sherwin L. Cook: *Torchlight Parade: Our Presidential Pageant* (New York, 1929), p. 258; *The New York Times,* June 25, 1924, p. 1.
[3] "The Damn Fool Democrats," *American Mercury,* IV (March 1925), 257.

Senator Pat Harrison of Mississippi, the keynote speaker, remarked: "What this country needs . . . is . . . Paul Revere," he
received a round of boos. According to one observer, some of
the disgruntled prohibitionist delegates apparently confused the
speaker's words with the pronouncements they had grimly
suspected they would be hearing: "What this country needs
. . . is . . . real beer." Bryan himself revised a reference to the bier
of President Harding, and McAdoo apologized for eating cake
soaked in sherry. The convention seemed fated to ill harmony:
the Georgia delegation bristled when the band, thinking perhaps
that it was a treasured southern tune, accompanied a Cracker
demonstration with "Marching Through Georgia." As for
Smith's song, "The Sidewalks of New York," Westbrook Pegler
remarked that it had been "inspired by beer"; and he also noted
that Smith's home territory of the East Side was "the best protected bootleg territory in New York today." In point of fact,
Bryan and McAdoo many times had ample reason to complain
about the abundance of liquor made available to distract thirsty
country delegates. McAdoo charged that the Smith men had
kept many of his supporters drunk since they arrived in New
York. And when the Imperial Wizard of the Klan mysteriously
fell ill of ptomaine poisoning, Klansmen from the Texas delegation resolved to burn a cross outside the meeting hall. But the
1200 city police assigned to prevent any disturbance were not in
the mood. One C. Lewis Fowler, a former college president, had
been jailed for selling his anti-Catholic *American Standard*
outside the doors.[4]

[4] On his way to the Vanderbilt Hotel, McAdoo said he was accosted by
two women. "You will not desert us?" one breathed. "No," he replied.
She dropped to her knees in prayer. Quoted in Edwin P. Hoyt, Jr.:
Jumbos and Jackasses (New York, 1960), pp. 315–16. Roper: *Fifty Years
of Public Life*, p. 224; William Allen White: *Politics: The Citizen's Busi-
ness* (New York, 1924), p. 80; Atlanta *Constitution*, June 28, 1924, p. 1;
July 9, 1924, p. 2; Claude Bowers: Oral History Memoir, Columbia
University, 1954, p. 52; *The Outlook*, CXXXVII (July 9, 1924), 386.

James Cox wrote to John H. Clarke of "a foolish platform given to us
by Hearst, Bryan, and McAdoo." October 1, 1924, Clarke Papers. On
McAdoo's responsibility for the Wilsonian League plank, see Norman H.

Senator Walsh, chairman of the convention—Catholic and dry, a supporter of McAdoo, he was acceptable to both factions—presided over the adoption of the platform. Here the first event of note was a speech and minority report on the League of Nations by Newton D. Baker, who thought of stampeding the delegates with what was indeed an eloquent plea for American entry. The platform itself sidestepped this and most other controversial issues; yet its sympathies were as wide as its recommendations were thin: it deplored child labor, but offered no remedy; neglecting McNary-Haugen or the equalization fee, it pitied the farmer. A measure of radicalism was brought into the platform through the influence of Bryan, a member of the Committee on Platforms and Resolutions, and other progressives; included were peremptory demands out of harmony with the rest of the document: for "strict public control and conservation of all the nation's natural resources, such as coal, iron, oil, and timber . . ."; for federal aid to education, an excess profits tax in wartime, and vigorous prosecution of monopolies; and for laws requiring a popular vote on certain further constitutional amendments and a referendum on entry into any war not begun by "actual or threatened" enemy attack. Bryan called the platform the best the Democrats had ever written.[5]

A crucial moment came with a platform committee report on whether to censure the Ku Klux Klan by name. McAdoo controlled three of the four convention committees, including this one, and the majority report declared against naming the Klan—although all the committee members agreed that the bigotry and intolerance of the Klan should be condemned. Every effort had been made to avoid the necessity of a direct commitment on the issue. According to Mark Sullivan, "The leading Catholics and Jews in the convention and out of it did

---

Davis to Charles Hamlin, September 24, 1924, Hamlin Papers. On Bryan see also Paxton Hibben: *The Peerless Leader: William Jennings Bryan* (New York, 1929), p. 380.
[5] Lawrence Levine: *Defender of the Faith: William Jennings Bryan; the Last Decade, 1915–1925* (New York, 1965), pp. 303–16. *Official Report of the Proceedings . . . [of] . . . 1924* (Indianapolis, 1925), pp. 228–45, 260.

not want to mention the Klan by name." But the proponents of Smith's candidacy were anxious to identify McAdoo closely with the Klan and possibly to defeat him in a test of strength before the balloting began; the Smith faction, led by George Brennan of Illinois, demanded that the specific denunciation of the Klan uttered by the committee minority become official. Bryan, whose aim was to keep the party together and to maintain harmony among his rural followers, argued that naming the Klan would popularize it, as had the publicity given the organization by the New York *World*. It was also good politics to avoid the issue, Bryan said, since naming it would irredeemably divide the party. Worse still, Bryan believed, denouncing the Klan by name would betray the McAdoo forces, since it had been Smith's strategy to raise the issue. In contrast to Bryan, former Mayor Andrew Erwin of Athens, Georgia, spoke for the anti-Klan plank—but again the band struck up "Marching Through Georgia." In the ensuing vote, the Klan escaped censure by a hair's breadth; the vote itself foretold McAdoo's own defeat in the balloting.[6]

The role of Bryan at the 1924 convention has often been twisted to make him seem a bigot or a charlatan; in truth, his performance has been misrepresented. He delivered an address on social injustice that Elmer Davis called "brilliant." If his speech on the Klan was tempered, it nevertheless represented a sincere repudiation of prejudice, and was fully consistent with the Bryan who in earlier days had praised the appointment to the Supreme Court of Louis D. Brandeis as strongly as he had denounced Henry Ford's use of the fabricated "Protocols of the Elders of Zion." Much to the delight of an audience at the

[6] Bryan himself had introduced a controversial resolution at the 1912 Democratic Convention that denounced by name J. Pierpont Morgan, Thomas F. Ryan, and August Belmont. For the sake of harmony, Brennan had agreed earlier in 1924 to leave the "three little words" out of his state's Democratic platform, but he insisted upon them in New York. The vote, as officially reported, was 541 3/20 to 542 3/20. New York *Herald-Tribune*, June 29, 1924, pp. 1, 2; *Official Report of the Proceedings* ... [of] ... *1924*, p. 333; *Century*, CX (May 1925), 94–100.

Brooklyn Jewish Center, Bryan in 1923 wore a yarmulke while he delivered his speech; at the convention his brother Charles wore a similar black skullcap over his bald spot to avoid catching cold. And Bryan had once noted: "Those who have come into intimate acquaintance with representative Catholics do not need to be informed that they do not concede to the church authorities the right to direct their course in political matters, but many Protestants, lacking this knowledge . . . , have been misled." Not all of Bryan's remarks on religion in his later years are free of intellectual intolerance; some of his pamphlets on fundamentalism are an intellectual disgrace. But it should be remembered that excellent political reasons undoubtedly motivated his position against naming the Klan—a position in which, incidentally, he was supported by the Catholic senator from Montana, Thomas J. Walsh. In fact, amid the different circumstances of the campaign, Bryan altered his stand. In August, after John W. Davis had denounced the nativist group by name, Bryan joined him.[7]

The New York Times, later comparing the vote on the Klan with the vote on the first ballot for President, found a high degree of coincidence between the McAdoo element at the convention and the element that opposed explicit condemnation of the Klan. It could not be doubted that at least in some sense McAdoo was the Klan's candidate. According to Claude Bowers, Daniel Roper of South Carolina (the real force behind David Ladd Rockwell, McAdoo's official campaign manager), jokingly referred to the "three years I have been working for the nomination of such a Klansman and all around rascal as McAdoo." Still, McAdoo's support was by no means exclusively drawn from the order: in Texas, for example, at least two large anti-Klan papers supported him, and in the primaries counties that had opposed local Klan candidates favored McAdoo over Underwood. Senator Thomas Walsh, a Catholic, and Bernard Baruch, a Jew, both supported McAdoo. In a seconding speech

[7] Levine: *Defender of the Faith*, pp. 258, 310; *The New York Times*, December 4, 1923, p. 5; August 30, 1924, p. 4.

for McAdoo, J. F. T. O'Connor of North Dakota explicitly repudiated the hooded order. But if it was only by way of appearance, and the polarities of the moment, that McAdoo was identifiable with the Klan, much of his following had no like fastidiousness. Brennan perhaps did not realize the full impact the Klan vote would have on the convention. He intended that it should harden feeling against McAdoo, and it did; but just as surely, even before the balloting began, Brennan had by his own strategy killed all hope of nominating Al Smith.[8]

The balloting for President began on June 30. McAdoo and Smith had each evolved a strategy to build up his total slowly: Smith's trick was to plant his extra votes for his opponent, so that McAdoo's strength might later appear to be waning; the Californian countered by holding back his full force, though he had been planning a strong early show. But by no sleight of hand could the convention have been swung around to either contestant. With the party split into two assertive parts, the rule requiring a two-thirds majority for nomination crippled the chances of both candidates by giving a veto each could—and did—use. McAdoo himself wanted to drop the two-thirds rule, but his Protestant supporters preferred to keep their veto over

[8] According to Richard C. Bain, all but one of Smith's first-ballot supporters favored the minority plank, while McAdoo supporters earned a +.63 correlation with the majority plank. See the statistical technique used in *Convention Decisions and Voting Records* (Washington, D.C., 1960), p. 225. For evidence of the Klan's considerable attachment to McAdoo, see Herbert Bayard Swope to Bernard Baruch, October 25, 1923, Baruch Papers; W. J. Vollor to Frank P. Walsh, June 9, 1924, and Kevin Kane of East St. Louis, who insisted to Walsh that "the only ones who are shouting McAdoo are those who wear the hood and sheet"; June 17, 1924, Walsh Papers. In Georgia, Texas, and some other states the Klan officially ordered its membership to support McAdoo. Atlanta *Constitution*, April 27, 1924, p. 1; July 1, 1924, p. 9; July 7, 1924, p. 1. Charles C. Alexander: "Secrecy Bids for Power: The Ku Klux Klan in Texas Politics in the 1920's," *Mid-America*, XLVI (January 1964), 18. Klan strength in the various states is estimated in *The New York Times*, July 1, 1924, p. 3. Love to Thomas L. Chadbourne, May 8, 1924; Love to McAdoo, September 6, 1923, Love Papers; Bowers to Samuel Ralston, August 21, 1924, Ralston Papers; Long Diary, March 15, 1924, Long Papers; *Official Report of the Proceedings . . .* [of] *. . . 1924*, pp. 188–9.

a Catholic candidate; and the South regarded the rule as a protection of its minority interests. The deadlock that developed might as well have been a political contest between the Pope and the Imperial Wizard of the Klan, so solidly did the Catholic delegates support Smith and the Klansmen support McAdoo. At no point in the balloting did Smith receive more than a single vote from the South and scarcely more than the twenty from the states west of the Mississippi; he never won more than 368 of the 729 votes needed for nomination, though even this performance was impressive for a Roman Catholic. McAdoo's strength fluctuated more widely, reaching its highest point of 528 on the seventieth ballot. Since both candidates occasionally received purely strategic aid, the nucleus of their support was probably even less. The remainder of the votes was divided among dark horses and favorite sons who had spun high hopes since the Doheny testimony; understandably, they hesitated to withdraw their own candidacies as long as the convention was so clearly divided.[9]

As time passed, the maneuvers of the two factions took on the character of desperation. Daniel Roper even went to Franklin Roosevelt, reportedly to offer Smith second place on a McAdoo ticket. For their part, the Tammany men tried to prolong the convention until hotel bills should mount beyond the means of the outlanders; the Smith backers also attempted to stampede the delegates by packing the galleries with noisy rooters. But the rudeness of Tammany, and particularly the booing accorded to Bryan when he spoke to the convention, only steeled the resolution of the country delegates. McAdoo and Bryan both tried to reassemble the convention in another city, perhaps Washington, D.C., or St. Louis. As a last resort, McAdoo supporters introduced a motion to eliminate one candidate on each ballot until

[9] Tammany forces tantalized favorite sons with hints of support later should they remain in the race. *Century*, CX (May 1925), 97. Lee N. Allen: "The Underwood Presidential Movement of 1924," unpublished doctoral dissertation, University of Pennsylvania, 1955, p. 239 and *passim;* Atlanta *Constitution*, July 1, 1924, p. 1; *Kiplinger Washington Letter*, June 13, 1924; Frank R. Kent: *The Democratic Party* (New York, 1928), p. 484.

only five remained, but Smith delegates and those supporting favorite sons managed to defeat the McAdoo strategy. Smith countered by suggesting that all delegates be released from their pledges—to which McAdoo agreed on condition that the two-thirds rule be eliminated—although Smith fully expected that loyalty would prevent the disaffection of Indiana and Illinois votes, both controlled by political bosses friendly to him. Indeed, Senator David I. Walsh of Massachusetts expressed the sentiment that moved the Smith backers: "We must continue to do all that we can to nominate Smith. If it should develop that he cannot be nominated, then McAdoo cannot have it either."[1]

On the sixty-first inconclusive round, the convention set a record for length of balloting. In the ensuing days the major candidates held a series of conferences to break the stalemate. After the eighty-second ballot, the convention adopted Smith's resolution to nullify all pledges. On the next round McAdoo led Smith by only fifty votes; on the eighty-seventh the count stood at 361½ for McAdoo, 333½ for Smith; and on the ninety-ninth McAdoo led by a bare one and one-half vote margin. Finally resolved to drop out while he was still a shade ahead, the Californian halfheartedly accepted Smith's suggestion that both withdraw their candidacies; the New Yorker, however, maintained his strength on the one-hundredth ballot, with a count of 351½.

It had seemed for a time that the nomination could go to Samuel M. Ralston, an Indiana Senator and popular ex-governor. Advanced by the indefatigable boss Tom Taggart, Ralston's candidacy might look for some support from Bryan, who had written that "Ralston is the most promising of the compromise

---

[1] Senator James D. Phelan of California, among others, complained of "New York rowdyism." Phelan to George L. Duval, July 21, 1924, Phelan Papers. Breckinridge Long wrote in his diary that Smith had been drunk when McAdoo tried to compromise with him. October 17, 1924. Harry L. Watson to William Watts Ball, July 12, 1924, Ball Papers; *Official Report of the Proceedings . . . [of] . . . 1924*, pp. 748–9, 754–5, 783, 816–17; New York *Evening World*, July 7, 1924, p. 1; *Christian Science Monitor*, July 5, 1924, p. 11.

candidates." Ralston was also a favorite of the Klan and a second choice of many McAdoo men. In 1922 the Indianian had made an attack on parochial schools that the Klan saw as an endorsement of its own views; and he won several normally Republican counties dominated by the Klan. Much of Ralston's support came from the South and West—states like Oklahoma, Missouri, and Nevada, with their strong Klan elements. McAdoo himself, according to Claude Bowers, said: "I like the old Senator, like his simplicity, honesty, record"; and it was reported that he told Smith supporters he would withdraw only in favor of Ralston. As with John W. Davis, Ralston had few enemies, and his support from men as divergent as Bryan and Taggart cast him as a possible compromise candidate. He passed Davis, the almost consistent third choice of the convention, on the fifty-second ballot; but Taggart then discouraged the boom for the time being because the McAdoo and Smith phalanxes showed no signs of weakening. On July 8, the eighty-seventh ballot showed a total for Ralston of ninety-three votes, chiefly from Indiana and Missouri; before the day was over, the Ralston total had risen to almost 200, a larger tally than Davis had ever received. Most of these votes were drawn from McAdoo, to whom they later returned.[2]

Numerous sources indicate that Taggart was not exaggerating when he later said: "We would have nominated Senator Ralston if he had not withdrawn his name at the last minute. It was as near a certainty as anything in politics can be. We had the pledges of enough delegates that would shift to Ralston on a certain ballot to have nominated him." Ralston himself had wavered on whether to make the race; despite his doctor's stern

[2] Ralston, commenting on the Klan issue, believed that it would set a bad precedent to denounce any organization by name in the platform. Ralston to Fred Van Nuys, May 21, 1924; see also Bowers to Ralston, May 24, 1924, and June 21, 1924, Ralston Papers. Bryan to John J. Centz, March 21, 1923, Bryan Papers; McAdoo to Love, September 18, 1923, Love Papers; Chalmers: *Hooded Americanism*, p. 167; Hoyt: *Jumbos and Jackasses*, p. 315; *The Outlook*, CXXXVII (June 18, 1924), 267; *The New York Times*, June 24, 1924, p. 1; June 30, 1924, p. 12; Bain: *Convention Decisions*, p. 224.

recommendation not to run and the illness of his wife and son, the Senator had told Taggart that he would be a candidate, albeit a reluctant one. But the 300-pound Ralston finally telegraphed his refusal to go on with it; sixty-six years old at the time of the convention, he was to die the following year.[3]

TABLE VII

The Last Ballots of the 1924 Democratic Convention

Ballot	McAdoo	Smith	Underwood	Davis	Meredith	Walsh
100	190	351	41	203	75	52
101	52	121	229	316	13	98
102	21	44	307	415	66	123
103	Davis by acclamation					

The very last ballots of the convention suggest some interesting possibilities about the nature of the conflict. Table VII shows that Senator Underwood, a wet, and Senator Walsh, a Catholic,

[3] After the convention, Ralston's doctor wrote to the Senator: "In my deliberate judgment, after having given the matter very careful consideration, you did the only wise thing possible. . . . Foreseeing what was liable to happen, I urged you many months ago not to allow yourself to be nominated." Dr. Sterling Raffin to Ralston, July 22, 1924. But Ralston had written to Taggart on June 19: "If . . . the Convention should turn to me, I shall do all in my power to bring success to our party this fall." In reality, he had been very indecisive; in August he told Senator Pat Harrison: "On more than one occasion, I said to you that I had never made up my mind I should want the nomination to come to me. In making that statement, I spoke truthfully. . . ." August 1, 1924. "I am very conscious," wrote the modest Ralston, "of not being in the presidential class." Ralston to Thomas C. Rye, May 12, 1924, Ralston Papers. See also the Atlanta *Constitution*, July 6, 1924, p. 12, and Sexson E. Humphreys: "The Nomination of the Democratic Candidate in 1924," *Indiana Magazine of History*, XXXI (March 1925), 1–9. Taggart's remark is in an unpublished biography of the Indiana boss by A. C. Sallee, Indiana State Library.

together received 327 votes on the one hundred and first ballot, as opposed to Smith's 121. The total for the three candidates, all wet or Catholic, was 448—far greater than Smith's highest vote. Walsh, for instance, received some of the McAdoo votes that are susceptible of being traced. Apparently the objection to Smith was broadly based; it was a resistance more to the whole complex of urban attributes he represented and of which his religion and stand against prohibition were only parts, while the Catholicism of Walsh and the anti-prohibitionist position of Underwood stood in isolation, free of larger contexts.[4]

The nomination, all honor stripped from it, finally went to John W. Davis, a compromise candidate who won on the one hundred and third ballot after the withdrawal of Smith and Mc-Adoo. Davis had never been a genuine "dark horse" candidate; he had almost always been third in the balloting, and by the end of the twenty-ninth round he was the betting favorite of New York gamblers. But, as Charles Hamlin wrote in his diary, Davis "frankly said . . . that he was not seeking [the nomination] and that if nominated he would accept only as a matter of public duty." For Vice President, the Democrats nominated Charles W. Bryan, Governor of Nebraska, brother of William Jennings Bryan and for many years editor of *The Commoner*. Bryan received little more than the necessary two thirds vote, and no attempt was made to make the choice unanimous: boos were sounding through the Garden. The incongruous teaming of the distinguished Wall Street lawyer and the radical from a prairie state provided not a balanced but a schizoid ticket; and because the selection of Bryan was reputed to be a sop to the radicals, many delegates unfamiliar with Davis' actual record came to identify the lawyer with a conservatism in excess even of that which he did indeed represent.[5]

The significance of Davis' victory was that it was also a tacti-

---

[4] Walsh was offered the support of the organized drys in the closing ballots. Justin Steuart: *Wayne Wheeler, Dry Boss* (New York, 1928), p. 220. *Official Report of the Proceedings . . .* [of] *. . . 1924*, pp. 974, 979.
[5] Wilbur Marsh wrote to George White that there had been a Davis movement at San Francisco in 1920 "of pretty good sized proportions." October

cal victory for the Smith forces over those of McAdoo. For though a West Virginian by birth, Davis had the support of urban politicians, and as a Wall Street lawyer—he had been partner in a distinguished law firm that from 1889 to 1892 included Grover Cleveland—he had a certain symbolic connection with the forces of urbanism. The shift of votes from the city areas to Davis did not occur until the very last ballot, since Davis was their second choice after Underwood. Indeed, the attempt of some urban leaders to nominate Underwood probably sent some McAdoo delegates to the support of the less objectional Davis—particularly southerners reassured by his West Virginia background. But long before, frequent reports had appeared that Smith, Roosevelt, Taggart, Edmond Moore, George White (an old friend of Davis), Wilbur Marsh, Key Pittman, and James Cox were all "talking Davis." George Brennan, the Illinois boss, particularly backed him.[6] At the same time, strong anti-Davis sentiment developed in the McAdoo camp, where Senator Carter Glass of Virginia was the reserve candidate.

10, 1923, George White Papers. William Jennings Bryan threatened to desert Davis unless a westerner were placed on the ticket. Robert Woolley, manuscript memoir, Chap. xxxii, pp. 10–11. *The New York Times,* July 2, 1924, p. 4; Hamlin Diary, February 5, 1924.

[6] Moore to White, August 13, 1923; Marsh to White, October 16, 1923, and September 23, 1926; White to Davis, March 27, 1924, and White to Fred C. Martin, May 10, 1924, George White Papers; Samuel Ralston to Henderson S. Martin, May 2, 1924, Ralston Papers; Maurice P. Murphy to the Honorable Joseph B. Shannon, June 18, 1924, copy in Ralston Papers (July 1924); Norman Davis to Senator Key Pittman, July 18, 1924, and Samuel W. Belford to Pittman, July 28, 1924, Pittman Papers; Grady Miller to Bush Binley, July 28, 1924, copy in Joseph T. Robinson Papers; William Allen White: *Politics: The Citizen's Business,* p. 95; New York *World,* July 9, 1924, p. 1; Chicago *Daily Tribune,* June 21, 1924, p. 1; Humphreys: "The Nomination of the Democratic Candidate," pp. 1–8; *The New York Times,* April 16, 1928, p. 6. To all of these sources showing strong urban support for Davis can be added the *Kiplinger Washington Letter,* which observed that the "program of the anti-McAdoo leaders is to push the Al Smith boom as far as it will go, then try to transfer it to John W. Davis. This has been their real plan all along." June 27, 1924; see also May 16, 1924, and June 13, 1924.

Claude Bowers reported that McAdoo "looks upon Davis as the tool of his Wall Street enemies." Bryan was particularly distressed by the possibility that Davis might be the Democratic candidate; he stated to the Mississippi delegation the same sentiments that had influenced his shift from Champ Clark to Woodrow Wilson in 1912: "The Convention must not nominate a Wall Street man."[7] When Davis was nominated, Smith appeared before the meeting to congratulate the candidate, while McAdoo was conspicuously absent. Months later after he returned from a European trip, McAdoo let it be known that he could not support the nominee.

In his acceptance speech Davis made the perfunctory statement that he would enforce the prohibition law; but his conservatism prejudiced him in favor of personal liberty and home rule and he was frequently denounced as a wet. After the convention Davis tried to satisfy both factions of his party, but his support came principally from the same city elements that had backed Cox in 1920. Frank Hague of New Jersey replaced Bruce Kremer of Montana, McAdoo's floor manager, as a vice chairman of the party. Those McAdoo men who remained in the party organization worked badly with Davis' eastern headquarters in New York. McAdoo himself failed even to reply to Senator Key Pittman's request from Davis headquarters that the Californian speak in the campaign, and some of McAdoo's followers actively supported La Follette or Coolidge in 1924 and Herbert Hoover in 1928. Daniel Roper wrote to Thomas B. Love of Davis' "bad environment." In the sense that the Davis

[7] New York *Herald-Tribune*, June 2, 1924, p. 2; Bowers to Samuel Ralston, June 21, 1924. In another letter to Ralston, Bowers added that "the Catholic bloc [was] unquestionably in league with the Reactionary or Wall Street bloc throughout." July 10, 1924. Later in the campaign Bowers wrote to Ralston that he was "afraid that [Davis] has been captured too much by this eastern crowd." August 28, 1924, Ralston Papers. *The New York Times*, July 2, 1924, p. 1. Actually Davis practiced law in New York for only three of his twenty-five professional years. *The New York Times*, May 3, 1924, p. 1; July 2, 1924, p. 3.

victory was also a Smith victory, the 1924 convention was a prelude to the victory of Smith at Houston four years later. Davis himself served as a Smith delegate in 1928.[8]

Even before the Democratic convention had ended, a third-party candidate had intruded into the balance of political forces —a candidate whose radical stance would serve as a foil as much to the conservatism of Davis as to that of Coolidge. The decision of Senator Robert La Follette of Wisconsin to run for President in 1924 gave the campaign a unique flavor, spicing it with a fresh and pungent radicalism that attempted to bring together the strength of factory and farm.

The new party movement had its impetus in 1919 when J. A. H. Hopkins, earlier a prominent Bull Mooser, organized the Committee of Forty-Eight as a progressive political action group. The work of political mobilization begun by the committee was taken up in 1922 by two conferences of progressives in Chicago, where La Follette established his position as head of the young movement. The majority of participants at the second meeting were trade union officials; the delegations included William Green of the United Mine Workers and Sidney Hillman of the Amalgamated Clothing Workers. A quarter of the delegates came from the Non-Partisan League, the Farmer-Labor party, and Morris Hillquit's flexible new Socialist party, while individual farmers and labor spokesmen comprised the remainder of the progressive conclave. Although majority sentiment for independent party action did not crystallize in Chicago, the dream of a monolithic new liberal party, reawakening the spirit and power of the insurgents of 1912, captured the loyalty

---

[8] The dry leader Wayne Wheeler complained of Davis' "constant repetition of wet catch phrases like 'Personal Liberty,' 'illegal search and seizure,' and 'home rule.'" Steuart: *Wayne Wheeler*, pp. 225–6. Another Smith man, James W. Gerard, served as treasurer of the party. Both Love and Roper supported Hoover in 1928. *Official Report of the Proceedings . . . [of] . . . 1924*, pp. 1012 ff.; *The New York Times*, November 7, 1924, pp. 1, 3; personal interview, Warren Kiplinger, September 8, 1964; New Orleans *Item*, August 26, 1928, p. 7; Roper to Love, July 3, 1924, Love Papers.

of many delegates who subsequently turned away from the major parties in 1924.[9]

Out of the Committee of Forty-Eight, some earlier organizations formed by La Follette, and the Chicago conventions grew the Conference for Progressive Political Action; and in 1924 the CPPA sponsored the Progressive party. La Follette had told reporters the previous summer that there would be no need for a third ticket unless both parties nominated reactionaries. Then came the Doheny scandals; and as for a time it seemed likely that the scandals would eliminate McAdoo, who was popular among railroad unions and other labor groups, the way was paved for the party which was launched in June of 1924. It was the dream of the Progressives that they might replace the Democrats, and thereby bring a clearer ideological alignment to American politics.

As Progressive candidate for President, La Follette became leader of the first formal prominent alliance in American political history between members of organized labor and farm groups, and of these with Socialists and independent radicals. Even the American Federation of Labor, although weakened by a precipitous decline in its membership since the war, gave La Follette mild backing and so officially supported a presidential candidate for the first time. The Progressive vice presidential candidate was Senator Burton K. Wheeler of Montana, only one of many Democrats who abandoned the chaos of their own party for the crusading vigor of La Follette's, and found there an idealism and dedication unparalleled within any of the other major political organizations of the 1920's.

At the foundation of La Follette's program was an attack on monopolies. His Socialist supporters took this as an attack on the capitalistic system in general; to non-Socialists, including the Senator himself, it signified a revival of the policy of trust-busting. The Progressive platform also called for government

[9] *Century*, CX (May 1925), 94–100; Kenneth MacKay: *The Progressive Movement of 1924* (New York, 1947).

ownership of water power and a gradual nationalization of the railroads. But the election did not become a pure test of his program. La Follette was criticized for his pacifism by the patriots of the Klan, and for his radicalism by both of the major party candidates. Labor was not strong enough to contribute heavily to its champion's campaign. Yet Daniel Tobin of the Teamsters spoke for a significant portion of organized labor when he rejected the Democrats for being "just as reactionary" as the Republicans; and the commendation of the AFL must have been of some aid to the Progressive candidate. Most of all, La Follette suffered from a host of election technicalities. In California, for example, he was forced to run as a Socialist; in Florida, he failed to meet the state election requirements—the submission of petitions signed by twenty-five voters in each of fifty-four counties; in Ohio, the exclusion of La Follette poll-watchers invited fraud. But the five million votes he actually received in the election—despite the candidate's age, sixty-four, his stand against prohibition, his antiwar record, his opposition to the Klan, his history of serious illness, and the rise in wheat prices over the summer—were a personal tribute to the senator and a sizable endorsement of his reform and isolationist views.[1]

Of the three presidential candidates, La Follette, Davis, and Coolidge, Davis had the most trouble in casting an appealing

---

[1] Senator Wheeler explained his defection in his autobiography: "When the Democratic Party goes to Wall Street for a candidate, I must refuse to go with it." *Yankee from the West* (New York, 1962), p. 249. In an examination of the La Follette candidacy, it should be remembered that the most halcyon days of Republican prosperity had not yet been reached; unemployment, in fact, was higher in 1924 than at any time between 1923 and 1929. United States Bureau of the Census: *Historical Statistics of the United States, Colonial Times to 1957* (Washington, D.C., 1960), p. 73. La Follette, running in California on the Socialist party ticket, received there four times as many votes as Davis; and La Follette also ran ahead of the Democrat in forty-seven out of forty-eight California counties. Yet William Allen White thought that "La Follette lost about forty per cent of his normal vote because of the Klan." White to Oswald Garrison Villard, October 19, 1924, White Papers. MacKay: *The Progressive Movement of 1924*, pp. 180 ff.; Samuel Lubell: *The Future of American Politics* (New York, 1952), p. 140.

image; to many voters, he appeared to be merely a shadow of the conservative Coolidge. "The framework of his mind was formed in West Virginia [his birthplace]," wrote Walter Lippmann in "The Setting for John W. Davis," an article in the *Atlantic Monthly*. "It is that of the traditional Democrat with the Jeffersonian distrust of centralization, the parochial dislike of bureaucracy, and a strong prejudice in favor of home rule." Lippmann concluded that Davis' nomination reflected confidence in his character rather than studied agreement with his views. Born on Jefferson's birthday, Davis had signed "The American's Creed," a clear affirmation of Jeffersonian principles widely circulated by businessmen in 1924; it included the maxim, paraphrasing Jefferson, "that government is best which governs least." As a member of the House Judiciary Committee, Davis had, it is true, written the final drafts of the anti-injunction and anticonspiracy features of the Clayton Act; but this and similar acts of duty as Solicitor General need imply no commitment further than that of loyalty to the administration, and indeed trust busting itself was in the grain of Jeffersonian decentralization. Just before the campaign of 1920, Wilson had said of Davis that he was "a fine man, but he is a formalist. If you want a standstill, he is just the man to nominate." And it was in character for Davis when he appeared among the conservative backers of the Republican Alf Landon in 1936.[2]

When Davis implied that he would not repudiate his friends to win the presidency, it was widely concluded that he had somehow endorsed his firm's clients, notably J. P. Morgan, and of course the name of Morgan evoked distrust among progressives and opponents of Wall Street. Davis, moreover, had recently managed to get an increase in rates for the New York Telephone Company. In several law cases, Davis had sided with management against hard-pressed unions, which made Samuel

[2] Henry D. Clayton wrote of Davis: "He helped me to formulate the conspiracy, injunction and contempt proceedings of the Clayton Act." Clayton to William B. Wilson, October 10, 1924, W. B. Wilson Papers. *Atlantic Monthly*, CXXXIV (October 1924), 530–5; Homer Cummings File of Ray Stannard Baker Papers, May 31, 1920.

Gompers skeptical of Davis as a friend to labor. In truth, the Democratic nominee had also defended the American Federation of Labor and had protected the right of West Virginia coal miners to strike. Apparently he took his clients without bias; but the impression persisted of Davis as a markedly conservative candidate.[3]

During the campaign Davis found the nominee of the Progressive party more distasteful than the more formidable and conservative Republican opponent. Although La Follette's program was for the most part fairly moderate, and the Wisconsin statesman rejected Communist support, he preached what to the lawyer Davis was a dangerous doctrine: the weakening of the power of the Supreme Court. La Follette, disgusted by judicial nullification of important labor laws, proposed that Congress might nullify a decision of the Court by passing a law a second time—a scheme different in design from that later advanced by Franklin Roosevelt, but similar in purpose; herein, Davis believed, the Progressive candidate had posed the most important issue of the campaign. In attacking La Follette, Davis ignored the sense of William Jennings Bryan's advice to stay clear of states that looked safe for the Progressives.[4]

As for Davis' campaign technique, Colonel House caught its flavor when he confided to his diary:

[3] Davis' statement is quoted in Theodore A. Huntley, *The Life of John W. Davis* (New York, 1924), pp. 133-4. Davis' record as advocate for management in labor cases did not escape the editors of *The Nation*. CXIX (August 20, 1924), 176. See also James Derieux to W. W. Ball, May 15, 1924, Ball Papers, and Samuel Gompers to William B. Wilson, August 6, 1924, Gompers Papers. Fellow-lawyer Frank P. Walsh wrote: "In my opinion, the most reactionary man in that Convention was the nominee, Mr. John W. Davis." Walsh to William Zimmerman, July 21, 1924, F. P. Walsh Papers. In a letter to Breckinridge Long, George Fort Milton speaks of the candidate's failure to answer the prevailing question: "How does Davis feel about Wall Street?" August 13, 1924, Long Papers; see also Hiram Johnson to Charles H. McClatchy, July 10, 1924, Johnson Papers. Matthew Page Andrews to Davis, January 9, 1924, and William J. Barker to Davis, August 24, 1924, Davis Papers.
[4] In a speech in Wilmington, Delaware, Davis pictured La Follette as "rawhead and bloody bones." John H. Holt of Huntington, West Vir-

Frankly, I am disappointed in him as a candidate. . . . I have tried to stir him to action and to make his speeches more forceful and pertinent to the trend of the times. He was candid enough to say that he had been all his life trying to eliminate his emotions from his briefs and addresses to the courts and that it was impossible at this late date to put this quality in his speeches for political effect.

Franklin Roosevelt dismissed Davis as an orator: "His little speeches are always charming and beautifully expressed." Tall, dignified, and manly, Davis lacked not conviction itself, but the oratorical fire and intensity with which to give conviction verbal form. Late in August of 1924, Claude Bowers wrote to Ralston of Davis' shortcomings as a candidate. "The moment I touched on politics," Bowers wrote, "he [Davis] seemed shy and embarrassed." Then Bowers proceeded to relate a story—no doubt overdrawn—about Davis: "I was in Spellacy's room [Thomas Spellacy, in charge of Eastern campaign headquarters in New York] when a delegation of Tammany Irishmen . . . came in to offer their services. . . . They were of the laborer type. After while [*sic*], to my surprise the door opened and Davis came in. . . . Everyone rose and Davis passed down the line shaking hands in a manner almost too dignified and gentlemanly, saying nothing. Then, evidently embarassed [*sic*] and at loss as to what was expected of him, he turned and looked at them in silence.

" 'These men are here to help elect you,' said Spellacy.

" 'Strength to their arms,' said Davis.

"Then he seemed at the end of his rope for a minute after which he added: 'We want every man in the boat and every man with an oar!'

"Then after another long period of silence which was finally interrupted by Spellacy with the astounding suggestion made

ginia, to Davis, October 1, 1924, Davis Papers. Russell B. Nye: *Midwestern Progressive Politics* (East Lansing, Mich., 1951), pp. 330–1, 338–9; Belle and Fola La Follette: *La Follette*, II, 1128; Bryan to Davis, September 29, 1924, Davis Papers.

almost impatiently and of course out loud:—'Tell them that you are an organization man.'

" 'Oh yes, I am an organization man,' said Davis.

"After that he turned to speak to a correspondent of the Boston *Globe* and the thing was over."[5]

But colorless as the West Virginian's candidacy must be judged, it had the strength of integrity. At Sea Girt, New Jersey, he joined his voice to La Follette's in explicit denunciation of the Klan. As Colonel House noted, Coolidge, who would not repudiate the organization, remained the only contestant likely to receive its substantial support.[6]

Davis' campaign was destined to failure. The candidacy of an alleged extremist awakens latent conservatism in an electorate, and this tendency usually benefits the current officeholder; and in an era dominated by one political party, that party tends to attract the new voters, especially when the minority party does not sharply differentiate itself from the majority. Neither Davis nor Frank Polk and Lincoln Dixon, his managers, took issue with the Republicans. And Clement L. Shaver, Davis' new Democratic National Chairman, was charged by one observer with having "none of the qualifications of a leader." Shaver, a little-known lawyer and coal-mine operator from Lost Creek, West Virginia, was as interested in Indian lore and fishing as in politics.

[5] Robert Woolley of Democratic National Headquarters criticized Davis for not being a "flaming crusader." Woolley to Davis, October 7, 1924, Davis Papers. House Diary, October 15, 1924; Franklin Roosevelt to Glenn Frank, August 12, 1924, Roosevelt Papers; Bowers to Ralston, August 21, 1924, Ralston Papers.

[6] The significance of Davis' condemnation was in his naming of the Klan; this had been the critical point at the Democratic convention. After William Jennings Bryan supported his disavowal of the Klan, the candidate regularly made digs at the order. Chalmers: *Hooded Americanism*, p. 214. Claiming credit for having defeated Smith in New York, Hiram Evans of the Klan surveyed the field and pronounced Coolidge the "safe" candidate. House Diary, November 14, 1924; *The New York Times*, June 30, 1924, p. 1; November 10, 1924, p. 1; *World's Work*, LV (January 1928), 10; Benjamin H. Avin: "The Ku Klux Klan, 1915–1925: A Study in Religious Intolerance," unpublished doctoral dissertation, Georgetown University, 1952, p. 27.

Though he had served as Democratic chairman of West Virginia, Shaver was an amateur: in September he told reporters that as matters then stood Davis was licked, but that the tables would turn. Shaver had only one wish for 1928: "If we could take Secretary of the Treasury [Mellon] away from the Republicans, we could win easily." Shaver's wife was an ardent prohibitionist, and her fanatical statements on the subject served to embarrass her husband and his party. When a reporter asked him in 1928 why his wife had endorsed Hoover, he replied: "Are you married?"[7]

But in the final analysis it was the convention itself, and the intraparty divisions that the convention both symbolized and widened, that spelled the doom of the Democratic party in the presidential election. One Minnesotan wrote to Roosevelt: "We defeated ourselves in New York in June." Davis himself recalled:

> They got into that North-South fight, at the end of which time the nomination wasn't worth purchase by anybody. They had to put a name on the ticket, and so they turned and put mine on. . . . Every time I'd reach out into the Eastern group personalized by Al Smith, the McAdoo group would run away from me. Then when I'd reach out and try to get the McAdoo group somewhere back into the corral, the Smith group would run away from me.[8]

[7] *Time* spoke of Shaver as the "alleged ineffectual Chairman of the Davis campaign." IV (September 29, 1924), 5. Key Pittman indicted the entire campaign staff: "From the chairman down most of them are incompetent and inexperienced." Pittman to William McKnight, October 23, 1924, Pittman Papers. For chairman, McAdoo had suggested Thomas L. Chadbourne; Smith, Thomas J. Spellacy. So Davis picked the inoffensive Shaver. Angus Campbell *et al.*: *The American Voter* (New York, 1960), pp. 156–8; *Mirrors of the Year* (New York, 1928), p. 126; *The New York Times*, June 26, 1928, p. 6; Julia Landers to Davis, November 14, 1924, Davis Papers; Breckinridge Long, manuscript diary, September 19, 1924; Robert Woolley, manuscript memoir, Chap. xxxii, pp. 18-19.

[8] H. H. Gillen to Franklin Roosevelt, December 30, 1924, Roosevelt Papers; see also Newton W. Powell to Davis, November 11, 1924, Davis Papers; Davis: Oral History Memoir, Columbia University, 1954, p. 149.

Calvin Coolidge, meanwhile, ran on a platform written almost wholly by monotonously conservative Republicans: Ogden Mills of New York, William Vare of Pennsylvania, Martin Madden of Illinois, and Reed Smoot of Utah. The President's technique was to destroy issues by ignoring them. The most ingenious argument the Republicans devised to injure Davis (whom they usually chose to overlook) was evolved by George Harvey in an article in the *North American Review*. La Follette's candidacy, Harvey maintained, would capture enough electoral votes from the other two parties to throw the presidential choice into the House, then marginally Republican. Democratic and Progressive Representatives would together prevent the selection of a President, while in the Senate, a coalition of Democrats and progressive Republicans would choose Charles W. Bryan as Vice President; and in the absence of a presidential choice, Bryan would succeed to the highest office. So argued Harvey, and the Republicans clinched this point with many voters by skillfully portraying the competent Charles Bryan as a sort of half-witted brother to the allegedly dangerous silver-tongued orator. Even those who could not understand the Republican reasoning might respond to their bizarre slogan: "A vote for La Follette is a vote for Bryan and a vote for Davis is a vote for Bryan. A vote for Coolidge is a vote for Coolidge."[9]

The 1924 election demonstrated again the chronic weakness of the Democratic party on the executive level. Coolidge won 382 electoral votes, leaving Davis with 136 in twelve states and La Follette with Wisconsin's 13. Coolidge received 15,719,921 popular votes (54.0 per cent); Davis, 8,386,704 (28.8 per cent); and La Follette, 4,988,398 (17.2 per cent). Coolidge won the eastern states and all of the West except Wisconsin. The farm states had worried the Republicans, but victory there had been

[9] George Harvey: "The Paramount Issue: Coolidge or Chaos," *North American Review*, CCXX (September 1924), 1–9. Numerous correspondents of Davis confided their fear of Charles Bryan; see, for example, Thomas W. Gregory to Davis, November 8, 1924, and James O'Donnell, November 19, 1924. See also typescript of a news conference of Nicholas Murray Butler, October 12, 1924, Davis Papers.

assured by a moderate rise in agricultural prices prior to the election. Yet the congressional returns did not sustain the appearance of Democratic decline so vividly suggested by Davis' paltry popular vote. The regular Republicans gained only twenty-one votes in the then closely divided House of Representatives. There was another somewhat encouraging sign: on the basis of counties, an important unit in party management, the Republican party showed itself weaker than in 1920 and the Democratic party stronger. Davis led in 1279 counties, a gain of 183 over Cox's in 1920, while Coolidge carried 377 counties fewer than did Harding.[1]

In the cities the voting strength of the Democrats on the presidential level was at an ebb, as it was to be in the countryside in 1928. But the Republicans also declined in the largest cities, to the advantage of La Follette. In that year the Progressive candidate won 23.6 per cent of the vote in the ten major cities, compared to his national average of 17.2 per cent. These industrial areas between Chicago and Boston went largely to Smith in 1928, but it was La Follette, not Smith, who first won the workingmen from the Republican party in great numbers. And these same workingmen, largely immigrants in the cities, had voted Republican or Socialist in their protest of 1920, or had not yet participated in any American election. The Progressive party seems to have functioned for many voters as a way station between the Republican and Democratic parties.[2]

[1] United States Bureau of the Census: *Historical Statistics*, p. 691; United States Department of Agriculture: *Yearbook of Agriculture, 1928* (Washington, D.C., 1929), pp. 686, 714, 957; Chester C. Davis to George Peek, November 8, 1924, C. C. Davis Papers; Edgar Eugene Robinson, *The Presidential Vote, 1896–1932* (Stanford, 1934), pp. 23–4.

[2] In Illinois La Follette drew most of his strength from Harding's supporters of four years before, who could well have been ethnic voters temporarily alienated from the Democracy; most of La Follette's votes went to Smith in 1928. The authors of a recent study argue that third parties prepare the way for major periods of political realignment, that the road to the Roosevelt coalition of 1936, in other words, begins in 1924. Duncan MacRae, Jr., and James A. Meldrum: "Critical Elections in Illinois: 1888–1958," *American Political Science Review*, LIV (September 1960), 674–7. Of the 230 counties that voted Republican in 1920 and

The nature of the La Follette vote is particularly revealing of the forces at work in the 1924 election. Upon which party did the Progressive candidate make heavier inroads? One might observe that fifty-eight per cent of the La Follette counties had been part of the Wilson coalition of 1916; but the Democrats in

TABLE VIII

A Comparison of the 1924 Congressional and Presidential Vote

	Dem.	Per Cent	Rep.	Per Cent	Prog.	Per Cent
House	10,676,076	42	14,818,143	58		
President	8,386,704	29	15,719,921	54	4,988,398	17

that year won normally Republican areas. The election of 1920 caught the party at its weakest point in decades. An examination of the nationwide vote in 1924 for the House of Representatives should be more telling; this more than any other constant would represent the normal Democratic and Republican strength in that year. Even these figures do not tell the full story: there is often a sectional discrepancy between presidential and congressional voting, and perhaps one party consistently received more support on one level than on another. Still the comparison, expressed in Table VIII, is a better gauge than any other election

Progressive in 1924, fifty-one moved to the Democratic column in 1928 rather than back to the GOP. (The Democratic support for La Follette does not appear in a county comparison with 1920, since much of that vote was urban and since almost every midwestern county had been Republican in that year.) A *New York Times* analyst concluded: "The prevailing opinion of political experts was that the great body of Democratic voters in the cities, mostly workers, had deserted their party's presidential candidate to vote for the Wisconsin Senator." September 16, 1928, III, 1.

figures, and it tends to confirm the statement of Major George L. Berry, the main organizer of the Democratic Labor Committee in 1924: "La Follette's entry . . . will injure the cause of the Democratic Party infinitely more than it will the Republican Party." For while the Coolidge vote fell only three per cent

TABLE IX

*Percentages of 1924 Presidential and Congressional Vote by Sections**

	Congressional Vote		Presidential Vote		
Section	DEM.	REP.	DEM.	REP.	PROG.
I New England, North Atlantic	39	61	26	61	12
II Southern and Border	60	40	57	37	6
III Middle West, Western Middle West	36	64	23	56	21
IV Far West	32	68	16	53	31

* Section I includes those states that Edgar E. Robinson designates as New England and North Atlantic; II, South Atlantic, East South-Central, and West South-Central; III, East North-Central and West North-Central; IV, Mountain and Pacific. *The Presidential Vote, 1896–1932* (Stanford, 1934), *passim.*

below the Republican House vote, that of Davis dropped fourteen per cent below the Democratic figure for the House.[3]

[3] Miss Ruth Silva reaches a similar conclusion. *Rum, Religion, and Votes: 1928 Re-examined* (University Park, Pa., 1962), p. 10. See also MacRae and Meldrum: "Critical Elections in Illinois," 677. The figures in Tables VIII and IX are computed from *Statistics of the Congressional and Presidential Election of November 4, 1924* (Washington, D.C., 1925); Berry to Senator Lee Overman, August 2, 1924, Overman Papers.

In what sections of the country did the Democrats lose most heavily to the Progressives? Table IX divides the country into sections patterned on those in Robinson's *Presidential Vote*. In New England and the North Atlantic states, La Follette appears to have drawn almost all of his support from Democratic congressional voters; most of these states included heavily industrial areas, where labor supported the Progressive candidate. In the southern and border states, La Follette obtained his small vote almost equally from the two parties. In the Middle West and Western Middle West he drew somewhat more heavily from the Democrats than from the Republicans, and in the Far West he raided a large vote from both parties, but proportionately much more from the Democrats.

Fortunately for the Democrats, the Progressive party proved to be a short-lived organization. The American Federation of Labor organ, *American Federationist*, deserted La Follette, saying that "the launching of third-party movements has proved wasted effort. . . . Experience therefore has taught labor that to be successful politically it must continue in the future, as in the past, to follow its nonpartisan policy."[4] And La Follette's death in 1925 helped seal the fate of the insurgent party—and incidentally raised the question of to what extent the radicalism of his movement may have been merely a response to his personal magnetism.

In 1924 the Democratic party was in a ruinous condition; and a good part of its difficulty lay in its very fabric, whose poorly assimilated strands of city and country tore apart in open disintegration in the convention at New York. The party incorporated the extremities in the country's population, gaining its greatest support in wholly rural districts and in the most metropolitan of cities.[5] The Republicans, on the other hand, drew their following from the more numerous districts nearer the middle of the spectrum. Even though the peculiar challenge of

[4] XXXI (December 1924), 989–90; XXXII (January 1925), 55.
[5] Arthur Holcombe: *The Political Parties of Today* (2d edn.; New York, 1925), p. 418.

the Progressives soon passed, the Democratic party was left with its most fundamental problems. To recover its soundness it would have to shape both a program and an identity that would capture at the same instant both sets of voters upon which it relied.

CHAPTER V

Franklin D. Roosevelt and Party Organization in the Twenties

The administrative structure of the national Democratic party in the twenties was ill devised to offset those forces that were working toward the party's disintegration. Possibly a national political party should not be considered a continuing organization at all but merely a succession of hierarchies, each called into being for victory in the next election. But in the decade before, the firm hand of Woodrow Wilson had for a time molded the party into a strong and active unit. Under the President's guidance, William Gibbs McAdoo in particular gave vigor and progressive direction to the national party offices. But the same malady that in Wilson's second term weakened the executive branch of the government infected the party framework as well, and disorder spread throughout the Democratic echelons. Contrasting the state of the party offices in earlier days to their condition late in 1924, a reporter observed that "the Democratic National Headquarters in Washington are as Romish catacombs or Pompeiian atriums, elegantly preserved but destitute."[1]

[1] William Hard: "The One-Party System," *The Nation,* CXIX (December 24, 1924), 703.

In the twenties authority itself was decentralized, since the party had no President who could use his office to discipline a following. The political contenders strongly backed for each coming presidential nomination shared and divided party leadership, which after the 1924 convention fell in large part to the man who became the party's choice. It was he who then chose the chairman of the national committee, shaped party policy, and controlled the meager patronage. Between campaigns the unsuccessful candidate of the preceding election normally assumed the role of titular leader, if he were thought to be available as a candidate in the next presidential race. But Cox and Davis had been defeated too decisively and Smith was too controversial to assume any substantial authority.[2]

Since the party could not look to one political leader for direction, it had to depend on its chairman and national committee, who together performed a number of functions vital to party unity. They carried the financial burden of the presidential campaigns; they provided the press with propaganda; they staged the national conventions; they even managed, so National Chairman Cordell Hull indicated, to gain the cooperation of the congressional and senatorial election committees. "Their work and ours," declared Hull at a meeting of the National Committee in 1924, "has [*sic*] been virtually merged now with the most satisfactory results."[3]

[2] Paul T. David *et al.* discuss the repositories of authority in a party out of power in *The Politics of National Party Conventions* (Washington, D.C., 1960), pp. 75–110. According to the authors, the structure of the party out of power is neither "as strong, as clear, nor as far advanced" as that of the ascendant party (p. 107). See also Richard F. Fenno, Jr.: *The President's Cabinet* (New York, 1959), p. 179. The work of political scientists is particularly valuable here inasmuch as the official Democratic party records of the 1920's were destroyed in 1946. The Democratic women's organization did issue a forerunner to today's *Democratic Digest*, but *The Bulletin*, which first appeared in 1922, restricted itself to folksy criticism of the Republicans and to news of Democratic women. Richard Linthicum helped edit the short-lived *Wilsonian*, which appeared in 1922 with articles by George Creel and Joe Tumulty. Some other fugitive literature survives.
[3] *Official Report of the Proceedings of the Democratic National Convention . . .* [of] *. . . 1924* (Indianapolis, 1925), p. 1092.

Real leadership, however, was beyond the reach of the committee. Composed of over fifty members—more than one hundred after the addition of female representatives in 1920—it was too large for effective work. Worse still, its membership was chosen by the states, and hostile rural delegates sometimes tried to sabotage the urban national chairmen. The committee gathered only when its chairman called a meeting, and would usually meet for the purpose of turning over to the chairman, whom it did not select, the task of campaign management. The national headquarters was completely beyond the control of the committee. The chairman was potentially an effective force in the out-party leadership vacuum, but in the twenties he received no salary and did not even work full time for the party. Except for the years 1921 to 1924 when Cordell Hull took command, the committee was under the direction of a succession of chairmen, none of whom performed the work that could have been accomplished. John J. Raskob actually wielded his chairmanship not as an instrument of party harmony but as a tool of the anti-prohibitionist faction. Al Smith, who was to do much to strengthen the electoral base of the party, summed up the whole matter with pardonable exaggeration when he complained that "it has been the habit of the Democratic party to function only six months in every four years."[4]

The strife between the urban and rural factions was most intense during the chairmanship of George White. Thomas B.

[4] The backgrounds and campaign activities of White and the other national chairmen of the twenties are described in the respective election commentaries. The national chairmen from 1916 to 1932 and their home states were: 1916–19, Vance C. McCormick of Pennsylvania; 1919–20, Homer Cummings of Connecticut; 1920–1, George White of Ohio; 1921–4, Cordell Hull of Tennessee; 1924–8, Clement L. Shaver of West Virginia; and 1928–32, John J. Raskob of Maryland.

Roosevelt described headquarters as "two ladies occupying one room in a Washington office building." William N. Chambers: *The Democrats, 1789–1964* (Princeton, 1964), p. 76. MS of radio address, January 16, 1928, Smith Papers; Fred L. Israel: *Nevada's Key Pittman* (Lincoln, Neb., 1963), p. 45; William R. Palmer to Franklin Roosevelt, December 7, 1928, Democratic National Committee Papers.

Love, Robert Woolley, and other McAdoo supporters, who controlled as much as two-thirds of the National Committee, tried early in 1921 to unseat White. Love and a majority of the committee members petitioned the chairman to call a meeting in March, but White's tenure was guarded by Cox, Palmer, Underwood, and Pittman, all of whom opposed McAdoo. And Bernard Baruch of New York City, a major benefactor of the party, also wanted to give White a chance. Timely donations of money from Thomas Fortune Ryan and a telegram that Baruch sent to the committee may have been influential in prolonging White's stay in office. In the summer of 1921 Cox announced his continued support of White, but by this time Baruch and his fellow financier Thomas L. Chadbourne joined in the movement to retire the national chairman. A meeting of the National Committee was called for September 21, 1921, and when it was apparent that anti-White forces had obtained enough proxies to unseat him, White resigned on September 20. Early in 1921 White had been receiving general support from urban leaders and a few important congressmen. But rural opposition—particularly strong in the National Committee where each state elected two members—determined his defeat. It must be said, however, that no matter what his affiliations White would have found his tenure under attack. In the 1920 campaign he had not been able to overcome the severe disadvantages under which his party labored, nor was he successful after the election in getting the party out of debt—here his troubles were increased by the illness of Wilbur Marsh, the party treasurer who was too sick early in 1921 to answer letters from creditors.[5]

[5] See Bernard Baruch, telegram to White, February 9, 1921; Norman Mack to White, November 15, 1920; Senator Andrew Jones to White, February 9, 1921; White to Jones, February 15, 1921; White to Arthur Krock, February 22, 1921; White to Charles E. Morris [Governor Cox's secretary], January 18, 1921; White to Frederick C. Martin, December 27, 1920; White to Wilbur Marsh, February 5, 1921, April 27, 1921, January 16, 1925, April 3, 1925; White to John W. Davis, November 4, 1921; White to Edmond Moore, November 4, 1921; George White Papers. *Literary Digest*, LXVII (February 19, 1921), 17–18; *The New York Times*, February 9, 1921, p. 15.

It was clear enough that White opposed the choice of Cordell Hull, who finally took over the chairmanship late in 1921. But Hull was sufficiently a compromise choice that White, in a letter to Edmond Moore, could describe him as "free from any domination from McAdoo." And although the prohibitionist Hull, a Tennessean, was viewed by many Democrats as closer in background to McAdoo than to his opposition—Hull had exhibited a slight preference for the former cabinet member at the 1920 convention—Carter Glass and other McAdoo men had first attempted to secure the appointment of Breckinridge Long of Missouri, Robert Woolley of Washington, D.C., or Daniel C. Roper of South Carolina; only after the failure of these candidates had McAdoo acquiesced in the choice of Hull.[6]

The selection of Hull as chairman made the party organization for the moment an effective body and a force for harmony. Hull, who later said he "took charge of the Democratic Party when it was at its lowest ebb," left the party treasury with a surplus of $30,000, after having paid off a debt of almost $300,-000. The Tennessean made many sacrifices in serving the party: in the early months of his tenure he used his own Liberty Bonds as security for party loans and personally countersigned notes for thousands of dollars. Later, he began to request bimonthly reports on political conditions in key states. Among others, Senator Samuel M. Ralston of Indiana commended Hull, praising the "high degree of efficiency" he brought to the chairmanship.[7]

[6] For the effort to remove White, see Senator Carter Glass to Robert Woolley, August 23, 1921; Woolley to Glass, September 21, 1921; Bernard Baruch to Glass, September 22, 1921; Glass to White, August 23, 1921, Box 165, Glass Papers. See also William E. Dodd to Jouett Shouse, November 15, 1921, Dodd Papers; Breckinridge Long manuscript diary, November 1, 1921; Robert Woolley to Thomas Love, November 30, 1920; Daniel C. Roper to Woolley, July 5, 1921, Woolley Papers, and Chap. xxxi, p. 23, Woolley's unpublished memoir. *The New York Times,* January 21, 1921, p. 3; January 25, 1921, p. 17; February 5, 1921, p. 10; February 7, 1921, p. 15; February 9, 1921, p. 15; February 10, 1921, p. 4; October 25, 1921, p. 17; Louisville *Times,* November 2, 1921, p. 1.

[7] Until John J. Raskob initiated his large-scale financial operations, the national Democratic party prudently avoided spending itself into bankruptcy on hopeless campaigns. Before 1928 the party debt never went over

The tenure of Hull was indicative of the growing concern of congressional Democrats—for whom Hull, formerly a senior member of the House Ways and Means Committee, was a leading spokesman—over the plight of the party organization. And when Hull was succeeded by the undynamic Clement Shaver of West Virginia, Democrats of the House and Senate increasingly stepped in to fill the breach in the national organization. William Oldfield of Arkansas, the Democratic whip and chairman of the 1924 House campaign, was put in charge of national campaign planning. In 1926 Oldfield directed all activities of the congressional campaign from the House and Senate Office Buildings, where he was assisted by a steering committee composed of Democrats from both Houses. When a party is out of power in the White House, congressmen normally serve as party spokesmen by virtue of their offices.[8]

It was during the chairmanship of Clement Shaver that the party machinery of the National Committee came nearest to a complete halt. Party headquarters became virtually inactive between 1925 and 1927, little headway was made against a substantial debt; but Shaver cut the organization to the bone in order to raise money. Though a party publication, the *National Democrat*, appeared in 1925 under the editorship of Frederick W. Steckman, the organ was soon discontinued; it failed, according to Joe Tumulty who helped to finance it, because of "con-

about $400,000, but by the end of that campaign Raskob had incurred a debt of about $1,550,000. Gerard was chairman of the party's finance committee in 1920, Jones in 1924, and Lehman in 1928. Hull: *Memoirs*, I (New York, 1948), 116; Ralston to Hull, July 24, 1924, Ralston Papers; Hull to Thomas B. Love, July 27, 1923, Love Papers; George White to J. Henry Cooke, January 30, 1924, George White Papers; Bascom N. Timmons: *Jesse H. Jones* (New York, 1956), p. 148; James W. Gerard: *My First Eighty-Three Years in America* (New York, 1951), p. 308; Allan Nevins: *Herbert H. Lehman and His Era* (New York, 1963), p. 106; *The New York Times*, November 1, 1921, p. 3; June 7, 1925, p. 1; June 12, 1926, p. 2; March 8, 1928, p. 1; Herbert H. Lehman to John J. Raskob, April 30, 1928, December 30, 1928, and June 11, 1932, Lehman Papers; Raskob to Frank J. Donahue, June 25, 1929, Raskob Papers.

[8] The changes in congressional campaigning are described in *The New York Times*, February 2, 1926, pp. 1, 6; July 11, 1926, p. 24.

flicting interests and diverging viewpoints." And the publisher, J. W. Elrod, was exposed as a former editor of the *Fiery Cross*, an Indianapolis Klan magazine, and as "chief lookout" for the Klan at the 1924 political conventions. In "about '26 or '27," recalled Florence Harriman, "the Democratic Party didn't have enough money to keep a headquarters. The Women's National Democratic Club had to take all the archives and put them in the attic of their Club House. The Committee even kept their desks there, because they couldn't afford to have an office." Yet, ineffective as he was, Shaver did help to pave the way for the candidacy of Al Smith. Formerly the campaign manager for the conservative urbanite Davis, Shaver was supported in his tenure by many wealthy eastern contributors whose adherence to the party Shaver's presence strengthened. Even though not an outright partisan of Smith, Shaver was known to be cool to McAdoo, and his appointment and long tenure alike were indicative of a fall in McAdoo's fortunes after 1924.[9]

For McAdoo's career was distinctly in an eclipse. At a time of increasing conservatism he was in some ways a conspicuous progressive; in 1928, moreover, he would be sixty-five, quite old for a presidential candidate. He lost the support of his wealthy urban friends Baruch and Chadbourne, as well as that of his mentor Daniel Roper, all of whom turned to other candidates; Baruch said after 1924 that he would never again participate in nominating battles. In addition, one of McAdoo's staunchest backers, Thomas B. Love, was experiencing his own troubles in Texas politics. When McAdoo's remaining followers attempted early in 1926 to replace Shaver with Edwin Meredith of Iowa or even the conservative J. Bruce Kremer of Montana, they had not the power to effect their will. Late in 1927 the Californian finally terminated his presidential bid; in a letter to the editor of the Chattanooga *News*, George Fort Milton, who had been

[9] *The New York Times*, July 12, 1925, pp. 1, 5; Arthur Schlesinger, Jr.: *The Crisis of the Old Order* (Boston, 1957), p. 273; MS of radio address by Alfred E. Smith, January 16, 1928, Smith Papers; Alfred Rollins, Jr.: *Roosevelt and Howe* (New York, 1962), p. 221.

McAdoo's publicity director in 1924, he explained that he wanted to avoid a repetition of the "disastrous" fight at the 1924 convention. Yet he had not resigned from interest or involvement in nomination politics; in a speech at Richmond, Virginia, early in 1928, he sharply attacked the candidacy of Smith.[1]

With the dimming of McAdoo's chances, Governor Smith's star brightened when in 1926 he and the whole New York Democratic ticket won a statewide victory. Even before that election it had been reported that Bernard Baruch was financing George Peek, the agriculturalist, in an effort to convert a crucial bloc of western farmers to the McNary-Haugen Bill—and ultimately to the Democratic nominee. By 1928 Smith led the field as clearly as had McAdoo before the oil scandals of the early twenties, and the triumph of Smith ushered in a new era for the national organization.[2]

In the hands of Smith and National Chairman John J. Raskob, the party structure took on fresh power and unity. Its unity was now, however, that of exclusion, for Raskob preached repeal and Al Smith to such an extent and in such fashion that the headquarters could be said to speak only for a sector of the party. Raskob spent about a million dollars of his own personal fortune to produce a tightly knit and intent party headquarters. He did set up an executive committee under the direction of Jouett Shouse and during the depression appointed Charles Michelson director of publicity with a full staff and a quarter of a million dollars to attack Hoover. Thanks to Raskob's generos-

[1] *The New York Times*, January 18, 1926, p. 3; January 21, 1926, p. 6; February 2, 1926, pp. 1, 6; January 30, 1927, p. 1; January 3, 1928, p. 1. Margaret Coit: *Mr. Baruch* (Cambridge, Mass., 1957), p. 372.
[2] Against the financial forces of the East, McAdoo was now powerless; Wilbur Marsh, the former party treasurer, wrote to George White in 1926: "There is one thing you can depend upon. Governor Smith can have a campaign fund, the like of which no democrat [*sic*] has ever had before." Marsh to White, April 18, 1926. White to Marsh, January 16, 1925; April 3, 1925; Marsh to White, February 28, 1925, George White Papers; Peek to Gilbert N. Haugen, April 9, 1926, Chester C. Davis Papers; Jerry C. Bryan to Clement Shaver, November 19, 1927, in Elbert Thomas Papers, "Political Information, 1927."

ity, the Democratic party had a permanently functioning national headquarters years before the Republican party did. But Raskob's circle could not address the economic hardships that beset the country after 1929 as eloquently and sincerely as could Franklin Roosevelt, the country-based aristocrat who had twice nominated Smith for the presidency. To Roosevelt belonged the future of the Democratic party.

While Democrats in Congress, unsure of their aims and their philosophy, were slipping into an ill-defined conservatism that presented no clear alternative to the well-articulated conservative policy of their Republican opponents, this important and relatively progressive Democrat was thinking hard and shrewdly about the organizational troubles of his faltering party. Late in 1924, Roosevelt prepared a circular letter dealing with the plight of the Democracy and the means to reform, and sent it to some three thousand Democrats, including all the delegates who had attended the prolonged convention of that year. He suggested to his correspondents several revisions in party structure: that the national committee or its executive machinery be made to function continuously and come in closer touch with state organizations; that publicity be extended and a sound financial base be obtained for the party; and that party leaders representing different regions meet more frequently. Roosevelt urged his readers to reply to his circular letter, for he wished to discover "what seems [sic] to be the common meeting points of Democratic minds from the North, South, East and West."³ And, of course, he also wished to remind the party members of his own existence.

The answers Roosevelt received are interesting both in their analysis of Democratic organization and in their probings into the most fundamental weaknesses of the party. On the whole the respondents were pessimistic. One sardonic letter set down four rules for future conventions to ensure the continued failure to which the party seemed to have committed itself: change the two-thirds vote needed for nomination to three-fourths or nine-

³ Quoted in Frank Freidel: *Franklin D. Roosevelt: The Ordeal* (Boston, 1954), p. 201.

tenths; hold the convention in Maine or Vermont; make the Alabama law apply everywhere, so that no delegate might vote for anyone except a favorite son; nominate no man unless his aspirations were approved by all former candidates.[4]

Upon one point the letters were in substantial agreement. They recognized that the basic cause of the party's decline was the growing disunity within its ranks. They were speaking, of course, of the social and religious antagonisms that had seized upon the Democracy; but Roosevelt's correspondents conceived these same conflicts in sectional as well as social form, and described a party splintered into three sectional components: an urban Northeast—conservative, as most of Roosevelt's correspondents viewed it; a conservative rural South; and a somewhat radical and predominantly rural West. Gavin McNab, an important California Democrat, charged that "the Democratic party is not, and under these circumstances, cannot be, affirmative. Nor can it be truly national."[5]

Many delegates who responded to Roosevelt's letter urged that Democrats in the future simply evade the dangerous issues of prohibition and the Klan, as these had been evaded by the Republicans. But such advice may have had mixed and partially defensive motives, for it came almost invariably from dry states where the Klan was strong, notably Arizona, Colorado, Georgia, and Texas. Some correspondents blamed the party politicians for the divisive effects of the Klan and prohibition; it was argued that the convention fight over the Klan had materialized only because of the selfish ambitions of the candidates, while the controversy over prohibition had emerged after relentless prodding by dry and wet fanatics. Suggestions were made that

[4] Robert Prescott to Franklin Roosevelt, January 29, 1925, Roosevelt Papers.
[5] Compare the septuagenarian Herbert Hoover's analysis of the Democratic party of the twenties: an ultraconservative South, city machines bent on plunder, and semi-socialists and fanatical agrarians. *The Memoirs of Herbert Hoover.* II: *The Cabinet and the Presidency, 1920–1933* (New York, 1952), 33–4. McNab to Roosevelt, January 16, 1925, Roosevelt Papers.

McAdoo and Smith, the personalities who represented the divergent wings of the party, be eliminated from future consideration for the presidency.

There were echoes of 1918 when western correspondents ascribed the troubles of the Democracy in great part to the eminent position of the South within the party. In the twenties the South appeared to take on a coloration even more conservative than the rest of the nation, as the tradition of southern populism disappeared or transfigured itself into the Klan; and progressive western Democrats were unhappy in their forced union with southern reaction. Despite its own strains of anti-Oriental feeling, moreover, the West was hardly prepared to sympathize with a southern racism that in the 1920's was resurgent in the Klan and in new policies of discrimination. The Californian Gavin McNab coupled southern racism to southern reaction when he observed that the "presence of the Negro has necessarily given a certain cast to Southern minds and prevents, to some extent, [the South's] complete union of thought with the rest of the nation on some governmental problems"; and McNab found the static South to be a questionable political partner to the rest of socially mobile America.[6] In fact, the popularity of La Follette's Progressive party in western Democratic territory illustrated that Democrats in the West would continue restive under conservative leadership, northern as well as southern.

The replies confirmed Roosevelt in his conviction that the Democratic party needed basic structural reform. He called for a national conference, to meet in Washington, D.C., to consider plans for making the National Committee a permanently operating organization. The suggestion won the backing of many

[6] McNab to Roosevelt, January 16, 1925, Roosevelt Papers. An Iowan reminded Roosevelt in 1929 of the continuance among middle westerners of the anti-southern feeling that had injured the Democrats in the 1918 election: "It is the prejudice against the Southern Democrats that has made this Middle West country overwhelmingly Republican." John J. Sullivan to Roosevelt, December 4, 1929, Democratic National Committee Papers.

Democrats, including Thomas J. Walsh, highly respected as a convention moderator. More generally, the idea of strengthening the Democratic organization gained great currency, as was indicated when Colonel Edward House persuaded Bernard Baruch, John W. Davis, and others to meet for the purpose of setting up an organizational framework for the 1926 congressional election. But plans for a national party conference fell through. They were destroyed not only by Shaver's lack of cooperation but also by calls from McAdoo and the Bryans for a new alliance of the West and South against the East, and the refusal of this wing of the party to participate wholeheartedly.[7]

Although his scheme of a national Democratic gathering never came to fruition, Roosevelt himself conferred with many Democrats as he traveled between his Hyde Park home and Warm Springs, Georgia, where he continued to recuperate from the poliomyelitis that had struck him in 1921. And at the smaller conferences and dinners Roosevelt's plans were given weighty consideration. Yet in spite of the New Yorker's good intentions, T.R.B. of the *New Republic* was probably not wide of the mark when he suggested that "the way to promote harmony in the Democratic party is to keep the leaders apart, not bring them together."[8]

While Roosevelt was taking his own increasingly active measures to strengthen the Democracy, other forces even more significant were at work for the rejuvenation of the party. The death of La Follette in June of 1925 had silenced talk of a permanent third party, and the liberal journals and newspapers began again to consider how to make the major parties more progressive. Much of their advice was directed at the Democratic party, and the day would come when the friendship of

[7] Louis Howe to Roosevelt, n.d., and Howe to Roosevelt, February 20, 1925, Roosevelt Papers; Alfred B. Rollins, Jr.: "The Political Education of Franklin Roosevelt, His Career in New York Politics: 1909–1928," unpublished doctoral dissertation, Harvard University, 1952, I, 793–4, 798; *New Republic*, XLIII (June 3, 1925), 46; *The New York Times*, March 21, 1925, p. 12; February 1, 1926, p. 1.
[8] XLIII (June 3, 1925), 46.

the liberal journals would be an asset to the Democrats. Further-more, in the 1926 election the Republicans retained control of the Senate by only a single vote margin.[9]

This last represented the backwash of Harding's lopsided victory of 1920, which had carried Republicans into office in normally Democratic states; for of 34 senators whose terms expired in 1926, 27 were Republicans and the remaining 7 Democrats were southerners. At least 18 of the Republican seats would have had to be classified as doubtful, and in the election most of these passed to the Democrats. But the precariousness of the Senate division after 1926—48 Republicans to 47 Democrats—does illustrate that the Democratic donkey, as in every other off-year race since 1906, was capable of delivering a spirited kick. The party, moreover, continued to gain in urban strength—the strength upon which its future successes would in large measure lie. In the 1926 election, as in 1922, the Democrats made House gains in urban areas of the country, gaining 3 seats in New York City, 1 in Newark, 2 in Chicago, 1 in Denver, 1 in Baltimore, and 1 in St. Louis; in the Senate, the Democrats won new seats in Massachusetts and New York, as well as in other traditionally Democratic states.[1]

Meanwhile, the circular letter of 1924 and the call for a national conference were enhancing Roosevelt's prestige within the party. Alfred Rollins, Jr., writes that Roosevelt's activities

[9] See, for instance, the *New Republic*, XLIII (June 24, 1925), 124; see also Julius Pratt to William E. Dodd, June 24, 1920, and Dodd to W. E. Chenery [of *The Survey*], June 16, 1920, Dodd Papers.

[1] The western Republican progessives won even more stunning victories in 1926, defeating loyal administration candidates in the primaries; it was not the revival of Democratic strength but the threat of the independents of his own party that most dismayed the Coolidge Administration. Of Smith Wildman Brookhart's victory, one columnist wrote: "If Iowa had tumbled a ton of dynamite down on the dome of the national Capitol, it could not have produced a greater explosion in Washington." Quoted in Malcolm Moos: *The Republicans* (New York, 1956), p. 359. *Congressional Directory*, Sixty-ninth Congress, 1st Sess.; Seventieth Congress, 1st Sess.; W. F. Ardis to Richard H. Lee, April 1, 1926, McKellar Papers.

helped little to clarify a national Democratic position, for he dealt in "slogans and easy compromises."[2] But with a seemingly offhand thoroughness, the country gentleman from Hyde Park, aided by Louis Howe, went about his task of building his own political reputation. He kept his name before the public by giving aid to various causes, from the Boy Scouts to the Cathedral of Saint John the Divine. His pet project was the Woodrow Wilson Foundation, which he served as chairman. Periodically he issued statements, and always he continued a voluminous correspondence that enabled him to stay in touch with his acquaintances from the Wilson Administration and the 1920 presidential campaign. And from the replies to his circular letters Roosevelt discovered what kind of man the rank and file would most readily accept as party leader.

Throughout the twenties, Roosevelt took a cautious stand somewhere between the two factions of the Democratic party. His connections with the city Democrats were at first tenuous, but they became numerous and strong. Rarely an ally of Tammany Hall while state senator, indeed an outspoken critic of one of Charles Murphy's senatorial candidates, he had nevertheless done patronage favors for Tammany during the war, had spoken at the Wigwam, and was photographed with its chief in 1917; and he had been acceptable to Murphy as candidate for the vice presidency in 1920. Though one writer describes Governor Smith's speech seconding Roosevelt in 1920 as "reluctant," the former vice presidential candidate served as a manager for Smith in 1924 and replaced him as governor of New York in 1928. At the 1924 convention it was Roosevelt who, after eighty-seven ballots, united the delegates as author of a message of sympathy to President Coolidge on the death of his son; and it was also the upstate New Yorker who made the offer of Smith's withdrawal from the convention if McAdoo should withdraw also. Roosevelt early realized how inextricably his own political future was bound to Smith's. The governor would have to have

[2] Rollins: *Roosevelt and Howe*, p. 222.

his own day in the sun before Roosevelt's ambitions could be fulfilled; and until 1928 at least, victories for Smith counted also for Roosevelt.[3]

Even clearer were Roosevelt's attachments to the country. In 1911 he had led a group of New York State Democratic Assemblymen in opposition to Tammany, and in 1914 he had aligned himself with William Gibbs McAdoo in a faction within the Wilson Administration. He voted for McAdoo on most of the roll calls in the 1920 convention, but by 1924 he had deserted McAdoo in the Californian's bid for the presidential nomination. Temporarily retired from politics because of his paralysis, Roosevelt by 1924 was harassing the party regulars of New York City as he had earlier in his career—he openly switched to Governor Smith when the oil scandals appeared to implicate McAdoo; and the sudden death of Boss Murphy of Tammany on April 25, 1924, allowed him to strengthen his commitment to Smith. Yet Roosevelt still declined to cut the ties that bound him to the rural interests; even after 1928, the upstate country squire made promises not to abandon prohibition. After becoming governor of New York in 1929, he carefully edged Smith out of his future. Roosevelt's spectacular success in 1932 testified in part to his judgment in remaining not wholly committed to either the urban or the rural faction of the party.[4]

In the mid-twenties a Tennessean wrote Roosevelt: "I believe your nomination would come nearer to uniting the Democratic party than [that of] any man in America." Though at the 1924 convention he had placed Smith's name in nomination, Roosevelt emerged from that convention a widely popular national figure. If McAdoo and Smith should deadlock again in 1928, Roosevelt would be a logical compromise candidate. And in considering whether to run for governor of New York in 1928, he

[3] Rollins: "The Political Education of Franklin Roosevelt," p. 656; *Official Report of the Proceedings* . . . [of] . . . *1924*, pp. 852–3, 888.
[4] Rollins: "The Political Education of Franklin Roosevelt," pp. 737, 739; Arthur Link: *Wilson: The New Freedom* (Princeton, 1956), p. 171; Roosevelt to John K. Sague, March 1, 1920, and Roosevelt to Donald V. Stephens, June 16, 1924, Roosevelt Papers.

surely knew to what destination that office had been a well-traveled path. As a Democrat, moreover, Roosevelt was wedded to a party sufficiently loose in structure, divided in composition, and unattached to ideology to provide an open field for fresh ideas and fresh leadership. As Arthur Holcombe observed in mid-decade: "Ambitious and realistic politicians, who aspire to bring about a realignment of parties in national politics, should find a more promising field for their operations on the Democratic side than on the Republican."[5]

[5] H. H. Gouchenour of Greeneville, Tennessee, to Roosevelt, January 8, 1924, Roosevelt Papers; Freidel: *Franklin D. Roosevelt: The Ordeal*, p. 169; Holcombe: *The Political Parties of Today* (2nd edn.; New York, 1925), p. 419.

CHAPTER VI

The Congressional Democrats

Who were the congressional Democrats in the 1920's? In the Senate they were almost entirely men who had served under Woodrow Wilson. The 54 Democrats who sat in that body between 1920 and 1928 had served an average of 17 years, and the median term of service was 16 years. Only a handful were newly elected during the twenties—not enough to alter the make-up of the Senate Democratic leadership. In addition, most of the Democratic senators, never fewer than 60 per cent, came from the southern and border states. Included among these southerners were both progressives and conservatives, men who had urged Wilson further into the realm of new legislation and still others who had acted as a brake upon the administration. In the House a majority of Democrats also were holdover southerners from the Wilson era; Finis J. Garrett of Tennessee was the minority leader, John Nance Garner of Texas was the ranking member of the Ways and Means Committee, and William Oldfield of Arkansas served as party whip. In both the Senate and House important committees and other party posts were dominated by southerners, but a greater proportion of

Democratic House than Senate members came from the eastern urban areas where the party was gaining. In 1931, after the Democrats gained control of the House, some urban Democrats were awarded key committee positions in recognition of their growing numbers.

Despite its minority status in the national legislature, the Democratic party was in a not unenviable position. Throughout the decade Republicans as well as Democrats were severely factionalized and particularly in the crucial political battleground of the Senate; a clash between eastern conservatives and western progressives damaged the relationship between the White House and Republicans in Congress and thereby weakened the party's hold upon legislation. The Democratic party, moreover, had a much stronger and initially more vigorous membership in the Congress than its desperate presidential totals would indicate. Table X illustrates the strength of the party, particularly in off-year elections, in the state houses as well as in Congress. "When it comes," wrote Walter Lippmann, "to electing Governors, Senators, Congressmen, Mayors and the like, the Democrats are very much stronger than they are in Presidential elections. The record shows clearly that only rarely do the Democrats succeed in making a national showing equal to the sum of their local victories. They are a party which is much stronger in its parts than as a whole. . . ."[1]

Yet in the Congress as in the nation at large, antagonisms between city and country prevented a united Democratic party from flourishing. This division is revealed in the votes on the sectional issues of McNary-Haugen and Muscle Shoals, and, in 1919, on the Volstead Act. During a discussion of government

[1] Edgar Eugene Robinson wrote in 1920 that "the growth of definiteness of division within the Republican party membership in Congress has been one of the outstanding developments of the past two decades." *New Republic*, XXIV (November 3, 1920), 239. George H. Mayer: *The Republican Party, 1864–1964* (New York, 1964), p. 394; Andrew Sinclair: *Prohibition: The Era of Excess* (Boston, 1962), pp. 21–3; Mark Sullivan to Joseph M. Dixon, April 10, 1923, Sullivan Papers; Lippmann: *Interpretations, 1931–1932* (New York, 1932), p. 256.

ownership of Muscle Shoals, nativist Senator Dial of South Carolina blamed his party's ills specifically on its immigrant faction:

TABLE X

Party Strength in Percentages: Elections of 1920 Through 1930*

	House	Senate	Governor
1920	R70	61	56
	D30	39	44
†1922	R52	54	46
	D48	46	54
1924	R57	59	44
	D43	41	56
†1926	R55	52	50
	D45	48	50
1928	R62	59	56
	D38	41	44
†1930	R49	51	38
	D51	49	62

* United States Bureau of the Census, *Historical Statistics of the United States* (Washington, D.C., 1960), p. 691; *World Almanac* (New York, 1920–1928).
† Off-year elections.

We have infected ourselves and our party with political miasma and pestilence, brought here from fetid and sickening atmospheres of the old countries. We have permitted the great Democratic Party to be degraded and used by a small alien faction. . . . The Democratic Party must declare whether it will serve high, straight, outspoken American Democracy or some kind of shambling, bastard, shame-faced mixture of so-called Democracy and alien-conceived bolshevism or socialism or hell broth of all.[2]

The philosophy of the congressional Democrats underwent a transformation between 1921 and 1928. In the first two Congresses, a formidable alliance developed between the minority Democrats and a vigorous group of western progressive Republicans; in its handling of the administration's domestic program, this bipartisan bloc thoroughly frustrated President Harding and on numerous occasions stymied his successor, President Coolidge. William Jennings Bryan called the Congress elected in 1922 "the most progressive . . . we have had in years. . . . The Democratic Party in that Congress made the most progressive record that the Democratic Party had made since I have been acquainted with politics." The election returns of 1922 seemed a mandate for reform; and Bryan favored a permanent alliance of Democrats with progressive Republicans. But after the disastrous 1924 election, the older congressional Democrats specifically blamed their party's poor showing on its flirtation with radicalism, and many of the newer urban Democrats had no special attachment to the principles of the Republican insurgents. As a result, after 1924 Democrats more and more followed the lead of Coolidge and the Republican majority, and they nearly severed their relations with the western radicals.[3]

The shift in sentiment is apparent in an examination of vot-

2 Dial's speech, later stricken from the galleys of the *Congressional Record*, is quoted in *The New York Times*, January 4, 1925, p. 18.
3 When the Democrats in 1925 voted with the insurgents against confirming a Coolidge cabinet appointee, they staunchly denied engaging in an alliance. *The New York Times*, March 19, 1925, pp. 20, 25. *Official Report of the Democratic National Convention . . . [of] . . . 1924* (Indianapolis, 1925), p. 531; *The Nation*, CXVIII (June 18, 1924), 697, 701; *The New York Times*, March 10, 1924, p. 1; November 20, 1924, p. 1; January 6, 1925, p. 27; March 19, 1925, p. 20; November 6, 1925, p. 27; December 19, 1925, p. 1; December 20, 1925, p. 1; January 13, 1926, p. 1; February 1, 1926, pp. 1–2; February 2, 1926, pp. 1, 6; May 10, 1926, p. 11.

ing; but care must be taken in such an analysis. Finding the key vote on any given bill may itself be a delicate process; often a motion to recommit, rather than the final roll call, is the critical test on a bill. Then, too, the motive behind a vote may be obscure. A congressman may try to placate some of his constituents by voting for a measure he in fact opposes if he is sure it is destined for burial; or he may dissent in the final conference report after having supported some parts of a bill. Whole tallies may be unreliable if a party is committed to a similar goal but through different means, or in its voting one party may be trying to embarrass the other. And many votes, particularly in the House, go unrecorded under the pressure of time, or because it is cumbersome and expensive to print them; finally, the members by common consent may agree not to publish a roll call. Even the definition of progressive is often different in succeeding generations; for present purposes we can consider as progressive or liberal a measure so designated in the political rhetoric of the times.

The evolution during the decade of a congressional tax policy reveals a conservative trend among House and Senate Democrats. The progressivism of the Democrats in Congress during the early twenties set itself against the administration view. In his message to the Sixty-seventh Congress (1921–3), Andrew Mellon, the Republican Secretary of the Treasury, advocated repeal of the excess profits and estate taxes and reductions of levies on incomes, especially surtaxes on large incomes, to be replaced by levies on items as diverse as automobiles and bank checks. The excess profits tax was removed by a narrow margin in both Houses; most Democrats wanted to keep the tax, but its prospective demise had received the approval even of *The Nation* and James Cox had spoken against it in the 1920 campaign. Many Democrats, however, apparently favored high taxes upon the wealthy, for the rest of Mellon's program met firm opposition, especially in the Senate. Senator Furnifold Simmons, minority spokesman of the Senate Finance Committee, protested that under Mellon's program "the corporations and the ultra-rich" would pass their taxes on to the less fortunate. Senate Democrats contributed 22 of their 36 votes to pass a bill raising the tax to 25 per cent on gifts over $100,000; no Democrats opposed the rise, which was later dropped in conference. But the main issue concerned the setting of a surtax on incomes over $500,000. The administration proposed a gradual reduction from 65 to 25 per cent. The radical Senate Republicans, supported by 24 Democratic votes—or two thirds of that party's contingent, and again with no Democrats in opposition— wrote their own tax bill and forced on the administration a 50 per cent surtax on high incomes and a slight increase in corporation taxes to make up for the elimination of the tax on excess profits. Ninety-nine per cent of the 116 House Democrats who voted concurred in the high surtax. It was hardly a triumph for the conservatives whose candidate had won an overwhelming victory in the 1920 election.[4]

The next Congress, in which Democrats were more numerous, showed still greater resistance to Mellon's proposals. When Mellon called for a sharp decrease of the federal estate tax and reductions for all incomes, surtax rates to be lowered to 25 per cent in the highest bracket, Democrats and insurgent Republicans in both the Senate and House joined ranks against the Mellon program. Henry T. Rainey, a Ways and Means Committee Democrat, called it a "rich man's bill." The Senate by a vote of 43 to 40—29 Democrats contributing to the victory— maintained the surtax on high incomes at 40 per cent and reduced it substantially on small and middle incomes. "We may even have to go higher [than 40 per cent]," Simmons warned, "to satisfy our allies [the radical Republicans]." All but six

[4] After Mellon's defeat *The New York Times* stated that "militant progressivism is in control in Congress, and the Republican party is without direction in its most important legislative policies. . . ." October 20, 1921, p. 14. See also September 28, 1921, p. 1; October 1, 1921, p. 15; October 23, 1921, p. 14; October 27, 1921, p. 21; November 8, 1921, pp. 1, 7. A correspondent of Senator Pat Harrison complained about two parties, each ruled by "half a dozen radicals." J. H. Weston to Harrison, January 5, 1924, Harrison Papers. *Congressional Record, Senate,* October 22, 1921, p. 6648; November 7, 1921, pp. 7486–7; *House,* August 20, 1921, p. 5358.

Democrats in the House, where a published roll call was omitted on the proposal, were reported to favor the higher surtax figure advanced by Representative John Nance Garner, a leading opponent of Mellon's plan. About 31 Senate Democrats aided the passage of amendments opening income tax returns and claims for abatement or refund of taxes to public inspection. Congress further thwarted the administration by raising estate taxes from 25 to 40 per cent and levying a gift tax; the progressive Republican-Democratic coalition forced each of the two proposals to be adopted by common consent in the Senate, and in the House Democrats contributed most of their votes for them. William Gibbs McAdoo congratulated the Democratic legislators for standing firm on taxes; Judge Gary of United States Steel observed that "the worst thing we have at the present time is our American Congress."[5]

The 1924 election, in which John W. Davis won only 29 per cent of the total vote, demoralized the congressional Democrats. Failing to consider the extent to which the La Follette vote may have been in fact Democratic and liable to return to its allegiance, many of the faithful feared that the Democracy was traveling the road to obscurity. Predictions of like nature had been appearing for some time. In 1914 Edgar Eugene Robinson had observed: "If the decline in Democratic majorities continues in the future as it has since 1896, it is only a matter of time when conviction will overcome habit and the Democratic Party will disappear." The election of 1920 seemed on the surface to mark a further point in the same trend; and after the 1924 election one of Roosevelt's urban correspondents wrote: "The drift to this bad condition began in 1896 and, with

[5] The Democrats had been aided in January 1924 by a crucial rules victory in the House. *Congressional Record, Senate*, May 2, 1924, pp. 7692–3; May 5, 1924, p. 7849; *The New York Times*, December 30, 1923, p. 1; January 7, 1924, pp. 1, 3; January 9, 1924, p. 23; January 14, 1924, p. 1; February 14, 1924, p. 1; February 25, 1924, p. 1; February 26, 1924, p. 1; March 31, 1924, p. 6; April 11, 1924, pp. 1, 6; May 6, 1924, p. 1; May 8, 1924, pp. 1–2; May 11, 1924, IX, 3. Judge Gary is quoted in Randolph E. Paul: *Taxation in the United States* (Boston, 1954), p. 137.

the exception of a slight reaction during the Wilson Administration, has continued to the present time." Herbert Croly in the *New Republic* warned that the Democratic party in America would follow the path of England's Liberal party. Careful observers knew that the two-party system was far from extinct, but the Democrats in Congress were understandably frightened by the immediate prospects.[6]

In the shadow of its overwhelming defeat, the congressional Democracy, particularly in the Senate, for the most part adapted itself to the business temperament of the decade. When Secretary Mellon in December of 1925 recommended a further tax cut of $330 million, the Democrats on the Senate Finance Committee countered with a figure of $500 million. Democrats had earlier proposed great reductions in taxes on middle and lower incomes; but the Senate Democratic program now included an additional $93 million reduction in taxes on corporation capital stock and a further cut of $54 million on surtaxes for men with incomes between $20,000 to $1,000,000—men of moderate means, Senator Simmons of the Finance Committee called them. The last adjustment was "to make businessmen realize that the Democratic Party is not bent on taxing them or their enterprises exorbitantly." The Democratic plan made no mention at all of publicity for income tax payments, or of the gift tax, which was totally abandoned, or of estate taxes, which—with Democratic aid and in direct opposition to a plea from the Progressives—were later cut in half. Though western Republicans in the Senate joined the regulars to defeat key parts of the Democratic proposal, the Democrats' eagerness for tax cuts did cause the administration to make more reductions than it had intended. Charging that a deal had been made between the regulars and the minority party, Senator

[6] O. Douglas Weeks wrote after the election of 1928: "The Democratic party . . . seems to be nationally dead." *Southwestern Political and Social Science Quarterly*, IX (December 1928), 337. *American Journal of Sociology*, XV (November 1914), 334; William Foster to Roosevelt, January 26, 1925, Box 11, Circular Letter, Roosevelt Papers; *New Republic*, XLV (December 10, 1924), 10.

Norris of Nebraska commented sarcastically that the Democrats were entitled to greater campaign contributions for their share in "relieving wealth from taxation." Senator Lenroot of Wisconsin told the Democrats that they were "out-Melloning Mellon"; and Senator Reed, the Missouri Democrat, observed that "the poor old Democratic mule is being led in by the ear and Mr. Mellon's hand holds the ear."[7]

The votes in the Congresses from 1925 to 1928 clearly reflected the shift in Democratic sentiment. In the Sixty-ninth Congress (1925–7), only four out of forty Senate Democrats voted against keeping the maximum surtax at 40 per cent. No more than thirteen Democrats joined sixteen insurgent Republicans who proposed to graduate the rate to a maximum of 30 per cent; ten voted with thirteen western Republicans against the lowering of estate taxes; four, along with nine Republicans, wanted gifts of over $25,000 to be counted as gross income. Mellon's biographer noted: "The great difficulty with this Congress was to restrain its members, who had seen a great light on last election day, from voting a deficit in the treasury." Democrats vied with Republicans in cutting rates. In the House

[7] President Coolidge had entertained Senator Oscar W. Underwood at the White House after the 1924 election, an act viewed by some as evidence of a conciliatory spirit. At first Democrats had been divided over the tax program presented by the Senate leadership, but most of them eventually backed it as a party measure. Senator Pat Harrison opposed both estate and inheritance taxes and stood against any increase in the corporation tax in 1926. Senator Wheeler wrote of Harrison: "The trouble is . . . that the Democratic leader has simply turned the bill over to the Republican side, and the Democrats are now asked to follow the Republican leader." *Kiplinger Washington Letter*, December 12, 1924, and November 8, 1926; Harrison to Carl Marshall, January 23, 1926, Harrison Papers. Comments by Senators Wheeler, Norris, Reed, Lenroot, Norbeck, and others on the Democratic about-face are in the *Congressional Record*, February 3, 1926, pp. 3219, 3221–4; June 15, 1926, p. 11289; February 4, 1927, pp. 2925–31. *The New York Times*, June 15, 1925, p. 14; September 11, 1925, p. 1; November 20, 1925, p. 1; November 26, 1925, p. 1; January 5, 1926, p. 4; January 6, 1926, p. 2; January 11, 1926, pp. 1–2; January 12, 1926, p. 2; January 19, 1926, p. 1; February 2, 1926, pp. 1, 6; February 4, 1926, p. 25; February 11, 1926, p. 1; January 28, 1927, p. 3; February 4, 1927, p. 1.

Democrats were not yet of one mind on the matter of taxes; in 1926 Garner even managed to save the estate tax by reducing its highest rates. But in the first session of the Seventieth Congress—the last to meet before the stock market crashed—almost all Democrats, in company with the United States Chamber of Commerce, continued to clamor for reductions beyond the wishes of President Coolidge. In calling for an immediate reduction of half a billion dollars, Garner and Simmons undoubtedly spurred the speculative fever of the later 1920's. They specifically voted for a further surtax reduction on intermediate incomes and a lowering of corporation and consumption taxes. But except for a reduction in the corporation levy, these last proposals met with slight success, for now the Republican regulars were standing solidly with the western bloc of their party in opposition to cuts. In a crucial test the Republican progressives and regulars voted as a matter of principle to use the tax surplus to reduce the national debt; all but one Democrat opposed the motion, which carried. Later in the sessions heavy Democratic majorities failed to repeal taxes on original issues of capital stock or to lower the stock transfer tax, though the Democrats and Republican regulars defeated a La Follette attempt to publicize tax returns. In the House of Representatives roll calls on tax measures continued to be sparse, but in December 1927, Democrats voted to lower the corporation tax more than Mellon had recommended, though at the same time they voted along progressive lines on some issues. In their efforts to graduate taxes on small corporations they seemed to retain their identity as Wilsonian Democrats.[8]

On another financial issue, the tariff, Democrats in the con-

[8] *Congressional Record, Senate,* February 3, 1926, p. 3221; February 10, 1926, p. 3696; February 12, 1926, p. 3850; February 4, 1927, p. 2931; May 10, 1928, pp. 8279–80; May 12, 1928, pp. 8508, 8518; May 14, 1928, p. 8622; May 19, 1928, p. 9175; May 25, 1928, p. 9854; *House,* December 18, 1925, pp. 1164–5; December 15, 1927, p. 716; *The New York Times,* June 11, 1927, p. 18; October 24, 1927, p. 20; January 29, 1928, p. 1; April 5, 1928, p. 13; April 6, 1928, p. 16; April 20, 1928, p. 9; April 27, 1928, p. 6; May 11, 1928, p. 44; May 26, 1928, p. 1; Harvey O'Connor: *Mellon's Millions* (New York, 1933), p. 140.

gressional sessions of 1921 and 1922 adhered to the traditional philosophy of their party. They stood against the Fordney-McCumber bill, with its high rates in face of the struggling European economy, and termed the bill "irredeemably and universally vicious." Senator Underwood and William Gibbs McAdoo added that the tariff would raise the cost of living at home; other Democrats argued that a high tariff made it difficult for Europeans to repay outstanding loans. But on this issue western and eastern Republicans were of one mind, and the small contingent of Democrats in the Sixty-seventh Congress was powerless to stop them. In the Senate 22 Democrats—16 of them from the South—and only 3 Republicans voted against the bill, and in the House 70 Democrats—61 from the South—were joined in their opposition by 21 Republicans. Only 9 House or Senate Democrats voted for the tariff measure. Until about 1924 Democrats continued their attack on the tariff, but in the later Congresses they tended to be less outspoken on the issue. In the matter of the tariff, the Democratic platform of 1928 was similar in its vagueness to the Republican. Even in 1930, after the onset of the depression, Democratic opposition to the Smoot-Hawley bill was weaker than it had been earlier in the decade.[9]

Upon other issues Democrats in Congress rarely made a united and energetic effort for progressive legislation. Often purely sectional considerations restrained many Democrats from making common cause with progressive Republicans, or even others of their own party. Senator Key Pittman of Nevada observed that during this period "localism had replaced the broad Wilsonian slogans. . . ."[1] On the issue of agricultural reform, for

[9] *Congressional Record, Senate,* June 2, 1922, pp. 7992–5; August 19, 1922, p. 11627; March 24, 1930, p. 6015; *House,* September 15, 1922, p. 12718; May 1, 1930, pp. 8148–9; *The New York Times,* April 4, 1922, p. 19; May 7, 1922, p. 16; June 11, 1922, VII, 1; August 16, 1922, p. 1; *The Nation,* CXIII (July 20, 1921), 61.

[1] Certainly little Wilsonianism was present in Democratic attitudes on foreign policy. G. L. Grassmuck has shown that Democrats were usually less favorable to internationalist legislation than Republicans in the 1920's. *Sectional Biases in Congress on Foreign Policy* (Baltimore, 1951), pp. 32–

example, divisions appeared within the party most notably between South and West but also between city and country.

Agricultural legislation during the twenties may be attributed in considerable part to the American Farm Bureau Federation, which entered politics in May 1921. Under the leadership of its secretary Gray Silver, the nonpartisan Farm Bureau devised an effective method to make its point in Washington: it periodically sent questionnaires on farm problems to its members and distributed the responses to the appropriate congressmen. The work of the Bureau contributed significantly to the formation of a farm bloc in May 1921; it was especially effective in the Senate of the Sixty-seventh Congress, where the bloc was composed of 15 Republicans and 12 Democrats, 9 of them from the South. The Farm Bureau underwent a brief decline when it turned its principal attention from legislation to cooperative marketing; but by 1926, when Chester Gray replaced Silver as secretary and Sam Thompson succeeded O. E. Bradfute as president, it had returned to the legislative field, throwing its full weight behind the controversial McNary-Haugen bill.[2]

In the early days of the Bureau and the farm bloc, Democratic legislators from the South and West worked in substantial harmony with each other and with their Republican colleagues from agricultural areas. But on the question of McNary-Haugen, rural Democrats divided, and their contribution never equalled that of the Republican adherents of the measure. In addition, some of the most powerful opponents of McNary-Haugen were Democrats, including Congressmen James B. Aswell of Louisiana and David H. Kinchelow of Kentucky. When in 1924 the new farm bill came to a vote in the House, it contained provisions that would chiefly benefit wheat and hog growers of the western states. Farm organizations, moreover, gave it

---

70, 97 ff. Pittman is quoted in Fred L. Israel: *Nevada's Key Pittman* (Lincoln, Neb., 1963), p. 49.

[2] Grant McConnell: *The Decline of Agrarian Democracy* (Berkeley, 1953), pp. 57 ff.; Orville M. Kile: *The Farm Bureau Through Three Decades* (Baltimore, 1948), pp. 92–113; 136–51; *The New York Times*, August 28, 1921, p. 1.

slight support. As a result, a mere 48 Democrats—only 23 from the South, where cotton prices were reasonably high—voted for the bill, as against 107 Republicans, and it failed to pass. In May 1926, a revised and somewhat more feasible McNary-Haugen bill was again defeated in the House but 17 additional Democrats favored the measure. In the Senate, where only 14 Democrats supported the bill when it first came to a vote, its southern supporters were few and unenthusiastic. The objection of the southerners was to the tariff principle bolstered in the bill; cotton, the main southern crop, was exported in much larger quantity than was the agricultural produce of the West, and on this issue the South maintained its traditional antagonism to protection. Senator Carter Glass of Virginia, for example, declared the measure unconstitutional and discriminatory against the South; he suggested that a reduction of the tariff would help the farmer more. When cotton and rice prices declined late in 1926, however, the South did come to favor McNary-Haugen, but only as part of a sectional bargain, in which cotton—included for a time in the first bill—rice, and tobacco were also added to the list of price-supported crops, and westerners gave needed backing to proposals for fertilizer production at Muscle Shoals.[3]

On February 11, 1927, 24 Republicans and 22 Democrats joined to pass a new version of McNary-Haugen in the Senate, and the House followed suit on February 27, 214 to 178, with 113 Republicans, 97 Democrats, and 4 Independents in favor. In each house southern Democrats now gave the bill a heavy majority of their votes. In 1928, after Coolidge had vetoed the bill of 1927, Congress modified it to meet the criticisms of the

[3] *Congressional Record, House,* May 20, 1924, p. 9052; June 3, 1924, pp. 10340–1; May 21, 1926, p. 9862; *Senate,* June 15, 1926, p. 11289; June 22, 1926, pp. 11735–52; June 24, 1926, p. 11872; *Congressional Digest,* I (June 1922), 4; *The New York Times,* February 2, 1926, p. 1; June 25, 1926, p. 1; *North American Review,* CCXXI (1925), 417–30; John D. Hicks and Theodore Saloutos: *Agricultural Discontent in the Middle West, 1900–1939* (Madison, Wisc., 1951), pp. 321–403; Gilbert C. Fite: *George N. Peek and the Fight for Farm Parity* (Norman, Okla., 1954), pp. 64, 67–8, 71, 78, 91.

administration and then adopted it again. On this occasion, when strategy dictated a test on whether to retain the controversial equalization fee, 27 Senate Democrats voted with 19 Republicans to form a margin of 46 to 31; in the House 91 Democrats, along with 94 Republicans, hard-pressed by the White House to vote differently, supported the measure, which was again vetoed by the Republican President. But it was not the Democrats who could claim leadership in the agrarian protest that had crystallized into the battle for the McNary-Haugen scheme; the honor belongs to the progressive Republicans of the West. Many Democrats were chiefly interested only in embarrassing the President.[4]

In the determination of a progressive congressional policy on Muscle Shoals, a hydroelectric project in the northern Alabama basin of the Tennessee River Valley, the southern Democrats played a more important role than they did over the issue of McNary-Haugen. The project had been initiated during the war to insure an adequate supply of nitrates, for which we had previously relied upon Chile. In 1920 Congress shunned the pleas of Bernard Baruch and others to make Muscle Shoals into a government-owned fertilizer plant, and the whole problem was a subject of congressional fumbling for the remainder of the decade.

In 1922 Henry Ford, then alleged to be a Democratic presidential aspirant, made an equivocal but sweeping offer to lease the area from the government and develop it into a great new Detroit for the benefit of the American people. Southern Democrats were sympathetic to Ford's proposal, as they had been to the plan for government ownership, and President Coolidge thought it an excellent idea. But the West was more interested in development of the St. Lawrence Seaway, and only after prolonged agitation by the Farm Bureau did Ford's proposal for cheap production of fertilizer attract widespread support. Ford's bid

[4] *Congressional Record, Senate*, February 11, 1927, p. 3518; April 27, 1928, pp. 6278–9; *House*, August 20, 1921, p. 5358; February 17, 1927, p. 4099; May 3, 1928, pp. 7770–2; *The New York Times*, February 4, 1927, p. 7; February 12, 1927, pp. 1, 5; February 13, 1927, p. 1.

drew opposition, however, both from representatives of the power trust and from progressives who feared the possibility that the project would be exploited in violation of the Water Power Act of 1920 and its real conservationist values neglected. Also, the Teapot Dome scandals made legislators uneasy about government leases, and Ford seemed more interested in cheap electricity than in producing fertilizer. Ford himself added little to his cause when he denounced his opponents as the international Jews of Wall Street. In 1924 a bill embodying the Ford offer passed the House—with 90 per cent of the Democrats supporting it—but not the Senate. Recognizing the fact of congressional deadlock, Ford finally withdrew his offer.[5]

The fight was now joined between Senator Norris, who advocated public operation for flood control and cheap power, and Democratic Senator Oscar W. Underwood of Alabama, who sponsored a plan of the Coolidge Administration for leasing by private power interests. Norris held the spotlight: he hinted darkly of foreign control of the Alabama Power Company, and he exposed an offer from thirteen power companies as being in fact nothing other than the overture of one giant combine dominated by General Electric. Early in 1925 Norris failed in his attempt to substitute his proposal for government ownership; fewer than half of the Democrats supported the Republican Senator. Yet seizing upon a technicality in the conference report of the House and Senate committees, Norris succeeded in dealing to the Underwood measure, which allowed Coolidge to lease the property, a crippling delay. "We defeated [Muscle Shoals] even without a filibuster," he said later, "because it was known and believed by those who were behind the legislation

---

[5] Urban Democrats claimed that Ford's presidential candidacy was designed to pressure Congress into leasing Muscle Shoals to him. *The New York Times*, November 16, 1923, p. 1. *Congressional Record, House*, March 10, 1924, p. 3927; Preston J. Hubbard: *Origins of the TVA: The Muscle Shoals Controversy, 1920–1932* (Nashville, 1961), pp. 128 ff.; Jerome G. Kerwin: *Federal Water-Power Legislation* (New York, 1926), pp. 270–83; Judson King: *The Conservation Fight* (Washington, D.C., 1959), pp. 100, 103, 116, 124.

that we would filibuster." Senator Robinson, the Democratic minority leader, acidly attacked La Follette's Muscle Shoals plan all through the twenties. But by late 1926 Norris was probably right to observe that "the sentiment of the people is gradually turning our way"—though perhaps the shift in feeling represented chiefly a frustration at the failure of the national legislature to adopt any plan. In 1928 enough southern Democrats, realizing that the only possibility of action lay in the Norris plan, joined with western Republicans to pass a bill for government operation of Muscle Shoals. Twenty-seven Democrats voted Aye as did 21 Republicans, and 121 House Democrats joined 90 Republicans to send the bill to President Coolidge, who gave it a pocket veto. In his fight Norris had received needed support from some Democrats: Wheeler and Walsh of Montana and Dill of Washington, as well as McKellar of Tennessee and other southerners; and sectional needs forced many other Democrats to the progressive side. But as in the battle over McNary-Haugen, western Republicans had provided the initiative and leadership; some Democrats favored both bills for purely partisan reasons. The willingness of southern Democrats to support both private and public power bills indicated that development itself, not the method used, was uppermost in their minds.[6]

Democrats in the big cities seemed no more reform-minded than their rural counterparts. Though the small but expanding contingent of urban Democrats was progressive enough to vote almost solidly in favor of high surtaxes in 1921, and even in 1925 gave a strong majority for a similar motion, the McNary-Haugen bills of the decade never received more than fifteen per cent of the city Democratic vote. The 1928 conference report on Muscle Shoals received the support of only one-half of the urban Democrats. After the Great Depression, that con-

[6] Hubbard: *Origins of the TVA, passim;* King: *The Conservation Fight,* pp. 138, 156, 175; Alfred Lief: *Democracy's Norris* (New York, 1939), pp. 277, 295; *Kiplinger Washington Letter,* December 19, 1924; *Congressional Record, Senate,* January 8, 1925, pp. 1449–50; March 13, 1928, p. 4635; *House,* May 25, 1928, p. 9957; Norris to W. L. Locke, March 12, 1925, Norris Papers, Nebraska Historical Society.

tingent evidently became more radical on public power, giving majority support to a crucial bill in 1931; but they overwhelmingly favored the manufacturer's sales tax as a solution to the financial problems of 1932.[7]

In the 1920 and 1924 elections the AFL and many other labor groups had been able to see little difference between Republicans and Democrats. But in 1926 the mild William Green of the AFL wrote of the House Democratic leader: "Representative Garrett has not lost an opportunity during his long session in Congress to antagonize most bitterly every important measure that has been introduced in that body in the interest of labor. . . . He has used his position as leader of the minority to hamper and discredit bills of great importance to not only the wage earners but the people generally." Yet the organized worker could hardly complain: enjoying prosperous times, labor itself hewed to the conservatism of the decade. Mesmerized by attractive business paternalism, it confined itself mostly to protests against the use of the injunction and to some relatively ineffective lobbying in Washington.

In the late twenties, the viewpoint of the congressional Democrats remained for the most part provincial, divided, and predominantly conservative. Their votes on the tax bills clearly demonstrated their mood; their friendliness toward business was also apparent when in 1926 Democratic leaders attacked Coolidge for spending four times as much money as had President Wilson ten years earlier. By 1928 it had indeed become plain that the congressional Democrats of that day bore little trace of the crusading zeal that had been present during the Wilson Administration. "Congressionally," wrote the farm

[7] All 21 members of the Tammany delegation at first declared themselves in favor of the sales tax; on the vote itself they divided themselves 16 for and 5 against. *The New York Times,* March 17, 1932, pp. 1, 4. *Congressional Record, House,* August 20, 1921, p. 5539; March 10, 1924, p. 3927; December 18, 1925, p. 1164; May 3, 1928, p. 7771; May 25, 1928, p. 9957; February 20, 1931, p. 6666; *The New York Times,* March 25, 1932, p. 3.

correspondent Lynn Haines, "the Democratic record is not an asset for 1928"; he complained that the labors of Democrats in the House and Senate recently have not been "constructive or coherent or consistent or courageous." The Democratic record in Congress blended well with its conservative party platform of 1928: in that year the League for Independent Political Action concluded that "today in the United States there is no vital party of opposition. Democrats in the election of 1928 revealed the fact that they have not one fundamental economic issue to distinguish them from the Republicans." But it was not among Democrats alone that the reform impulse had begun to fade. Even the Republican progressives appeared late in the decade as tired liberals drained of their energies. Except on the special issues of Muscle Shoals and McNary-Haugen—and even here the veto had sufficed to stalemate the battle—the conservative Republicans had routed their opposition.[8]

The depression years brought with them an unprecedented challenge to the congressional Democrats. True to their recently deepened conservatism, they were slow to develop programs in alternative to Hoover's. After the 1930 elections, Speaker of the House John Nance Garner and Senate minority leader Joseph T. Robinson joined with Cox, Davis, Smith, Raskob, and Jouett Shouse, head of the Democratic Executive Committee, in assuring the public that Democrats would cooperate with President Hoover and not countenance "dangerous" legislation. Widely applauded by businessmen, the offer, complained the *New Republic*, would insure the failure of progressive legislation. But Hoover, who blamed the Senate for "playing politics at the expense of human misery," was himself too partisan and

[8] Senator Peter Norbeck wrote to a friend: "The *American Mercury* article is making quite a sensation around here because much of it is true." Quoted in Reinhard H. Luthin: "Smith Wildman Brookhart of Iowa: Insurgent Agrarian Politician," *Agricultural History*, XXV (October 1951), 194. *American Mercury*, XVI (April 1929), 385–93; Haines: "Al Smith and Certain Soothsayers," unpublished manuscript in the Chester C. Davis Papers, 1928.

tactless to work with the Democrats; and the leaders, at the behest of Democratic senators, eventually repudiated their statement. Yet the very kind of coalition the liberals feared had already passed the Hawley-Smoot tariff in 1930. According to John Dewey: "The Democratic party . . . was, on the whole, an accomplice to the passage of the bill, passive and even active." Five Democratic votes in the Senate salvaged the measure there; but even more striking is the action of about seventeen Democratic senators who voted for high rates on coal, oil, copper, and lumber. After the tariff vote *The Nation* cynically observed that the Democratic party differed from the Republican "only in that its desire to become the party of privilege has never been satisfied."[9]

The crucial issue before the Seventy-second Congress was that of taxation, for the demand of the economic emergency were draining the Treasury. In January 1932, Senators Robinson and Harrison warned that a radical increase in taxes would be "disturbing to business." Because of his fiery attacks on Secretary of the Treasury Mellon, John Nance Garner was considered by many to be a dangerous radical; but "Cactus Jack," who gave up his official car to dramatize his interest in economy, decided to promote the safe and sane measures of President Hoover. On the critical question of revenue, Garner agreed with Republican leaders to support a manufacturer's sales tax (in the early twenties he had opposed such a tax). His action was an admission of the failure of the Democratic congressional leadership to provide an alternative to the policies of the Republican administration; for example, the Democrats were uninterested in overtures by progressive Republicans who wanted to vote a raise in corporation taxes. The sales tax received enthusiastic

[9] Of Robinson even Smith wrote: "He has given more aid to Herbert Hoover than any other Democrat." Ray T. Tucker: *The Mirrors of 1932* (New York, 1931), p. 130. *New Republic*, LXV (November 19, 1930), 4–5; (December 17, 1930), 137; (December 24, 1930), 164; LXVI (March 25, 1931), 151; *The Nation*, CXXXII (January 28, 1931), 60; *The New York Times*, March 27, 1932, p. 1; Lippmann: *Interpretations*, p. 136.

backing from the national Democratic organization, and from Senator Robinson, who was preaching radical economies in public expenditures. Robinson's chief fear was the dole, and with his encouragement Senate Democrats contributed about forty per cent of the votes cast against the La Follette-Costigan relief bill late in February. In early March the *New Republic* mourned: "Up to this date we have had the spectacle of the Democratic party in the House and Senate voting with almost complete solidarity in favor of . . . one Hoover recommendation after the other. . . . The plain fact is that the Democratic party is at heart just as conservative as its opponent.[1]

But when finally roused in the spring of 1932 to the worsening crisis, they broke away from the caution of their leaders. There were many House Democrats who considered the sales tax proposed by Hoover and endorsed by the Democratic leadership as both a real and symbolic burden upon the poor—a sort of reverse income tax. Already aroused by Garner's limitation of the debate on the Glass-Steagall bill that made available to business a large quantity of government gold, about fifty Democrats, under the leadership of Robert Doughton of North Carolina, rebelled against the Speaker and managed to defeat the sales tax. In a rapid fire of votes the Democrats substituted a variety of progressive measures, including surtaxes of up to sixty-five per cent; the taxation policy they offered was reminiscent of that in effect during the war years and the early twenties. Later in the session Garner—who on March 29 had roused almost the entire membership to stand in favor of a balanced budget—himself decided to support a massive relief bill, and in the Senate Democrats proposed numerous reforms. At last, it appeared, some of the shackles of economic traditionalism were beginning to fall away from the Democratic party. Skeptics pointed out that even the sales tax revolt was sparked in some measure

[1] *New Republic*, LXVII (June 10, 1931), 97; LXVIII (December 23, 1931), 161–2; (January 20, 1932), 270; LXIX (March 9, 1932), 96; (March 16, 1932), 126; (March 30, 1932), 181.

by the self-interest of important mercantile groups. Yet in the next Congresses the same men who had hedged on ideology for almost a decade would contribute their votes unquestioningly for one advanced scheme after another.[2]

[2] Jordan A. Schwarz: "John Nance Garner and the Sales Tax Rebellion of 1932," *Journal of Southern History*, XXX (May 1964), 162–80; Bascom N. Timmons: *Garner of Texas* (New York, 1948), p. 138.

CHAPTER VII

The Brown Derby Campaign

A President must, without compromising his integrity of origin and manner, show that he is broadly representative of the nation over which he has been placed, and toward which he stands in so peculiarly symbolic a relationship. The task of squaring a social, ethnic, or regional with a national identity need not be an overwhelming one: Harry Truman and John Kennedy, both deeply stamped by their divergent breedings and places of origin, succeeded admirably. But some presidential candidates never transcend the political image that served them in local politics. To this category belongs Governor Alfred E. Smith of New York.

In studying the 1928 campaign, analysts have quite properly concentrated their attention upon the scurrilous tactics of Protestant bigots; almost by default, the New Yorker has emerged as a liberal martyr sacrificed to religious prejudice and prohibitionist morality. But this view of Al Smith is more myth than fact. It is now commonly recognized that any study of the 1928 campaign must begin upon the assumption that whatever the more flamboyant issues, economic prosperity probably pre-

destined the success of the party in power. As Richard Hofstadter has observed: "There was not a Democrat alive, Protestant or Catholic, who could have beaten Hoover in 1928."[1]
More serious, however, has been the reluctance to examine the
strategy within the Smith camp—to gauge the response on the
part of the candidate and his lieutenants to the charge that his
background ill fitted him to represent the whole American
people, rural as well as urban, Protestant as well as Roman
Catholic. Such an examination will reveal that Al Smith was less
than successful, and at moments less than tactful, in presenting
his case to that portion of American society which lay outside
his immediate cultural experience.

The failure of Smith to present himself as a national candidate—reflected in his choice of a brown derby as a campaign
symbol—was also a mark of his party's failure to unify itself. In
1928 the Democrats thrust upon the whole nation the same
conflict that had caused them internal chaos four years earlier
in New York. But no longer was Smith's political opposition
solely a fundamentalist rural America under the leadership
of William Jennings Bryan and William Gibbs McAdoo.
While this rural element undoubtedly contributed to his defeat,
Smith now faced in Herbert Hoover a powerful antagonist who
could command the respect of politically sophisticated Americans having little in common with the narrow ruralists of 1924.
And the whole controversy surrounding Smith's candidacy has
since obscured the solid appeal of his opponent almost as much
as it has romanticized the New Yorker himself.

To gain a deeper understanding of the campaign, we may first
call to mind the background of the 1928 Democratic nominee:
his big-city upbringing, and his political rise; and then examine
the campaign itself, in order to discover the kind of presidential

---

[1] "Could a Protestant Have Beaten Hoover in 1928?" *The Reporter*, XXII
(March 17, 1960), 31. For a sympathetic account of the Smith campaign
written by a warm admirer, see Oscar Handlin: *Al Smith and His America* (Boston, 1958), pp. 125–36; see also Edmund A. Moore: *A Catholic
Runs for President: The Campaign of 1928* (New York, 1956).

image the Smith forces created for their candidate, and the nature of their reply to the assaults of Protestantism, nativism, and rural politicians.

Smith's birthplace, now in the shadow of Brooklyn Bridge, stood in sharp contrast to President Coolidge's homestead in Vermont or Hoover's Quaker village in Iowa. Nor were both of Smith's parents American-born; his father was a native of Manhattan, but his mother's birthplace, according to Smith himself, was in West Meath County, Ireland.[2] Smith's boyhood was shaped to a pattern unprecedented among major presidential candidates. In place of the swimming hole, he had the East River; he attended not the one-room schoolhouse of rural nostalgia but the city's Roman Catholic parochial schools. He married Katie Dunn of the lower East Side, who bore him five children, all of whom attended the same church schools. And Smith's later career as governor in upstate New York never took him far from the mode of life he knew in the city.

Smith was born in 1873; his formal education was ended before he completed the ninth grade when his father died leaving young Al, age fifteen, to help support the family. Graduating, as he later would say, from the Fulton Street Fish Market, where he was a bookkeeper in a commission house, Smith entered ward politics at an age when boys from families of higher income entered college. In 1902 he was elected to the New York State Assembly and served there with increasing prominence until 1915. After distinguishing himself in that year's state constitutional convention, he became Sheriff of New York County and then President of the Board of Aldermen of New York City. Smith went on to win the governorship of New York in 1918. He lost in 1920, but won again in 1922, 1924, and 1926; altogether he served four terms, a record unequalled since the administration of George Clinton. William Allen White stigmatized Smith as a "town-lot Sir Galahad who never fared afield." H. L. Mencken, who voted for and frequently defended him, observed that

2 *The New York Times*, September 2, 1928, p. 2.

Smith's world "begins at Coney Island and ends at Buffalo."[3]

The governor had gotten his political start as the favorite of Charles Murphy of Tammany Hall. But though at first he was of necessity obedient to the political bosses of New York City— his record came under attack from the Citizens' Union of Manhattan—Smith later overshadowed them and developed his own independent Democratic organization. In affairs at Albany Smith depended not primarily on Murphy, but on advisers such as Mrs. Belle Moskowitz and Judge Joseph Proskauer. Mrs. Moskowitz in particular encouraged the governor to promote city welfare legislation that actually helped to diminish the influence of Tammany Hall, since it made voters less dependent on local politicians for favors. The governor also gained considerable power within the increasingly important Democratic machines in Brooklyn and the Bronx. After Murphy's death in 1924, Smith's following was powerful enough to name as his successor George W. Olvany. Yet this victory is itself evidence of Smith's ambivalent relationship toward Tammany bossism; while sufficiently strong and autonomous to be able to dictate terms to the organization, the Smith forces nevertheless found it necessary to support, in Olvany, a man whose ethics seem to have been in the Tammany vein. Smith's own integrity is certain, but he could never shake the stigma of Tammany; it remained a nettle to his rural and small-town opponents. Smith's association with the Wigwam put the Democrats in a defensive position in 1928, much as that in which the Teapot Dome oil scandals had earlier placed the Republicans.[4]

[3] Mencken wrote of Smith still more caustically: "Not only is he uninterested in the great problems facing the nation, but he has never heard of them." *A Carnival of Buncombe*, ed. Malcolm Moos (Baltimore, 1956), p. 143. White is quoted in Henry F. Pringle, *Alfred E. Smith* (New York, 1927), p. 97. Ralph D. Casey: "Scripps-Howard Newspapers in the 1928 Presidential Campaign," *Journalism Quarterly*, VII (September 1930), 228 ff.

[4] Charles Murphy was more sophisticated than some of his outrageous predecessors on Fourteenth Street, but he, too, took enormous sums in the form of "honest graft." Both he and Olvany left estates of over $2 million, although Tammany paid them no salary and they had held no

Smith drank in defiance of prohibition and won for himself the epithet "Alcohol Al." In the summer of 1923 he was presented with a bill repealing the state's prohibition-enforcement law. Franklin Roosevelt advised a veto; instead, the governor—in conformity to his own conscience as well as to the demands of Charles Murphy—signed the bill and issued a declaration that wine and beer should be legalized. When Smith stepped beyond state politics, his stand against prohibition became a major political liability, especially in the South and West. That same year Smith made an off-the-record remark to some newspapermen, which was widely quoted as: "Wouldn't you like to have your foot on the rail and blow the foam off some suds?" Early in 1924, in a letter to Franklin Roosevelt, a nervous Louis Howe remarked: "I took lunch today with some of the Albany boys and they told me in some ways at least Smith is much drier than he used to be. How long he has sworn off for this time, God knows. Let us trust until after the national convention." Even at the Executive Mansion in Albany, Edward Flynn recalled, "a cocktail or highball, in fact, was always available."[5]

The question of Smith's own conduct during prohibition days was to persist. "Does 'Al' drink and does he drink too much?" asked a correspondent of Oswald Garrison Villard, editor of *The Nation*, in 1927. "I am reliably informed," wrote Villard in reply, "that he drinks every day, and the number of his cocktails and highballs is variously estimated at from four

other jobs but that of Sachem. Dennis Lynch: "Friends of the Governor," *North American Review*, CCXXVI (October 1928), 426–7; *Outlook and Independent*, CLII (May 15, 1929), 86, 117. The censures of the Citizens' Union are discussed in "Governor Smith of New York," *World's Work*, XXIX (January 1920), 239; Norman Thomas and Paul Blanshard condemn Olvany in *What's the Matter with New York: A National Problem* (New York, 1932), pp. 52–4. See also "The New Tammany Under George W. Olvany," in William B. and John B. Northrop: *The Insolence of Office* (New York, 1932), pp. 193–203; William Allen White to Edward J. Woodhouse, July 20, 1923, White Papers; *The New York Times*, July 13, 1924, p. 1; July 14, 1924, p. 3; November 27, 1925, p. 1; November 10, 1931, p. 1.
[5] Pringle: *Alfred E. Smith*, p. 138; Howe to Roosevelt, February 25, 1924, Howe Papers.

to eight." The liberal editor was to regret the remark, for it was widely quoted, but later he assured Lillian Wald: "I am certain that it is true, or was true before the campaign began." A friend of William Allen White insisted: "I am told that he drinks regularly. If this is true, how does he get his liquor? He must be either violating the law or knowing that someone else does. If this is true he is not a fit man to be either Governor or President."[6]

The behavior of Smith, in face of national prohibition, during these years prior to 1928 provides one of the more startling instances of an urban provincialism or perhaps a mere personal stubbornness on his part. What was at issue here, of course, is not Smith's legitimate opposition to the prohibition laws but the manner of his opposition. Certainly it would be no great crime for a private citizen to engage in genial defiance of a law that appeared both senseless and obtrusive; Smith regarded the prohibitionist cause, moreover, as a covert attack on the immigrant and his culture, and he thought it hypocritical to camouflage his personal life. But Smith was no private citizen; he was occupant of one important position of public trust and aspirant to another, in which he would become the highest of the sworn defenders of the Constitution, the representative of the whole people. One of the most recent additions to the fundamental national law embodied a principle close to the heart of small-town American Protestantism; and the blatant refusal of Smith to submit to prohibition could be interpreted as a cocky defiance, almost a contempt for that considerable part of the nation that made the law. Having scorned one of our enactments, which of our remaining hopes will this man choose to dash if he becomes our President and representative? So might the query

[6] *The Nation*, CXXV (November 30, 1927), 596. According to Bishop Cannon, the information was supplied to Villard by Henry and Belle Moskowitz. *Bishop Cannon's Own Story*, ed. Richard L. Watson, Jr. (Durham, N.C., 1955), p. 413. Villard to Lillian Wald, June 19, 1928, Wald Papers; T. H. Barrow of Austin, Texas, to White, August 31, 1928, White Papers; Flynn: *You're the Boss* (New York, 1947), p. 66; Cannon to Carter Glass, December 11, 1928, Cannon Papers.

have come from the America that lay west of the Alleghenies and south of Staten Island.

The question of Smith's religion, too, was far from non-existent long before the presidential campaign of 1928. Smith embraced his church, simply and deeply. He took great pride in outward tokens of his faith; in the Executive Mansion in Albany, for instance, he displayed a portrait of Pope Pius XI autographed in 1924. And Katie Smith exhibited on the religious issue a similar openness. In 1925 Louis Howe was fidgeting over the loquacity of the governor's wife, who had just returned from a European trip that included a papal audience. "Mrs. Smith is back from Europe," Howe wrote to Roosevelt:

> and complains to your "Missus" that there were too many ruins in Rome. She is talking too much for Al's good, describing with much gusto and detail their special audience with the Pope and how he referred to Al as his son and the great knowledge he showed in the political campaign. One of her stories is particularly delicious. She says that the Pope turned to McCooey [John H. McCooey, Brooklyn Democratic leader], who was with them and said, "I know how hard you have worked for my beloved son, Governor Smith, but next time you must work even harder." She also is announcing that she brought back a photograph of the Pope personally inscribed "To my beloved son, Alfred E. Smith."[7]

Before 1928, Smith had also become innocently involved in a number of incidents that anti-Catholics could use against him. In 1915 he had offered a highly controversial amendment to the Commissioner of Education at the New York State Constitutional Convention. The measure proposed to strike out of the constitution a clause prohibiting the state from making direct appropriations to denominational schools. Actually, Smith had not pressed his resolution and later explained that he had intro-

[7] During the 1928 campaign, snobbery was unleashed against Mrs. Smith. When complimented by an ambassador's wife on her gown, for example, Mrs. Smith would supposedly reply: "You said a mouthful." Howe to Roosevelt, April 15, 1925, Howe Papers.

duced it to counter another amendment providing for the taxation of church property. Smith's record as governor might have
seemed invulnerable to attacks on religious grounds. But his opponents pointed out that New York City, with Smith's approval, paid as much as $4 million in one year to parochial
schools. Though a long-standing practice, it rebounded, of
course, against Smith.[8]

Joe Tumulty warned the governor in 1927: "You must flatly,
once and for all, dispose of the notion that the Pope will be the
Colonel House of your administration"; and before the 1928
presidential race got under way, Smith settled to his own satisfaction the "problem" of his religion. He did so by taking advantage of an invitation offered him by Ellery Sedgwick, editor
of the *Atlantic Monthly* and a supporter of McAdoo in 1924.
Sedgwick had persuaded Smith to clear the air by replying to an
Episcopal lawyer, Charles Marshall, who in an article published
in Sedgwick's magazine had alleged a conflict between the
American Constitution and the "Two Powers" dogma of the
Roman Church, and had assembled evidence to try to show
that American Catholics would have at best a divided allegiance
between church and state. The draft of Smith's reply was written by Judge Joseph Proskauer with the approval of two priests,
Francis P. Duffy and Francis J. Spellman; yet the sentiments
were patently Smith's own. If religious questions arose, he said,
he would follow the dictates of his own conscience. The governor also pointed to his own career as a pragmatic testament
that theological controversies did not bind the judgment of
Catholic statesmen. In fact, as governor of New York he had
approved a bill providing for an extension of the grounds for
divorce that the Catholic Church specifically opposed; and he
objected emphatically to most forms of public censorship. "I
believe," he wrote, "in the absolute separation of church and

[8] *New York State Constitutional Record, 1915* (Albany, 1916), I, 75;
Journal of the State Constitutional Convention of 1915 (Albany, 1916),
p. 188. *The Nation,* CXXVII (October 24, 1928), 426.

state. . . ." But other events were to show that ammunition far more powerful than a single magazine article would be necessary in face of the religious issue.[9]

Those voters who were prepared to look beyond Smith's religion and his stand on prohibition to his political and economic philosophy could ascertain that though he had won a well-deserved reputation as a progressive, he was in a deeper and more lasting sense a conservative. Here he contrasted with Bryan, who remained an economic radical to the end. In 1924 Smith promised, if elected President, to reassert states' rights and to halt the expansion of federal taxes, laws, and commissions; "We must stop the dangerous overcentralization of Federal power," he wrote during Coolidge's first year in the White House. As presidential aspirant in 1928, as well as in 1924, Smith chose to advertise himself as a Jeffersonian. He instructed the Houston convention to build a platform on "unflinching application of Jeffersonian principles to the problems of the day." Rexford Tugwell admonished the candidate in the *New Republic:* "Cannot Governor Smith understand that—ridiculous as it sounds—the stronghold of Jeffersonianism has shifted from the South to the Northeast and that its latter day prophet is Coolidge?" The testimony of friends and critics alike suggests that Smith's later opposition to New Deal reform may not have been the about-face that is so often portrayed. Walter Lippmann in 1925 called Smith "the most powerful conservative in urban America." His remark is echoed and expanded upon in dozens of commentaries, including ones by Henry F. Pringle, Robert Moses, Edward Flynn, Mrs. Franklin D. Roosevelt,

[9] Later, Michael Williams, editor of *Commonweal,* remarked on Charles Marshall's letter to Smith and his subsequent book, *The Roman Catholic Church in the Modern State* (New York, 1928): "We called him a variety of names. We accused him of misquotation and bad faith. But the point is we did not reply to his book." *The Commonweal,* IX (January 2, 1929), 251. On Proskauer's role, see his *A Segment of My Times* (New York, 1950), p. 55, and personal interview, January 8, 1963. Tumulty to Smith, March 31, 1927, Tumulty Papers; *Atlantic Monthly,* CXXXIV (April 1927), 540–9; (May 1927), 721–8.

John Gunther, Bernard Bellush, Richard Neuberger, and George Mowry.[1]

Set against all this, to be sure, is a remarkably progressive streak in Smith's thinking. His gubernatorial administration made some major legislative and executive advances in education and factory labor; a "mildly humanitarian" program, the historian George Mowry calls it, but for its own day a very impressive program indeed. And he completely reorganized the state government, following to a certain extent the example of Governor Frank Lowden of Illinois. The reformist and the conservative tendencies in Smith are in any case quite compatible; it is possible to find their common source in his upbringing and early manhood. The city streets had schooled him in the facts of economic hardship and the plight of the ghetto; they had also set him forth upon a self-made career—and the economic individualism of the self-made is a matter of common record.

As a self- made man Smith had experienced in his own person

[1] On Smith's conservatism, see Samuel B. Hand: "Al Smith, Franklin D. Roosevelt, and the New Deal: Some Comments on Perspective," *The Historian*, XIII (May 1965), 365–83; *The New York Times*, June 22, 1924, p. 1; *New Republic*, LIII (February 1, 1928), 285; LIII (May 10, 1928), 302; Norman Thomas: "Letter to the Editor," *The Nation*, CXXVII (September 5, 1928), 226–7; Paul A. Carter: "The Campaign of 1928 Re-examined," *Wisconsin Magazine of History*, XLVI (Summer 1963), 263–72; and Jordan A. Schwarz: "Al Smith in the Thirties," *New York History*, XLV (October 1964), 327–8. A group of remarks about Smith's conservatism is quoted in David Burner: "The Brown Derby Campaign," *New York History*, XLVI (October 1965), 363. See Eleanor Roosevelt: *Autobiography* (New York, 1961), p. 152; Edward Flynn: Oral History Memoir, Columbia University, 1950, p. 5; Pringle: *Afred E. Smith*, p. 237; Walter Lippmann: *Men of Destiny* (New York, 1927), pp. 5–6; Robert Moses: *A Tribute to Governor Smith* (New York, 1962), p. 39; John Gunther: *Roosevelt in Retrospect* (New York, 1950), pp. 249–50; Bernard Bellush: *Franklin D. Roosevelt as Governor of New York* (New York, 1955), p. 97; Richard L. Neuberger and Stephen B. Kahn: *Integrity: The Life of George W. Norris* (New York, 1937), p. 177; Hand: "Al Smith," 368; Martin Feldman: "An Abstract of the Political Thought of Alfred E. Smith," unpublished doctoral dissertation, New York University, 1963, p. ii; Smith: *The Road to Victory* (1924), unpaged.

some of the privations of the urban poor; and this was the grounds of a progressivism that is less moral and evangelistic than practical, addressed to specifics. And because he was a politician, and as long as he remained active in politics on the city and state level, Smith had to take major account of the problems of his constituents, and could not have taken on the hard, arrogant indifference of some of the self-made who go into business; as a politician, moreover, he had the kind of constant contact with the urban poor, at least at second or third hand, that would have kept his sympathies genuinely alive, his memories fresh. And since he was not a businessman, he did not need to undergo those painful encounters with labor unions or socially inspired taxation that can make an entrepreneur, risen from the streets or the backwater farm, turn his back upon those who must continue to endure the hardships he has overcome. The complexity and technical nature of urban problems and the sophisticated structure of the urban political machines also conduce to a pragmatic reform rather than one of an ideological origin. The machine in particular may in its demand for loyalty offset the more humane impulses of its workers and protégés—even if one of its members gets as far up as a legislative seat, he will not find it to his advantage to support clean-government legislation, or to oppose business interests allied to a Tammany.

But Smith's background may have had its even deeper effect. He grew up in the atmosphere of moral conservatism, of endangered values carefully preserved, so vividly portrayed by Oscar Handlin in *The Uprooted;* and his traditionalist attitude toward some issues of social and moral conduct is striking. For all his apparent hostility to the blue-law temperament, he signed the so-called Padlock Bill of 1927, a Draconic measure that would close a theater for one year if any play it presented should be declared indecent by the courts. This came about after he mistakenly attended a Broadway play depicting Lesbianism. He reacted to Edward Bourdet's classic by asking the city police to take action against theaters not only when formal complaints were made, but also to anticipate what productions might be violating the law. His devotion to civil liberties had its limits. The principles he upheld in denouncing the Red-baiting Lusk Committee he abandoned in signing a bill that almost outlawed the Ku Klux Klan. He also refused to speak against a clean literature bill, supported by the Catholic Church, which would place the definition of obscenity in the hands of a jury and declare irrelevant the testimony of literary critics. He was notably hostile to woman suffrage; he relied heavily on the political advice of a woman, it is true, but one who believed in the mental inferiority of her sex. A conservatism of this sort, nurtured within the ordered community, would leave its mark upon economic as well as moral considerations; concretely sensitive to the special economic needs of the community, it would at the same time react instinctively whenever the pace of reform seemed to threaten the traditions and the orthodoxies.[2]

In sum, the man the Democrats nominated in 1928 possessed a peculiar mixture of characteristics, some as yet new to national politics, and some as old as American statesmanship; a breeding and a religion foreign to Jackson, Lincoln, and Theodore Roosevelt; a conservatism cut in part to a conventional American mold.

As the Democratic Convention got under way at Houston in June of 1928, Smith had little competition. Edwin T. Meredith of Iowa had inherited some of McAdoo's strength but died ten days before the balloting commenced; the wet Maryland Governor Albert Ritchie was impeded by the relative obscurity of his name. Cordell Hull of Tennessee and Senator Walter F. George of Georgia were also mentioned as possible nominees. But Senator Thomas J. Walsh, a dry Catholic from Montana, was the only figure other than Smith who might have been a formidable candidate. Democrats remembered Walsh as the in-

---

[2] Miss Paula Eldot will soon publish her doctoral dissertation, which connects Smith's reforms with the New Deal. "Al Smith, Reforming Governor," Yale University, 1961. Mrs. Belle Moskowitz declared her belief in the intellectual inferiority of women at a Columbia University forum held on April 28, 1926. *The New York Times,* April 29, 1926, p. 25. Mowry: *The Urban Nation, 1920–1960* (New York, 1965), p. 55.

vestigator of Teapot Dome and as chairman of the 1924 convention. Because he was a dry, Walsh found himself acceptable as a candidate to the Methodist Board of Temperance, Prohibition, and Public Morals. His supporters urged that he was uniquely qualified to be at once the candidate of the dry, Protestant, rural South and the wet, Catholic, urban North. Unlike Smith, however, Walsh had no large personal following who would support him in the election, and after suffering a severe defeat in the California primary he withdrew weeks before the convention opened. The McAdoo group made a last-ditch effort to stop Smith by supporting Senator James A. Reed of Missouri, who had recently visited twenty-eight states and entered several primaries without winning any. Reed was a former wet, and it was disastrous for the McAdoo element to pin its hopes on him.[3]

Smith and his supporters made a conscious effort at the 1928 Democratic Convention to eradicate the poor impression that lingered in the minds of those who had attended the 1924 conclave in New York. At that time, James J. Hoey, a Smith man, had kept the galleries full of unruly crowds who infuriated the McAdoo and Bryan supporters, and a host of Catholic clergy had by their presence antagonized the rural delegates. After his defeat in the New York convention, Smith had not bothered to hide his resentment. In an address to the convention, he had told the skeptical delegates that New York was the greatest city in the world; the speech had a self-congratulatory and arrogant tone. But in 1928 the Smith contingent had mellowed and matured its tactics. Two upstate Democrats, George R. Van Namee, State Democratic Chairman, and Franklin Delano Roosevelt, led the floor fight for the governor, and the more urban politicians stayed sober and respectable. Senator Thomas J. Walsh remarked that "there was no finer looking, better

[3] Walsh believed that southerners could have escaped the charge of religious bigotry had they supported him against Smith. But in spite of help from McAdoo, Walsh gained negligible southern support. Walsh to Hope Fitzgerald, June 20, 1928, Thomas F. Walsh Papers; McAdoo to Ray Stannard Baker, March 25, 1928, Baker Papers; Thomas B. Love to E. J. Mantooth, June 4, 1928, Love Papers.

dressed, more polite, less demonstrative delegation in the convention than the delegates sent by Tammany Hall." Some New Yorkers carried books of poetry with them, others tomes written in a foreign language. In the selection of the New York delegates, preference had been given to those born in the South. Heeding the advice of Joe Tumulty to "let the demands for your election come from elsewhere in America," Smith made certain that speeches seconding his nomination be representative of all regions. In addition, he had given up his fight for repeal of the two-thirds rule; repeal would have denied the South a veto that its politicians had decided not to use on Smith. Finally, the governor assured the delegates that the lengthy deliberations of the 1924 convention would not recur, and promised to withdraw if as many as ten ballots had to be taken.[4]

At the convention "things went off like clockwork," remarked Franklin Roosevelt. The proceedings that opened on June 26 closed on June 29, and except for a fist fight among the Mississippi delegates and another skirmish over the prohibition plank, the Democrats behaved like an assembly of Republicans. Roosevelt, who one day would bring to the party the surface harmony that Smith had not achieved, nominated the governor as "one who has the will to win—who not only deserves success

[4] In 1924 Franklin Roosevelt had expressed concern at the way delegates from the South and West were treated in New York. *The New York Times,* July 3, 1924, p. 2. A few of the delegates imagined that they had been attending a convention of Catholics in 1924. James W. Orr of Kansas, for example, wrote to Roosevelt: "The Democrats of the 47 states left the New York Convention with the spectacle of Catholic Priests, Bishops, Nuns and Catholic Institutions [*sic*] parading the aisles of the Convention." December 17, 1924, Roosevelt Papers. Claude Bowers wrote to Senator Samuel Ralston of "priests by dozens on the floor . . . once as many as 40." July 10, 1924, Ralston Papers. Smith's speech to the 1924 convention is in *Official Report of the Proceedings of the Democratic National Convention* . . . [of] . . . *1924* (Indianapolis, 1925), pp. 1012–15. *The New York Times,* December 9, 1927, p. 20; March 1, 1928, p. 1; June 8, 1928, p. 2; July 5, 1928, p. 18; *The Outlook,* CIL (July 4, 1928), 374–7; Tumulty to Smith, March 23, 1927, Tumulty Papers; Norman Mack to Alfred E. Smith, September 30, 1926, Mack Papers.

but commands it. Victory is his habit—the happy warrior, Alfred E. Smith." Although street-corner evangelists predicted that God would intervene to avert the catastrophe, and a local Baptist church held all-day and all-night fundamentalist prayer meetings, it was to no avail; the governor of New York was nominated when Ohio switched its vote at the end of the first ballot. The delegates refused to name him by acclamation, but it was an impressive victory, astounding in contrast to the previous convention. Smith was joined on the ticket by Senator Joseph T. Robinson, an Arkansas dry. A southern seminary head described the pairing of Smith and Robinson as an attempt to carry fire and water in the same bucket. Robinson—who earlier had been reported "unalterably opposed" to Smith's candidacy —was the first southerner, aside from Woodrow Wilson, to have a place on the national ticket since the Civil War.[5]

A fortnight before Smith won the Democratic nomination, Herbert Hoover was awarded that of the Republican party. A great success in far-flung engineering projects, Hoover had gone on to acquire an even wider reputation as a result of European relief work. And in bringing to several high federal posts, during and after the Great War, a vision and an administrative skill acquired in big business, he won solid acclaim as a progressive. Beginning in 1921 Hoover served as Secretary of Commerce, strengthening his department so that its many functions

[5] Roosevelt's nominating speech is in the *Official Report of the Proceedings of the Democratic National Convention* . . . [of] . . . *1928* (Indianapolis, 1928), p. 104. Joseph Proskauer claims to have written this speech. Personal interview, January 8, 1963. Roosevelt had used the epithet "Happy Warrior" in nominating Smith four years before; the name was applied to Theodore Roosevelt in a speech F.D.R. heard at Harvard. *Official Report of the Proceedings* . . . [of] . . . *1924*, p. 128. Roosevelt remarked on the convention to Sara Delano Roosevelt; quoted in Alfred B. Rollins, Jr.: "The Political Education of Franklin Roosevelt, His Career in New York Politics: 1909–1928," unpublished doctoral dissertation, Harvard University, 1953, II, 844. New York *Herald-Tribune*, June 20, 1928, p. 6; June 24, 1928, p. 3; *The New York Times,* February 11, 1928, p. 3; June 28, 1928, p. 3; October 29, 1928, p. 2.

visibly served the business community. On the important issue of prohibition, his background was that of a teetotaler, although in early June 1918, he had urged Wilson to veto the wartime prohibition act. On the religious question, Hoover occupied unassailable ground. "By blood and conviction," the Quaker candidate could say in 1928, "I stand for religious tolerance both in act and spirit." He spoke during the campaign neither of Smith's religion nor his affiliation with Tammany. And while the jovial Smith permitted countless photographs of himself with a cigar in one hand and his brown derby in the other, the meticulous Republican candidate refused even to allow pictures to be taken while he smoked a pipe. By any measure, Hoover's candidacy seemed ideal for the Republicans.[6]

In his speeches during the 1928 campaign, Hoover gave body to the promise of his wartime career. Far more than Smith, the Republican candidate looked forward to a material fulfillment for America: to the day, when, in the words of his acceptance address, "poverty will be banished from this nation." Hoover continued: "There is no guarantee against poverty equal to a job for every man. That is the primary purpose of the economic policies we advocate." In the same speech, delivered at his alma mater, Stanford University, Hoover called for a shorter work-day and greater purchasing power for labor, for ending the abuse of the injunction, and for collective bargaining; more public works, greater educational opportunity publically financed, and the spending of "hundreds of millions" of dollars for farm relief. A week later he declared against the national-origins principle of the immigration law, complaining of its favoritism toward Great Britain and Ireland, and still later he called for a "humanizing" of the law. While endorsing a limited number of reforms, Smith in his acceptance speech complained of the proliferation of government agencies and their rising

[6] *The New York Times*, August 12, 1928, p. 2; George Peek to John J. Raskob, September 11, 1928, Chester C. Davis Papers; *Kiplinger Washington Letter*, March 5, 1924; Hoover: *The Memoirs of Herbert Hoover. II: The Cabinet and the Presidency, 1920–1933* (New York, 1952), 208.

costs; insisted that "Government should interfere as little as possible with business" and at the same time noted that a few corporations were making outrageous profits; advocated putting the tariff on "a strictly business basis"; and called for "fearless application of Jeffersonian principles." Neither candidate sought any general revision of taxes.[7]

Only on the matter of public power did Smith appear more progressive than Hoover. But as Norman Thomas, the Socialist candidate, put it: "He [Smith] accepts Hoover's general philosophy and reduces the battle between them to the comparatively insignificant question of power at Muscle Shoals and Boulder Dam." Elsewhere, Thomas criticized Smith for not having carried out his earlier proposals for regulating utilities. Hoover, on the other hand, tried to stand by his commitment not to let the government compete with private enterprise, but later in the campaign he did agree to public development of Muscle Shoals. And he had been a most active supporter of the proposed St. Lawrence Seaway, Boulder Dam, and the deepening of the Mississippi River. Smith's own willingness as governor to permit utility companies to contract for the transmission of power further narrowed the divergence between the two candidates on the question, yet Hoover condemned Smith's position as one of state socialism.[8]

[7] *Teamster's Magazine*, XXV (January 1928), 10–14; (June 1928), 13; *The New York Times*, August 12, 1928, pp. 1, 3; August 19, 1928, p. 3; August 23, 1928, pp. 2–3, October 17, 1928, pp. 1, 14.
[8] Smith called for a "fair and equal distribution of power through contractual agreements with the district companies." *Campaign Addresses of Governor Alfred E. Smith* (Washington, D.C., 1929), pp. 61–76. In his *Memoirs* Hoover listed development of water power resources as one of the subjects on which there was "no great difference between Governor Smith and myself." *Memoirs of Herbert Hoover*, II, 199. Senator George Norris, a Republican for whom a government program of flood control was of paramount importance, endorsed Smith with considerable reluctance; Norman Thomas sent Norris a list of public power topics on which Smith had never committed himself; and Franklin Roosevelt, Smith's successor in Albany, seemed in the recollection of Norris to be far more opposed to the utilities interests than Smith. Neuberger and Kahn: *Integrity*, pp. 176–7, 220. On the equivocal positions of both candidates, see Judson

On the issue of farm relief, Smith endorsed the "principle" of McNary-Haugen but not the equalization fee, and he was unspecific about possible remedies. During the campaign, Hoover dismissed the whole plan as unpromising—as indeed it was; it had earlier been rejected in the Republican Convention by a vote of 807 to 277. Instead, he proposed a special session of Congress—if the one ending in December 1928, should offer no solution—to set up a Federal Farm Loan Board, which would provide initial funds for a farmer-owned stabilization agency to offset "seasonal" and "periodic" surpluses. Speaking of the farm situation as the "most urgent economic problem in our nation today," Hoover hoped for the achievement of better than pre-war standards of agricultural prosperity, and his acceptance speech impressed Governor Frank Lowden of Illinois, although he still opposed Hoover on the farm issue. Understandably, farm support was divided between the two candidates.[9]

Hoover was more definite and more positive in his formulation of economic policy; he was, indeed, the more explicitly

King: *The Conservation Fight* (Washington, D.C., 1959), pp. 182–5. *The New York Times*, September 23, 1928, pp. 1–2; October 9, 1928, pp. 1–2; October 23, 1928, pp. 1, 3; October 25, 1928, pp. 1, 13; *The Nation*, CXVII (September 5, 1928), 226.

[9] Hoover was not duped by the agrarian myth: although "conscious of sentimental regret for the passing of . . . old-time conditions," he did not suggest a return to a more secure agricultural past. In reality, he said, the past had more toil, lower living standards, less leisure and recreation —"less of the comforts of home, less of the joy of living." *The New York Times*, August 22, 1928, p. 2. But in 1929 Senator George Norris remarked on how far Democratic leaders and his own Senate colleague, Smith Brookhart, had been deceived by what he called the "glittering generalities" in Hoover's campaign speeches. During the campaign Brookhart had reported that according to six congressmen Hoover had urged Coolidge not to veto the McNary-Haugen Bill. Norris to W. L. Locke, April 23, 1928, Norris Papers, Nebraska Historical Society. *The New York Times*, June 12, 1928, pp. 1, 3, 5; June 13, 1928, pp. 1, 9; June 15, 1928, pp. 1, 4, 12; August 12, 1928, pp. 2, 3; August 24, 1928, pp. 1, 3; August 27, 1928, p. 5; September 9, 1928, p. 3; September 20, 1928, pp. 1, 2; September 21, 1928, p. 1; September 22, 1928, p. 3; William T. Hutchinson: *Lowden of Illinois* (Chicago, 1957), II, 605–6; Gilbert C. Fite: *George Peek and the Fight for Farm Parity* (Norman, Okla., 1954), pp. 196–201.

progressive candidate—enough so that Coolidge's Secretary of the Treasury Andrew Mellon fiercely opposed his presidential candidacy. Of sixty-six social workers who responded to a pro-Smith campaign letter from Lillian Wald, forty-five declared for Hoover. Add to this progressivism a personal identity with the business community, a magnificently successful and splendidly humanitarian career, both public and private, and a manner and background appealing alike to urban and provincial voters; the Republican candidate would have presented an awesome challenge to any Democratic opponent.[1]

The conservative—or, at most, thinly progressive—cast of the Democratic campaign was reflected in its programs and personnel. The platform adopted at Houston was significant in its omissions and could be read as a passive endorsement of the status quo. A low tariff, one clearly traditional bulwark of the Democratic party, went unchampioned in a campaign financed by industrialists protected by Republican high tariffs. Reference to the League of Nations and the World Court was also omitted, while regard was paid to the isolationist sentiment of "freedom from entangling alliances." Newton Baker remarked of the platform that McKinley could have run on the tariff plank and Lodge on the one dealing with international relations. The convention gave only vague endorsement to the McNary-Haugen agricultural plan. Finally, the platform stressed economy, protection of states' rights, and "businesslike methods in Government."[2]

[1] *The New York Times*, June 11, 1928, pp. 1, 2; James E. Watson: *As I Knew Them* (Indianapolis, 1936), p. 256; Clarke A. Chambers: *Seedtime of Reform* (Minneapolis, 1963), p. 140.

[2] Smith clearly opposed a lowering of the tariff; see his statement in *The New York Times*, June 24, 1928, pp. 1, 2. Senator James E. Watson, on the other hand, complained that Hoover "was not a good protectionist." *As I Knew Them*, p. 259. Senator Peter Norbeck of South Dakota remarked to George Peek: "I see Mr. Work [the Republican National Chairman] is going to make the Tariff the issue. I do not suppose he read either platform, or he could not have talked that way." July 14, 1928, Chester C. Davis Papers. Clarence H. Cramer: *Newton D. Baker* (Cleveland, 1961), p. 224; Baker to William E. Dodd, November 16, 1928, Dodd

The governor's conservative strain, as well as his stubbornness, also revealed itself in his choice of John J. Raskob as National Chairman of the Democratic party. Raskob, in the manner of a Horatio Alger hero, had been born poor and had risen to the top as a secretary to Pierre S. DuPont; and this background appealed to Smith. In 1919 Raskob had acquired prominence as a business delegate at President Wilson's National Industrial Conference in Washington, where the position of the business representatives for the open shop and against labor's unimpeded right to organize and to bargain collectively brought the meeting to a halt. By 1928 Raskob was vice president of E. I. DuPont de Nemours and chairman of the finance committee of General Motors. He also served as a director of the Bankers Trust, American Surety, and County Trust companies. In the then current *Who's Who* he accurately listed himself as a capitalist; William Leuchtenburg describes him as an "arch reactionary."[3]

Raskob, like Smith, was a devout Catholic and an ardent wet. He had contributed more than a million dollars to the church, and in recognition of loyalty Pope Pius XI made him a Knight of the Order of Saint Gregory the Great. Raskob saw the Pope in 1927 and again in 1928 when the industrialist received a special benediction and was made a private chamberlain in the papal household. George Van Namee, who had served in the complementary position of preconvention manager, was also a Catholic, as were a number of state chairmen, like that of Iowa. As for

Papers; *The New York Times,* September 9, 1928, pp. 1, 3; *Official Report of the Proceedings* ... [of] ... *1928,* pp. 186–96.
[3] Roosevelt, Josephus Daniels, Josiah Bailey, and other Democrats saw in the appointment of Raskob a break with the conciliatory spirit of the convention. Roosevelt to Daniels, July 20, 1928, Roosevelt Papers; Daniels to George Fort Milton, n.d., copy in Furnifold Simmons Papers, 1928; Bailey to George Van Namee, July 20, 1928, and Bailey to Joseph Proskauer, July 12, 1928, Bailey Papers; Thomas B. Love to Davis S. Rose, July 21, 1928, Love Papers; *The New York Times,* October 11, 1919, p. 1; October 18, 1919, p. 2; October 20, 1919, p. 1; October 24, 1919, p. 1; October 25, 1919, III, 5; August 8, 1924, pp. 1, 3; *Who's Who in America, 1928–1929,* XV (Chicago, 1928), 1727; Leuchtenburg, *Franklin D. Roosevelt and the New Deal, 1932–1940* (New York, 1963), p. 5.

prohibition, Raskob pronounced it a "damnable affliction," and on receiving his appointment he called it the "chief issue" of the campaign. He was, in a way, a counterpart of the professional dry, for lately he had spent a large part of his time and energy as a director of the Association Against the Prohibition Amendment; and when he took on the job of National Chairman, he did so knowing that the Democratic party would serve the interests of the Association, which he energetically promoted until his retirement in 1932. In 1928 his remarks on the liquor issue were stronger even than those of Smith himself, and on this subject, at least, Raskob's influence surpassed that of Belle Moskowitz, one of Smith's longstanding advisers.[4]

Raskob was not a man to attract either organized labor or the hinterland; and as if this were not enough, southerners could not have found it to their liking that in the 1928–9 edition of *Who's Who* he had listed himself as a Republican. "I do not know Mr. Raskob personally," wrote Walter Lippmann after seeing him in action for three years, "but from watching his brief political career I have the impression that in politics he is an innocent lamb." The choice of Raskob, which was made against the objection of his closest advisers, foreshadowed the way in which in the course of the campaign Smith would react to the charges of his opponents. He seemed determined to flaunt what was most controversial about his candidacy.[5]

The new chairman did bring to the campaign a skill in money raising unprecedented in previous Democratic history, and no

[4] *The New York Times,* April 11, 1928, p. 15; July 12, 1928, p. 1; *Christian Science Monitor,* July 13, 1928, p. 1; Mabel Walker Willebrandt to Bishop Cannon, July 16, 1928, Cannon Papers; Belle Moskowitz to Josiah Bailey, July 26, 1928, Bailey Papers; Nathan Miller to Hoover, July 12, 1928, Hoover Papers.
[5] *The New York Times* intimated that Smith's personal preference for governor of New York was not the popular Franklin Roosevelt but Owen D. Young, Chairman of the Board of General Electric. July 16, 1928, p. 1. *Who's Who in America, 1928–1929,* p. 1927; *The New York Times,* July 12, 1928, p. 1; August 29, 1928, p. 5; Vaughn D. Bornet: *Labor and Politics in a Democratic Republic* (Washington, D.C., 1964), p. 76; Lippmann, *Interpretations, 1931–1932* (New York, 1932), p. 257.

doubt his own enormous wealth and his connections dictated his choice as chairman. Thomas Fortune Ryan, who had made some $200,000,000 in street railway franchises, William Kenny, a wealthy New York building contractor, former Senator Clarence W. Watson of West Virginia, John W. Davis, and other conservatives generously responded to his requests for contributions. In all Raskob's Democratic National Committee disbursed $5,342,000 against $3,529,000 for the Republican headquarters: in 1928, for the second time in American history, the Democrats spent more than the Republicans in the national campaign. Raskob himself underwrote Smith's campaign in the amount of half a million dollars, and gifts to the two parties were roughly proportionate in size, although Hoover's preconvention campaign was clearly financed by smaller gifts than Smith received. Yet the addition of Raskob to the Smith retinue deepened the already existing problems attached to the Happy Warrior's candidacy.[6]

During the convention a measure of peace had been maintained between North and South; the very choice of Houston as the convention city had been aimed at appeasing southern Democrats, for not since 1860 had a Democratic convention met in the South. But even before appointing Raskob, Smith shattered the harmony that prevailed at Houston when he sent an important telegram to the adjourning delegates declaring for "fundamental changes in the present provisions of national prohibition." The statement was taken as a rejection of the more moderate platform plank. Franklin Roosevelt later wrote of that "fool telegram," Josephus Daniels called it "unnecessary and ill-timed," and the Anti-Saloon League reacted by an immediate endorsement of Hoover—the first candidate the League had ever officially supported. Actually, it was not clear what course Smith would pursue with regard to prohibition should he

[6] On campaigns for all levels of government combined, the Republicans continued to outspend the Democrats by about $9 to $7 million. *The New York Times,* May 12, 1928, p. 1; Raskob to Bernard Baruch, November 17, 1928, Baruch Papers; James K. Pollock, Jr.: "Campaign Funds in 1928," *American Political Science Review,* XXIII (February 1929), 63, 65.

achieve the presidency. Walter Lippmann predicted that he would follow a moderate policy of law enforcement; certainly, Lippmann observed, the Democrats could do no worse job of it than the Republicans had beeen doing. To other commentators, "fundamental change" suggested repeal. As the campaign progressed, Smith's meaning became clearer. In August he took an advanced stand when he called for state control of liquor, and later he said he would lead a nationwide fight for a change in the prohibition law.[7]

The good fellowship of the convention was dissolved by the Smith telegram and the Raskob appointment. The campaign would henceforth take on a new tone, but nowhere more emphatically than in the South. Bishop James Cannon, Jr., of the Methodist Episcopal Church, South, and Dr. Arthur J. Barton, Chairman of the Committee on Social Service of the Southern Baptist Convention, met in Asheville, North Carolina, in July to form an anti-Smith group. Cannon in particular worked indefatigably in directing the *ad hoc* association in its mission of defeating the New Yorker; he raised ample funds, some of them donated by the Republican National Committee, to spread propaganda into every area of the South.[8]

Through the Anti-Smith Democrats and other organizations the South was encouraged to refuse Smith its traditional hospitality when he made a campaign trip there—he had first visited the region in April of 1928. Newspapers patronizingly reported that at the town of Biltmore, North Carolina, Smith had said to a cheering crowd: "I hope to meet yez-all personally." In his autobiography, Smith wrote that in Louisville a policeman accused

[7] At the convention a petition had been displayed that purportedly represented 6.4 million southerners opposed to any candidate not fully committed to prohibition. Roosevelt to James C. Bonbright, March 11, 1930, Roosevelt Papers; *The New York Times*, June 30, 1928, p. 1; July 1, 1928, pp. 1, 6; August 22, 1928, p. 1; September 23, 1928, p. 1; September 30, 1928, pp. 1–2; October 12, 1928, p. 1; *Harper's Magazine*, CLVI (January 1928), 133–9.

[8] *The New York Times*, November 2, 1928, p. 24; Rembert G. Smith to Cannon, August 4, 1928, Bishop Warren A. Candler Papers.

him of being drunk, the whole police force was rude, and someone turned the heat too high in the auditorium where he delivered a speech. After a series of discourtesies on October 11,
Smith was "solemn, silent and sullen." It appeared that although
most of the southern politicians had accepted Smith in the convention the majority of voters would not support him. "Of the
Southern delegates who voted for Smith," wrote one observer,
"not one reflected the real wishes of his constituents."[9]

While it was most pronounced in the South, the denominational attack on Smith was national in scope. A large contingent
of ministers, including the popular Billy Sunday, fought Smith
by every means available. Sunday called himself the "Ambassador of God" out "to defy the forces of hell—Al Smith and the
rest of them."[1] A Methodist paper with countrywide circulation
declared: "Governor Smith has a constitutional right to run for
President, even though a Catholic. This we confess. And we have

[9] John E. Sullivan, Smith's physician who accompanied him on the campaign, recalled that when the candidate's bodyguard, William Roy, went
down to the steamroom to see what the matter was, he found a cordon
of policemen protecting the engineers who were stoking the furnace.
Personal interview, March 25, 1963. *Time*, VIII (April 23, 1928), 8; Alfred
E. Smith: *Up to Now* (New York, 1929), pp. 400-1; Stuart Deskins: "The
Presidential Election of 1928 in North Carolina," unpublished doctoral
dissertation, University of North Carolina, 1944, p. 81; Sherwin L. Cook:
Torchlight Parade (New York, 1929), p. 274.
[1] Sunday called Smith's male supporters "the damnable whiskey politicians,
the bootleggers, crooks, pimps and business men who deal with them,"
while the New Yorker's female supporters were "street-walkers." After
the election Vice President Charles Curtis sent Sunday a letter thanking
him for his "valued assistance" and "good work in the South." One of the
most intemperate of the churchmen who opposed Smith came not from
the South but from the Calvary Baptist Church in New York City: in a
speech in Dallas, John Roach Straton announced that "Smith is the
nominee of the worst forces of hell." And in Riverside Park, New York,
Dr. Ed Bywater delivered his popular sermon "To Hell with the Pope."
The New York Times, August 26, 1928, p. 3; September 4, 1928, p. 6;
Memphis *Commercial Appeal*, October 25, 1928, p. 5. William G. Mc-
Loughlin, Jr.: *Billy Sunday Was His Real Name* (Chicago, 1955), p. 285.
The New York Times, September 24, 1928, p. 2; *Book of Horror* (a col-
lection of inflammatory literature used in the 1928 campaign), Columbia
University Library.

a constitutional right to vote against him because he is a Catholic. This we assert." The Moral Welfare Department of the Presbyterian Church of America adopted a resolution denouncing any prospective wet candidate. And the leaders of four million Baptists voted in convention to warn the Democratic party against a Catholic candidate. Dr. Mordecai Ham of the First Baptist Church, the largest in Oklahoma City, made the penalty for voting Democratic clear enough: "If you vote for Al Smith, you're voting against Christ and you'll all be damned." Lutherans were most emphatic in opposing Smith for his religion. Even the Unitarian leader, Dr. Alfred C. Dieffenbach, called to mind the Roman Catholic persecution of Unitarians in other countries and declared that no Catholic should be elected to the presidency. One scholar later noted that "the people seemed to have one thing in their minds—Al Smith's religion."[2]

Such was the denominational opposition to Smith; the nation-wide attack it fostered was in most cases the least fair of the campaign, for it was the most difficult to combat. Smith was accused of all the crimes of the Spanish Inquisition and the medieval popes. Bishop Edwin Mouzon of the Methodist Episcopal Church, South, compiled in the North Carolina *Christian Advocate* a list of "Catholic crimes" in Mexico and England. In the same periodical Mouzon suggested topics for political-religious sermons. In New Jersey a confectioner sent along with his invoices copies of "The Inquisitorial Horrors of the Roman Catholic Church, as Described by an Officer in Napoleon's Army." The fundamentalist *Fellowship Forum* caricatured Smith driving a beer truck bearing the sign "Make America

---

[2] Bishop Warren A. Candler of Emory University, among others, ventured the hope that his fellow Methodists would not bring their church into politics. Cook: *Torchlight Parade*, p. 274; Wesleyan *Christian Advocate* of Atlanta: quoted in Michael Williams: *The Shadow of the Pope* (New York, 1932), pp. 192, 195; *The New York Times*, May 28, 1928, p. 3; August 17, 1928, pp. 1, 2; August 21, 1928, p. 4; October 3, 1928, p. 3; *America*, XXXIV (October 3, 1928), 654; *The Commonweal*, VIII (October 3, 1928), 654; *Christian Register*, CVII (November 22, 1928), 948–9; William G. Carleton: "The Popish Plot of 1928: Smith-Hoover Presidential Campaign," *The Forum*, CXII (September 1949), 145.

100 per cent Catholic, Drunk, and Illiterate," and another cartoon, showing a buxom woman giving a cup to a reclining cleric, bore the caption "The Pope Converted the Vatican into a House of Ill Fame." The flavor of the *Fellowship Forum* is caught in its advertisement for an "eye-opening" ten-cent pamphlet: "Can a Bobbed-Haired Woman Go to Heaven?" The *Forum* and other such publications gave wide circulation to a spurious Knights of Columbus oath: "I will spare neither sex, age nor condition, and [I swear] that I will hang, waste, boil, flay, strangle and burn alive these infamous heretics [Protestants]; rip up the stomachs and wombs of their women and crush infants' heads against the wall, in order to annihilate forever their execrable race. That when the same cannot be done openly, I will secretly use the poison cup, the strangulation cord, the steel of the poniard, or the leaden bullet [and so forth]."[3]

Senator Thomas Heflin of Alabama delivered some of the most vitriolic anti-Catholic attacks on record. Initially he used the floor of the Senate to denounce Smith and the Pope, and to urge the deportation of all Catholics; but in 1928 he carried his message throughout the country. In that year as before, one of the groups to pay his speaking expenses was the Ku Klux Klan. With Heflin, anti-Catholicism became a mania, growing into a conviction that the Catholics were planning to murder him. The Cincinnati *Catholic Telegram* said of the Alabamian—who slept with a gun under his pillow—that he had "strangely overlooked what is probably the most striking proof of the papal invasion of the United States. The telegraph pole bears the form of the cross from one end of the country to the other. . . . The plan was devised by none but a mastermind."[4]

[3] Mouzon: "The Roman Catholic Question," North Carolina *Christian Advocate*, August 2, 1928, p. 9; *The New York Times*, September 29, 1928, p. 3.
[4] A Holy Name Society sent Heflin a check for $250 "in appreciation of aid to the Catholic church." *The New York Times*, June 20, 1928, p. 5. A fellow senator described Heflin's delusion as "the airiest bubble that

With a co-religionist as a major presidential candidate for the first time in the nation's history, American Catholics were naturally on the defensive in 1928. A study of Catholic periodicals has shown that few openly urged the election of Smith. Many Catholics thought that only when one of their number became President could they achieve full social status in America, and they did not choose to forfeit their opportunity by confirming the fears of Protestants. Ellery Sedgwick of the *Atlantic Monthly* complimented the Catholic clergy on its good manners and restraint. Their discretion in the campaign contrasted with the behavior of many Protestant ministers who chose not to respect the principle for which they spoke, the separation between religion and politics. In Ohio two thousand of them willingly heard Mrs. Mabel Walker Willebrandt, Assistant Attorney General of the United States, urge them to use their pulpits and clerical influence against Smith. A public outburst would have greeted a comparable appeal for Smith before an assembly of Catholic priests.[5]

---

had ever found lodgment in an empty head." Circular letter of W. Earl Hotales: "Tom Heflin National Legion Secretary," May 5, 1930, Heflin Papers, Howard College [Alabama] Library. The Catholic paper is quoted in *America*, XXXIV (June 9, 1938), 197. For Heflin's harangues in the Senate, see the *Congressional Record, Senate*, May 3, 1928, pp. 7697–700; May 8, 1928, pp. 8050–9; May 11, 1928, pp. 8381–2; May 17, 1928, pp. 8835–42; May 23, 1928, pp. 9542–51; May 28, 1928, pp. 10209–21 and 10283–7. *The New York Times*, June 1, 1928, p. 1; June 16, 1928, p. 1; June 18, 1928, p. 1; September 25, 1928, p. 6. Virginius Dabney: *Liberalism in the South* (Chapel Hill, N.C., 1932), p. 273; *The Commonweal*, VIII (June 20, 1928), 176.

5 Mrs. Willebrandt spoke at the request of the Republican National Committee. "There are 2,000 pastors here," she said. "You have in your churches more than 600,000 members of the Methodist Church in Ohio alone. That is enough to swing the election." *The New York Times*, September 8, 1928, pp. 1, 3; October 25, 1932, p. 15. Moore: *A Catholic Runs for President*, pp. 175–8; Helen M. Matzke: "The Attitude of the Catholic Periodicals in the Election of 1928," unpublished Master's essay, Columbia University, 1929, p. 13; *Current History*, XXIX (December 1928), 377–81.

Could there be a well-founded suspicion of Smith on religious grounds? Some Catholic leaders, it is true, had indicated a willingness to bring the church into politics. In 1922, for example, two priests, John A. Ryan—the New Deal liberal of a later day—and Moorhouse F. X. Millar had published *The State and the Church,* a work that might offend many Protestants too sophisticated to base their thinking upon stories of the inquisitorial atrocities of other lands and centuries. Ryan and Millar used as one of their texts the famous 1895 Encyclical of Pope Leo, which stated in part that "it would be very erroneous to draw the conclusion that in America is to be sought the type of the most desirable status of the Church. . . . She would bring forth more abundant fruits if, in addition to liberty, she enjoyed the favor of the laws and the patronage of public authority." In one of his essays included in the book, Ryan argued that "the State should officially recognize the Catholic religion as the religion of the Commonwealth. . . . Should [non-Catholics] be permitted to practice their own form of worship?" he asked. "If these are carried on within the family, or in such an inconspicuous manner as to be an occasion neither of scandal nor of perversion to the faithful. . . ." Ryan insisted that in America the Church would never be so recognized and that tolerance was a precious part of the American Catholic heritage; but he added that "error has not the same rights as truth."[6]

It was not alone the autocratic remarks of individual priests that antagonized many intelligent Protestants toward the presi-

[6] (New York, 1922), pp. 33–6. *The Manual of Christian Doctrine,* a Catholic text for parochial elementary schools, was scandalous to Ryan; he claimed, hopefully, that "there is no evidence that the section on the relations of Church and State has been taken seriously by the average teacher. . . ." Francis L. Broderick: *Right Reverend New Dealer, John A. Ryan* (New York, 1963), pp. 118–20, 176. In addition, the reproofs the Church offered to liberal American Catholics such as Bishop Keane and Archbishop Ireland seemed to underscore the foreign and autocratic character of the Church. Some Catholic churchmen, it should be noted, had insisted upon the separation of Church and State even if Catholics someday predominate. Robert D. Cross: *The Emergence of Liberal Catholicism in America* (Cambridge, Mass., 1958), pp. 74, 195–205.

dency of a Roman Catholic. The example of several European and Latin American countries, where the Catholic Church had inexorably attempted to control political as well as spiritual affairs, was particularly disturbing. As Catholics became more numerous, might not the same fate befall America? At an International Eucharistic Congress held in Chicago during the summer of 1926, Smith was kept forward as the major lay figure; and before attending the meeting he had held a reception for eight cardinals at City Hall in New York, knelt before two of the visiting prelates, and kissed the ring of the papal legate, Cardinal Banzano. The Vatican itself made known that it would rejoice to see a Catholic President of the United States. Rome, apparently, was interested, and it is not odd that some Protestants—even though the threat of papal control was absurd—believed they had ample reason to take offense at that interest. Smith's unequivocal stand in the *Atlantic Monthly* in 1927 was not enough to dispel these fears.[7]

Here again, the conduct of Smith requires commentary. A Catholic both loyal and stalwart in the assertion of his faith, Smith had before 1928 engaged in many small expressions of his Catholicism remarkable for a hardened politician aiming for national election, and as constitutional delegate and governor had taken political actions perhaps reflective of his religion. During the presidential campaign of 1928 he continued to follow the path he had always trod, making no apparent concessions to the instinctive revulsion shared by much of America against the

[7] Instances were reported of the participation of Catholic churchmen in politics. Bishop Alma B. White: *Heroes of the Fiery Cross* (Zarephath, N.J., 1928), p. 122; Edgar I. Fuller: *The Visible of the Invisible Empire* (Denver, 1925), pp. 40–8; William Hall Allen to William Allen White, July 19, 1928, White Papers, Library of Congress; Caroline I. White to Bishop James Cannon, Jr., August 21, 1928, Cannon Papers. There also were frequent reports of Republicans aiding the anti-Catholic crusade; see, for instance, *The New York Times*, November 2, 1928, p. 24. Smith himself listed the Klan as a Republican ally, saying that it got a great deal of encouragement from Republican leaders. *The New York Times*, October 30, 1928, pp. 1, 4; June 16, 1926, p. 1; June 22, 1926, p. 14; *Christian Register*, CVII (January 6, 1927), 3.

symbols of Catholicism. In September he even volunteered to serve as an acolyte during a New Jersey church service.[8] Smith's conduct on the matter of religion must, it is true, be judged on grounds somewhat different from those by which his defiance of prohibition is tested. In showing at least some respect for the law of the constitution and for that large segment of the people who had called for the prohibition amendment, Smith would have combined good politics with good morals. But with regard to the religious question, morality and political strategy had to diverge; the minutest compromise of religious faith and observance would have been as morally questionable as it would be politically shrewd. Of course, it may be pointed out that the display of an autographed picture of the Pope in Smith's Albany office, for example, falls outside the scope of religious duty. Yet even here, Al Smith's conscience might have equated the least coyness in the affirmation of his faith with moral cowardice.

But all this does not free Smith from the charge of provincialism on the religious issue. For if he could not shirk his religion itself, or modify the slightest symbolic act of allegiance, he could at least have addressed himself more fully to the fears in which so many of his fellow Americans had been reared. Even assuming that the Smith forces may at first have pinned their hopes on the *Atlantic Monthly* article—which the governor had been reluctant to write—and reasoned that further reference on their part to the religious controversy would only more inflame the issue, it should have become apparent during the course of the camaign that nothing could have worsened the situation as it already stood. Smith might have acknowledged the occasional alliance between Latin Catholicism and political tyranny and then pointed to the historical American tradition of religious harmony, as embodied in Lord Baltimore; he and his supporters might even have made explicit contrast between their position, along with the position of countless of their fellow religionists in the United States, and that of Catholic reactionaries; he might have sought out the support of Protestant

[8] *The New York Times,* September 5, 1928, pp. 1, 4.

clergymen or outstanding laymen; he might have increased the Protestant contingent in his campaign committee.[9] In short, Smith might have acted as though he were aware of the anxiety, however silly or bigoted, that was felt by much of rural American Protestantism, as one who shared with it a sense of America's role in preserving religious liberty. A provincial Protestant ruralism and a provincial Catholic urbanism stared at each other in uncomprehending hostility, and with the single exception of Smith's article of 1927, neither attempted to break the impasse with a liberal word or gesture.

The contrast between Al Smith's handling of the religious question and John Fitzgerald Kennedy's is compelling. Smith discussed the issue once during the campaign. In his speech at Oklahoma City he lashed out angrily at a hostile audience, whom he attacked for hiding under the cloak of antiprohibition. He overpersonalized the religious debate and used explosive gesticulations to match his words.[1] Kennedy, on the other hand, spoke often and directly to critics of his religion. "My experience . . . shows it is a matter of great concern," he said. "I am delighted

[9] Senator Burton K. Wheeler, Democrat of Montana, asked that prominent Norwegians and Swedes be enlisted in his state to defend Smith on the religious issue: "The need for that kind of approach ought to be pounded into the heads of those simple-minded people in New York who think the whole world revolves around that section of the country east of the Hudson River. The Smith forces may be playing fine politics as far as the East is concerned, but they did not display very much intelligence thus far with reference to the West in the selection of their advisers." Wheeler to Key Pittman, July 21, 1928, Pittman Papers. Lynn Haines, a journalist who wrote an unpublished manuscript, "Al Smith and Certain Soothsayers," added to Wheeler's criticisms with a warning for Smith: "He must go west—not merely west of Broadway, not west of the Hudson, but west of the Alleghanies [*sic*]. From Ohio west and northwest and southwest, clear to the coast, is electoral territory ripe for Smith conquest. The key to the situation is the great agricultural depression—that plus a fighting progressive slant to the whole campaign. . . . Governor Smith will be nominated; if he goes far enough west of Broadway—in understanding and sympathy and spirit and purpose—he will easily be elected"; Chester C. David Papers. Tom Connally also considered Smith's background "provincial." *My Name Is Tom Connally* (New York, 1954), p. 132.

[1] *Daily Oklahoman,* September 21, 1928, p. 1.

to answer any questions about it. . . . There is nothing improper in discussing it." In a speech to the Greater Houston Ministerial Association, he gave his audience the benefit of the doubt for opposing him. He was specific, moreover, in his remarks about what worried that audience: "No church or church school," he said, should be granted "public funds or political preference." Kennedy asserted his opposition to state control of religion; and on the matter of birth control he promised to follow his own conscience without regard to outside religious pressures. Nor had Kennedy compounded the religious problem by politically amateurish appointments. As National Chairman, for example, he named Senator Henry M. Jackson of Washington, after passing over a prominent Catholic congressman. Undoubtedly, Kennedy had profited from Smith's mistakes, as he had also profited from the liberalization of his church.[2]

Smith's religion did not stand alone as an issue in the campaign; opponents saw it as but one of a complex of characteristics that marked the New Yorker as a personality alien to the American grain. Smith was not merely a wet; he was a "Bowery wet," and his position toward alcohol, like his faith, affronted not only the most ignorant but also Americans of a genteel, middle-class tradition—offended their gentility or their conception of Americanness as much or more than their morals. As a social liability, Smith's wet position vied with a number of mannerisms that stamped him as a Gotham Cockney. Over the radio, then a new and impressive contribution to presidential campaigns, Smith's voice could be heard only with difficulty, for he spoke indistinctly and insisted on dashing from one side of the microphone to the other. His speeches themselves lacked grace and symmetry. He employed "ain't" and "he don't," and changed "work" to "woik"—forms of speech defended by the Johns Hopkins philologist Kemp Malone. His language, gestures, and physical appearance, all of which the new motion-picture newsreels conveyed, stamped him as an intruder in national politics. Even the two spittoons in Smith's Albany office

[2] *The New York Times,* August 29, 1960, p. 1; September 13, 1960, pp. 1, 22.

seemed to speak loudly of his social origins. His eighth-grade education was insufficient, critics insisted, to equip him to face national and world problems, and on more than one occasion Smith himself admitted that he was interested only in the concrete and did not read books. When Smith visited Lincoln's birthplace in Kentucky, he bought a corn-cob pipe at the souvenir stand and immediately stuck it between his teeth. On another occasion, he joked with reporters about the needs of the states west of the Mississippi: "What states *are* west of the Mississippi?" he asked. When he met Babe Ruth, Smith—who had signed bills legalizing boxing and Sunday baseball—remarked: "Say, I read in a paper somewhere that in some place —I think in Pennsylvania—somebody wouldn't let the series be announced on Sunday. Well, I'd like to see that place," mused the Governor, "it must be a hot one." He did not even hesitate to make a potentially abrasive public demonstration of fellowship with Tammany Hall, that embodiment of big-city politics and values. Before the national convention Smith visited Tammany, where, after a two-years absence from the annual ceremonies, he was reinstated as an honorary Sachem. Because Tammany Hall had lasted a century, he said, it must be "all right."[3]

In sum, the matter of Smith's Catholicism, his obliviousness to Tammany's bad name, and his intransigence toward the Eighteenth Amendment blended with other characteristics less explicitly reflective of Smith's political outlook, yet combining to

[3] Mildred Duncan to Lillian Wald, October 22, 1928, Wald Papers; New York *Sun,* August 24, 1932, p. 1; *The New York Times,* November 1, 1928, p. 3; Pringle: *Alfred E. Smith,* p. 338. The various anecdotes are in Cook: *Torchlight Parade,* p. 295; Pringle: *Alfred E. Smith,* p. 97; Geoffrey Parsons: Oral History Memoir, Columbia University, 1949, p. 30; *The New York Times,* October 11, 1928, p. 1—the Babe Ruth story, quoted in the *Times,* appeared as a human interest item at the top of p. 1. *The New York Times,* July 15, 1928, p. 2; October 27, 1928, p. 12. On Smith and Tammany Hall, see the *New Republic,* LVI (October 10, 1928), 188–90, and the more critical article in *The Nation,* CXXVI (June 13, 1928), 659. On his becoming a Sachem, see *The New York Times,* May 15, 1928, p. 1; July 5, 1928, p. 1.

create a total impression of the man. A Florida Democrat told Roosevelt that "the sidewalks of New York didn't synchronize with my thought . . . of the dignity of the job." One woman wrote to Roosevelt:

> There were vast numbers who did not regard him as a fit man, either by birth, culture, dignity, or breadth of vision, to fill the great office of President of the United States. One who had never until middle life traveled beyond the counties of his native state could not possibly have other than a provincial viewpoint. His superficial knowledge of nationwide affairs, hastily acquired, could not give him the understanding or sympathetic outlook necessary in dealing with great national and international problems.

Another correspondent of Roosevelt identified a mélange of reasons for voting Republican; this is one of many "know-nothing" letters written to political figures in 1928:

> Mr. Roosevelt: Birds of a feather flock together, and if you uphold Smith and help him get in it is obvious you are in Tammany's pay. Of course he may be better than the ordinary man but Tammany has not become honest. . . . Everyone knows that Tammany uses Public School surplus to supply parochial schools so god knows what they will do when he gets to be President. . . . If you ever heard the Knights of Columbus oath I am sure you a Protestant would be through with [Roman Catholics]. They say it is all right to steal or cut out the bellies (the exact words used) of Protestants. . . . Why people are saying that he will make us have war with Mexico and he will so he can kill off some Protestants. . . . We can't trust them, don't you know that their church and the Pope come first, and they will be subject as it was to them first, and to America and her ideals second. . . . You ought to know the corruption there is in New York with Smith having a private telegraph wire to Tammany Hall, so of course he'll have a private wire to Tammany if he is made President. . . . An eyewitness saw him carried on the train

dead drunk after his mother's funeral. He'd make a fine President, getting the Protestants drunk like he did when he was speaker or leader of the floor, in Albany, just so they would vote his way. And everyone knows his sons had to get married. And what kind of a woman would that be in the White House. Some difference from Mrs. Coolidge, who is educated and refined and cultured. Mrs. Smith's father was a saloon keeper, and kept Prostitute Houses and yet you'd help those kind of people get in. Well, all I can say is God help you and all of us, if they do get in.

From an American who wants an American President who will protect America's Ideals, first, last, and always.[4]

Even in his choice of an executive committee, Smith displayed a lack of sensitivity toward the touchy social and ethnic issues of the campaign. The selection of Raskob has already been mentioned; the rest of the committee came principally from New York and was largely composed of first- or second-generation Jews and Irish Catholics. Some of them were adept at urban politics and most had no connection with Tammany, but in general they showed the limited outlook of their candidate. One of Smith's closest advisers was James J. Hoey, the man who led the raucous galleries at the 1924 convention as they cheered "Oil! Oil!" to embarrass McAdoo. Joe Cohn of the tabloid New York *Evening Graphic,* Smith's press contact man, was another bad choice; as Smith himself observed in an interview some ten years later, his snappy clothes and overbearing manner made it almost impossible for him to win over conservative, middle-aged newspapermen of the West and South. Conversely, Smith ignored advice from most western and southern Democrats. As early as May 1927, Joe Tumulty had criticized him for failing to consult out-of-state Democrats traveling through New York. Franklin Roosevelt, who was definitely not a member of Smith's inner circle, objected vigorously to the way Smith ran his presi-

[4] G. G. Dodge of Tampa to Franklin Roosevelt, August 20, 1931, Democratic National Committee Papers; Mary Robbins Long to Franklin Roosevelt, February 12, 1929, Roosevelt Papers.

dential campaign, especially to the publicity organization, which he described as a combination of Mrs. Moskowitz and the advertising section of General Motors. On his campaign train Smith took with him Tammany judges and other New Yorkers; the only noneasterners to accompany him for very long were J. Bruce Kremer, the conservative Montanian closely associated with the Anaconda Copper Company, and former Senator Gilbert Hitchcock, who had voted against the prohibition amendment in 1920. Senator Robinson, the southern vice presidential candidate, who considered Raskob's acceptance remarks "inadvisable and unnecessary," did not hear from Smith for almost two weeks after the notification ceremonies.[5]

Are the Smith forces free of responsibility for the misunderstandings and antagonisms of the campaign? In answer, we may first acknowledge that no amount of political skill on their part,

[5] In complaining of Smith's tactics to Harry Byrd of Virginia, Roosevelt said: "Things depend so much on the way they are put." August 20, 1928, Roosevelt Papers. F.D.R. complained bitterly of being treated as "window dressing" in the campaign. Memorandum, April 6, 1938. Elliott Roosevelt, ed. *Franklin D. Roosevelt: His Personal Letters*, II, 771–3. George Peek, managing the campaign in the farm states, explained to one supporter why he was being ignored at Smith's headquarters: "Things are moving so lively with them in New York that it is pretty difficult for me to get anything over to them now about what is to go in Governor Smith's speeches." Peek to Julien N. Friant, October 10, 1928, Chester C. Davis Papers. Even at the Houston convention, Judge Proskauer had allegedly been antagonistic to supporters of Smith from outside the East. *The New York Times*, June 27, 1928, p. 4. In 1928 the national Democratic headquarters and Congressman Oldfield's Democratic National Congressional Committee were transferred to the General Motors Building in New York. Roosevelt to Van Lear Black, July 25, 1928; George Foster Peabody to Franklin Roosevelt, September 11, 1928, Roosevelt Papers; H. D. Carre to Senator Kenneth McKellar, January 26, 1928, McKellar Papers. Joe Tumulty to Alfred E. Smith, May 16, 1927, Tumulty Papers; Robinson to Raskob, August 10, 1928, Robinson Papers; Bascom N. Timmons: *Jesse H. Jones: The Man and Statesman* (New York, 1956), p. 149; Frances Perkins: *The Roosevelt I Knew* (New York, 1946), pp. 52–3; Arthur Schlesinger, Jr.: *Crisis of the Old Order* (Boston, 1957), p. 380; *Time*, VII (October 1, 1928), 12–13; Leona F. Becker: "Alfred E. Smith [Personal interview, May 3, 1937]," unpublished Master's essay, University of Chicago, 1938, pp. 96–7.

no conceivable effort at conciliation, could have obliterated the bigotry with which they had to contend. But it was not bigotry alone that ruled the emotions of the campaign; was there not a legitimate concern, on the part of some of the anti-Smith voters, at the possibility that the kind of America they had known might cease to find its symbol in the Executive Mansion[6] —a concern that need not have been unduly aroused by Smith's candidacy, had he only taken the proper steps to still it? Failing this, a candidate can hardly complain if voters sense the mutual estrangement. And in 1928, a special responsibility rested upon Smith to harmonize his America with that beyond the Hudson. For at that time America had only begun to recognize that the "urban frontier," as well as the rural, had composed the substance of her past; she had not had time fully to absorb that more teeming frontier—of which Smith is today almost a folk hero— into her self-image. Smith might have tried to make 1928 a year of reconciliation between the two American cultures, but to do so he would have had to reach out, beyond the eastern city, to rural and small-town Protestant America, address it and show that he understood its feelings as well as the feelings of the lower East Side and the Bowery.

Instead, he sometimes displayed during his candidacy an exclusionist provinciality unequalled even during the bids of William Jennings Bryan. His taste for the Sunday manner of New York was laudable; his sniping at the Protestant blue laws

[6] Three years prior to the 1928 campaign, Walter Lippmann wrote: "The older American stocks in the South and the West, and in the East, too, are not all Ku Kluxers, and the Governor's more hasty friends show an intolerance when they believe that Al Smith is the victim of purely religious prejudice. Quite apart even from the sincere opposition of the prohibitionists, the objection to Tammany, the sectional objection to New York, there is an opposition to Smith which is as authentic and, it seems to me, as poignant as his support. It is inspired by the feeling that the clamorous life of the city should not be acknowledged as the American ideal. . . . The Ku Kluxers may talk about the Pope to the lunatic fringe, but the main mass of the opposition is governed by an instinct that to accept Al Smith is to certify and sanctify a way of life that does not belong to [their America]." *Men of Destiny*, pp. 8–9.

of small-town Pennsylvania was not good politics. His identification with the sidewalks of New York was of course legitimate; his reluctance to campaign in the South—against the advice of his strategists[7]—and his jocular reference to "the states west of the Mississippi" made him doubly vulnerable to the charge of remaining a provincial New Yorker. To oppose prohibition was his prerogative; flagrantly to defy it was not. In fact, it may be suggested that had Smith entered the White House, rural America—and genteel urban Protestants as well— would have had as much cause to suffer a sense of alienation from the Presidency as would H. L. Mencken, for example, at the election of Bryan. Smith was at once a victim of prejudice and of his own clinging loyalty to his special environment. In 1932 he blamed his defeat on "bigotry"; but in an interview in May of 1937, he admitted that he had lacked a sensitivity to the social and cultural condition of those Americans he should have addressed.[8]

[7] *The New York Times*, June 15, 1926, p. 3; August 18, 1928, p. 2; August 21, 1928, pp. 1, 2; August 30, 1928, p. 1; October 9, 1928, pp. 1, 2; October 10, 1928, p. 2.
[8] *The New York Times*, October 26, 1932, p. 15; Becker: "Alfred E. Smith," p. 162.

CHAPTER VIII

The Composition of the 1928 Vote

The presidential election of 1960, in which a Catholic faced a Protestant for the second time in American history, prompted new interest in the 1928 election and led to an extensive reexamination of the earlier contest. But only one point seems to have been established with finality: that in 1928 Hoover would have won over any Democratic candidate. No Democrat, whatever his faith and whatever his political program, could have vanquished the party that was presiding over the feverish prosperity of the later twenties.

While historians have recently come to assign to prosperity the central role in the defeat of Smith, they have been less successful in evaluating the importance of the more spectacular issues of religion and prohibition; yet the weighing of these two factors as elements in the defeat of Smith has been a preoccupation of political commentators since 1928. One of the first attempts at an analysis of the election was a contemporary article written by William Ogburn and Nell Talbot, who concluded that prohibition was by far the more influential of the two issues. The authors had contrived a rather cumbersome method by which to measure statistically the relative importance of major issues in the election; but since their investigation is confined to the Smith vote and takes no account of the vote for Hoover, it in fact does not take wholly into consideration the anti-Catholic and antiprohibitionist sentiment. Other objections may be raised against the study: the authors accepted as a definition of "urban" the census bureau's misleading standard of 2,500 people; they used "foreign-born" as an all-inclusive term, and thereby ignored crucial differences in nationality; the 1920 Democratic vote, which Ogburn and Talbot set against that of 1928, was almost the worst example of "party regularity" available; for some states they measured the "wetness" factor by the slanted *Literary Digest* figures; finally, their study is limited to 173 counties chosen at random in eight states and the same statistical weight is given to each county, regardless of population.[1]

Other statistical studies of the 1928 election present contradictory findings. The most ambitious, Miss Ruth Silva's *Rum, Religion, and Votes: 1928 Re-examined* (published in 1962), concludes that Smith's membership in the Democratic party was a greater liability to him than his membership in the Roman Catholic Church and that like religion, the vote for liquor had virtually no impact on Smith's strength at the polls in 1928. The major flaw in Miss Silva's admirable pioneering work is that the Davis vote of 1924 is taken as a standard measure of Democratic strength, while it was in fact the nadir of Democratic power. This study, which is also limited to the Smith vote, needs some correction on other points: it is based on a state-by-state approach and fails to contend with possible interaction among discrete factors, it relies on the untrustworthy government census of religious groups made in 1926, it projects backward a 1934 vote on the Eighteenth Amendment for use in analyzing the 1928 vote, and it fails to take into account the strength of party organization, which may have been an important determinant of Smith's vote in the cities. Two state analyses have been made.

[1] Ogburn and Talbot: "A Measurement of the Factors in the Presidential Election of 1928," *Social Forces,* VIII (December 1929), 175–83.

One, an account of the Democratic vote in Missouri, contends that both Catholicism and repeal were important correlates of the Smith vote, but that non-Catholics were relatively unaffected by the religious factor. The other, based on the Democratic tally in Pennsylvania, finds only Catholicism to correlate with the Smith vote.[2]

The belief persists among many historians that prohibition—insofar as it can be separated from the Protestant churches—overshadowed religion as an element in the Hoover-Smith contest. In 1958 one writer asserted that "prohibition was not a straw man. . . . To millions of Protestants prohibition was . . . an issue of transcendent importance. . . . When Protestants said they opposed Smith because of his wetness, they meant precisely what they said.[3] Unquestionably, some of the professional prohibitionists—and some politicians, too—thought of nothing else; but other dry leaders were Protestant ministers for whom Catholicism was the historic enemy. More important, what of the less fanatical and more numerous drys, the rank and file of the Protestant churches? It was the mass of these voters to whom Reinhold Niebuhr referred after the election when he said that the real issues of the campaign "were hid under the decent veil of loyalty to a moral ideal —prohibition." Niebuhr argued that "there will . . . be many who will hide anti-Catholic sentiment behind their opposition to his [Smith's] prohibition views. This is certainly true in the South, where there are more dry voters

2 Ruth Silva: *Rum, Religion, and Votes: 1928 Re-examined* (University Park, Pa., 1962). See the review of Miss Silva's book by a government statistician, Philipps Cutright of the Social Security Administration, in the *American Sociological Review*, XXVIII (June 1963), 484–5, and that by Edmund A. Moore in the *American Historical Review*, LXVIII (April 1963), 840–1. Richard A. Watson: "Religion and Politics in Mid-America: Presidential Voting in Missouri, 1928 and 1960," *Mid-Continent American Studies Journal*, V (Spring 1964), 33–55; Lola S. Hobbs: "A Catholic Runs for President: 1928 in Pennsylvania," unpublished Master's essay, Pennsylvania State University, 1961, pp. 24–6. See also Harold F. Gosnell, who holds that the prohibition issue was not important. *Machine Politics: Chicago Model* (Chicago, 1937), p. 111.
3 Robert M. Miller: *American Protestantism and Social Issues, 1919–1939* (Chapel Hill, N.C., 1958), p. 51.

than teetotalers." Moreover, the number of people who drank but felt a stake in Protestantism was considerable. The secret ballots and magazine polls that were indicating a sharply waning support for prohibition provide some evidence to back up Niebuhr's charge that in 1928 the issue had become a polite veneer spread over the unsightly reality of anti-Catholicism.[4]

That prohibition was of transcendent importance in 1928 appears, in fact, most dubious, and especially in the light of evidence recently accumulated illustrating the vital role religion may play for American voters. When a Roman Catholic candidate has run for office, there has apparently emerged both a Catholic and an anti-Catholic vote. The most authoritative of the many studies indicating the significance of religion in American politics—one conducted by the Survey Research Center of the University of Michigan[5]—investigates the election of 1960 and finds that in some areas as many as forty per cent of the Democratic Protestant voters who regularly attended church threw their vote against Kennedy, and the incidence of defection was highest among the most constant of churchgoers. At the same time, claimed the Michigan survey, Kennedy received more consistent Catholic support than had any recent Democratic presidential candidate. After examining both the Protestant and Catholic vote, the authors judged that religion had deprived Kennedy, on balance, of approximately 2.2 per cent of the two-party

---

4 Reverend Bob Jones, the ardent prohibitionist, said he would rather see a saloon on every corner or a "nigger" as President than a Catholic in the White House. Gustavus Myers: *History of Bigotry in the United States* (New York, 1943), p. 326. Scott McBride, Superintendent of the Anti-Saloon League, intimated that regardless of whether the Democrats should adopt a dry plank he would vote for Hoover if Smith were nominated, as did Mrs. Booe, President of the WCTU. San Antonio *Express,* June 19, 1928, p. 4; *The New York Times,* January 10, 1928, p. 16; *World Tomorrow,* XI (December 1928), 493; *Christian Century,* XLV (September 13, 1928), 1107–8; Andrew E. Lee to George Peek, November 17, 1928, Chester C. Davis Paper. See Chap. iii, footnote 1. p. 99.

5 Angus Campbell *et al.: Elections and the Political Order* (New York, 1966), pp. 78–124.

vote. Outside the South the faith of the Democratic candidate gained him about 1.6 per cent of the vote, and in the South it lost him roughly 16.5 per cent.[6]

That in 1960 religion could still constitute so imposing a political force suggests its importance in the earlier election. For in 1928 Catholics were at a cruder stage of assimilation into Ameriman society; and their own parochialism rivaled that of their Protestant foes. In 1928, for example, many Irish and Italian election districts in New York that had shown no comparable political homogeneity in any previous presidential election gave Smith all but two or three per cent of their vote. And, of course, the Catholic support of Smith in 1928 may have been a response to the anti-Catholicism of the campaign as well as a positive affirmation of religious solidarity.

There is therefore reason to believe that religion outweighed prohibition as an election issue. Senator George Norris of Nebraska stated the case emphatically: "The greatest element involved in the landslide was religion. Regret it and conceal it as we may, religion had more to do with the defeat of Governor Smith than any other one thing." Bishop Mouzon, a leader of the anti-Smith Democrats in the South, admitted that "Whatever else may appear above the surface, this [religion] is in the deep undercurrent of our thinking." Among those who believed religion to have been a more influential issue than prohibition

[6] Campbell *et al.: Elections and the Political Order*, p. 83. Catholic support, of course, aided Kennedy in the most crucial states, and probably his minority group status won him some compensating Jewish and Negro support. Other studies of voting along religious lines include John H. Fenton: *The Catholic Vote* (New Orleans, 1960); Peter H. Odegard, ed.: *Religion and Politics* (New York, 1960); Louis Bean: *How to Predict Elections* (New York, 1940), pp. 99–104; David H. Gold: "The Influence of Religious Affiliation on Voting Behavior," unpublished doctoral dissertation, University of Chicago, 1953; Madge M. McKinney: "Religion and Elections," *Public Opinion Quarterly*, VIII (Spring 1944), 110–14; Scott Greer: "Catholic Voters and the Democratic Party," *Public Opinion Quarterly*, XXV (Winter 1961), 611–25; and Andrew R. Baggaley: "Religious Influences on Wisconsin Voting, 1928–1960," *American Political Science Review*, LVI (March 1962), 66–70.

were Smith himself, his running mate, Robinson of Arkansas, Senators Kenneth McKellar of Tennessee, Thomas P. Gore of Oklahoma, James A. Reed of Missouri, and Key Pittman of Nevada, Mark Sullivan, Bernard Baruch, James Cox, Harold Ickes, Wilbur Cash, and many others. Even Dr. Arthur J. Barton, speaking as a member of the Anti-Saloon League, said in Birmingham that religion was a more important concern than prohibition, and warned that America might come under the domination of a foreign religious "sect." Before the election *The New York Times* had predicted that Smith would lost a million votes on account of his religion; later, the paper commented on the returns: "Most of [the votes] were cast against the Democratic candidate because he is a Catholic; the rest were because he is an antiprohibitionist." "Without doubt," pronounced *Time*, "the religious question was foremost."[7]

Prohibition and religion together constituted the most flamboyant issues of the campaign. The final tally, however, reflects a conjunction of these with a number of other concerns; and a more satisfactory understanding of the election requires a closer scrutiny into the nature of the campaign and vote among several regions and classes. This inquiry must be tentative, for in the final analysis the motives of an electorate are hidden—perhaps even from itself. During the campaign it had become clear that so abstract a consideration as the image of the presidency played a key role in turning many Americans against Smith. It is this

[7] Norris is quoted in the Charlotte *Observer*, November 10, 1928, p. 5; Mouzon in *The Commonweal*, VIII (October 3, 1928), 541. Robinson to Pittman, November 21, 1928, Robinson Papers; McKellar to James D. Phelan, November 10, 1928, McKellar Papers; Gore to John J. Raskob, December 15, 1928, Gore Papers; Pittman to Franklin Roosevelt, November 13, 1928, Roosevelt Papers; Lee Meriwether: *Jim Reed, "Senatorial Immortal"* (Webster Groves, Mo., 1948), pp. 176–7; *La Follette's Magazine*, XX (December 1928), 181, 185; Sullivan to Bernard Baruch, February 28, 1928, and Baruch to Winston Churchill, September 6, 1928, Baruch Papers. The opinions of Cox, Ickes, Cash, and others are noted in Andrew Sinclair: *Prohibition: The Era of Excess* (Boston, 1962), pp. 301–2. *The New York Times*, December 23, 1927, p. 12; July 10, 1928, p. 1; November 7, 1928, p. 24.

reason that helps to explain, for example, why Smith as governor was able to carry New York State by a substantial margin only to lose it by a landslide in the presidential contest. Still, a formal investigation of some of the returns has its value.

In the South, where in 1928 there was massive defection from the Democratic party, an uneven decline in Democratic strength had been under way for some time. The beginnings of the textile industry in the cities of that section created business groups for whom the high-tariff Republican party had its attractions; guardians of free enterprise would give ear to Hoover's assertion that Smith preached "state socialism." "In Georgia, in North Carolina, in Alabama, in fact all through the South," commented *The Nation*, "the industrial development has been enormous. The manufacturers and the managers of mills and factories and many of their employees have become Republicans because they felt it was to their financial interests to do so." Smith, after all, had earned much of his reputation by sponsoring labor reforms. The Republican inroads had come first in Florida, where an influx of northerners was rapidly building a two-party system. Between 1916 and 1924 the Republican vote in that state had doubled; and it doubled again between 1924 and 1932, in spite of the depression. In Texas also the Republican vote was on the increase during the twenties. Other states, such as Virginia, North Carolina, and Tennessee, had long registered strong Republican minorities. In 1920 Tennessee had even given the Republican candidate its electoral vote, while the border states of Kentucky, West Virginia, Maryland, and Oklahoma also voted for Harding.[8]

[8] According to the 1927 manufacturing census, the South's share of the cotton textile industry was, by yardage, sixty-seven per cent. "The community acknowledged the standing of the industry," writes a labor historian, "by yielding to its management the decisive voice in shaping southern affairs." Irving Bernstein: *A History of the American Worker: The Lean Years* (Boston, 1960), pp. 2–3. Dewey M. Grantham, Jr., observed that "it was becoming easier [in the twenties] to think of Republican affiliations in a region so strongly committed to the gospel of business expansion and economic diversification." *The Democratic South* (Athens, Ga., 1963), p. 66. *The Nation*, CXXVII (November 21, 1928), 537;

The election of 1928 simply introduced new and more powerful factors to widen a small but already discernible crack in the
South. Al Smith's stand against prohibition ended an alliance
between the drys and the Democrats that had prevailed in the
region for decades. The region was strongly susceptible to the
religious issue; the loss of southern clergymen was a major
handicap, for in the South the churches wielded great power.
Sporting Al Smith barber shops and Herbert Hoover butcher
stores, the South in 1928 enjoyed its first real presidential campaign since Reconstruction. Even that part of the region which
had most clearly represented the "Solid South" nearly went
Republican; the popular vote in the eleven former Confederate
states from Virginia to Texas was 47.8 per cent for Hoover and
52.2 per cent for Smith. The border states of Oklahoma,
Kentucky, West Virginia, Maryland, and Delaware gave
Hoover 60 per cent of the vote and Smith only 40 per cent.

But in 1928 the overriding political concern throughout much
of the South was not prosperity, nor religion, nor prohibition;
it was, as usual, loyalty to the Democratic party—and beyond,
of course, loyalty to the racial commitment ingrained in the
southern Democracy. In 1928 the claims of the party that symbolized regional tradition and white supremacy clashed for a
moment with the claims of Protestant Anglo-Saxonism. "Southerners were frankly skeptical," according to an observer of the
campaign, "of maintaining white supremacy in a two-party
system." Throughout the southern countryside the strength of
the Democratic presidential vote varied directly with the ratio
of Negro to white. The New York *World* observed that in 1928
this pattern held true on the statewide level; that it held on a
local level as well, V. O. Key carefully verified in his *Southern
Politics*.⁹ Counties such as those composing "Little Dixie" in

---

New Republic, XLVII (August 4, 1926), 296–7; Deskins: "The Presidential
Election in North Carolina," *passim*; *Literary Digest*, IC (November 24,
1928), 8–9.
9 "The Democratic solidity of the several [southern] states," noted the
World, "varies directly with the proportion of Negroes in the population;
and the Solid South—what is left of it—was not voting against the
Eighteenth Amendment. It was still voting against the Fifteenth." Quoted

Missouri, once containing a large Negro population though now preponderantly white, also remained loyal to Smith; so did counties in the Ozarks and elsewhere that had been settled by emigrating white families from slaveholding areas. Democrats spread unlikely stories about Hoover courting Negro girls while directing flood relief in 1927, and dancing with a Mary Booze, a colored Republican committeewoman, in Mound Bayou, Mississippi. They observed that Hoover had abolished segregation in the Department of Commerce. Southern Republicans in turn tried to portray Smith as a liberal on the race question: pictures of him dictating to a Negro secretary were widely circulated, and in Maryland Senator Millard Tydings charged that Republicans hired drinking Negroes to ride through the East Shore area in cars emblazoned with Smith signs.[1]

But if the campaign disrupted the Democratic party in the South, it invigorated the party in other areas. Among these were a number of farming regions.[2] In the twenties the farmers had

---

in the *Literary Digest,* IC (November 24, 1928), 8. V. O. Key: *Southern Politics in State and Nation* (New York, 1949), pp. 318–29.

[1] In some states, such as Mississippi, the Republican organization was controlled by Negroes. *The Independent,* XXX (March 10, 1928), 227. Senator Heflin's ravings against Smith in the Senate often settled down eventually on the Negro issue; see, for example, the *Congressional Record, Senate,* May 3, 1928, pp. 7698–9. Heflin defined the issues as "Race, Rum, Romanism, and Raskob." On racial appeals, see Herbert Hoover to Henry W. Anderson, October 11, 1928; Lizzie Bankhead Hotchkiss to Hoover, Box L/512; Eugene P. Booze to Hoover, October 22, 1928, Hoover Papers. Frank Mitchell: "Embattled Democrats: Missouri Democratic Politics, 1919–1932," unpublished doctoral dissertation, University of Missouri, 1964; John H. Fenton: *Politics in the Border States* (New Orleans, 1957), p. 10; Paul Lewinson: *Race, Class, Party: A History of Negro Politics and White Suffrage in the South* (New York, 1932), p. 180; Hugh D. Reagan, "Race as a Factor in the Presidential Election of 1928 in Alabama," *Alabama Review,* XIX (January 1966), 5–19.

[2] In contrast to the farm revolt, labor had no major grievance in 1928. Most AFL leaders preferred Smith, whose labor record in New York was longstanding and impressive, but some important unionists, including John L. Lewis, William L. Hutchinson, and Daniel Tobin, endorsed Hoover. "It is noteworthy," Vaughn D. Bornet writes, that "union leaders who came to the support of Smith in the campaign seldom, if ever, attacked Hoover." *Labor Politics in a Democratic Republic* (Washington, D.C.,

suffered more perhaps than at any time in the recent past, and the prolonged agricultural depression was wearing down their patience with Calvin Coolidge. By the summer of 1928 the prices of wheat, corn, and wool had reached their lowest point in two years, and there was no fortuitous rise before the election, as there had been in 1924. At the Houston convention, a number of farm leaders, angered at Coolidge's vitriolic opposition to the McNary-Haugen bills and at the silence of the Republican platform upon the scheme the bills had embodied, were officially welcomed into the fold by Clement Shaver and Jesse Jones. Hoover's long residence in England was also a count against him with isolationist midwesterners.

The agricultural leaders George Peek and Chester C. Davis, who had helped Senator McNary to draft the farm bill, were sent into their native territory as early as the spring of 1927 to direct the Smith campaign; there they were aided by grants from the New York Democratic headquarters totaling more than half a million dollars. Both men were well aware of Smith's hesitation to commit himself on the farm problem, particularly the controversial McNary-Haugen plan for which he had declared himself "in principle"—then repudiated as it had been worked out in the three congressional bills of 1924, 1927, and 1928. Peek and particularly Davis recognized that Republicans had actually suggested proposals more specific for the solution of the farm problem than had the Democrats. Yet they also believed that the Democrats would be more likely to experiment with McNary-Haugen, since the Republican administration had fixed upon its party a policy of opposition to the plan. And they thought that Hoover, from his Food Administration days onward, had shown little genuine concern or understanding for the farmer. During the summer and fall Davis and Peek contributed all their energies to the campaign, particularly in

---

1964), pp. 132-3, 163, 166-7, 236. Organized labor was not only divided but weak and cautious, having lost almost forty per cent of its membership during the past decade. Bernstein: *The Lean Years*, pp. 96-104. Donald Richberg to Martin F. Ryan, June 4, 1928, and B. M. Jewell to D. B. Robertson, July 16, 1928, Richberg Papers.

the ten states in which the combined votes of John W. Davis and La Follette would have comprised a majority in 1924.[3]

The work of the two agricultural spokesmen, and the desertions of a few important Republican officeholders, such as Governor Frank W. Murphy of Minnesota, and Governor Adam McMullen and Senator George Norris of Nebraska, resulted in a degree of Democratic success in the 1928 presidential returns. "Republican majorities in most of the farm states from Illinois to Montana," wrote Gilbert Fite, "were drastically reduced." And reduced they were in some Protestant as well as in numerous Catholic rural counties; and as Fite shows, most of the 1924 Progressive vote went to Smith rather than to the Republican party from which a considerable part of the Progressive electorate had been drawn in that area. "The significant fact," Fite concluded "is that the drift was Democratic in a substantial number of farm states as early as 1928."[4] If Smith had been a

[3] Peek confessed that "it may be true that we do not know what the Democratic administration would do for agriculture, but on the other hand there is probably some hope in that direction and none with Hoover." Peek to S. P. Bush, July 19, 1928, Peek Papers. Gilbert C. Fite: "The Agricultural Issue in the Presidential Campaign of 1928," *Mississippi Valley Historical Review*, XXXVII (March 1951), 659–60, 662, 664. Fite in his book on Peek refers to Hoover as an "arch enemy of American agriculture." *George N. Peek and the Fight for Farm Parity* (Norman, Okla., 1954), pp. 125–30. Bernard Baruch, in a letter to Smith, also noted that "the farmers look upon Hoover as their arch enemy." July 3, 1928, Baruch Papers. The manuscripts in the new Hoover Library may alter this view of his farm policies. United States Department of Agriculture, *Yearbook of Agriculture, 1928* (Washington, D.C., 1929), pp. 686, 714, 959; *The New York Times*, August 3, 1928, p. 1; August 4, 1928, pp. 1, 4; James K. Pollock, "Campaign Funds in 1928," *American Political Science Review*, XXIII (February 1929), 66.

[4] Senator Peter Norbeck observed: "It was not the strength of the Republican position and Mr. Hoover that entirely account [*sic*] for victory —it was fully as much the weakness of the opposition." Norbeck had earlier written to Peek that "Smith with the Tammany connections and New York residence seems so remote and unpromising." Norbeck to Mrs. E. R. Doering, November 9, 1928, Norbeck to Peek, July 14, 1928, Peek Papers. Chester C. Davis, in a memorandum written two weeks before the election, named the religious factor as the chief obstacle to a Democratic success. September 15, 1928, Chester C. Davis Papers.

candidate more personally appealing to the prairie voter, the Democratic showing might have been still more impressive.

The sign of new life in the Democratic party was as visible in the Far West as in the Northeast and farm belt. In the Pacific states, where the La Follette vote had cut deep into the Democratic vote, that party's share of the two-party vote jumped from 28 per cent in 1920 and 16 in 1924 to 42 in 1928. In the Mountain states the increase was only slightly less. No issue such as that of peace restored the balance between the parties struck in the West in 1916, but the Democratic identity was apparently progressive enough to retrieve some of the Far West's radical vote lost to third-party candidates in 1920 and particularly in 1924.

More important than these gains, however, was the expansion in the urban Democratic vote. And because of its effect upon Democratic fortunes in the cities the candidacy of Governor Smith, regardless of his personal shortcomings as a campaigner, was undoubtedly a significantly healthy event in the evolution of the Democracy. Smith won the nation's two most urbanized and most Catholic states, Massachusetts and Rhode Island, where a slump in textile production also played a part. Throughout the new America of the metropolis, the immigrant, and the Catholic Church the story was the same. Because of Smith's remarkable performance in these areas, Walter Lippmann wrote that the chief result of the Smith candidacy was the reconstruction of the Democratic party and its liberation from Bryan and the South. The Smith victory was not a conversion of Republicans; that party apparently had used up its male voting potential in the cities in 1916 and its female potential in 1920. It was not that Hoover lacked urban support: on the contrary, he won more urban votes than any former Republican presidential candidate, building his strength on old-stock and Negro communities strong in the cities. But in metropolitan America taken as a whole, the Democrats gained more.[5]

5 Carl Degler has shown that in 1928 Democratic strength in cities with a high population of foreign stock expanded enormously, while in preponderantly old-stock urban centers it fluctuated little in comparison with

The massive immigration of 1900 to 1914 was apparently paying dividends in votes in 1928. Part of the explanation for Smith's strength in the immigrant cities, however, was an apparent rise in voting among Roman Catholic women, a phenomenon that Samuel Lubell has noted. In Boston it is possible to measure the voting by sex of those ethnic groups that appear in large numbers in unpublished government lists of 1930 census reports. Unfortunately, the largest Roman Catholic group—the Irish—no longer appear markedly as "foreign-born" in the 1930 census. Within heavily Italian census tracts, however, we find the voting precincts where female registration rose by twenty-nine per cent, and precincts identified as strongly Irish by names appearing on voting lists show a comparable rise in registration of women. But in another section of the country there were other women of conservative tradition who, hitherto reluctant to assume the prerogative of the vote, were drawn to the polls by the angry issues of 1928. In the South as well as in the Northeast the total vote rose so sharply, as Table XI indicates, as to suggest a considerably increased participation by women.[6]

1920. And in cities of native population outside the South, the Republican vote showed no comparable rise. It must be observed, however, that this analysis has only limited value, since 1920, when the immigrant disaffected more sharply from the Democratic party than at any other presidential election in this century, is the worst year to choose for a comparison of urban voting. Degler: "American Political Parties and the Rise of the City: An Interpretation," *Journal of American History*, LI (June 1964), 50–9. Samuel J. Eldersveld analyzes the expanding political strength in urban areas since 1920 in "The Influence of Metropolitan Party Pluralities in Presidential Elections Since 1920," *American Political Science Review*, XLIII (December 1949), 1189–1206, and "A Study of Urban Electoral Trends in Michigan, 1920–1940," unpublished doctoral dissertation, University of Michigan, 1946. The Republican National Chairman, Dr. Hubert Work, had earlier designated the East as the battleground of the campaign. *The New York Times*, August 26, 1928, p. 5. *Yale Review*, XVIII (September 1928), 18–27.

[6] Lubell: *The Future of American Politics* (New York, 1952), p. 40. The reluctance of women in southern and border states to vote had been for several years a matter of concern to Cordell Hull and other national chairmen. A rise in female registration in predominantly Catholic New York City is noted in *The New York Times*, October 11, 1928, p. 2, and

The unusually high 1928 presidential ethnic vote could be considered in a sense deviant, since it went to a candidate who would have a striking appeal for Americans of immigrant background. And the election was one of a series in which peculiar circumstances existed capable of deflecting the immigrant ballot

TABLE XI

The Ten States with the Greatest Increase
in Presidential Voting, 1924 to 1928

East	Per Cent Increase	South	Per Cent Increase
New Jersey	40	Florida	50
Massachusetts	35	Louisiana	50*
Pennsylvania	30	Virginia	50
New York	25	Arkansas	30
		Alabama	30
		Georgia	28

* The population of Louisiana was 40 per cent Roman Catholic in 1928.

---

the Greensboro, North Carolina, *Daily News* observed a large turnout of women in its locality, November 6, 1928, p. 1. In the nation at large registration rose from twenty-nine to forty-three million. *The New York Times,* October 29, 1928, pp. 1, 2; United States Bureau of the Census: "Machine Lists of Ethnic Characteristics in the 1930 Census" (unpublished); "Registered Voters (Women), State Election, November 4, 1924, and November 6, 1928," *Boston City Document Number Eleven,* pp. 142, 152. The complete redistricting of Boston in 1925 hinders comparisons between the elections of 1924 and 1928. In the measurement of Italian female registration, precincts 1, 2, 3, 5, and 7 in ward three and precinct 5 in ward one in 1928 were compared with almost identical areas in 1924: precincts 1, 2, 3, 5, and 6 in ward five, and precinct 5 in ward two.

from its normal course: in 1920 several immigrant communities usually loyal to the Democratic party reacted to Versailles by turning to the Republican nominee; the 1924 candidacy of La Follette, which drew votes away from the major parties, attracted many of the city poor; the depression worked violence upon the politics of 1932. But in 1928 the immigrants did more than respond to the nomination of Al Smith; their presence in the Democracy effected that nomination—and the Republicans had no comparable electorate that could have won its party to a Smith. However special its context, moreover, the election of 1928 must have permanently strengthened some immigrant Democratic machines and thereby contributed to the massive party victory among immigrant-stock Americans in the depression vote of 1932. For an indication of the trend in the ethnic electorate during those years and the period immediately preceding them, at least two cities—New York and Chicago—are susceptible of close statistical analysis; within these two cities, in fact, along with Boston which has been the subject of a close study in this period, lived nearly half of America's foreign-born and their children.

Nowhere in America have immigrant communities remained more politically self-assertive than in Manhattan, where in 1920, 76.5 per cent of the white stock were themselves foreign born or the children of foreign-born parents;[7] and for a study of ethnic groupings and voting habits during the years that spanned the Versailles conference and the candidacy of Roosevelt, the pioneering census work of Walter Laidlaw, a skilled statistician employed by the New York City Department of Health, provides an excellent foundation. In an attempt to make more efficient the activity of New York's public and private social-service agencies, Laidlaw in 1920 gathered census data of richly inclusive scope on a number of territories in and around the city; and included, of course, was information on the race and national origins of the inhabitants. The Welfare Council of

[7] Walter Laidlaw, ed.: *Statistical Sources for Demographic Studies of Greater New York, 1920* (New York, 1922), p. xxix.

Greater New York collected similar materials for 1930. In both surveys, the data were obtained for relatively small census areas known then as sanitary districts—areas considerably smaller than assembly districts but more sizable than election districts. The information on geographic ethnic patterns obtainable from the Laidlaw and Welfare Council reports is especially trustworthy, since the investigators determined origins not upon the occasionally deceptive basis of surname, but upon personal interviews.[8]

The two surveys can therefore be of great use in the delineation of national and racial communities within the city of New York. To determine something of the nature of ethnic voting for the presidency in the twenties, the historian has to isolate on the basis of the Laidlaw and Welfare Council findings as many ethnically homogeneous sanitary districts as possible, seek out election districts lying wholly within these areas, and examine the presidential vote within those smaller sections. The 1920 ethnic figures may be used for the elections of 1916, 1920, and 1924; the 1930 data for the elections of 1928 and 1932.

Such an approach has its flaws. It does not take into account differences in the social or economic composition of the districts similar in ethnic stock. But in the early twentieth century such differences within ethnic groups were by no means so common as today, and sufficiently varied areas are ordinarily included in an examination to offset any danger of social or economic bias. Another shortcoming to our method lies in the possibility that any particular election district might represent an enclave of people ethnically divergent from those who dominate the larger

[8] Laidlaw, ed.: *Statistical Sources for Demographic Studies of Greater New York, 1920;* a summary of Laidlaw's earlier work may be found in *The New York Times,* April 1, 1923, IV, 11–12. See also Laidlaw, ed.: *Population of the City of New York, 1890–1930* (New York, 1932); Florence DuBois, ed.: *Population in Health Areas: New York City, 1930–1931,* Research Bureau, Welfare Council of New York City, Section 7 of Study 10 of the Research Bureau; *Heads of Families by Color and Nativity and Country of Birth of Foreign Born Head, by Health Areas, New York City, 1930–1934,* Research Bureau, Welfare Council of New York City, Section 9 of Study 10 of the Research Bureau.

sanitary district. Here, surnames appearing on voter registration lists—while less reliable than were the interviews employed by Laidlaw—can help to indicate whether an election district seems to correspond ethnically to the sanitary area that includes it. In the last analysis, aggregate voting studies are always hampered by the incompleteness of the data upon which they rely. Yet such figures as are within reach throw considerable light upon the politics of New York's national and racial communities.

Four immigrant groups—the German, the Irish, the Italian, and the Jewish—are sufficiently populous to warrant examination; and to these we may add the Negro, more isolated than the immigrants from native white society and headed for a major role in big-city ghetto politics. The Irish and Germans came to New York too early to count heavily as foreign-born even in the 1920 Laidlaw census; therefore it has been necessary to rely somewhat more heavily upon surnames on registration lists. The German-American vote can be followed closely. In 1916 the New York *Staats-Zeitung und Herald* declared for the Republican candidate, but its appeal went unheeded among the city's Germans. After the war they may have been motivated by what Samuel Lubell, in referring to the McCarthy era, calls the "politics of revenge" and by a desire to rid themselves of the inferior status they had acquired during the war. A vote for isolation could serve both ends; it could work vengeance upon Wilson, and it could demonstrate that German-Americans, like their fellow countrymen, wished to preserve separate the purity of the American motherland. The election issue, declared the *Staats-Zeitung*, was Wilson and the League versus Harding and Americanism. Germans in Manhattan gave Harding a spanking majority in 1920.[9]

Yet the traditional attachment held by New York's Germans for the Democratic party seems to have been only temporarily disrupted by World War I. In 1924 the Democratic German

[9] New York Bureau of Elections, *The City Record*, *passim*; *Staats-Zeitung und Herald*, November 1, 1916, p. 6; November 2, 1920, p. 4; *Harper's Magazine*, CCXII (April 1956), 29-35.

vote eclipsed the Republican; the percentages would probably have approached those of 1916 but for the candidacy of Robert La Follette, who had the endorsement of the *Staats-Zeitung*. La Follette was attractive to many German-Americans as an opponent of American involvement in the war, and he had a pro-

The German Vote, 1916–32: Support for Political Parties in Sanitary Districts of New York County Having a German Population of Approximately 70 Per Cent.

Year	Democratic Per Cent	Republican Per Cent	Third Party Per Cent
1916	62	38	—
1920	28	61	11 (Socialist)
1924	46	37	17 (Progressive)
1928	73	27	—
1932	80	20	—

gressive German following in the Middle West. By 1928 the Germans in New York county had arrived at a firm commitment to the Democratic party that many voters were not to attain until 1932. Possibly the local origins and popularity of Smith accounted for much of his strength among the German-Americans of New York, but his stand against prohibition increased their attachment. In addition, many Germans were Roman Catholic. The *Staats-Zeitung* supported both Smith and Roosevelt, calling the latter the "hope of America."[1]

In 1916 the Irish *World* and *Gaelic American* condemned

[1] November 3, 1924, p. 6; November 1, 1928, p. 6; October 21, 1932, p. 2; November 9, 1932, p. 6.

Wilson as an anti-Irish bigot.[2] But no widespread Irish defection from the Democracy occurred until 1920, when Wilson was excoriated by the Irish press for his part in the hated peace conference that bolstered the position of the British Empire.[3] After deserting Wilson in a predictable but not a striking

The Irish Vote, 1916–32: Support for Political Parties in Sanitary Districts of New York County Having an Irish Population of Approximately 70 Per Cent.

Year	Democratic Per Cent	Republican Per Cent	Third Party Per Cent
1916	64	36	—
1920	47	50	3 (Socialist)
1924	63	25	12 (Progressive)
1928	82	18	—
1932	81	19	—

fashion, the Irish returned to the Democratic-Tammany fold in 1924.[4] And in 1928 they gave to the Democratic party a vote higher than that of any other major nationality group—a vote that was not to be exceeded even in 1932. A prominent consideration in 1928 was Hoover's identification with England; he was denounced by the *Gaelic American* as an Anglophile.[5]

[2] Irish *World*, October 28, 1916, p. 4; *Gaelic American*, October 21, 1916, p. 4.

[3] See, for example, *Gaelic American*, October 30, 1920, p. 4. Cox said he was opposed by "a militantly anti-Wilson Catholic oligarchy." *Journey Through My Years* (New York, 1946), pp. 273–4.

[4] The newspapers declared for La Follette; Irish *World*, November 1, 1924, pp. 3–4; *Gaelic American*, October 25, 1924, p. 1.

[5] July 7, 1928, p. 1; Irish *World*, October 13, 1928, p. 4.

But John W. Davis, the Democratic candidate in 1924, had himself been Ambassador to England under Wilson and yet had won the support of the Irish. Smith's appeal, we may presume, was chiefly as a fellow religionist and fellow son of Erin. The

The Italian Vote, 1916–32: Support for Political Parties in Sanitary Districts of New York County Having an Italian Population of Approximately 85 Per Cent.

Year	Democratic Per Cent	Republican Per Cent	Third Party Per Cent
1916	63	37	—
1920	47	50	3 (Socialist)
1924	48	44	8 (Progressive)
1928	77	23	—
1932	79	21	—

depression, of course, brought its own reason for Irish working-class support of the Democrats.

The vote of the Italian Catholic bloc offers no surprises. In spite of *Il Telegrafo*'s declaration for Hughes in 1916, the Italian community supported Wilson enthusiastically. In 1920 the Italians recoiled from the hated Wilson Democracy; in 1924 they were again preponderantly Democratic. As presidential candidate, Governor Smith scored an overwhelming victory among his Italian coreligionists whose ties to the Democratic party were later strengthened by the depression years. *Il Telegrafo*, indifferent to politics since the defeat of Cox, implicitly declared both for Smith and Roosevelt.[6]

[6] November 2, 1916, p. 5; November 3, 1916, p. 5; October 25, 1928, p. 4; November 6, 1928, p. 4; November 4, 1932, p. 4; November 5, 1932, p. 6; November 7, 1932, p. 6.

The Manhattan Negro remained faithful to the Grand Old Party until after 1928. The ties of loyalty that bound the Negro when he cast his first vote were not broken until the depression. In 1916 the New York *Age* vigorously condemned the southerner in the White House and charged him with wholesale dis-

The Negro Vote, 1916–32: Support for Political Parties in Sanitary Districts of New York County Having a Negro Population of Approximately 95 Per Cent.

Year	Democratic Per Cent	Republican Per Cent	Third Party Per Cent
1916	26	74	—
1920	3	94	3 (Socialist)
1924	28	69	3 (Progressive)
1928	41	59	—
1932	58	42	—

crimination in making federal appointments; the newspaper could also have mentioned the practice of racial segregation in the executive departments, which southern cabinet members had introduced or strengthened. In 1920 the *Age* insisted that "the important thing at the moment for the Negro is the destruction of the national political power of the South." The unusually high Negro Republican vote in 1920 probably resulted from Cox's pronouncement, which was not aimed specifically at Negroes, that this was a "white man's country," his stated belief that Negroes could never attain social equality in this country, and the widely publicized stories that Harding had some Negro ancestry. In contrast, the Republican National Committee in 1920 barred local conventions at hotels discriminating against

Negroes, the party platform strongly endorsed a federal anti-lynching law, and Harding himself spoke out for such a measure. In 1924 the *Age* endorsed Coolidge; third parties, which included anti-Negro unions, won few votes in Harlem.[7]

In 1928 the newspaper, its support thrown to Hoover, ran a picture of the "Jim Crow wire cage," a fenced-off area in which Negroes were forced to sit at the Houston convention. The paper noted the vice presidential candidate's denunciation of "Niggers" while he was governor of Arkansas; and it made much of the lynching of a Negro at Houston on the eve of the convention—the first lynching that had occurred in the city in more than fifty years. The new *Amsterdam News* also endorsed Hoover in 1928. Raskob's Democratic National Committee donated $125,000 to the Smith Colored League for proselytizing among Negroes in the large cities, but Smith himself expressed few sentiments calculated to win the Negro vote. Yet the Democrats gained impressively among the colored voters in the presidential election. The Negro vote may perhaps be explained in part by the Republicans' refusal to seat a number of Negro representatives at their Kansas City convention; the act amounted to an endorsement of "Lily White" organizations in the South. More important, Al Smith had already won the majority support of the Negroes in Manhattan's nineteenth and twenty-first assembly districts: in these areas of Harlem enough Negroes had split their tickets in 1924 to swing their districts

7 Henry Blumenthal: "Woodrow Wilson and the Race Question," *Journal of Negro History*, XLVIII (January 1963), 1–21; Richard B. Sherman: "The Harding Administration and the Negro: An Opportunity Lost," *Journal of Negro History*, XLIX (July 1964), 151–68. A Negro leader in Ohio complained to Democratic National Chairman George White about a state Democratic pamphlet that warned of "Negro domination" in case Harding should win. Fairbank Tucker to White, December 12, 1920, George White Papers. Arthur S. Link: *Wilson: The New Freedom* (Princeton, 1956), pp. 246–53; Wesley Bagby: *The Road to Normalcy* (Baltimore, 1962), pp. 162–3; New York *Age*, October 19, 1916, p. 4; October 26, 1916, p. 4; October 20, 1920, p. 1; October 25, 1924, p. 4; *The New York Times*, June 4, 1920, p. 1; September 18, 1920, p. 14; October 15, 1920, p. 3; October 27, 1920, p. 9.

to Smith as gubernatorial candidate; and again in 1926 Smith won more of the Negro vote than did his Republican opponent. In 1932, while the *Amsterdam News* again favored Hoover, the *Age* withheld its support. Unsure itself where the hope for equality might lie, the *Age* left the decision to the economically

The Jewish Vote, 1916–32: Support for Political Parties in Sanitary Districts of New York County Having a Jewish Population of Approximately 90 Per Cent.

Year	Democratic Per Cent	Republican Per Cent	Third Party Per Cent
1916	55	45	—
1920	19	43	38 (Socialist)
1924	51	27	22 (Progressive)
1928	72	28	—
1932	82	18	—

distressed Negro voters, for whom, it would appear from the result, the depression was the paramount issue.[8]

Jewish voters in 1916 could bear in mind Wilson's appointment of Louis D. Brandeis to the Supreme Court. The first Jew to receive such an appointment, Brandeis was a leading Zionist. In addition, Jews wanted to avoid war with Germany, whose record toward the Jews contrasted favorably with that of its

[8] New York *Age*, October 13, 1928, p. 1; October 20, 1928, p. 1; October 24, 1928, p. 16; November 3, 1928, p. 1; November 5, 1932, p. 4; *Amsterdam News*, October 24, 1928, p. 6; October 2, 1932, p. 6; *The New York Times*, November 6, 1924, p. 6; November 3, 1926, p. 2; August 25, 1928, p. 4; *New Republic*, CXXVII (October 17, 1928), 392–4; Pollock: "Campaign Funds in 1928," 66; Elbert L. Tatum: *The Changed Political Thought of the Negro, 1915–1940* (New York, 1951), pp. 94–112.

great eastern rival, Russia. Aroused perhaps by the eastern European territorial settlements, the failure at Versailles to create a new Jewish homeland, and the administration's treatment of radicals, many of whom were Jewish, Jews voted against the Democrats in 1920. They gave a heavier vote to the jailed Socialist candidate Eugene Debs than to Cox; and in 1924 Robert La Follette also won considerable Jewish support. But during the twenties, urban Jews voted more and more heavily Democratic. Governor Smith's extensive employment of Jewish advisers, such as Judge Joseph Proskauer and Belle Moskowitz, helped him to win the Jewish vote. Jews, moreover, could consider Smith a fellow victim of Klan bigotry. Franklin Roosevelt —who made overtures to Jewish voters, claiming Henry Morgenthau, Jr., as his friend and neighbor among the farmers of Dutchess County—won in 1932 the overwhelming approval of Manhattan's Jews.[9]

For Chicago, population figures almost as useful as those for Manhattan reveal the voting of Germans, Jews, Poles, and Negroes between 1916 and 1932. The vote in Chicago during this period followed some of the Manhattan patterns, but it also also reacted to variations in region, religion, and degree of cultural homogeneity. Particularly noticeable is the absence of Governor Smith as a familiar and popular Democrat. Chicago's Germans adhered to the Democratic party in considerably smaller proportion than the Germans of Manhattan; the election of 1932 was perhaps the first in which they gave a majority to the national Democratic ticket, while Manhattan Germans voted Republican only once between 1916 and 1932. The comparative weakness of Roman Catholicism among Chicago Germans may in part account for the difference; and because of their location in the American heartland, Chicago's Germans may have been more isolationist than Manhattan's. In 1928 Hoover was remembered for his postwar German relief work in the face of adverse opinion at home, as well as his rejection of national

[9] Lawrence H. Fuchs: *The Political Behavior of American Jews* (Glencoe, Ill., 1956), pp. 57–69.

Chicago, *1916–32: Support for Political Parties in Sanitary Districts Having German, Jewish, Polish, and Negro Populations of 70 to 95 Per Cent.*

	Democratic Per Cent	Republican Per Cent	Third Party Per Cent
1916			
German	44	56	
Jewish	57	43	
Polish	73	27	
Negro	31	69	
1920			
German	10	80	10
Jewish	28	61	11
Polish	50	45	5
Negro	6	93	1
1924			
German	18	52	30
Jewish	37	43	20
Polish	51	37	12
Negro	5	91	4
1928			
German	45	55	
Jewish	78	22	
Polish	83	17	
Negro	29	71	
1932			
German	59	41	
Jewish	85	15	
Polish	85	15	
Negro	30	70	

origins for computing immigration figures, while Smith was an unfamiliar figure.[1]

Jewish voters in Chicago failed to return to the Democratic fold in 1924, and in this they resembled Jews in the nation at large who remained Republican until 1932. Though the Chicago *Defender* did break its Republican traditions by supporting Smith in 1928, Negroes in that city were slower to become Democrats than were those of Manhattan, where Governor Smith could work his influence upon the colored minority. Initially Democratic but alienated from Wilson in 1920, the Poles gave enormous support to Smith and Roosevelt.

In Boston the first statistics on ethnic composition by sanitary district were gathered by the federal government in 1930, and they remain unpublished. The voting of Boston's Irish, who supported Smith as enthusiastically as they repudiated Wilson, is well chronicled on the ward level in J. Joseph Huthmacher's *Massachusetts People and Politics, 1919–1933* (Cambridge, 1958). Of the other ethnic groups in Boston, only the Italian is numerous enough in the government lists to assure accurate measurement. The Boston Italians showed unusual loyalty to Wilson in 1916 before deserting him in 1920. And not even in New York did they vote in more solid ranks for Al Smith in 1928.

In sum, that there was a vote cast specifically against Smith and against his social background tends to obscure the genuine assets his candidacy brought to his party. After the election a friend wrote to Roosevelt: "The Democratic Party is stronger

[1] The table on Chicago voting is based on election ward maps of the city and on Ernest W. Burgess and Charles Newcomb: *Census Data of the City of Chicago, 1920* (Chicago, 1931); *Census Data of the City of Chicago, 1930* (Chicago, 1933). Chicago *Defender*, October 20, 1928, p. 4. Harold F. Gosnell estimates the 1920 Negro vote in Chicago at 95 per cent Republican (as against 93 per cent recorded above) and declares that Hoover received 15 per cent less Negro support than Coolidge (as against 20 per cent above). *Negro Politicians: The Rise of Negro Politics in Chicago* (Chicago, 1935), pp. 28–9. Arthur W. Thurner, "The Impact of Ethnic Groups on the Democratic Party in Chicago, 1920–28," unpublished doctoral dissertation, University of Chicago, 1966.

than it has been since the Civil War."[2] Roosevelt agreed. And it could be expected that if this Protestant Democrat were nominated in 1932 he would draw back into the party the South and other areas where anti-Catholic sentiment had damaged it. At the same time, the Democratic ethnic vote, already clearly

The Italian Vote in Boston, 1916–32: Support for Political Parties in Sanitary Districts in Boston Having an Italian Population of Approximately 75 Per Cent.

Year	Democratic Per Cent	Republican Per Cent	Third Party Per Cent
1916	67	33	—
1920	43	50	7 (Socialist)
1924	45	35	20 (Progressive)
1928	95	5	—
1932	78	22	—

growing early in the decade, and now firmed and made assertive in the candidacy of Smith, would probably remain in that column in 1932, even if Smith were not renominated. The reconstruction of the party had been handsomely begun by Governor Smith; when Governor Roosevelt won the next presidential election, the party had established its strength far more soundly than ever before in the twentieth century.

[2] William F. Haywood to Roosevelt, December 11, 1928, Democratic National Committee Papers, Box 80, Colorado.

Franklin D. Roosevelt
and the Depression

The depression of 1929 offered Democrats of varying outlook the first concrete issue in many years upon which they might take common ground. Political as well as economic realities would appear at first sight to have made almost certain a new progressive course for the Democracy. As the party in power at the time of the crash, the GOP was in some degree politically identifiable with it, and would have a hard time trying to present itself as the representative of fresh departures and energies. Hoover himself, despite the notable innovations of his presidential years, simply would not think his way into certain possibilities—massive direct federal relief, for example. Conceivably, he needed more time than was to be allotted him. And if the Republicans could neither convincingly nor willingly seize the progressive standard we might expect that with something that approaches the inevitability of dialectic, the Democratic would become the party of reform.

But the reasoning here is retrospective. In fact, the politics of the thirties might have taken any number of logically definable courses. The bitterness of the previous decade need not have dissipated within the Democratic party; finding their mutual company intolerable, the leaders along with the factions for which they spoke could have found their separate ways into other political organizations more directly expressive of depression ideologies: the Republican and Socialist parties, some Dixiecrat splinter of populist hue. Or the party leadership might have taken on a hard rightist character. Al Smith, whose origins and career had made of him an ambivalent mixture of the urban progressive and the individualist conservative, was fast settling into the latter mode, and other important Democrats were of similar persuasion. In 1931 John W. Davis condemned Hoover for "following the road to socialism at a rate never before equaled in time of peace. . . ." At the Jackson and Jefferson Day dinners of 1932, Governor Cox was demanding a balanced budget and a sales tax, Davis was warning against persecution of the rich, and Smith—who did go so far as to declare for a federal bond issue to pay for unemployment relief—was implicitly labeling as a "demagogic appeal" Roosevelt's plea for the "forgotten man at the bottom of the economic pyramid." There were progressive stirrings among the congressional Democrats— at least in 1932, when the rank and file in the House broke away from the generally conservative policy its leaders had been pursuing and threw its weight behind such measures as a surtax of up to sixty-five per cent. But there was nothing to ensure that the congressional revolt could translate itself into a firm and organized movement. Had the views of Smith, Davis, and Cox prevailed within the Democratic hierarchy, the party might have crumbled under economic stress; or if a Democratic conservative had won the presidency in 1932, quite conceivably the Republicans in time of defeat, rediscovering their progressive tradition recently embodied in Theodore Roosevelt and Hoover and still maintained in Senator George Norris and his followers, would have shifted to the unoccupied left.[1]

[1] *New Republic*, LXV (December 17, 1930), 137; *The New York Times*, March 27, 1932, p. 1; Arthur Schlesinger, Jr.: *The Crisis of the Old Order* (Boston, 1957), p. 417.

The role of the Roosevelt candidacy in the rebirth of the Democratic party is therefore of a double nature; for F.D.R. gave the Democracy both a degree of harmony and a progressive cast. Both achievements owe much to his special temperament—inductive, experimental, even opportunistic rather than philosophically reformist—relishing the plasticity of the social and political materials in which he worked.

Roosevelt's progress to the White House began with his gubernatorial victory of 1928. He brought to the governorship the strenuous life of his cousin Teddy, and also a measure of T.R.'s Bull-Moose radicalism. His career as governor is not easily judged against that of his predecessor, Al Smith, since the problems of the depression demanded unprecedented response. At any rate, Roosevelt's actions in the early depression years, though episodic, showed imagination. At the Governors' Conference of 1930 he led the nation by endorsing unemployment insurance, though in the state banking crisis he acted with little foresight. An advocate of economy and retrenchment in government, he nevertheless called for two important bond issues: one to finance relief, which he at first had held to a crippling pay-as-you-go basis; the other to provide for a far-reaching reforestation program in 1931. Al Smith firmly opposed the reforestation bond; the success of the conservation referendum was in fact a victory at the polls for the incumbent governor. Roosevelt also fought earnestly for public power in a way that drew the admiration of Senator Norris. Despite his occasional hesitancy no governor was more responsive to the depression than Roosevelt, and he emerged in 1932 as the liberal in opposition to the now dominantly conservative candidacy of Al Smith.[2]

2 John J. Raskob, in a personal letter to Jouett Shouse, drew firm ideological lines: "When I think of the Democratic party being headed by such radicals as Roosevelt, Huey Long, Hearst, McAdoo, and Senators Wheeler and Dill, as against the fine, conservative talent in the party as represented by such men as you, Governor Byrd, Governor Smith, Carter Glass, John W. Davis, Governor Cox, Pierre S. duPont, Governor Ely and others . . . , it takes all one's courage and faith not to lose hope completely." July 7,

In his quest for the presidency Roosevelt had also to solve the more distinctively political problem of reconciling to a single candidacy the varied and divided elements within the Democratic party and within the larger electorate. His success was foreshadowed in his gubernatorial re-election victory of 1930 against United States Attorney Charles H. Tuttle. Not unexpectedly, that election brought him a heavy vote in the city, where he had yet to begin his attacks on the administration of Mayor Jimmy Walker and the forces of Tammany. But the upstate party organization had been a shambles, and it was there that Roosevelt had concentrated his energies. It was his intention, he said, to make "country life in every way as desirable as city life"; and he supported farm legislation and redistributed to the cities some of the tax burden formerly carried by the countryside. A Prohibition party candidate drew votes from Tuttle and helped Roosevelt to carry forty-two of the state's fifty-seven counties; he won the election with a plurality of 725,000, a record far superior to Smith's highest margin of 339,000 in 1922 and a full compensation for the title "one-half of one per cent governor" that Roosevelt had borne after his hair's breadth victory of 1928.[3]

The congressional elections of 1930 also boded well for Roosevelt or any man who should attain national Democratic leadership. In normally Democratic districts, voters who had favored Republicans in 1928 were returning to the fold— notably in southern and border states: North Carolina, Virginia, West Virginia, Maryland, Kentucky, Missouri, and Oklahoma. Outside the South, agricultural states that had reacted against

1932, Raskob Papers. Frank Freidel: *Franklin D. Roosevelt: The Triumph* (Boston, 1956), pp. 139, 186–92, 217–27, 231–3; Bernard Bellush: *Franklin D. Roosevelt as Governor of New York* (New York, 1955), *passim;* Schlesinger: *Crisis of the Old Order*, p. 111. On the reforestation amendment see also Samuel B. Hand: "Al Smith, Franklin D. Roosevelt, and the New Deal: Some Comments on Perspective," *The Historian*, XXVII (May 1965), 366–81.

[3] Franklin D. Roosevelt: *Public Papers, 1930* (Albany, 1931), pp. 700–2; *The New York Times*, November 7, 1932, p. 1; *Farm Economics*, LXX (June 1931), 1541; Bellush: *Franklin D. Roosevelt*, pp. 76–102.

Smith's alien manner and failure to formulate a program were disillusioned over Hoover's promises to alleviate the plight of the farmers; Democrats won Republican-held seats in Ohio, Indiana, Illinois, Wisconsin, and Nebraska. Finally, the districts Smith had helped to gain in urban areas in 1928 remained Democratic in 1930, and additional ones were won for the party in such localities as Chicago, northern New Jersey, southeastern Connecticut, and Pittsfield, Massachusetts. When the new Congress met in the winter of 1931, the Democrats were able to organize the House; and in the Senate, where six new Democrats were sworn in, the Republicans had an edge of only one vote.[4]

For Roosevelt the task of winning nationwide support for the presidency was an exercise in consensus. F.D.R. had first to dissociate himself sufficiently from the policies of the city faction to demonstrate that he was not the hand-picked and tractable successor of Governor Smith. "Out here," complained a Californian, "you seem to have the brand of Tammany Hall and its 'clique.' " On the issue of prohibition, Roosevelt in 1930 went damp, calling for repeal and, in the interim, for proscription of saloons and for state prohibition laws to be enforced by the federal government. After the gubernatorial election he kept quiet on the issue, subordinating it to the depression in his 1932 slogan "Bread, Not Booze": thereby he outmaneuvered Raskob, who wished to make him appear so antiprohibitionist that southerners would promote favorite sons. To put further distance between himself and Tammany, Roosevelt called Mayor Walker on the carpet in Albany, appointed Judge Samuel Seabury to investigate the Tammany District Attorney, and supported a Republican-controlled state investigation of New York City government. And in 1932 Roosevelt decided on a southern Protestant, John Nance Garner, for the vice presidential nomination—a choice only partially offset by that of James Farley for National Chairman. In other respects, Roosevelt's program in the years preceding the presidential contest

---

[4] *Congressional Directory*, Seventieth Congress (2nd Sess., July 1930); Seventy-first Congress (1st Sess., April 1931).

was attractive to city voters: he extended workmen's compensation, promoted restraints on the injunction, attempted remedies for unemployment, and expanded the state park area. He even hedged his attack on Tammany corruption by insulting Judge Seabury and prolonging the tenure in office of Mayor Walker. Finally, Roosevelt's overtures to the older Wilsonians brought more inclusive strengths and appeals to his cause. He won over Colonel Edward House, Albert Sidney Burleson, A. Mitchell Palmer, Homer Cummings, and other men of the Wilson era. The identification with Wilson came easily to that President's Assistant Secretary of the Navy; and the support of some of the Wilsonians helped impart a liberal tone to the Roosevelt candidacy.[5]

By the time the Democrats met in Chicago to choose a presidential candidate in 1932, Roosevelt held a commanding lead among the aspirants. Though Smith and Garner had each won some important primaries, only Roosevelt had distinguished himself as a man with a positive approach to the depression. It was pointed out that his liberal rhetoric sometimes outdistanced his intentions; he only puzzled voters in May, for instance, when he suggested that the "National Income" be redistributed by means of social planning that would give more money to workers and less to owners. But set against the platitudinous statements of the urban Democrats and the confusion of the congressional party men, Roosevelt provided the hope his party and nation needed. At the convention the candidacies of Smith and Garner seriously threatened to block F.D.R.'s nomination. Had Smith given up his own ambitions and released his delegates he might have satisfied his aversion to the Governor, for many of the

[5] For a detailed account of Roosevelt's maneuvers on prohibition, there is Earland I. Carlson: "Franklin D. Roosevelt's Fight for the Presidential Nomination, 1928–1932," unpublished doctoral dissertation, University of Illinois, 1955; on Roosevelt's sometimes inept handling of his relations with Tammany, see Freidel: *Franklin D. Roosevelt: The Triumph*, p. 54; on his labor program, Bellush: *Franklin D. Roosevelt*, pp. 191–207; Casper T. Gee to F.D.R., February 19, 1929, Roosevelt Papers; Edward House to Albert Sidney Burleson, May 7, 1931, House Papers.

votes for Roosevelt were cast out of fear that Smith might win—while the Happy Warrior's own supporters would not favor the man who liked to style himself a Dutchess County farmer. But Garner and his chief backer, William Randolph Hearst, conceded the prize to F.D.R. on the fourth ballot, and Smith had to bear the ignominy of having William Gibbs McAdoo throw California's votes and the nomination to Roosevelt. McAdoo's speech before jeering galleries recalled Bryan's effort to address the convention of 1924, but this time a trump card was in hand, and McAdoo undoubtedly relished his dramatic opportunity to play it. Roosevelt flew from Albany to Chicago, bucking storms along the Great Lakes, to deliver his acceptance speech.

The brief party platform, called by one journalist "ten or fifteen percent more progressive" than the Republican, phrased its scanty remedies in a formidable language. Among other crimes, the unnamed opposition "[had] robbed millions of our people of their life savings"; and there must be a "drastic change in economic governmental policies." But that change turns out to be "an immediate and drastic reduction of governmental expenditures . . . to accomplish a saving of not less than twenty-five per cent in the cost of the Federal Government." The Farm Board was extravagant, so were government subsidies; at most, the federal government should promote "necessary and useful" public works and help impoverished states to pay their relief bills, while foreign nations should be held to the debts they owed us. Walter Lippmann noted that "the platform is the handiwork of men composing the right wing of the Roosevelt following."[6]

Neither was the campaign itself an especially articulate one, for Roosevelt had not at this time found his empirical way into a clearly progressive national policy—as he had into a program of statewide scope. Earlier in the year Hearst had prevailed upon

[6] Kirk H. Porter and Donald Bruce Johnson: *National Party Platforms, 1840–1956* (Urbana, Ill., 1956), pp. 331–3; *New Republic* LXXI (July 13, 1932), 220; Lippmann: *Interpretations, 1931–1932* (New York, 1932), p. 310.

Roosevelt to make a statement denigrating the League of Nations, and during the electioneering he practically ignored foreign policy except for attacking the debt moratorium. He also preached government economy in a way that was later to prove most embarrassing. He hedged on the tariff; he practically ignored labor; he hailed agriculture in the most general terms. Hoover called his opponent a chameleon on plaid. Only occasionally in gestures such as his meeting with the Bonus Army, or in speeches like that delivered at the Commonwealth Club in San Francisco—where he spoke of the major role in store for the national government—did Roosevelt anticipate future policies.

Still, through it all he seemed a far more sensitive humanitarian than Hoover, and the expected Democratic landslide came. As the vote in 1920 was anti-Wilson, so that in 1932 was anti-Hoover rather than pro-Roosevelt. Contemporary observers had scant reason to predict that Roosevelt would be an outstanding President, but at least he had managed, both in New York politics and in prenomination strategy, to become the representative of a party rather than a faction; and this achievement in political skill—not the least of skills for a statesman—should have been perceived as a favorable portent.

In 1932 Roosevelt won slightly over sixty per cent of the two-party vote in the nation's ten largest cities; in 1936 he would win sixty-four per cent. And in the House of Representatives, Democrats occupied seventy-five per cent of the seats in the ten largest cities in 1932 and would win ninety-seven per cent in 1936. The figures appear to demonstrate that the depression years were a time of urbanization for the Democratic party, and indeed the legislative politics and the legislative accomplishments of the party during the thirties fixed upon it a character more enduringly urban than rural: in the years since, the city has proven more faithful to the Democrats than the country. And why has this been so? Perhaps the party, thrust by the crisis into a role of emergency leadership and economic innovation, would have turned by necessity to a politics of the city where America's complex economic future, along with the majority of its electorate, would lie; and if the conservative posture of the Republicans had relatively little to attract the farmer with his own continuing burden of overproduction, it had less to attract the urban voter. But the history of the years prior to 1932 suggests that the depression merely accelerated, within the Democratic party at any rate, a process that was already well under way. The phenomenon of Smith, the rear-guard politics of the Klan, the drama of the 1924 convention and the 1928 presidential campaign all demonstrate at least impressionistically the increasing strength of the urban Democracy, and the increasing significance of its immigrant-stock component; the congressional vote beginning in 1922, and the presidential returns of 1928, chart the trend with some precision.

Yet in 1932 Roosevelt won almost as large a portion of the hinterland as the metropolis. For his total popular vote was fifty-nine per cent. Indeed, the Roosevelt coalition of 1932 included elements comparable to those in the Wilson coalition of 1916. In 1932 Roosevelt's candidacy sealed together in common cause farmers and laborers, natives and foreign stock, country and city. The revolution is traceable to many sources: the victories of Smith among the immigrants and their children, the political craft of Roosevelt, the dilemmas and bad fortune of the Republican administration, and the crucible of the depression— which substituted for the divisions of culture and ancestry the common identity of the dispossessed. The victory of Roosevelt in 1932 was only a step toward the more lasting conquest of the electorate. But it was the new President who saw the revolution through and fulfilled the wishes of his old friend Josephus Daniels: "I am ambitious that your administration shall be followed by a repetition of the strengthening of the Democratic party so that it will not henceforth be dependent upon the southern states and three or four pivotal states, but that it shall be, as in the early days of the Republic, the dominant party in all parts of the country."[7]

7 Daniels to Roosevelt, November 10, 1932, Roosevelt Papers.

APPENDIX

Homogeneous Election Districts
Used in Voting Samples for Chapter VIII

(AD = assembly district; ED = election district; Pcts = precincts)
I. Manhattan
  A. The German Vote
    1916: AD 23; ED 9, 11–21.
    1920: AD 16; ED 4, 5, 25–35, 37, 40, 46.
    1924: AD 16; ED 2–5, 25–33, 38.
    1928: AD 16; ED 1–8, 16–19, 22–29, 31–40.
    1932: AD 16; ED 1–7, 12, 14, 16–20, 23–30, 32–40.

  B. The Irish Vote
    1916: AD 11; ED 6, 11–16. AD 14; ED 20, 21.
       AD 16; ED 20. AD 23; ED 16. AD 27; ED 17, 22.
    1920: AD 5; ED 16, 18, 19, 24–27. AD 11; ED 31, 33.
       AD 12; ED 28, 29, 31–33.
    1924: AD 5; ED 16, 18, 19, 23–26. AD 12; ED 28, 31–33, 51.
    1928: AD 5; ED 29–31, 33, 34, 36.
    1932: AD 5; ED 31, 33, 35, 36, 38.

  C. The Italian Vote
    1916: AD 1, ED 17, 18. AD 2; ED 5–8. AD 3; ED 2, 3, 7, 8, 11–13.
       11–13. AD 5; ED 2–4.
    1920: AD 1; ED 14–16. AD 2; ED 17, 20, 21. AD 10; ED 16.
    1924: AD 1; ED 15–17, 24, 26. AD 2; ED 23, 28, 30.
       AD 10; ED 18, 19, 21, 22.
    1928: AD 1; ED 2–8. AD 2; ED 14, 16–19, 23, 24.
       AD 4; ED 1, 3. AD 6; ED 6–10, 12–14, 16–20.
    1932: AD 1; ED 1–7. AD 2; ED 2–5, 8. AD 4; ED 1, 3, 4, 10.
       AD 6; ED 6–12, 14–18.

D. The Negro Vote

1916: AD 21; ED 20, 22, 26–28. AD 23; ED 1–5. AD 30; ED 25–30.
1920: AD 19; ED 36, 38–43. AD 21; ED 21, 23, 24.
1924: AD 19; ED 39–43. AD 21; ED 17, 18, 21–30, 32, 33.
1928: AD 13; ED 22, 23, 28, 30. AD 19; ED 16, 18, 20, 23, 24.
        AD 21; ED 12–14, 19–22.
1932: AD 13; ED 16–23, 25–30, 32.

E. The Jewish Vote

1916: AD 2; ED 16, 18. AD 4; ED 6–11, 13, 15.
        AD 6; ED 3–7. AD 8; ED 6. AD 18; ED 16, 19–24.
        AD 26; ED 9, 11.
1920: AD 1; ED 1–5. AD 4; ED 4, 9–11, 14–17.
        AD 6; ED 1–4, 6, 7. AD 14; ED 25–26, 31.
        AD 15; ED 47–50. AD 17; ED 1, 2.
1924: AD 1; ED 1–5. AD 4; ED 8–12, 17–20. AD 6; ED 1–8.
1928: AD 1; ED 2–8. AD 2; ED 5, 6. AD 4; ED 1, 3.
        AD 6; ED 6–10, 12–14, 16–20.
1932: AD 1; ED 1–7. AD 2; ED 2–5, 8. AD 4; ED 1, 3, 4, 10.
        AD 6; ED 6–12, 14–18.

II. Chicago

A. The German Vote

1916: Ward 24; Pcts 11–17.
1920: Ward 24; Pcts 13–19.
1924: Ward 45; Pcts 9–19.
1928: Ward 45; Pcts 9–19. Ward 47; Pcts 22–26.
1932: Ward 45; Pcts 1, 10–13, 15, 34–43, 45, 50.

B. The Jewish Vote

1916: Ward 12; Pcts 45–47. Ward 15; Pcts 1–18.
        Ward 20; Pcts 4–12.
1920: Ward 10; Pcts 2–5. Ward 11; Pcts 6–8. Ward 12; Pcts 41–47.
        Ward 14; Pcts 1–16, 18, 44–50, 52.
1924: Ward 20; Pcts 3–9. Ward 24; Pcts 3–10, 13–23.
        Ward 26: Pcts 7, 9, 11–16, 23. Ward 34; Pcts 8–16.
1928: Ward 24; Pcts 15, 16, 18–24, 30. Ward 29; Pct 15.
1932: Ward 24; Pcts 19–22, 24–29, 33, 35–39.

C. The Polish Vote

1916: Ward 8; Pcts 9, 18–20. Ward 16; Pcts 15–24.
1920: Ward 8; Pcts 9, 18–20. Ward 17; Pcts 1–7.
1924: Ward 31; Pcts 1–7. Ward 33; Pcts 12–19.
1928: Ward 31; Pcts 1–7, 18, 19. Ward 33; Pcts 13–22.
1932: Ward 26; Pcts 16, 17, 19–23, 25, 27, 28. Ward 32; Pcts 39–47.

D. The Negro Vote
    1916: Ward 2; Pcts 17, 20, 22–30, 34, 55–59, 62–74.
    1920: Ward 2; Pcts 20–35, 50–74.
    1924: Ward 2; Pcts 20, 24–37, 49, 50, 54–58. Ward 3; Pcts 1–17.
    1928: Ward 2; all Pcts. Ward 3; Pcts 1–70. Ward 4; Pcts 12–42.
    1932: Ward 2; all Pcts. Ward 3; Pcts 1–40, 64–69.
        Ward 4; Pcts 44–66.

III. Boston

A. The Italian Vote
    1916: Ward 1; Pcts 1, 2. Ward 2; Pcts 1–7. Ward 5; Pcts 1, 2.
    1920: Ward 1; Pcts 1, 2. Ward 2; Pcts 1–7. Ward 5; Pcts 1.
    1924: Ward 1; Pcts 1, 2. Ward 2; Pcts 1–7. Ward 5; Pcts 1, 2.
    1928: Ward 1; Pcts 2, 4–6, 12. Ward 3; Pcts 1, 2.
    1932: Ward 1; Pcts 2, 4–6, 12. Ward 3; Pcts 1, 2.

BIBLIOGRAPHY

I. *MANUSCRIPTS*

American Civil Liberties Union, Princeton University Library.

Chandler P. Anderson, Library of Congress.

Association Against the Prohibition Amendment, Library of Congress.

Josiah W. Bailey, Duke University Library.

Newton D. Baker, Library of Congress and Western Reserve University Library.

Ray Stannard Baker, Library of Congress.

William Watts Ball, Duke University Library.

William B. Bankhead, Department of Archives and History, State of Alabama.

Alben W. Barkley, University of Kentucky Library.

Bernard Baruch, Princeton University Library.

William E. Borah, Library of Congress.

Gutzon Borglum, Library of Congress.

William Bruce, University of Virginia Library.

Charles W. Bryan, Nebraska State Historical Society.

William Jennings Bryan, Library of Congress and Nebraska State Historical Society.

Albert S. Burleson, Library of Congress.

Nicholas Murray Butler, Columbia University Library.

Warren A. Candler, Emory University Library.

James Cannon, Jr., Duke University Library.

John H. Clarke, Western Reserve University Library.

William Bourke Cockran, New York Public Library.

Tom Connally, Library of Congress.

Royal Copeland, Michigan Historical Collections, University of Michigan.

George Creel, Library of Congress.

James M. Curley Scrapbooks, College of the Holy Cross Library.

Bronson Cutting, Library of Congress.

Josephus Daniels, Library of Congress.

Chester C. Davis, Western Historical Manuscripts Collection, University of Missouri Library.

John W. Davis, Yale University Library.
Democratic National Committee Papers, 1929–1933, Franklin D. Roosevelt Library.
Mary Dewson, Franklin D. Roosevelt Library.
Nathaniel B. Dial, Duke University Library.
Edward A. Dickson, University of California Library (Los Angeles).
William E. Dodd, Library of Congress.
Robert L. Doughton, Southern Historical Collection, University of North Carolina.
Woodbridge Ferris, Michigan Historical Collections, University of Michigan.
Henry Ford, Ford Motor Company Archives.
Carter Glass, University of Virginia Library.
Samuel Gompers, New York Public Library.
Thomas Gore, University of Oklahoma Library.
Theodore Green, Library of Congress.
Thomas Gregory, Library of Congress.
Charles S. Hamlin, Library of Congress.
Frank A. Hampton, Duke University Library.
Byron Patton Harrison, The Mississippi Collection, University of Mississippi Library.
Will H. Hays, Indiana State Library.
James Thomas Heflin, Howard College Library.
Gilbert Hitchcock, Library of Congress.
Herbert Hoover, Herbert Hoover Presidential Library.
Edward House, Yale University Library.
David Houston, National Archives.
Louis Howe, Franklin D. Roosevelt Library
Cordell Hull, Library of Congress.
Arthur M. Hyde, Western Historical Manuscripts Collection, University of Missouri.
William M. Jardine, Library of Congress.
Hiram Johnson, Bancroft Library, University of California.
Edwin P. Kilroe, Tammany Hall Collection, Columbia University Library.
Franklin K. Lane, Library of Congress.
Robert Lansing, Library of Congress.
League of Women Voters, Library of Congress.
Breckinridge Long, Library of Congress.
Thomas B. Love, Dallas Historical Society.
Norman Mack, Buffalo Historical Society.
Thomas R. Marshall, Indiana State Library.
William Gibbs McAdoo, Library of Congress.

Vance McCormick, Yale University Library.

Kenneth D. McKellar, Memphis Public Library.

Charles McNary, Library of Congress.

George Fort Milton, Library of Congress.

Meredith Nicholson, Indiana State Library.

Peter Norbeck, University of South Dakota Library.

George W. Norris, Library of Congress and Nebraska Historical Society.

Lee Overman, Southern Historical Collection, University of North Carolina.

Robert L. Owen, Library of Congress.

Alexander Mitchell Palmer, Library of Congress and National Archives.

George Peek, Western Historical Manuscripts Collection, University of Missouri.

James D. Phelan, Bancroft Library, University of California.

Gifford Pinchot, Library of Congress.

Key Pittman, Library of Congress.

Louis Post, Library of Congress.

Chester D. Pugley, Duke University Library.

Henry Rainey, Library of Congress.

Samuel Ralston, Indiana University Library.

Joseph E. Ransdell, Louisiana State University Library.

John J. Raskob, Eleutherian Mills Historical Library.

Donald R. Richberg, Chicago Historical Society.

Franklin D. Roosevelt, Franklin D. Roosevelt Library.

Jared Y. Sanders, Louisiana State University Library.

Jouett Shouse, University of Kentucky Library.

Furnifold M. Simmons, Duke University Library.

Alfred E. Smith, New York State Library.

Augustus O. Stanley, University of Kentucky Library.

Mark Sullivan, Herbert Hoover Institute on War, Revolution, and Peace.

Claude A. Swanson, Duke University Library and University of Virginia Library.

Thomas Taggart, Indiana State Library.

Elmer Thomas, University of Oklahoma Library and Franklin D. Roosevelt Library.

Joe Tumulty, Library of Congress.

Lawrence D. Tyson, University of North Carolina Library.

Oscar W. Underwood, Department of Archives and History, State of Alabama.

Lillian Wald, New York Public Library.

David I. Walsh, College of the Holy Cross Library.

Frank P. Walsh, New York Public Library.

Thomas J. Walsh, Library of Congress.
Lindsey Warren, University of North Carolina Library.
James Watson, Indiana State Library.
Tom Watson, University of North Carolina Library.
Henry Watterson, Library of Congress.
George White, The Ohio Historical Society.
William Allen White, Library of Congress.
John Sharp Williams, Library of Congress.
William B. Wilson, Historical Society of Pennsylvania.
Woodrow Wilson, Library of Congress.
Robert Woolley, Library of Congress.

II. *BOOKS: Primary Sources*

Baker, Ray Stannard: *Woodrow Wilson, Life and Letters.* 8 vols. New York, 1931.
Barkley, Alben: *That Reminds Me—.* Garden City, N.Y., 1954.
Behind the Scenes in Politics. Anonymous. New York, 1924.
Bowers, Claude: *My Life.* New York, 1962.
Burgess, Ernest W., and Charles Newcomb: *Census Data of the City of Chicago, 1920.* Chicago, 1931.
———: *Census Data of the City of Chicago, 1930.* Chicago, 1933.
Campaign Book of the Democratic Party, Candidates and Issues in 1928. New York, 1928.
Campaign Book of the Democratic Party, Candidates and Issues in 1932. New York, 1932.
Cannon, James: *Bishop Cannon's Own Story,* ed. Richard L. Watson, Jr. Durham, N.C., 1955.
Colby, Lewis Sells: *I'll Take the Democrats.* New York, 1964.
Connally, Tom, and Alfred Steinberg: *My Name is Tom Connally.* New York, 1954.
Coolidge, Calvin: *The Autobiography of Calvin Coolidge.* New York, 1929.
Cox, James M.: *Journey Through My Years.* New York, 1946.
Creel, George: *How We Advertized America.* New York, 1920.
———: *Rebel at Large.* New York, 1947.
———: *The War, the World, and Wilson.* New York, 1920.
Daniels, Josephus: *The Cabinet Diaries of Josephus Daniels, 1913–1921,* ed. E. David Cronon. Lincoln, Neb., 1963.
———: *The Wilson Era: Years of War and After, 1917–1923.* Chapel Hill, N.C., 1946.

Darrow, Clarence: *The Story of My Life.* New York, 1932.

Davis, Julia: *Legacy of Love.* New York, 1961.

Dawes, Charles G.: *Notes as Vice-President, 1927–1928.* Boston, 1935.

The Democratic Campaign Book, 1924. New York, 1924.

The Democratic Text Book, 1916. New York, 1916.

The Democratic Text Book, 1920. New York, 1920.

Farley, James A.: *Jim Farley's Story.* New York, 1948.

Flynn, Edward J.: *You're the Boss.* New York, 1947.

Gerard, James W.: *My First Eighty-Three Years in America.* New York, 1951.

Gompers, Samuel: *Seventy Years of Life and Labor.* Vol. II. New York, 1925.

Guzman, Jessie P. *et al.*, eds.: *The Negro Yearbook, 1952.* New York, 1952.

Harris, Joseph P.: *Registration of Voters in the United States.* Washington, D.C., 1929.

Hays, Will H.: *Memoirs.* Garden City, N.Y., 1955.

Hoover, Herbert: *The Memoirs of Herbert Hoover.* Vol. I. *Years of Adventure, 1874–1920;* Vol. II. *The Cabinet and the Presidency, 1920–1933.* New York, 1952.

——: *The New Day, Campaign Speeches of Herbert Hoover, 1928.* Stanford, 1928.

Houston, David F.: *Eight Years with Wilson's Cabinet, 1913–1920.* Vol. II. New York, 1926.

Howe, Frederic C.: *The Confessions of a Reformer.* New York, 1925.

Hull, Cordell: *Memoirs.* Vol. I. New York, 1948.

Ickes, Harold L.: *The Autobiography of a Curmudgeon.* New York, 1943.

Laidlaw, Walter, ed.: *Population of the City of New York, 1890–1930.* New York, 1932.

——: *Statistical Sources for Demographic Studies of Greater New York, 1920.* New York, 1922.

Lane, Franklin K.: *The Letters of Franklin K. Lane, Personal and Political,* eds. Anne W. Lane and Louis H. Wall. Boston, 1922.

Le Brun, George: *It's Time to Tell.* New York, 1962.

Lodge, Henry Cabot: *The Senate and the League of Nations.* New York, 1925.

March, Peyton C.: *The Nation at War.* Garden City, N.Y., 1932.

Marshall, Thomas R.: *Recollections of Thomas R. Marshall: A Hoosier Salad.* Indianapolis, 1925.

McAdoo, Eleanor Wilson: *The Woodrow Wilsons.* New York, 1937.

McAdoo, William Gibbs: *Crowded Years.* Boston, 1931.

Norris, George W.: *Fighting Liberal: The Autobiography of George W. Norris.* New York, 1945.

Official Report of the Proceedings of the Democratic National Convention ... [of] ... *1920.* Indianapolis, 1920.

Official Report of the Proceedings of the Democratic National Convention ... [of] ... *1924.* Indianapolis, 1925.

Official Report of the Proceedings of the Democratic National Convention ... [of] ... *1928.* Indianapolis, 1928.

Percy, William Alexander: *Lanterns on the Levee.* New York, 1941.

Petersen, Svend: *A Statistical History of the American Presidential Elections.* New York, 1963.

Porter, Kirk H., ed.: *National Party Platforms, 1840–1960.* Urbana, Ill., 1961.

Proskauer, Joseph M.: *A Segment of My Years.* New York, 1950.

Quint, Howard H., and Robert H. Ferrell, eds.: *Talkative President: The Off-the-Record Press Conferences of Calvin Coolidge.* Amherst, Mass., 1964.

Robinson, Edgar E.: *The Presidential Vote, 1896–1932.* Stanford, 1934.

Roosevelt, Eleanor: *The Autobiography of Eleanor Roosevelt.* New York, 1961.

Roosevelt, Elliott, ed.: *Roosevelt, Franklin D.: His Personal Letters: 1905–1928.* Vol. II. New York, 1948. *His Personal Letters: 1928–1945.* Vol. III. New York, 1950.

Roper, Daniel C.: *Fifty Years of Public Life.* Durham, N.C., 1941.

Simmons, Furnifold M.: *Memoirs and Addresses,* ed. J. Fred Rippy. Durham, N.C., 1936.

Smith, Alfred E.: *Campaign Addresses of Governor Alfred E. Smith.* Washington, D.C., 1929.

———: *Up to Now.* New York, 1929.

Steffens, Lincoln: *The Autobiography of Lincoln Steffens.* New York, 1931.

———: *The Letters of Lincoln Steffens,* eds. Ella Winter and Granville Hicks. 2 vols. New York, 1938.

Stevens, Doris: *Jailed for Freedom.* New York, 1920.

Syrett, Harold C., ed.: *The Gentleman and the Tiger: The Autobiography of George B. McClellan, Jr.* Philadelphia, 1956.

Thompson, Warren S.: *Population: The Growth of Metropolitan Districts in the United States: 1900–1940.* Washington, D.C., 1947.

Tumulty, Joseph P.: *Woodrow Wilson As I Knew Him.* New York, 1921.

Underwood, Oscar W.: *Drifting Sands of Party Politics.* New York, 1928.

United States Bureau of the Census: *Fifteenth Census, 1930.* Washington, D.C., 1933.

———: *Fourteenth Census, 1920.* Washington, D.C., 1923.

———: *Historical Statistics of the United States, Colonial Times to 1957.* Washington, D.C., 1960.

———: *Religious Bodies, 1926.* Vol. I. Washington, D.C., 1930.

———: *Religious Bodies, 1926.* Vol. II. Washington, D.C., 1929.

———: *Thirteenth Census, 1910.* Washington, D.C., 1913.

———: *Twelfth Census, 1900.* Washington, D.C., 1903.

United States Department of Agriculture: *Second Annual Report.* Federal Farm Loan Board. Washington, D.C., 1918.

United States Department of Agriculture: *Yearbook of Agriculture, 1920.* Washington, D.C., 1921.

United States Department of Agriculture: *Yearbook of Agriculture, 1928.* Washington, D.C., 1929.

United States Department of Labor: *Annual Report of the Commissioner of Immigration, 1920.* Washington, D.C., 1921.

Watson, James E.: *As I Knew Them.* Indianapolis, 1936.

Wheeler, Burton K., and Paul F. Healy: *Yankee from the West.* New York, 1962.

White, William Allen: *The Autobiography of William Allen White.* New York, 1946.

———: *Politics: The Citizen's Business.* New York, 1924.

———: *Selected Letters of William Allen White, 1899–1943,* ed. Walter Johnson. New York, 1947.

Wilson, Edith Bolling: *My Memoir.* Indianapolis, 1939.

Wilson, Woodrow: *War and Peace: Presidential Messages, Addresses, and Public Papers (1917–1924),* eds. Ray Stannard Baker and William E. Dodd. 2 Vols. New York, 1927.

III. *BOOKS: Secondary Sources*

Aaron, Daniel, ed.: *America in Crisis.* New York, 1952.

Acheson, Sam Hanna: *Joe Bailey: The Last Democrat.* New York, 1932.

Adams, Frank C.: *Texas Democracy.* Austin, Tex., 1937.

Adler, Selig: *The Isolationist Impulse: Its Twentieth-Century Reaction.* New York, 1957.

Agar, Herbert: *Pursuit of Happiness: The Story of American Democracy.* Boston, 1938.

Alexander, Charles C.: *The Ku Klux Klan in the Southwest.* Lexington, Ky., 1965.

Allen, Frederick Lewis: *Only Yesterday.* New York, 1931.

Allen, William Harvey: *Al Smith's Tammany Hall: Champion Political Viper.* New York, 1928.

Anderson, William H.: *The Church in Action Against the Saloon.* Westerville, Ohio, 1910.

Angle, Paul M.: *Bloody Williamson.* New York, 1952.

Asbury, Herbert: *The Great Illusion: An Informal History of Prohibition.* Garden City, N.Y., 1950.

Bagby, Wesley: *The Road to Normalcy.* Baltimore, 1962.

Bailey, Thomas A.: *Woodrow Wilson and the Great Betrayal.* New York, 1945.

———: *Woodrow Wilson and the Lost Peace.* New York, 1944.

Bain, Richard C.: *Convention Decisions and Voting Records.* Washington, D.C., 1960.

Barnes, Harry Elmer: *Prohibition Versus Civilization.* New York, 1932.

Bartlett, Ruhl J.: *The League to Enforce Peace.* Chapel Hill, N.C., 1944.

Baruch, Bernard M.: *Baruch: The Public Years.* New York, 1960.

———, and John M. Hancock: *War and Postwar Adjustment Policies.* Washington, D.C., 1944.

Bates, J. Leonard: *The Origins of Teapot Dome: Progressives, Parties, and Petroleum, 1909–1921.* Urbana, Ill., 1963.

Bean, Louis: *Ballot Behavior: A Study of Presidential Elections.* Washington, D.C., 1940.

———: *How to Predict Elections.* New York, 1948.

Beasley, Norman, and Rixey Smith: *Carter Glass.* New York, 1939.

Bell, Herbert C. F.: *Woodrow Wilson and the People.* Garden City, N.Y., 1945.

Bellush, Bernard: *Franklin D. Roosevelt as Governor of New York State.* New York, 1955.

Benedict, Murray R.: *Farm Policies in the United States, 1790–1950.* New York, 1953.

Benson, Lee: *The Concept of Jacksonian Democracy: New York as a Test Case.* Princeton, 1961.

Bent, Silas: *Strange Bedfellows.* New York, 1928.

Berelson, Bernard, *et al.: Voting; A Study of Opinion Formation in a Presidential Campaign.* Chicago, 1954.

Berman, Edward: *Labor Disputes and the President of the United States.* New York, 1924.

Bernstein, Irving: *The Lean Years: A History of the American Worker, 1920–1933.* Boston, 1960.

Berridge, William A.: *Cycles of Unemployment in the United States, 1903–1922.* Boston, 1923.

Binkley, Wilfred E.: *American Political Parties: Their Natural History.* 3rd edn. New York, 1958.

Blum, John M.: *Joe Tumulty and the Wilson Era.* Boston, 1951.

————: *Woodrow Wilson and the Politics of Morality.* Boston, 1956.

Bone, Hugh: *American Politics and the Party System.* New York, 1949.

————: *Party Committees and National Politics.* Seattle, 1958.

Booth, Edgar Allen: *The Mad Mullah of America.* Columbus, 1927.

Booth, Edward Townsend: *God Made the Country.* New York, 1946.

Bornet, Vaughn D.: *Labor Politics in a Democratic Republic: Moderation, Division, and Disruption in the Presidential Election of 1928.* Washington, D.C., 1964.

Boulding, Kenneth: *The Image.* Ann Arbor, Mich., 1956.

Bowden, Robert D.: *Boies Penrose.* New York, 1937.

Bowers, Claude G.: *Beveridge and the Progressive Era.* Cambridge, Mass., 1932.

Bowers, David F., ed.: *Foreign Influences in American Life.* Princeton, 1944.

Broderick, Francis L.: *Right Reverend New Dealer, John A. Ryan.* New York, 1963.

Brody, David: *Labor in Crisis: The Steel Strike of 1919.* Philadelphia, 1965.

Brooks, Robert C.: *Political Parties and Electoral Problems.* 3rd edn. New York, 1933.

Brown, William Burlie: *The People's Choice: The Presidential Image in Campaign Biography.* Baton Rouge, 1960.

Bryce, James: *The American Commonwealth.* Vol. II. New York, 1895.

Burdick, Eugene, and Arthur J. Brodbeck, eds.: *American Voting Behavior.* Glencoe, Ill., 1959.

Burnham, Walter Dean: *Presidential Ballots, 1836–1892.* Baltimore, 1955.

Burns, James M.: *The Deadlock of Democracy: Four-Party Politics in America.* Englewood Cliffs, N.J., 1963.

————: *John Kennedy: A Political Profile.* New York, 1961.

Butler, Robert A.: *So They Framed Stephenson.* Huntington, Ind., 1940.

Campbell, Angus, *et al.: The American Voter.* New York, 1960.

————: *Elections and the Political Order.* New York, 1966.

————: *The Voter Decides.* Evanston, Ill., 1954.

Campbell, Christiana M.: *The Farm Bureau: A Study of the Making of National Farm Policy, 1933–1940.* Urbana, Ill., 1962.

Capper, Arthur: *The Agricultural Bloc.* New York, 1922.

Carroll, Mollie R.: *Labor and Politics: The Attitude of the AF of L Toward Legislation and Politics.* New York, 1923.

Carter, Paul A.: *The Decline and Revival of the Social Gospel; Social and Political Liberalism in American Protestant Churches, 1920–1940.* Ithaca, N.Y., 1956.

Cash, Wilbur: *The Mind of the South.* New York, 1941.

Cash, William T.: *History of the Democratic Party in Florida*. Tallahassee, Fla., 1936.

Catt, Carrie C., and Nettie R. Shuler: *Woman Suffrage and Politics: The Inner Story of the Suffrage Movement*. New York, 1923.

Chaffee, Zechariah, Jr.: *Free Speech in the United States*. Cambridge, Mass., 1941.

Chalmers, David M.: *Hooded Americanism: The First Century of the Ku Klux Klan, 1865–1965*. New York, 1965.

Chambers, Clarke A.: *Seedtime of Reform: American Social Service and Social Action, 1918–1933*. Minneapolis, 1963.

Chambers, William N.: *The Democrats, 1789–1964*. Princeton, 1964.

Child, Clifton J. *The German-Americans in Politics, 1914–1917*. Madison, Wisc., 1939.

Churchill, Winston S.: *The Aftermath*. London, 1929.

Claghorn, Kate H.: *The Immigrant's Day in Court*. New York, 1923.

Clark, Norman H.: *The Dry Years: Prohibition and Social Change in Washington*. Seattle, 1965.

Cleveland, Frederic A., and Joseph Schafer, eds.: *Democracy in Reconstruction*. Boston, 1919.

Cohen, Stanley: *A. Mitchell Palmer: Politician*. New York, 1963.

Cohn, David L.: *The Fabulous Democrats*. New York, 1956.

Coit, Margaret L.: *Mr. Baruch*. Boston, 1957.

Coletta, Paolo E.: *William Jennings Bryan*. Vol. I. *Political Evangelist, 1860–1908*. Lincoln, Neb., 1964.

The Commonweal: Catholicism in America. New York, 1953.

Connable, Alfred, and Edward Silberfarb: *Tigers of Tammany: Nine Men Who Ran New York*. New York, 1967.

Cook, Sherwin L.: *Torchlight Parade: Our Presidential Pageant*. New York, 1929.

Cotter, Cornelius P., and Bernard C. Hennessy: *Politics Without Power: The National Party Committees*. New York, 1964.

Cramer, Clarence H.: *Newton D. Baker*. Cleveland, 1961.

Cross, Robert D.: *The Emergence of Liberal Catholicism in America*. Cambridge, Mass., 1958.

Crowell, Benedict, and Robert Forrest Wilson: *Demobilization: Our Industrial and Military Demobilization After the Armistice, 1918–1920*. New Haven, 1921.

Cummings, Homer, and Carl MacFarland: *Federal Justice*. New York, 1937.

Dabney, Virginius: *Below the Potomac: A Book About the New South*. New York, 1942.

———: *Dry Messiah, The Life of Bishop Cannon*. New York, 1949.

———: *Liberalism in the South*. Chapel Hill, N.C., 1932.

Daniels, Jonathan: *The End of Innocence*. Philadelphia, 1954.

Daniels, Roger: *The Politics of Prejudice: The Anti-Japanese Movement in California and the Struggle for Japanese Exclusion*. Berkeley, 1962.

David, Paul T., *et al.*: The Politics of National Party Conventions. Washington, D.C., 1960.

Denison, John D. *Iowa Democracy*. Vol. I. Iowa City, 1939.

Dickinson, Thomas H.: *The Portrait of a Man as Governor*. New York, 1928.

Dobyns, Fletcher: *The Amazing Story of Repeal*. Chicago, 1940.

———: *The Underworld of American Politics*. New York, 1932.

Dodd, William E.: *Woodrow Wilson and His Work*. New York, 1922.

Dos Passos, John: *U.S.A.* Vol. II. *Nineteen Nineteen*. New York, 1930.

Douglas, Paul H.: *The Coming of a New Party*. New York, 1932.

Duffield, Marcus: *King Legion*. New York, 1931.

Dunn, Robert W., ed.: *The Palmer Raids*. New York, 1948.

Dunnington, Miles W.: *Thomas J. Walsh, Independent Democrat in the Wilson Years*. Chicago, 1940.

Durden, Robert F.: *The Climax of Populism*. Lexington, Ky., 1965.

Eaton, Herbert A.: *Presidential Timber: A History of Nominating Conventions, 1868–1960*. New York, 1964.

Ellis, David M. *et al.*: *A Short History of New York State*. Ithaca, N.Y., 1957.

Ellis, John Tracy: *American Catholicism*. Chicago, 1956.

Ewing, Cortez A.: *Presidential Elections from Abraham Lincoln to Franklin D. Roosevelt*. Norman, Okla., 1940.

Fenno, Richard F., Jr.: *The President's Cabinet*. New York, 1959.

Fenton, John H.: *The Catholic Vote*. New Orleans, 1960.

———: *Politics in the Border States*. New Orleans, 1957.

Field, Carter: *Bernard Baruch*. New York, 1944.

Fite, Gilbert C.: *George N. Peek and the Fight for Farm Parity*. Norman, Okla., 1954.

Fleming, Denna F.: *The Treaty Veto of the American Senate*. New York, 1930.

———: *The United States and the League of Nations, 1918–1920*. New York, 1932.

Flexner, Eleanor: *Century of Struggle: The Woman's Rights Movement in the United States*. Cambridge, Mass., 1959.

Freidel, Frank: *Franklin D. Roosevelt: The Ordeal*. Boston, 1954.

———: *Franklin D. Roosevelt: The Triumph*. Boston, 1956.

Friedman, Elisha M., ed.: *American Problems of Reconstruction*. New York, 1918.

Frost, Stanley, and Milton Elrod: *The Challenge of the Klan*. Indianapolis, 1924.

Fry, Henry P.: *The Modern Ku Klux Klan*. Boston, 1922.

Fuchs, Lawrence H.: *The Political Behavior of American Jews*. Glencoe, Ill., 1956.

Fuller, Edgar I.: *The Visible of the Invisible Empire*. Denver, 1925.

Furniss, Norman F.: *The Fundamentalist Controversy, 1918–1931*. New Haven, 1954.

Garraty, John: *Henry Cabot Lodge*. New York, 1953.

———: *Right-Hand Man: The Life of George W. Perkins*. New York, 1960.

———: *Woodrow Wilson*. New York, 1956.

Garrett, Garet: *The Wild Wheel*. New York, 1952.

Garrison, Winfred E.: *Catholicism and the American Mind*. Chicago, 1928.

Gerson, Louis L. *The Hyphenate in Recent American Politics and Diplomacy*. Lawrence, Kan., 1964.

Gibson, Florence E.: *The Attitude of the New York Irish Toward State and National Affairs, 1848–1892*. New York, 1951.

Gilbert, Clinton W.: *You Takes Your Choice*. New York, 1924.

Gist, Noel P.: *Secret Societies*. Columbia, Mo., 1940.

Glad, Paul W.: *McKinley, Bryan, and the People*. Philadelphia, 1964.

———: *The Trumpet Soundeth: William Jennings Bryan and His Democracy, 1896–1912*. Lincoln, Neb., 1960.

Glass, Carter, Jr., and Robert C. Glass: *Virginia Democracy*. Springfield, Ill., 1937.

Goldman, Eric F.: *Rendezvous With Destiny*. New York, 1952.

Gosnell, Harold F.: *Getting Out the Vote*. Chicago, 1927.

———: *Machine Politics: Chicago Model*. Chicago, 1937.

———: *Negro Politicians: The Rise of Negro Politics in Chicago*. Chicago, 1935.

Gossett, Thomas F.: *Race: The History of an Idea in America*. Dallas, 1963.

Graham, Frank: *Al Smith: American*. New York, 1945.

Grant, Madison: *The Passing of the Great Race*. New York, 1916.

Grantham, Dewey W., Jr.: *The Democratic South*. Athens, Ga., 1963.

———: *Hoke Smith and the Politics of the New South*. Baton Rouge, 1958.

Grassmuck, George L.: *Sectional Biases in Congress on Foreign Policy*. Baltimore, 1951.

Greer, Thomas H.: *What Roosevelt Thought: The Social and Political Ideas of Franklin D. Roosevelt*. East Lansing, Mich., 1958.

Gunther, John: *Roosevelt in Retrospect*. New York, 1950.

Gusfield, Joseph R.: *Symbolic Crusade: Status Politics and the American Temperance Movement.* Urbana, Ill., 1963.

Hagedorn, Herman: *Leonard Wood.* Vol. II. New York, 1931.

Handlin, Oscar: *Al Smith and His America.* Boston, 1958.

———: *The American People in the Twentieth Century.* Cambridge, Mass., 1954.

———: *The Uprooted.* Boston, 1951.

Hapgood, Norman, ed.: *Professional Patriots.* New York, 1928.

———, and Henry Moskowitz: *Up From the City Streets.* New York, 1927.

Harbaugh, William Henry: *Power and Responsibility: The Life and Times of Theodore Roosevelt.* New York, 1961.

Harris, Warren G.: *Herbert Hoover and the Great Depression.* New York, 1959.

Havard, William C., and Loren P. Beth: *The Politics of Mis-representation; Rural-Urban Conflict in the Florida Legislature.* Baton Rouge, 1962.

Hays, Samuel P.: *The Response to Industrialism, 1885–1914.* Chicago, 1957.

Hennessy, Michael E.: *Four Decades of Massachusetts Politics, 1890–1935.* Norwood, Mass., 1935.

Herrick, Genevieve Forbes, and John Origin Herrick: *The Life of William Jennings Bryan.* Chicago, 1925.

Herring, Pendleton E.: *The Politics of Democracy.* New York, 1940.

Hibben, Paxton: *The Peerless Leader: William Jennings Bryan.* New York, 1929.

Hicks, John D.: *Republican Ascendancy, 1921–1933.* New York, 1960.

———, and Theodore Saloutos: *Agricultural Discontent in the Middle West, 1900–1939.* Madison, Wisc., 1951.

High, Stanley: *The Church in Politics.* New York, 1930.

Higham, John: *Strangers in the Land.* New Brunswick, N.J., 1955.

Hinton, Harold B.: *Cordell Hull.* New York, 1942.

Hirsch, Mark D.: *William C. Whitney, Modern Warwick.* New York, 1948.

Hofstadter, Richard: *The Age of Reform: From Bryan to F.D.R.* New York, 1955.

———: *The American Political Tradition and the Men Who Made It.* New York, 1948.

———: *Anti-Intellectualism in American Life.* New York, 1963.

Holcombe, Arthur: *The New Party Politics.* New York, 1933.

———: *The Political Parties of Today.* 2nd edn. New York, 1925.

———: *State Government in the United States.* 2nd edn. New York, 1926.

Hollingsworth, J. Rogers: *The Whirligig of Politics: The Democracy of Cleveland and Bryan.* Chicago, 1963.

Holt, W. Stull: *Treaties Defeated by the Senate.* Baltimore, 1933.

Hoover, Herbert: *The Ordeal of Woodrow Wilson.* New York, 1958.

Howe, Frederic C.: *The Confessions of a Reformer.* New York, 1925.

Howe, M. A. DeWolfe, ed.: *John Jay Chapman and His Letters.* Cambridge, Mass., 1937.

Hoyt, Edwin P.: *Jumbos and Jackasses.* Garden City, 1960.

Hubbard, Preston J.: *Origins of the TVA: The Muscle Shoals Controversy, 1920–1932.* Nashville, 1961.

Humes, D. Joy: *Oswald Garrison Villard, Liberal of the 1920's.* Syracuse, 1960.

Huntley, Theodore A.: *The Life of John W. Davis.* New York, 1924.

Hutchinson, William T.: *Lowden of Illinois.* Vol. II. Chicago, 1957.

Huthmacher, J. Joseph. *Massachusetts People and Politics, 1919–1933.* Cambridge, Mass., 1959.

Hyman, Herbert: *Political Socialization.* Glencoe, Ill., 1959.

Inglehart, Frederick M.: *King Alcohol Dethroned.* New York, 1917.

Ise, John: *The United States Oil Policy.* New Haven, 1926.

Israel, Fred L.: *Nevada's Key Pittman.* Lincoln, Neb., 1963.

Jefferson, Charles E.: *Roman Catholicism and the Ku Klux Klan.* New York, 1925.

Jefferson, Thomas: *Notes on Virginia,* ed. William Peden. Chapel Hill, N.C., 1954.

Johnson, Claudius O.: *Borah of Idaho.* New York, 1936.

Johnson, Donald: *The Challenge to American Freedoms: World War I and the Rise of the American Civil Liberties Union.* Lexington, Ky., 1963.

Johnson, Walter: *William Allen White's America.* New York, 1947.

Johnson, Willis F.: *George Harvey.* Boston, 1929.

Jones, Richard S.: *A History of the American Legion.* Indianapolis, 1946.

Jones, Stanley L.: *The Presidential Election of 1896.* Madison, Wisc., 1964.

Jones, Winfield: *Knights of the Ku Klux Klan.* New York, 1941.

Kane, John J.: *Catholic-Protestant Conflicts in America.* Chicago, 1955.

Karson, Marc: *American Labor Unions and Politics, 1900–1918.* Carbondale, Ill., 1958.

Keller, Morton: *In Defense of Yesterday: James M. Beck and the Politics of Conservatism, 1861–1936.* New York, 1958.

Kent, Frank R.: *The Democratic Party: A History.* New York, 1928.

———: *The Great Game of Politics.* New York, 1935.

Kerwin, Jerome G.: *Federal Water-Power Legislation.* New York, 1926.

Key, V. O., Jr.: *Politics, Parties, and Pressure Groups*. 4th edn. New York, 1958.

——: *A Primer of Statistics for Political Scientists*. New York, 1954.

——: *Southern Politics in State and Nation*. New York, 1949.

Kile, Orville M.: *The Farm Bureau Through Three Decades*. Baltimore, 1948.

Kilpatrick, Carroll, ed.: *Roosevelt and Daniels: A Friendship in Politics*. Chapel Hill, N.C., 1952.

Kilroe, Edwin P., *et al.*: *The Story of Tammany*. New York, 1924.

King, Judson: *The Conservation Fight: From Theodore Roosevelt to the Tennessee Valley Authority*. Washington, D.C., 1959.

Kinzer, Donald L.: *An Episode in Anti-Catholicism: The American Protective Association*. Seattle, 1964.

Komarovsky, Mirra, ed.: *Common Frontiers of the Social Sciences*. Glencoe, Ill., 1957.

La Follette, Belle C., and Fola La Follette: *La Follette*. 2 vols. New York, 1953.

Lally, Francis J.: *The Catholic Church in a Changing America*. Boston, 1962.

Lane, Robert E.: *Political Life*. Rev. edn. New York, 1965.

Lasch, Christopher: *The American Liberals and the Russian Revolution*. New York, 1962.

Lasswell, Harold: *Psychopathology and Politics*. Chicago, 1930.

Latham, Earl, ed.: *The Philosophy and Policies of Woodrow Wilson*. Chicago, 1958.

Lee, Henry W.: *How Dry We Were: Prohibition Revisited*. New York, 1963.

Lee, Robert, and Martin E. Marty, eds.: *Religion and Social Conflict*. New York, 1964.

Lenski, Gerhard: *The Religious Factor*. Garden City, N.Y., 1961.

Leuchtenburg, William: *Franklin D. Roosevelt and the New Deal, 1932–1940*. New York, 1963.

——: *The Perils of Prosperity, 1914–1932*. Chicago, 1958.

Levine, Edward M.: *The Irish and Irish Politicians: A Study of Cultural and Social Alienation*. Notre Dame, Ind., 1966.

Levine, Lawrence: *Defender of the Faith: William Jennings Bryan; The Last Decade, 1915–1925*. New York, 1965.

Lewinson, Paul: *Race, Class, Party: A History of Negro Suffrage and White Politics in the South*. New York, 1932.

Lief, Alfred: *Democracy's Norris*. New York, 1939.

Lindley, Ernest K.: *The Roosevelt Revolution*. New York, 1933.

Link, Arthur S.: *Wilson: Confusions and Crises, 1915–1916.* Princeton, 1964.
———: *Wilson: Campaigns for Progressivism and Peace.* Princeton, 1965.
———: *Wilson the Diplomatist: A Look at His Major Foreign Policies.* 2nd edn. Chicago, 1963.
———: *Wilson: The New Freedom.* Princeton, 1956.
———: *Wilson: The Road to the White House.* Princeton, 1947.
———: *Woodrow Wilson.* New York, 1963.
———: *Woodrow Wilson and the Progressive Era, 1910–1917.* New York, 1954.
———, and Bruce Catton: *American Epoch.* 2nd edn. New York, 1963.
Lippincott, Isaac: *Problems of Reconstruction.* New York, 1919.
Lippmann, Walter: *Interpretations, 1931–1932.* New York, 1932.
———: *Men of Destiny.* New York, 1927.
Lipset, Seymour M.: *Political Man; The Social Bases of Politics.* Garden City, N.Y., 1960.
Littleton, Martin W.: *The Democratic Party of the State of New York.* Vol. II. New York, 1905.
Livermore, Seward W.: *Politics Is Adjourned: Woodrow Wilson and the War Congress, 1916–1918.* Middletown, Conn., 1966.
Lombardi, John: *Labor's Voice in the Cabinet: A History of the Department of Labor from Its Origin to 1921.* New York, 1942.
Loucks, Emerson H.: *The Ku Klux Klan in Pennsylvania.* New York, 1936.
Lowitt, Richard: *George W. Norris: The Making of a Progressive, 1861–1912.* Syracuse, 1963.
Lubell, Samuel: *The Future of American Politics.* New York, 1952.
———: *The Revolt of the Moderates.* New York, 1956.
Lynd, Robert S., and Helen Merrell Lynd: *Middletown: A Study in Contemporary American Culture.* New York, 1929.
Lyons, Eugene: *Herbert Hoover.* Garden City, N.Y., 1964.
MacKay, Kenneth C.: *The Progressive Movement of 1924.* New York, 1947.
MacKaye, Milton: *The Tin Box Parade: A Handbook for Larceny.* New York, 1934.
Manchester, William: *H. L. Mencken: Disturber of the Peace.* New York, 1950.
Mann, Arthur. *La Guardia: A Fighter Against His Times, 1882–1933.* Philadelphia, 1959.
———: *La Guardia Comes to Power.* Philadelphia, 1965.
Marshall, Charles C.: *The Roman Catholic Church in the Modern State.* New York, 1928.
Mason, Alpheus T.: *Brandeis, A Free Man's Life.* New York, 1946.

Maury, Reuben: *The Wars of the Godly*. New York, 1928.

Maxey, Chester C.: *Urban Democracy*. Boston, 1929.

May, Ernest R.: *The World War and American Isolation, 1914–1917*. Cambridge, Mass., 1959.

Mayer, George H.: *The Republican Party, 1854–1964*. New York, 1964.

McAdoo, William Gibbs: *The Challenge: Liquor and Lawlessness Versus Constitutional Government*. New York, 1928.

McBain, Howard Lee: *Prohibition, Legal and Illegal*. New York, 1928.

McConnell, Grant: *The Decline of Agrarian Democracy*. Berkeley, 1953.

McCoy, Donald R: *Calvin Coolidge: Quiet President*. New York, 1967.

McDougall, William: *Ethics and Some Modern World Problems*. New York, 1924.

———: *Is America Safe for Democracy?* New York, 1921.

McGovney, Dudley O.: *The American Suffrage Medley*. Chicago, 1949.

McGrath, James H.: *The Power of the People*. New York, 1948.

McGurrin, James: *Bourke Cockran*. New York, 1948.

McKay, Claude: *Harlem: Negro Metropolis*. New York, 1940.

McKean, Dayton D.: *The Boss: The Hague Machine in Action*. Boston, 1940.

McKenna, Marian C.: *Borah*. Ann Arbor, Mich., 1961.

McLoughlin, William G., Jr.: *Billy Sunday Was His Real Name*. Chicago, 1955.

McMaster, John Bach: *The United States in the World War, 1918–1920*. New York, 1920.

Mecklin, John M.: *The Ku Klux Klan: A Study of the American Mind*. New York, 1924.

Mencken, H. L.: *A Carnival of Buncombe*, ed. Malcolm Moos. Baltimore, 1956.

———: *Making a President*. New York, 1932.

———: *Prejudices: First Series*, 1919; *Second Series*, 1920; *Third Series*, 1922; *Fourth Series*, 1924; *Fifth Series*, 1926; *Sixth Series*, 1927. New York.

Meredith, Ellis, ed.: *Democracy at the Crossroads: A Symposium*. New York, 1932.

Meriwether, Lee: *Jim Reed, 'Senatorial Immortal.'* Webster Groves, Mo., 1948.

Merriam, Charles E.: *Chicago: A More Intimate View of Urban Politics*. New York, 1929.

———: *Four American Party Leaders*. New York, 1926.

———, and Harold F. Gosnell: *Non Voting: Causes and Methods of Control*. Chicago, 1924.

Merz, Charles: *The Dry Decade*. New York, 1931.

————: *And Then Came Ford*. Garden City, N.Y., 1929.

Meyer, Donald B.: *The Protestant Search for Political Realism*. Berkeley, 1960.

Michie, Allan, and Frank Ryhlick: *Dixie Demagogues*. New York, 1939.

Miller, Robert M.: *American Protestantism and Social Issues, 1919–1939*. Chapel Hill, N.C., 1958.

Mims, Edwin: *The Advancing South: Stories of Progress and Reaction*. New York, 1926.

Minor, Henry A.: *The Story of the Democratic Party*. New York, 1928.

Mitgang, Herbert: *The Man Who Rode the Tiger*. New York, 1963.

Mock, James R., and Cedric Larson: *Words That Won the War: The Story of the Committee on Public Information, 1917–1919*. Princeton, 1939.

————, and Evangeline Thurber: *Report on Demobilization*. Norman, Okla., 1944.

Monteval, Marion: *The Klan Inside Out*. Claremore, Okla., 1924.

Moore, Edmund A.: *A Catholic Runs for President: The Campaign of 1928*. New York, 1956.

Moos, Malcolm: *The Republicans*. New York, 1956.

Morgan, H. Wayne, ed.: *The Gilded Age: A Reappraisal*. Syracuse, 1963.

Morris, Richard B.: *Encyclopedia of American History*. 2nd rev. edn. New York, 1965.

Morrison, Joseph L.: *Josephus Daniels: The Small-d Democrat*. New York, 1967.

Moses, Robert: *A Tribute to Governor Smith*. New York, 1962.

Mowry, George E.: *The Era of Theodore Roosevelt, 1900–1912*. New York, 1958.

————: *Theodore Roosevelt and the Progressive Movement*. Madison, Wisc., 1946.

————: *The Urban Nation, 1920–1960*. New York, 1965.

Mullen, Arthur F.: *Western Democrat*. New York, 1940.

Munro, William B.: *Personality in Politics*. New York, 1934.

Murphy, John C.: *An Analysis of the Attitudes of American Catholics Toward the Immigrant and the Negro, 1825–1925*. Washington, D.C., 1940.

Murray, Robert K.: *Red Scare: A Study in National Hysteria, 1919–1920*. Minneapolis, 1955.

Myers, Gustavus: *The History of Tammany Hall*. 2nd edn. New York, 1917.

————: *History of Bigotry in the United States*. New York, 1943.

Myers, William S.: *The Republican Party: A History*. New York, 1931.

Myrdal, Gunnar.: *An American Dilemma: The Negro Problem and Modern Democracy*. New York, 1942.

Nations, Gilbert O.: *The Political Career of Alfred E. Smith*. Washington, D.C., 1928.

Nelson, William H., ed.: *Theory and Practice in American Politics*. Chicago, 1964.

Neuberger, Richard L., and Stephen B. Kahn: *Integrity: The Life of George W. Norris*. New York, 1937.

Nevins, Allan: *Henry White: Thirty Years of American Diplomacy*. New York, 1930.

———: *Herbert H. Lehman and His Era*. New York, 1963.

———, and Frank E. Hill: *Ford, Expansion and Challenge, 1915–1932*. New York, 1957.

Noggle, Burl: *Teapot Dome: Oil and Politics in the 1920's*. Baton Rouge, 1962.

Northrop, William B., and John B. Northrop: *The Insolence of Office: The Story of the Seabury Investigations*. New York, 1932.

Nye, Russel B.: *Midwestern Progressive Politics*. East Lansing, Mich., 1951.

O'Connor, Harvey: *Mellon's Millions*. New York, 1933.

Odegard, Peter H.: *Pressure Politics*. New York, 1928.

———, ed.: *Religion and Politics*. New York, 1960.

Ogburn, William F., ed.: *Social Changes in 1928*. Chicago, 1929.

O'Keane, Josephine: *Thomas J. Walsh*. Francestown, N.H., 1955.

Ostrander, Gilman: *The Prohibition Movement in California, 1848–1933*. Berkeley, 1957.

Overacker, Louise, and Victor J. West: *Money in Elections, 1920–1928*. New York, 1932.

Palmer, Frederic: *Newton D. Baker: America at War*. Vol. II. New York, 1931.

Panunzio, Constantine: *The Deportation Cases of 1919–1920*. New York, 1932.

Paul, Randolph: *Taxation in the United States*. Boston, 1954.

Paxson, Frederic L.: *The Great Demobilization and Other Essays*. Madison, Wisc., 1941.

———: *Postwar Years: Normalcy, 1918–1923*. Berkeley, 1948.

Peck, Mary Gray: *Carrie Chapman Catt*. New York, 1944.

Peel, Roy V.: *The Political Clubs of New York City*. New York, 1935.

Peel, Roy V., and Thomas C. Donnelly: *The 1928 Campaign: An Analysis*. New York, 1931.

———: *The 1932 Campaign: An Analysis*. New York, 1935.

Penniman, Howard R.: *Sait's American Parties and Elections*. 5th edn. New York, 1952.

Perkins, Frances: *The Roosevelt I Knew.* New York, 1946.

Perlman, Selig, and Philip Taft: *History of Labor in the United States, 1896–1932.* New York, 1935.

Petersen, H. C., and Gilbert C. Fite: *Opponents of War, 1917–1918.* Madison, Wisc., 1957.

Pike, James A.: *A Roman Catholic in the White House.* New York, 1960.

Pinchot, Gifford: *The Power Monopoly: Its Makeup and Its Menace.* Milford, Pa., 1928.

Pollock, James Kerr, and Samuel Eldersveld: *Michigan Politics in Transition.* Ann Arbor, Mich., 1942.

Pollock, Norman: *The Populist Response to Industrial America: Midwestern Populist Thought.* Cambridge, Mass., 1962.

Pomper, Gerald: *Nominating the President: The Politics of Convention Choice.* Evanston, Ill., 1963.

Porter, Kirk H., and Donald Bruce Johnson: *National Party Platforms, 1840–1956.* Urbana, Ill., 1956.

Post, Louis: *The Deportations Delirium of Nineteen Twenty.* Chicago, 1923.

Preston, William, Jr.: *Aliens and Dissenters: Federal Suppression of Radicals, 1903–1933.* Cambridge, Mass., 1963.

Pringle, Henry F.: *Alfred E. Smith: A Critical Study.* New York, 1927.

Pritchett, C. Herman: *The Tennessee Valley Authority: A Study in Public Administration.* Chapel Hill, N.C., 1943.

Puryear, Elmer: *Democratic Party Dissension in North Carolina, 1928–1934.* Chapel Hill, N.C., 1962.

Pusey, Merlo J.: *Charles Evans Hughes.* 2 vols. New York, 1951.

Randel, William Peirce: *The Ku Klux Klan: A Century of Infamy.* Philadelphia, 1965.

Rank, S. E.: *Prices of Farm Products in New York State, 1841–1935.* Ithaca, N.Y., 1936.

Raper, Arthur F.: *The Tragedy of Lynching.* Chapel Hill, N.C., 1933.

Rauschenbusch, Stephen: *High Power Propaganda.* New York, 1928.

Rayback, Joseph G.: *A History of American Labor.* New York, 1959.

Rice, Arnold S.: *The Ku Klux Klan in American Politics.* Washington, D.C., 1962.

Rice, Stuart A.: *Farmers and Workers in American Politics.* Washington, D.C., 1942.

———: *Quantitative Methods in Politics.* New York, 1928.

Richards, William C.: *The Last Billionaire: Henry Ford.* New York, 1948.

Richter, Edward J., and Berton Dulce: *Religion and the Presidency: A Recurring American Problem.* New York, 1962.

Rischin, Moses: *The Promised City: New York's Jews, 1870–1914.* Cambridge, Mass., 1962.

Roberts, Edward F.: *Ireland in America.* New York, 1931.

Robertson, William J.: *The Changing South.* New York, 1927.

Robinson, Claude F.: *Straw Votes.* New York, 1932.

Rodman, Bella, and Philip Sterling: *Fiorello La Guardia.* New York, 1962.

Rollins, Alfred B., Jr.: *Roosevelt and Howe.* New York, 1962.

Romasco, Albert U.: *The Poverty of Abundance: Hoover, the Nation, the Depression.* New York, 1965.

Root, Grace C.: *Woman and Repeal.* New York, 1934.

Roseboom, Eugene H.: *A History of Presidential Elections.* New York, 1957.

Ross, Edward A.: *The Old World in the New.* New York, 1913.

Ryan, John A.: *Social Doctrine in Action.* New York, 1941.

Ryan, John A. and Moorhouse F. X. Millar: *The State and the Church.* New York, 1922.

Salter, John Thomas: *Boss Rule: Portraits in City Politics.* New York, 1935.

Samuelson, Paul A., and Everett E. Hagen: *After the War—1918–1920: Military and Economic Demobilization of the United States.* National Resources Planning Board. Washington, D.C., 1943.

Scammon, Richard M.: *America at the Polls: A Handbook of American Presidential Election Statistics, 1920–1964.* Pittsburgh, 1965.

Scheiber, Harry: *The Wilson Administration and Civil Liberties, 1917–1921.* Ithaca, N.Y., 1960.

Schiavo, Giovanni E.: *The Italians in Chicago.* Chicago, 1928.

Schlesinger, Arthur, Jr.: *The Age of Roosevelt.* Vol. I. *Crisis of the Old Order, 1919–1933.* Boston, 1957.

Schriftgiesser, Karl: *This Was Normalcy.* Boston, 1948.

Schroeder, Theodore: *Al Smith, the Pope, and the Presidency.* Cos Cob, Conn., 1928.

Seller, James B.: *The Prohibition Movement in Alabama, 1703–1943.* Chapel Hill, N.C., 1943.

Seymour, Charles: *Woodrow Wilson and the World War.* New Haven, 1921.

Shannon, William V.: *The American Irish.* New York, 1963.

Shideler, James H.: *Farm Crisis, 1919–1923.* Berkeley, 1957.

Shuler, Antoinette, and Carrie Chapman Catt: *Woman Suffrage and Politics.* New York, 1926.

Siegfried, André: *America Comes of Age.* New York, 1927.

Silva, Ruth C.: *Rum, Religion, and Votes: 1928 Re-examined*. University Park, Pa., 1962.

Simmons, William J. *The Klan Unmasked*. Atlanta, 1923.

Sinclair, Andrew. *The Available Man: The Life Behind the Masks of Warren Gamaliel Harding*. New York, 1965.

——: *The Better Half: The Emancipation of the American Woman*. New York, 1965.

——: *Prohibition: The Era of Excess*. Boston, 1962.

Sinclair, Upton B.: *The Flivver King: A Story of Ford–America*. Pasadena, Calif., 1937.

Slosson, Preston William: *The Great Crusade and After, 1914–1928*. New York, 1930.

Smith, Alfred E.: *The Citizen and His Government*. New York, 1935.

Smith, Daniel M.: *The Great Departure: The United States and World War I, 1914–1920*. New York, 1965.

Smith, Emily W., and Daniel Hawthorne: *The Happy Warrior*. New York, 1950.

Smith, Gene: *When the Cheering Stopped: The Last Years of Woodrow Wilson*. New York, 1964.

Smith, Mortimer: *William J. Gaynor, Mayor of New York*. Chicago, 1951.

Smith, Rembert: *Politics in a Protestant Church*. Atlanta, 1930.

Socolofsky, Homer E.: *Arthur Capper*. Lawrence, Kan., 1962.

Soule, George H.: *Economic Forces in American History*. New York, 1952.

——: *Prosperity Decade*. New York, 1947.

Sparrow, John C.: *History of Personnel Demobilization in the United States Army*. Washington, D.C., 1951. (Mimeographed.)

Speranza, Gino: *Race or Nation*. Indianapolis, 1925.

Stanwood, Edward: *A History of the Presidency*. Boston, 1898.

Stephenson, George M.: *A History of American Immigration, 1820–1924*. Boston, 1926.

Steuart, Justin: *Wayne Wheeler, Dry Boss*. New York, 1928.

Stiles, Lela: *The Man Behind Roosevelt*. Cleveland, 1954.

——: *It Costs To Be President*. New York, 1936.

Stoddard, Henry L.: *Presidential Sweepstakes: The Story of Political Conventions and Campaigns*. New York, 1948.

Stokes, Anson Phelps: *Church and State in the United States*. Vol. II. New York, 1950.

Stokes, Thomas L.: *Chip Off My Shoulder*. Princeton, 1940.

Stone, Irving: *They Also Ran*. Garden City, N.Y., 1943.

Stromberg, Roland: *Republicanism Reappraised*. Washington, D.C., 1952.

Stuart, William H.: *The Twenty Incredible Years.* Chicago, 1935.

Sullivan, Mark: *Our Times, The United States: 1900–1925.* 6 vols. New York, 1926–35.

Surface, Frank M.: *The Grain Trade During the World War.* New York, 1928.

Sward, Keith: *The Legend of Henry Ford.* New York, 1948.

Synon, Mary: *McAdoo: The Man and His Times.* Indianapolis, 1924.

Taft, Philip: *The AF of L from the Death of Gompers to the Merger.* New York, 1959.

———: *The AF of L in the Time of Gompers.* New York, 1957.

Tannenbaum, Frank: *Darker Phases of the South.* New York, 1924.

Tatum, Elbert L.: *The Changed Political Though of the Negro, 1915–1940.* New York, 1951.

Taylor, Mack: *Alfred E. Smith: A Psychoanalytical Study.* Fort Worth, 1928.

Thomas, Norman, and Paul Blanshard: *What's the Matter with New York: A National Problem.* New York, 1932.

Timberlake, James H.: *Prohibition and the Progressive Movement, 1900–1920.* Cambridge, Mass., 1963.

Timmons, Bascom N.: *Garner of Texas.* New York, 1948.

———: *Jesse H. Jones: The Man and the Statesman.* New York, 1956.

———: *Portrait of an American: Charles G. Dawes.* New York, 1953.

Tucker, Ray T.: *The Mirrors of 1932.* New York, 1931.

Van Devander, Charles W.: *The Big Bosses.* New York, 1944.

Vinson, John Chalmers: *Referendum for Isolation.* Athens, Ga., 1961.

Wahlke, John C., and Heinz Eulau, eds.: *Legislative Behavior.* Glencoe, Ill., 1959.

Wall, Joseph: *Henry Watterson, Unreconstructed Rebel.* New York, 1956.

Wallace, Henry: *Our Debt and Duty to the Farmer.* New York, 1925.

Wallis, J. H.: *The Politician.* New York, 1935.

Walsh, Thomas J., Lindsay Rogers, and John Dickson: *The Future of Party Government.* Winter Park, Fla., 1929.

Walworth, Arthur: *Woodrow Wilson.* Vol. II. *World Prophet.* New York, 1958.

Warren, Harris G.: *Herbert Hoover and the Great Depression.* New York, 1959.

Wayman, Dorthy G.: *David I. Walsh: Citizen-Patriot.* Milwaukee, 1952.

Wecter, Dixon: *The Hero in America.* New York, 1941.

———: *When Johnny Comes Marching Home.* Cambridge, Mass., 1944.

Weeks, Oliver D.: *The Democratic Victory of 1932.* Dallas, 1933.

Werner, Morris R.: *Bryan.* New York, 1929.

———: *Tammany Hall*. Garden City, N.Y., 1928.

Werner, Morris R., and John Starr: *Teapot Dome*. New York, 1959.

White, Alma B.: *Heroes of the Fiery Cross*. Zarephath, N.J., 1928.

———: *The Ku Klux Klan in Prophecy*. Zarephath, N.J., 1925.

White, Morton, and Lucia White: *The Intellectual Versus the City: From Thomas Jefferson to Frank Lloyd Wright*. Cambridge, Mass., 1962.

White, Theodore H.: *The Making of the President, 1960*. New York, 1961.

White, Walter: *A Man Called White*. New York, 1948.

White, William Alanson: *Thoughts of a Psychologist on the War and After*. New York, 1919.

White, William Allen: *Masks in a Pageant*. New York, 1928.

———: *A Puritan in Babylon: The Story of Calvin Coolidge*. New York, 1938.

Whitener, Daniel Jay: *Prohibition in North Carolina, 1715–1945*. Chapel Hill, N.C., 1945.

Wiebe, Robert: *Businessmen and Reform*. Cambridge, Mass., 1962.

Willebrandt, Mabel Walker: *The Inside of Prohibition*. Indianapolis, 1929.

Williams, Michael: *Shadow of the Pope*. New York, 1932.

Winter, Paul: *What Price Tolerance?* Hewlitt, N.Y., 1928.

Wittke, Carl: *German-Americans and the World War*. Columbus, 1936.

———: *The Irish in America*. Baton Rouge, 1956.

Woddy, C. H.: *The Case of Frank L. Smith*. Chicago, 1930.

Wolfe, Harold: *Herbert Hoover*. New York, 1956.

Zink, Harold: *City Bosses in the United States*. Durham, N.C., 1930.

Zinn, Howard: *La Guardia in Congress*. Ithaca, N.Y., 1958.

Zucker, Norman L.: *George W. Norris: Gentle Knight of American Democracy*. Urbana, Ill., 1966.

IV. SCHOLARLY ARTICLES

Abrams, Richard M.: "Woodrow Wilson and the Southern Congressmen, 1913–1916," *Journal of Southern History*, XXII (November 1956), 417–37.

Acheson, Sam: "Al Smith and the Solid South," *Southwest Review*, XIII (October 1927), 119–22.

Adler, Selig: "The Congressional Election of 1918," *South Atlantic Quarterly*, XXXVI (October 1937), 447–65.

———: "Isolationism Since 1914," *American Scholar*, XXI (Summer 1952), 335–44.

Alexander, Charles C.: "Defeat, Decline, Disintegration: The Ku Klux Klan in Arkansas, 1924 and After," *Arkansas Historical Quarterly,* XXII (Winter 1963), 311–31.

——: "Kleagles and Cash: The Ku Klux Klan as a Business Organization, 1915–1930," *Business History Review,* XXIX (Autumn 1965), 348–67.

——: "The Ku Klux Klan in Texas, 1920–1930," *The Historian of the University of Texas,* I (1962), 21–43.

——: "Secrecy Bids for Power: The Ku Klux Klan in Texas Politics in the 1920's," *Mid-America,* XLVI (January 1964), 3–28.

——: "White Robes in Politics: The Ku Klux Klan in Arkansas, 1922–1924," *Arkansas Historical Quarterly,* XXII (Fall 1963), 195–214.

——: "White-Robed Reformers: The Ku Klux Klan Comes to Arkansas, 1921–1923," *Arkansas Historical Quarterly,* XXII (Spring 1963), 8–23.

Allan, Howard W.: "Isolationism and German-Americans," *Journal of the Illinois State Historical Society,* LVI (Summer 1964), 321–39.

Allen, Lee: "The Democratic Presidential Primary Election of 1924 in Texas," *Southwestern Historical Quarterly,* LVI (April 1958), 474–93.

——: "The McAdoo Campaign for the Presidential Nomination in 1924," *Journal of Southern History,* XXIX (May 1963), 211–38.

——: "The 1924 Underwood Campaign in Alabama," *Alabama Review,* IX (July 1956), 176–87.

——: "The Underwood Presidential Movement of 1924," *Alabama Review,* XV (April 1962), 83–99.

Bagby, Wesley M.: "William Gibbs McAdoo and the 1920 Democratic Presidential Nomination," *East Tennessee Historical Society Publication,* XXXI (1959), 43–58.

——: "Woodrow Wilson, a Third Term, and the Solemn Referendum," *American Historical Review,* LX (April 1955), 567–75.

Baggaley, Andrew R.: "Religious Influences on Wisconsin Voting, 1928–1960," *American Political Science Review,* LVI (March 1962), 66–70.

Barclay, Thomas S.: "The Publicity Division of the Democratic Party, 1929–1930," *American Political Science Review,* XXV (Fall 1931), 68–73.

Bates, J. Leonard: "The Teapot Dome Scandal and the Election of 1924," *American Historical Review,* LX (January 1955), 303–22.

Berman, Daniel M.: "Hugo Black, Southerner," *American University Law Review,* XXI (1961), 35–42.

Billington, Ray A.: "The Origins of Middle Western Isolationism," *Political Science Quarterly,* LX (March 1945), 44–64.

Blum, John: "Nativism, Anti-Radicalism and the Foreign Scare, 1917–1920," *Midwest Journal,* III (1950–51), 46–53.

Blumenthal, Henry: "Woodrow Wilson and the Race Question," *Journal of Negro History,* XLVIII (January 1963), 1–21.

Bohn, Frank: "The Ku Klux Klan Interpreted," *American Journal of Sociology,* XXX (January 1925), 385–407.

Borg, Walter T.: "Food Administration Experiment with Hogs, 1917–1919," *Journal of Farm Economics,* XXV (May 1943), 444–57.

Brown, D. A.: "Historical Prices of Farm Products of States: A Bibliography," *Agricultural History,* XXXVI (July 1962), 169–70.

Burner, David B.: "The Breakup of the Wilson Coalition of 1916," *Mid-America,* XLV (January 1963), 18–35.

———: "The Democratic Party in the Election of 1924," *Mid-America,* XLVI (April 1964), 92–113.

———: "The Brown Derby Campaign," *New York History,* XLVI (October 1965), 356–80.

Burnham, Walter Dean: "The Changing Shape of the American Political Universe," *American Political Science Review,* LIX (March 1965), 7–28.

Carleton, William G.: "Isolationism and the Middle West," *Mississippi Valley Historical Review,* XXXIII (December 1946), 377–90.

———: "A New Look at Woodrow Wilson," *Virginia Quarterly Review,* XXXVIII (Autumn 1962), 545–66.

———: "The Popish Plot of 1928: Smith-Hoover Presidential Campaign," *The Forum,* CXII (September 1949), 141–7.

Carlson, Earland I.: "Franklin D. Roosevelt's Post-Mortem of the 1928 Election," *Midwest Journal of Political Science,* VIII (August 1964), 298–308.

Carter, Paul A.: "The Campaign of 1928 Re-examined," *Wisconsin Magazine of History,* XLVI (Summer 1963), 263–72.

———: "The Other Catholic Candidate: The 1928 Presidential Bid of Thomas J. Walsh," *Pacific Northwest Quarterly,* LV (January 1964), 1–8.

Casey, Ralph D.: "Scripps-Howard Newspapers in the 1928 Presidential Campaign," *Journalism Quarterly,* VII (September 1930), 207–31.

Chalmers, David: "The Ku Klux Klan in the Sunshine State: The 1920's," *Florida Historical Quarterly,* XLII (January 1964), 209–15.

Christenson, Alice M.: "Agricultural Pressure and Governmental Response, 1919–1929," *Agricultural History,* XI (January 1937), 33–42.

Coben, Stanley: "A Study in Nativism: The American Red Scare of 1919–1920," *Political Science Quarterly,* LXXIX (March 1964), 52–75.

Converse, Philip *et al*.: "Stability and Change in 1960: A Reinstating Election," *American Political Science Review*, LV (June 1961), 269–80.

Corwin, Edward S.: "Woodrow Wilson and the Presidency," *Virginia Law Review*, XLII (October 1956), 761–83.

Darling, H. Maurice: "Who Kept the United States Out of the League of Nations?" *Canadian Historical Review*, X (Spring 1929), 196–211.

David, Henry: "Labor and Politics After World War I: 1919–1924," *Labor and Nation*, I (February–March 1946), 27–32.

Davis, James H.: "Colorado Under the Klan," *Colorado Magazine*, XLII (Spring 1965), 93–115.

Degler, Carl N.: "A Century of the Klans: A Review Article," *Journal of Southern History*, XXXI (November 1965), 435–43.

———: "American Political Parties and the Rise of the City: An Interpretation," *Journal of American History*, LI (June 1964), 41–59.

———: "The Great Reversal: The Republican Party's First Century," *South Atlantic Quarterly*, LXV (Winter 1966), 1–11.

———: "The Ordeal of Herbert Hoover," *Yale Review*, LII (Summer 1963), 563–83.

Diamond, William: "Urban and Rural Voting in 1896," *American Historical Review*, XLVI (January 1941), 281–305.

Dimock, Marshall E.: "Woodrow Wilson as a Legislative Leader," *Journal of Politics*, XIX (February 1957), 3–19.

Doherty, Herbert J., Jr.: "Florida and the Presidential Election of 1928," *Florida Historical Quarterly*, XXVI (October 1947), 174–86.

Edelman, Murray: "Symbols and Political Quiescence," *American Political Science Review*, LIV (September 1960), 695–704.

Eldersveld, Samuel J.: "The Influence of Metropolitan Party Pluralities in Presidential Elections Since 1920," *American Political Science Review*, XLIII (December 1949), 1189–1206.

Farris, Charles D.: "Prohibition as a Political Issue," *Journal of Politics*, XXIII (August 1961), 507–25.

Fite, Gilbert: "The Agricultural Issue in the Presidential Campaign of 1928," *Mississippi Valley Historical Review*, XXXVII (March 1951), 653–72.

Fletcher, Ralph, and Mildred Fletcher: "Consistency in Party Voting, 1896–1932," *Social Forces*, XV (1936), 281–5.

Gosnell, Harold F., and Norman Gill: "Analysis of the 1932 Presidential Vote in Chicago," *American Political Science Review*, XXIX (December 1935), 967–84.

Grantham, Dewey W., Jr.: "The Southern Senators and the League of Nations," *North Carolina Historical Review*, XXVI (April 1949), 187–205.

Greer, Scott: "Catholic Voters and the Democratic Party," *Public Opinion Quarterly*, XXV (Winter 1961), 611–25.

Hand, Samuel B.: "Al Smith, Franklin D. Roosevelt, and the New Deal: Some Comments on Perspective," *The Historian*, XXVII (May 1965), 366–81.

Hanneman, Max: "Das Deutschtum in den Vereigten Staaten," *Zu Petermans Milteilungen. Erganzungbund*. CCXXIV (1936), Tafel 9.

Hattery, John W.: "The Presidential Election Campaigns of 1928 and 1960: A Comparison of *The Christian Century* and *America*," *A Journal of Church and State*, IX (Winter 1967), 36–50.

Hennings, Robert E.: "California Democratic Politics in the Period of Republican Ascendance," *Pacific Historical Review*, XXXI (August 1962), 667–80.

Hicks, John D.: "Some Parallels with Populism in the Twentieth Century," *Special Education*, VIII (November 1944), 297–301.

Hines, Tom S., Jr.: "Mississippi and the Repeal of Prohibition," *Journal of Mississippi History*, XXIV (January 1962), 1–39.

Hofstadter, Richard: "Could a Protestant Have Beaten Hoover in 1928?" *The Reporter*, XXII (March 17, 1960), 31–3.

Howenstine, E. Jay, Jr.: "Demobilization After the First World War," *Quarterly Journal of Economy*, LVIII (November 1943), 91–105.

———: "Lessons of World War I," *Annals of the American Academy of Political and Social Science*, CCXXXVIII (April 1945), 180–7.

———: "Public Works Program After World War I," *Journal of Political Economy*, LI (December 1943), 523–37.

Humphreys, Sexson E.: "The Nomination of the Democratic Candidate in 1924," *Indiana Magazine of History*, XXXI (March 1935), 1–9.

Hutchmacher, J. Joseph: "Charles Evans Hughes and Charles Francis Murphy: The Metamorphosis of Progressivism," *New York History*, XLVI (June 1965), 25–40.

———: "Urban Liberalism and the Age of Reform," *Mississippi Valley Historical Review*, XLIX (September 1962), 231–41.

Jackson, Charles O.: "William J. Simmons: A Career in Ku Kluxism," *Georgia Historical Quarterly*, L (December 1966), 351–65.

Johnson, Donald: "The Political Career of A. Mitchell Palmer," *Pennsylvania History*, XXV (October 1958), 345–70.

Johnson, Hildegard B.: "The Location of German Immigrants in the Middle West," *Annals of the American Association of Geographers*, XLI (March 1951), 1–41.

Kelley, Darwin N.: "The McNary-Haugen Bills, 1924–1928," *Agricultural History*, XIV (October 1940), 170–80.

Kelley, Donald B.: "Deep South Dilemma: The Mississippi Press in the

Presidential Election of 1928," *Journal of Mississippi History*, XXV (April 1963), 63–92.

Kerr, Thomas J., IV: "German-Americans and Neutrality in the 1916 Election," *Mid-America*, XLIII (April 1961), 95–105.

Key, V. O., Jr.: "The Future of the Democratic Party," *Virginia Quarterly Review*, XXVIII (Spring 1952), 161–75.

———: "Secular Realignment and the Party System," *Journal of Politics*, XXI (May 1959), 198–210.

———: "A Theory of Critical Elections," *Journal of Politics*, XVII (February 1955), 3–18.

Kirschner, Don S.: "Conflicts and Politics in the 1920's," *Mid-America*, XLVIII (October, 1966), 219–33.

Kutler, Stanley I.: "Labor, the Clayton Act, and the Supreme Court," *Labor History*, III (Winter 1962), 19–38.

Leary, William M., Jr.: "Woodrow Wilson, Irish Americans and the Election of 1916," *Journal of American History*, LIV (June 1967), 57–72.

Link, Arthur S.: "The Enigma of Woodrow Wilson," *American Mercury*, LXV (September 1947), 303–13.

———: "The Federal Reserve Policy and the Agricultural Depression of 1920–21," *Agricultural History*, XX (July 1946), 166–75.

———: "The Middle West and the Coming of World War I," *Ohio Archaeological and Historical Quarterly*, LXII (April 1953), 109–21.

———: "The South and the 'New Freedom': An Interpretation," *American Scholar*, XX (Summer 1951), 314–24.

———: "What Happened to the Progressive Movement in the 1920's?" *American Historical Review*, LXIV (July 1959), 833–51.

———: "Woodrow Wilson and the Democratic Party," *Review of Politics*, XVIII (April 1956), 145–56.

Lippmann, Walter: "Our Predicament Under the Eighteenth Amendment," *Harper's*, CLIV (July 1926), 51–60.

———: "Reconstruction of the Democratic Party," *Yale Review*, XVIII (September 1928), 18–27.

———: "The Setting for John W. Davis," *Atlantic Monthly*, CXXIV (October 1924), 530–5.

———: "Two Leading Democratic Candidates," *New Republic*, XXIII (June 2, 1920), 10–11.

———: "The Wetness of Al Smith," *Harper's*, XLVI (January 1928), 133–9.

Lipset, Seymour Martin: "Some Statistics on Bigotry in Voting," *Commentary*, XXX (October 1960), 286–90.

Livermore, Seward: "The Sectional Issue in the 1918 Congressional Election," *Mississippi Valley Historical Review*, XXXV (June 1948), 29–60.

Lubell, Samuel: "The Politics of Revenge," *Harper's*, CCVI (April 1956), 29–36.

———: "Who Votes Isolationist and Why?" *Harper's*, CCII (April 1951), 29–36.

Margulies, Herbert F.: "The Election of 1920 in Wisconsin: The Return to 'Normalcy' Reappraised," *Wisconsin Magazine of History*, XLI (Autumn 1957), 15–22.

———: "Recent Opinion on the Decline of the Progressive Movement," *Mid-America*, XLV (October 1963), 250–68.

McKinney, Madge W.: "Religion and Elections," *Public Opinion Quarterly*, VIII (Spring 1944), 110–14.

Merriam, Charles E., and Norman N. Gill: "An Analysis of the 1932 Presidential Vote in Chicago," *American Political Science Review*, XXIX (December 1933), 967–84.

Merritt, Richard L.: "Woodrow Wilson and the 'Great and Solemn Referendum,' 1920," *Review of Politics*, XXVII (January 1965), 78–194.

Miller, Robert M.: "A Footnote to the Role of the Protestant Churches in the Election of 1928," *Church History*, XXV (June 1956), 145–59.

———: "A Note on the Relation Between the Protestant Churches and the Revival of the Ku Klux Klan," *Journal of Southern History*, XXII (August 1956), 355–68.

Murphy, Paul L.: "Normalcy, Intolerance, and the American Character," *Virginia Quarterly Review*, XL (Summer 1964), 445–59.

———: "Sources and Nature of Intolerance in the 1920's," *Journal of American History*, LI (June 1964), 60–76.

Nash, Gerald D.: "Herbert Hoover and the Origins of the Reconstruction Finance Corporation," *Mississippi Valley Historical Review*, XLVI (December 1959), 455–68.

Neal, Nevin E.: "The Smith-Robinson Arkansas Campaign of 1928," *Arkansas Historical Quarterly*, XIX (Spring 1960), 3–11.

Niebuhr, H. Richard: "Fundamentalism," *Encyclopaedia of Social Sciences*, eds. E. R. A. Seligman and Alvin Johnson. New York, 1937. III, 527.

Noggle, Burl: "Conservation in Politics: A Study of Teapot Dome," *Mississippi Valley Historical Review*, XLIV (September 1957), 237–60.

Ogburn, William F., and Nell S. Talbot: "A Measurement of the Factors in the Presidential Election of 1928," *Social Forces*, VIII (December 1929), 178–85.

Osgood, Robert E.: "Woodrow Wilson, Collective Security, and the Lessons of History," *Confluence*, V (Winter 1957), 341–54.

Pollock, James K., Jr.: "Campaign Funds in 1928," *American Political Science Review*, XXIII (February 1929), 59–69.

Posner, Russell: "California's Role in the Nomination of Franklin D. Roosevelt," *California Historical Society Quarterly*, XXXIX (Winter 1960), 120–40.

Rankin, Robert S.: "The Future of the Democratic Party," *South Atlantic Quarterly*, XXVIII (July 1929), 225–35.

Reagan, Hugh D.: "Race as a Factor in the Presidential Election of 1928 in Alabama," *Alabama Review*, XIX (January 1966), 5–19.

Rice, Stuart A.: "Differential Changes of Political Preference Under Campaign Stimulation," *Journal of Abnormal and Social Psychology*, XXI (October–December 1926), 297–303.

Rice, Stuart A., and Malcolm M. Willey: "American Women's Ineffective Use of the Vote," *Current History*, XX (July 1924), 641–7.

———: "A Sex Cleavage in the Presidential Election of 1920," *Journal of the American Statistical Association*, XIX (December 1928), 519–20.

Richa, Karel Denis: "Liberalism Frustrated: The League for Independent Political Action, 1928–1933," *Mid-America*, XLVIII (January 1966), 19–28.

Robinson, Edgar E.: "The Decline of the Democratic Party," *American Journal of Sociology*, XX (November 1914), 331–4.

Rollins, Alfred B., Jr.: "Franklin Roosevelt's Introduction to Labor," *Labor History*, III (Winter 1962), 3–18.

———: "Young F.D.R. and the Moral Crusaders," *New York History*, XXXII (January 1956), 3–16.

———: "Young F.D.R. as the Farmer's Friend," *New York History*, XLIII (April 1962), 186–98.

Rothschild, Donald S.: "F.D.R.: Leader in a Time of Drift," *Colby Library Quarterly*, V (September 1960), 143–50.

Sayre, Wallace S.: "Personnel of the Republican and Democratic National Committees," *American Political Science Review*, XXVI (April 1932), 360–3.

Schruben, Francis W.: "William Jennings Bryan, Reformer," *Social Studies*, LV (January 1964), 12–17.

Schwarz, Jordan A.: "Al Smith in the Thirties," *New York History*, XLV (October 1964), 316–30.

———: "John Nance Garner and the Sales Tax Rebellion of 1932," *Journal of Southern History*, XXX (May 1964), 162–80.

Scott, Anne Firor: "A Progressive Wind from the South," *Journal of Southern History*, XXIX (February 1963), 53–70.

Sherman, Richard B.: "The Harding Administration and the Negro: An Opportunity Lost," *Journal of Negro History*, XLIX (July 1964), 151–68.

——: "Republicans and Negroes: The Lessons of Normalcy," *Phylon*, XXVII (Spring 1966), 63–79.

Shideler, James H.: "The La Follette Progressive Party Campaign of 1924," *Wisconsin Magazine of History*, XXXIII (June 1950), 444–57.

——: "The Disintegration of the Progressive Party Movement of 1924," *The Historian*, XIII (Spring 1951), 189–201.

Smith, John S.: "Organized Labor and Government in the Wilson Era; Some Conclusions," *Labor History*, III (Fall 1962), 265–86.

Smylie, James H.: "The Roman Catholic Church, the State, and Al Smith," *Church History*, XXIX (September 1960), 321–43.

Snodgrass, Katharine: "Price Fluctuations in the Woolen Industry," *Annals of the American Academy of Political and Social Science*, LXXXIX (May 1920), 55–60.

Stratton, David H.: "Behind Teapot Dome: Some Personal Insights," *Business History Review*, XXXI (Winter 1957), 385–402.

——: "Splattered with Oil: William G. McAdoo and the 1924 Democratic Presidential Nomination," *Southwestern Social Science Quarterly*, XLIV (June 1963), 62–75.

Taft, Philip: "The Federal Trials of the IWW," *Labor History*, III (Winter 1962), 57–91.

Taner, Ralph M.: "Senator Tom Heflin as Story Teller," *Alabama Review*, XV (January 1962), 54–60.

Tindall, George B.: "Business Progressivism: Southern Politics in the Twenties," *South Atlantic Quarterly*, LXII (Winter 1963), 92–106.

Toy, Eckard V., Jr.: "The KKK in Tillamook, Oregon," *Pacific Historical Quarterly*, LIII (April 1962), 60–4.

Wallace, Anthony F. C.: "Revitalization Movements," *American Anthropologist*, LVIII (March 1956), 264–81.

Warth, Robert D.: "The Palmer Raids," *South Atlantic Quarterly*, XLVIII (January 1949), 1–23.

Watson, Richard A.: "Religion and Politics in Mid-America: Presidential Voting in Missouri, 1928 and 1960," *Midcontinent American Studies Journal*, V (Spring 1964), 33–55.

Watson, Richard L., Jr.: "A Political Leader Bolts—F. M. Simmons in the Presidential Election of 1928," *North Carolina Historical Review*, XXXVII (October 1960), 516–43.

Weeks, O. Douglas: "The Election of 1928," *Southwest Political and Social Science Quarterly*, IX (December 1928), 337–48.

Wesser, Robert F.: "Charles Evans Hughes and the Urban Sources of

Political Progressivism," *New York Historical Society Quarterly*, L (October 1966), 365–400.

Wimer, Kurt: "Woodrow Wilson and a Third Term," *Pennsylvania History*, XXIX (April 1962), 193–211.

———: "Woodrow Wilson Tries Conciliation: An Effort That Failed," *The Historian*, XXV (August 1963), 419–38.

Wolfinger, Raymond E.: "The Development and Persistence of Ethnic Voting," *American Political Science Review*, LIX (December 1965), 896–908.

Woodward, C. Vann: "The Populist Heritage and the Intellectual," *American Scholar*, XXIX (Winter 1960), 55–72.

V. SERIALS

A. MAGAZINES

America
The American Federationist
The American Mercury
The Atlantic Monthly
Christian Register
Collier's
The Commoner
The Commonweal
Congressional Digest
The Literary Digest
The Nation
The New Republic
The North American Review
The Outlook
Progressive Farmer
Review of Reviews [American]
The Saturday Evening Post
The Survey
Time
Wallace's Farmer
World's Work
Yale Review

B. NEWSPAPERS

Atlanta *Constitution*
Boston *Herald*
Chicago *Daily Tribune*
Denver *Post*

Los Angeles *Times*
The New York Times
New York *World*
St. Louis *Post-Dispatch*
C. GOVERNMENT PUBLICATIONS
Congressional Record
Monthly Labor Review

VI. *ORAL HISTORY COLLECTION,* Columbia University

Will W. Alexander, 1952
William H. Anderson, 1950
Martin C. Ansorge, 1949
William S. Bennet, 1951
Robert S. Binkerd, 1949
Hobart S. Bird, 1949
Claude Bowers, 1954
John W. Davis, 1954
Samuel Dickstein, 1950
Edward Flynn, 1950
Joseph A. Gavagan, 1950
James W. Gerard, 1950
Florence Harriman, 1950
Marvin Jones, 1953
Samuel Koenig, 1950
Jeremiah T. Mahoney, 1949
Geoffrey Parsons, 1949
Herbert Pell, 1951
Lindsay Rogers, 1958
George Rublee, 1951
William Schieffelin, 1949
Francis R. Stoddard, 1949
Louis Taber, 1952
Eva Valesh, 1954
Lawrence Veiller, 1949
James Wadsworth, 1952

VII. *PERSONAL INTERVIEWS*

Charles W. Berry, March 25, 1963
Warren Kiplinger, September 8, 1964
Joseph M. Proskauer, January 8, 1963

VIII. *UNPUBLISHED DOCTORAL DISSERTATIONS*

Adrian, Frederick W.: "The Political Significance of the Prohibition Party." The Ohio State University, 1942.

Allen, Lee: "The Underwood Presidential Movement of 1924." University of Pennsylvania, 1955.

Almond, Gabriel: "Plutocracy and Politics in New York City." University of Chicago, 1938.

Avin, Benjamin H.: "The Ku Klux Klan, 1915–1925: A Study in Religious Intolerance." Georgetown University, 1952.

Bates, James L.: "Senator Walsh of Montana, 1918–1924: A Liberal Under Pressure." University of North Carolina, 1952.

Bean, Walton E.: "George Creel and His Critics: A Study of the Attacks on the Committee of Public Information, 1917–1919." University of California (Berkeley), 1941.

Boothe, Leon E.: "Woodrow Wilson's Cold War: The President, The Public, and the League Fight, 1919–1920." University of Illinois, 1966.

Carlson, Earland I.: "Franklin D. Roosevelt's Fight for the Presidential Nomination, 1928–1932." University of Illinois, 1955.

Casey, Ralph D.: "Campaign Techniques in 1928." University of Wisconsin, 1929.

Chatham, Marie: "The Role of the National Party Chairman from Hanna to Farley." University of Maryland, 1953.

Chinn, Ronald E.: "Democratic Party Politics in California, 1920–1956." University of California (Berkeley), 1958.

Christensen, Alice M.: "Agricultural Pressure and Government Response in the United States, 1919–1929." University of California (Berkeley), 1937.

Clark, Norman H.: "Liquor Reform and Social Change: A History of the Prohibition Movement in the State of Washington." University of Washington, 1964.

Cuddy, Joseph E.: "Irish-America and National Isolation, 1914–20." State University of New York (Buffalo), 1965.

Dalrymple, Gordon: "The Repeal of the Eighteenth Amendment." Vanderbilt University, 1951.

Davis, John A.: "The Ku Klux Klan in Indiana," Northwestern University, 1966.

Delmatier, Royce D.: "The Rebirth of the Democratic Party in California, 1928–1938." University of California (Berkeley), 1955.

Deskins, Stuart C.: "The Presidential Election of 1928 in North Carolina." University of North Carolina, 1945.

Dohn, Norman H.: "The History of the Anti-Saloon League." The Ohio State University, 1959.

Eldersveld, Samuel J.: "A Study of Urban Electoral Trends in Michigan, 1920–1940." University of Michigan, 1946.

Eldot, Paula: "Alfred E. Smith, Reforming Governor." Yale University, 1961.

Feldman, Martin I.: "An Abstract of the Political Thought of Alfred E. Smith." New York University, 1963.

Ferguson, Jenniellen W.: "Presidential Election Trends in the United States, 1900–1950: A Statistical Study." University of California (Los Angeles), 1956.

Fite, Gilbert C.: "Peter Norbeck: Prairie Statesman." University of Missouri, 1945.

Flynt, James W.: "Duncan Upshaw Fletcher: Florida's Reluctant Progressive." Florida State University, 1965.

Gold, David: "The Influence of Religious Affiliation on Voting Behavior." University of Chicago, 1953.

Goodman, T. William: "The Presidential Campaign of 1920." The Ohio State University, 1951.

Gravell, Grady J.: "A Rhetorical Study of Franklin D. Roosevelt's 1920 Campaign." Louisiana State University, 1963.

Greenlee, Howard S.: "The Republican Party in Division and Reunion, 1913–1920." University of Chicago, 1950.

Hanks, Raymond J.: "The Democratic Party in 1920: The Rupture of the Wilsonian Synthesis." University of Chicago, 1960.

Harrell, Kenneth E. "The Ku Klux Klan in Louisiana, 1920–1930." Louisiana State University, 1966.

Harris, Arvil E.: "Organized Labor in Party Politics, 1906–1932." State University of Iowa, 1936.

Heckman, Dayton E.: "Prohibition Passes: The Story of the Association Against the Prohibition Amendment." The Ohio State University, 1939.

Henderson, Bancroft: "The Democratic National Committee." University of Minnesota, 1958.

Jamison, Edward A.: "Irish-Americans, the Irish Question and Irish Diplomacy, 1895–1921." 2 vols. Harvard University, 1944.

Jennings, David H.: "President Wilson's Tour in September, 1919: A Study of Forces Operating During the League of Nations Fight." The Ohio State University, 1958.

Johnson, Dorothy E.: "Organized Women and National Legislation, 1920–1941." Western Reserve University, 1960.

Jones, Bartlett C.: "The Debate Over National Prohibition, 1920–1933." Emory University, 1961.

Jones, Dallas Lee: "The Wilson Administration and Organized Labor, 1912–1919." Cornell University, 1954.

Kendrick, Jack E.: "The League of Nations and the Republican Senate, 1918–1921." University of North Carolina, 1953.

Kirschner, Don S.: "Conflict in the Corn Belt: Rural Response to Urbanization, 1919–1929." State University of Iowa, 1964.

Manning, Eugene A.: "Old Bob La Follette: Champion of the People." University of Wisconsin, 1966.

McCleiren, Beryl F.: "The Southern Baptist State Newspapers and the Religious Issue During the Presidential Campaigns of 1928 and 1960." Southern Illinois University, 1964.

Milner, Cooper: "The Public Life of Cordell Hull." Vanderbilt University, 1960.

Mitchell, Frank: "Embattled Democrats: Missouri Democratic Politics, 1919–1932." University of Missouri, 1964.

Morsell, John A.: "The Political Behavior of Negroes in New York City." Columbia University, 1950.

Nathan, Meyer J.: "The Presidential Election of 1916 in the Middle West." Princeton University, 1966.

Neal, Nevin E.: "A Biography of Joseph T. Robinson." University of Oklahoma, 1957.

Nugent, Gloria W.: "James A. Farley and the Politics of Victory: 1928–1936." 2 vols. University of Southern California, 1966.

Olsen, Keith: "Franklin K. Lane: A Biography." University of Wisconsin, 1964.

Paone, Rocco M.: "The Presidential Election of 1920." Georgetown University, 1949.

Patterson, Robert E.: "Gilbert M. Hitchcock: A Study of Two Careers." University of Colorado, 1940.

Payne, John W.: "David Franklin Houston: A Biography." University of Texas, 1953.

Reagan, Hugh D.: "The Presidential Campaign of 1928 in Alabama." University of Texas, 1961.

Rofinot, Henry L.: "Normalcy and the Farmer: Agricultural Policy Under Harding and Coolidge, 1920–1928." Columbia University, 1958.

Rollins, Alfred B., Jr.: "The Political Education of Franklin Roosevelt, His Career in New York Politics: 1909–1928." 2 vols. Harvard University, 1953.

Ruetten, Richard T.: "Burton K. Wheeler of Montana." University of Oregon, 1961.

Schapsmeier, Frederick T.: "The Political Philosophy of Walter Lippmann: A Half Century of Thought and Commentary." University of Southern California, 1965.

Schofield, Kent M.: "The Figure of Herbert Hoover in the 1928 Campaign." University of California (Riverside), 1966.

Shideler, James: "The Neo-Progressives: Reform Politics in the United States, 1920–1925." University of California (Berkeley), 1945.

Silbert, Edward M.: "Support for Reform Among Congressional Democrats, 1897–1913." University of Florida, 1966.

Silver, Paul L.: "Wilsonians and the New Deal." University of Pennsylvania, 1964.

Silveri, Louis D.: "The Political Education of Alfred E. Smith: The Assembly Years, 1904–1915." St. John's University, 1964.

Skolnik, Richard.: "The Crystallization of Reform in New York City, 1890–1917." Yale University, 1964.

Smith, John S.: "Organized Labor and Government in the Wilson Era, 1913–1921." Catholic University, 1963.

Smith, William David: "Alfred E. Smith and John F. Kennedy: The Religious Issue During the Presidential Campaigns of 1928 and 1960." Southern Illinois University, 1964.

Springen, Donald K.: "A Rhetorical Analysis of the Speaking of Senator Oscar Underwood in His 1924 Campaign for the Democratic Presidential Nomination." State University of Iowa, 1962.

Stillings, Edwin J.: "Turnout and Electoral Trends, 1870–1950." University of Chicago, 1953.

Thurner, Arthur W.: "The Impact of Ethnic Groups on the Democratic Party in Chicago, 1920–1928." University of Chicago, 1966.

Watts, James F., Jr.: "The Public Life of Breckinridge Long, 1916–1944." University of Missouri, 1964.

Weaver, Norman F.: "The Knights of the Ku Klux Klan in Wisconsin, Indiana, Ohio, and Michigan." University of Wisconsin, 1954.

INDEX

Agar, Herbert: quoted, 11
agriculture: in election of 1918, 35–9; in 1919–20, 45, 72, 72 *n.*; and LaFollette, 130; and congressional Democrats, 169–71; 196; and 1928 election returns, 226–8; *see also* McNary-Haugen plan
AFL (American Federation of Labor), 130, 140, 174
American Protective League, 47
Anderson, William H., 96
anti-Catholicism: spread by Klan, 87–8; 96; and Smith, 185–7; in 1928 campaign, 202–4; and 1928 election returns, 217–22
Anti-Saloon League: anti-urban character, 94; allied with Protestant churches, 95; effective lobby, 96–7; endorses Hoover, 200; *see also* prohibition
Anti-Smith Democrats, 201
Association Against the Prohibition Amendment (AAPA): exposes Anti-Saloon League, 95–6; political activities, 97–8; investigated, 98
Aswell, James B., 169

Baker, Newton D., 60, 117, 197
Banzano, Cardinal, 207
Barton, Bishop Arthur, Jr., 201, 222
Baruch, Bernard, 109, 112, 145, 149, 153
Berry, George L.: quoted, 139

Booze, Mary, 225
Borah, Senator William E.: quoted, 40
Borglum, Gutzon, 86
Boston, ethnic voting in (1916–32), 242–3
Bourdet, Edward, 189
Bowers, Claude: quoted, 13, 65, 127
Bradfute, O. E., 169
Brandeis, Louis, 30, 239
Brennan, George, 100, 118, 120
Bryan, Charles, 125, 136, 153
Bryan, William Jennings: and free silver, 6–7; in election of 1896, 6–7, 20; supports reform, 6–9, 12–15; and Wilson, 8–11; quoted, 11, 59, 64, 109, 111, 122–3, 127, 161; role in 1916 convention, 11 *n.*; contrasted with McAdoo, 11–12; votes for Cox, 12, 64; Prohibition party tenders him presidential nomination, 12; sustains reform impulse in 1920's, 13–15; at Scopes trial, 14–15; no formal tie to Klan, 82; hero of Klan, which he denounces, 94; 97; arrives at 1924 convention, 114; 116; defends implicit censure of Klan, 118–19; 153; favors alliance with Republican insurgents, 161; his provincialism, 215
Burke, John W., 39
Burleson, 10, 53, 247
Butler, Nicholas Murray, 101–2

Caminetti, Anthony, 48

campaign of 1920: party organization, 65–6; George White chosen National Chairman, 66; Cox's shifting stands, 67; overshadowed by Wilson, 68; *see also* election of 1920

campaign of 1924: Davis' conservatism, 131–2; Davis attacks LaFollette, 132; Davis' inability to project himself, 133–4; inadequacies of national chairman, 134–5; party disharmony, 135; *see also* election of 1924

campaign of 1928: Raskob named National Chairman, 198–200; Protestants fight Smith, 201–5; anti-Catholic issue analyzed, 206–10; objections to Smith, 210–13; his provincialism, 213–16; *see also* election of 1928

campaign of 1932, 250–1; *see also* election of 1932

Candler, Warren A., 203 *n.*

Cannon, Bishop James, Jr., 96, 97, 98, 201

Catholic Association Movement, 16

Catts, Governor Sidney J., 88

census of 1920, 5 and *n.*, 106

census of 1930, 5 *n.*

Chadbourne, Thomas L., 109, 112, 145

Chicago, ethnic voting in (1916–32), 240–2

civil liberties, Smith's record on, 27, 189–90

Clarke, Edward Y., 80, 86

Cohn, Joe, 213

Colcord, Lincoln: quoted, 52

Committee of Thirty-One, 57

Committee on Public Information, 42, 46

Conference for Progressive Political Action (CPPA), 129

congressional Democrats: personnel, 158–9; urban-rural division, 159–61; conservatism, 161–2; votes on taxation, 162–7; split with Republican insurgents, 165–7; opposition to tariff wanes, 167–8; votes on agricultural legislation, 169–71; and Muscle Shoals, 171–3; urban no more liberal than rural, 173–4; response to depression, 175–8

congressional elections of 1910–18, 33

congressional election of 1918, agricultural defections, 35–9

congressional election of 1922, strengthens urban Democrats, 103–6

congressional election of 1924, 137–40

congressional election of 1926, 154

congressional election of 1930, 247–8

convention of 1920: selection of candidates, 62–3; platform, 64

convention of 1924: Klan fulfills aim at, 89; candidates arrive, 114–15; atmosphere, 115–16; platform, 117; fight on Klan plank, 117–19; Bryan's role, 118–19; balloting, 120–5, 192 *n.*

convention of 1928: candidates, 190–1; politeness of Tammany delegates, 191–2; Smith chosen, 192–3; platform, 197

convention of 1932, 249–50

Coolidge, Calvin, 86, 107, 136, 226, 233–43 *passim*

Cox, James, 12, 32; fear of foreigners, 48 *n.*; candidate for presidential nomination in 1920, 59, 62–3; nominated, 62–3; and party organization, 65–6; shifting position in 1920, 67; overshadowed by Wilson, 68; defeat, 68; reasons for defeat, 68–71; quoted, 110; 162; immigrant support, 233–43 *passim;* for sales tax in depression, 245

Creel, George, 46, 49

Creel Committee, 46–7

Croly, Herbert, 165

Cummings, Homer, 249

Daniels, Josephus, 200, 252

Davis, Chester C., 226

Davis, John W., 123; wins
presidential nomination in 1924,
125; meaning of nomination,
125–7; conservatism, 131–2;
attacks LaFollette, 132; projects
self poorly, 133–4; picks Shaver
as National Chairman, 134–5; and
party disharmony, 135; 153, 200;
immigrant support, 233–43
passim
Debs, Eugene V., immigrant
support, 233–43 *passim*
Degler, Carl, 18, 228 *n.*
Depression, effect of on politics,
244–52
Dewey, John: quoted, 176
Dial, Senator: quoted, 160–1
Dieffenbach, Alfred C., 203
Dixon, Lincoln, 134
Doheny, Edward L., 107–10
Donahey, Vic, 85
Doughton, Robert, 177
Duffy, Francis P., 186
Dunn, Katie: *see* Smith, Mrs.
Alfred E.
DuPont, Pierre S., 100, 198

election of 1896, 6–7, 7 *n.*
elections of 1910–18, 33
election of 1918, 34–40
election of 1920: candidates for
presidential nomination of 1920,
59–62; Cox and Roosevelt chosen,
62–3; platform, 64; party
organization, 65–6; campaign,
67–8; analysis of returns, 68–73;
role of woman suffrage, 68–70;
immigrant defection, 70–1;
national debacle, 70–2
election of 1922, strengthens urban
Democrats, 103–6
election of 1924: primaries, 111–12;
candidates arrive at convention,
114–15; colorful scene, 115;
sensitivity to prohibition, 115–16;
vote on Klan plank, 117–18; role
of Bryan, 118–19; balloting,
120–3; Davis chosen, 125–8;
La Follette candidacy, 128–30;
Davis' campaign, 130–5;
Coolidge's campaign, 136;

outcome, 136–7; congressional
and presidential returns
contrasted, 137–40
election of 1926, 154
election of 1928: religious *vs.*
prohibition issue, 217–22;
Hoover's appeal in South, 223;
race issue, 224–5; agricultural
issue, 225–8; analysis of
immigrant voting, 228–43
election of 1930, 247–8
election of 1932, 251–2
Elrod, J. W., 148
Esch-Cummins law, 45, 46, 70; *see
also* Transportation Act of 1920
Evans, Hiram, 76, 80, 81, 86, 89
evolution, 14–15

Federal Reserve Board:
anti-inflation policy of 1919,
43–4; agricultural policy in
1919–20, 46
Fite, Gilbert: quoted, 227
Flynn, Edward: quoted, 183
Ford, Henry: thought to be
candidate, 111; and Muscle
Shoals, 171–3
Fosdick, Harry Emerson, 78
free silver, 6, 9
French Lick Springs, 62, 86
Fundamentalist movement: and
Bryan, 14–15; ties to Klan, 91–2;
ties to prohibitionist movement,
92–3; discredited, 96

Garner, John Nance, 158, 164, 167,
175–8, 248
Garrett, Finis J., 158, 174
Garvey, Marcus, 81
Gary, Judge, 164
General Leasing Act, 54
George, Senator Walter, 190
German-American voting
(1916–32): Chicago, 240–2; New
York, 223–4
Glass, Carter, 52, 146, 170
Gompers, Samuel, 45, 71, 131–2
Grain Standards Act, 35–6
Grant, Madison, 75
Gray, Chester, 169

Grayson, Dr. Cary T., 51
Green, William, 128; quoted, 174

Hague, Frank, 127
Haines, Lynn: quoted, 174–5, 209 *n*.
Hamlin, Charles: quoted, 125
Handlin, Oscar, 108 *n*., 189
Harding, Warren G., 32, 233–43
    passim
Harkness, Edward S., 101
Harriman, Florence: quoted, 148
Harrison, Senator Pat, 116
Harvey, George, 136
Hays, Will, 66, 86, 104
Hearst, William Randolph, 101, 250
Heflin, Tom: quoted, 87; 88, 204
Higham, John, 75
Hillquit, Morris, 128
Hillman, Sidney, 128
Hitchcock, Gilbert, 214
Hoey, James J., 191, 213
Hofstadter, Richard: quoted, 180
Holcombe, Arthur: quoted, 157
Hoover, J. Edgar, 47–8
Hoover, Herbert, 43, 57, 59, 175–8,
    180, 193–7, 217, 223, 225, 233–43
    passim, 245, 248, 251
Hopkins, J. A. H., 128
House, Colonel Edward, 109, 133,
    134, 153, 249
Houston, David F., 45, 52
Howe, Louis, 155, 183, 185
Hughes, Charles Evans, 24–5, 31,
    57, 233–43 *passim*
Hull, Cordell, 143–4, 146–7, 190
Huthmacher, J. Joseph: quoted, 25

immigration restriction, 76–7, 194
immigrants: urban, 6; voting
    participation, 19, 22–3; antipathy
    to Treaty of Versailles, 57–8;
    defection in 1920, 70–1; target of
    nativists, 74–102 *passim;* become
    increasingly Democratic, 106;
    voting, 1916–32, 228–43; *see also*
    new immigrants; nativism
Irish-American voting (1916–32):
    in New York City, 234–6; in
    Boston, 242
Irish-Americans: suited to
    American politics, 15–16; support

for Democratic party, 15–19,
    23–4; temporary defections, 18
Italian-American voting (1916–32):
    in New York City, 236; in
    Boston, 242–3

Jackson, Senator Henry, 210
Jewish voting (1916–32): in New
    York City, 239–40; in Chicago,
    240–2
Jones law, 98

Kennedy, John F., handling of
    religious issue in 1960 campaign,
    209–10
Kenny, William, 199
Key, V. O., Jr., 224
Kinchelow, David H., 169
Kremer, J. Bruce, 214
Kresge, S. S., 101
Krock, Arthur: quoted, 115
Ku Klux Klan: naturalization
    ceremonies, 74; 76, 79; origins,
    80–1; sources of appeal, 82–3;
    political activities, 83–9; decline,
    89–90; ties to fundamentalist
    movement, 91–2; ties to
    prohibitionist movement, 92–3;
    94; Wizard falls ill in New York
    City, 116; censure not voted,
    117–18; likes Ralston, 123

labor: in 1916 coalition, 30–1; in
    election of 1918, 40; in 1919, 44–5;
    in election of 1920, 71–2; and
    La Follette, 128–9; and Davis,
    133–4; in 1924 election returns,
    137; Smith and Hoover stands,
    194; election of 1928, 225–26 *n*.;
    see also Esch-Cummins law
La Follette, Robert: receives liberal
    support, 111; 1924 Progressive
    presidential candidate, 128–30;
    examination of his voting
    support, 138–40; death of, 140,
    153; 167, 228; immigrant support,
    233–43 *passim*
Laidlaw, Walter, 231
Lane, Robert: quoted, 19

Lane, Franklin K.: on leaving cabinet, 51; quoted, 67
Lansing, Robert, 52
League for Independent Political Action, 175
League of Nations, 13, 54–9
Lenroot, Senator Irving: quoted, 166
Leuchtenberg, William: quoted, 198
Lever Act, 35
Levine, Lawrence, 13 and *n.*
Link, Arthur S.: quoted, 73
Lippmann, Walter: quoted, 14, 54, 99, 110, 131, 159, 199, 201, 215 *n.*, 250; 187, 228
Love, Thomas B., 107, 144–5
Lowden, Frank, 188, 196
Lubell, Samuel: quoted, 23, 233; 229

MacDougall, William, 75
Madison Square Garden, 115
Malone, Kemp, 210
Marsh, Wilbur, 145
Marshall, Charles, 186
McAdoo, William Gibbs: contrasted with Bryan, 11–12; quoted, 46, 53, 123; resigns from cabinet, 51; undeclared candidate for 1920 presidential nomination, 59–62; on party organization, 65, 142; alleged meeting with Klan leader, 86; Klan support, 86–7; Doheny tie injured his 1924 candidacy, 107–10; Klan support not rejected, 110; unpopular with some liberals, 110–11; wins primaries, 111–12; presents party with dilemma, 113; chances to win election contrasted with Smith's, 113–14; accepts New York City as convention site, 114; arrives at convention, 114; condemns New York City, 114–15; 115–16; supports Klan plank, 117–19; strategy, 120–2; drops out of balloting, 122; opposed to Davis, 126–7; leaves for Europe, 127; career in eclipse, 148–9; 156, 164, 168; supports Roosevelt, 250

McCooey, John H., 185
McKellar, Senator Kenneth: quoted, 76
McMullen, Governor Adam, 227
McNab, Gavin: quoted, 151, 152
McNary-Haugen plan, 169–71, 196, 226
Mellon, Andrew, 62–7, 197
Mencken, H. L., 12–13; quoted, 82, 181–2, 182 *n.*; 216
Meredith, Edwin T., 45, 149, 190
Millar, Moorhouse F. X., 206
Mouzon, Bishop Edwin, 203; quoted, 221
Moore, Edmond H., 62, 115
Morgan, J. P., 131
Morgenthau, Henry, Jr., 240
Moskowitz, Belle, 27, 182, 214, 240
Mowry, George: quoted, 188
Murphy, Charles: snubbed by Wilson, 10; and Smith, 24–7, 182–3; periodical comment on, 25–6; death of, 25–6, 156; supports Cox, 62–3; and Roosevelt, 155
Murphy, Governor Frank W., 227
Muscle Shoals, 171–3, 195

National Committee, unwieldy body, 144
National Democrat, 147
National Industrial Conference, 44, 198
nativism: intensifies with new immigrants, 74–5; theories supporting, 75–6; "foreign" element embodied in New York City, 77–8; in back of rural-urban conflict, 79; in Klan, 80–91; 92 *ff.*; *see also* immigrants; new immigrants
Negro voting (1916–32): Chicago, 240–2; New York City, 237–9
new immigrants: and Democratic party, 17, 19, 21–3; presence spurs nativism, 74–7
New York City: embodiment of foreign influence, 77; ethnic voting (1916–32), 231–40
Niebuhr, Reinhold: quoted, 219

Norbeck, Peter: quoted, 227 *n.*
Norris, Senator George: quoted, 166, 221; and Muscle Shoals, 172-3; 227, 245

Ogburn, William, 217
Oldfield, William, 147, 158
Olvany, George W., 182

Pabst, Fred, 100
Palmer, A. Mitchell, 41; obtains injunctions, 44; fear of foreigners, 47; persecutes aliens, 48-9; during Wilson's sickness, 51-2; candidate for 1920 presidential nomination, 59, 62-3; 249
party organization: in 1920, 65-6; weakness, 142-4; congressional influence, 143, 147; weakened by rural-urban conflict, 144-6; decline under Shaver, 147-8; revived by Raskob, 149-50
patronage, under Wilson, 52-3
Peek, George, 43, 149, 226
Pegler, Westbrook: quoted, 116
Pittman, Key, 72, 127; quoted, 168
Pius XI, Pope, 185, 198
Plumb plan, 44
Polish-American voting in Chicago (1916-32), 240-2
polls, on prohibition, 99 and *n.*, 100 *n.*
Post, Louis, 49-50
Progressive party of 1924: origins, 128-9; candidates, 129; program, 129-30; hindered by election technicalities, 130
prohibition: 1920 platform, 64; relation to Protestantism, 95-6; and political action, 95-9; loses popularity, 98-100; defeat, 100-2; Smith's behavior in regard to, 183-5; and 1928 election returns, 217-22; *see also* Anti-Saloon League; Association Against the Prohibition Amendment (AAPA)
Proskauer, Joseph, 182, 186, 240

race issue in 1928, 224-5
Rainey, Henry T.: quoted, 163
Ralston, Samuel M., 122-4, 146
Raskob, John J., 98, 149-50, 198-200; quoted, 246 *n.*
Red scare of 1919, 46-9
Reed, Senator James A., 9, 100; quoted, 166; 191
Republic Iron and Steel, 109
Republican insurgents, 159, 161, 163-7, 171, 173
Republican National Committee, 201
Republican party, factions in Congress, 159
Ritchie, Governor Albert, 190
Roberts, Kenneth, 75-6
Robinson, Edgar E.: quoted, 164
Robinson, Joseph T., 175, 176 *n.*, 193, 214, 238
Rockefeller, John D., 101-2
Rollins, Alfred, Jr., 154-5
Roosevelt, Franklin D.: vice-presidential candidate in 1920, 63; works to strengthen party organization, 150 *ff.*; circular letter of 1924, 150-2; steers middle course in aiming for presidency, 154-7; 191; quoted, 192, 214 *n.*; nominates Smith in 1928, 192-3; 200; immigrant support, 233-43 *passim;* and depression, 245-52; as governor of New York, 246 *ff.*; wins re-election in 1930, 247; dissociates self from Smith, 248; on prohibition, 248; support for presidential nomination, 248-50; is nominated, 249-50; 1932 campaign, 251-2; electoral success, 251-2
Roper, Daniel: quoted, 119, 127; 121
Ruppert, Colonel Jacob, 100
rural-urban tension, 77-80 and *passim*
Ryan, John A.: quoted, 100, 206
Ryan, Thomas Fortune, 200

sales tax (manufacturer's), 176-7
Samuelson, Paul: quoted, 42
Scopes trial, 14-15

Seabury, Judge Samuel, 249
sectionalism, 39, 151–2
Sedgwick, Ellery, 186, 205
Shaver, Clement, 134–5, 147–8, 153
Shouse, Jouett, 98
Shupp, W. C., 96
Siebold, Louis, 61
Silva, Ruth, 218
Silver, Gray, 169
Simmons, Senator Furnifold:
    quoted, 162–3, 165
Simmons, William J., 80, 87, 89
Sinclair, Andrew: quoted, 96
Smith, Alfred E.: spokesman of
    urban Democrats, 24; and
    Charles Murphy, 24–6, 182; and
    Tammany Hall, 24–7, 182; in
    state assembly, 24–5; his
    conservatism, 24–5, 187–90; and
    immigrant quotas, 76; signs laws
    permitting Sunday
    entertainment, 77; *vs.* Klan, 88–9,
    117–18; 95; 1924 presidential
    candidacy, 113 *ff.*; raises party
    dilemma, 113; chances for
    election contrasted with
    McAdoo's, 113–14; arrives at
    convention, 115; strategy, 120–2;
    drops out of balloting, 122; Davis
    victory raises his standing, 125–8;
    137; quoted, 144; improved
    chances for 1928, 149; liberal
    martyr, 177; his provincialism,
    180, 213–16; background, 181 *ff.*;
    attitude toward prohibition,
    183–5; and religious issue, 185–7,
    206–10; tactics in 1928, 191–2;
    nominated by Roosevelt, 192–3;
    espouses views similar to
    Hoover's, 193–7; repeal telegram,
    200; Protestants against, 201–4;
    objections to, 210–13;
    anti-Catholicism *vs.* prohibition,
    217–22; other reasons for
    southern losses, 223–4; race,
    224–5; agriculture, 225–8;
    immigrant support, 228–43
    passim; and depression, 245;
    opposes Roosevelt, 240, 249–50
Smith, Mrs. Alfred E., 181, 185 *n.*;
    quoted, 185

South, the, 38–9, 151–2, 223, 224–5
    and *passim*
Spellacy, Thomas, 133–4
Spellman, Francis J., 186
Steckman, Frederic W., 147
Stephenson, David, 89
Sullivan, Mark, 43, 67; quoted, 79,
    117–18
Sullivan, Roger, 9
Sunday, Billy, 202
Survey Research Center, 220–1

Taggart, Tom, 85, 122–4
Tammany Hall: Irish influence in,
    16–7; and Smith, 24–7, 211; and
    Roosevelt, 155–6
tariff, 167–8, 197
taxation, 162–7
Teapot Dome scandals, 107–10
Thomas, Norman, 195
Thompson, Sam, 109
Tobin, Daniel, 71, 130
Transportation Act of 1920, 54; *see
    also* Esch-Cummins law
T.R.B. (writer for *New Republic*):
    quoted, 153
Tugwell, Rexford: quoted, 187
Tumulty, Joe, 23; quoted, 65, 147–8,
    192; 108, 186, 213
Turner, Frederick Jackson, 5
Tuttle, Charles H., 247
Tydings, Senator Millard, 225
Tyler, Elizabeth, 80

Underwood, Oscar W., 111, 124–5,
    126, 168, 172

Van Namee, George R., 191, 198
Villard, Oswald Garrison: quoted,
    183–4

Wald, Lillian, 197
Walker, Mayor Jimmy, 247, 249
Walsh, David I., 80
Walsh, Frank P., 30
Walsh, Thomas J.: investigator of
    Harding scandals, 107–8; tells
    McAdoo not to run, 109–10;
    presides over 1924 convention,

Walsh, Thomas J. (*con't.*)
117; votes for Walsh on last
ballots, 124–5; 153; presidential
candidacy in 1928, 190–1; quoted,
191–2, 191 *n.*
Watson, Clarence W., 200
Watson, Tom, 87–8
wheat, 35–8, 130, 226
Wheeler, Burton K., 129, 209 *n.*
Wheeler, Wayne, 97
White, George, 66, 144–6
White, Stanford, 115
White, William Allen: quoted, 8,
181; 14
Willebrandt, Mabel Walker:
quoted, 95; 205
Williams, Michael, 187 *n.*
Williams, Wayne: quoted, 95
Wilson, William B., 45
Wilson, Woodrow: and Bryan,
8–11; snubs Boss Murphy, 10;
coalition of 1916, 10–11, 28–32;
appeal for vote of confidence in
1918, 35 *n.*, 40; votes rise in wheat
ceiling, 36; breakup of 1916
coalition, 41 *ff.*; quoted on labor,
44–5; abroad in 1918–19, 50; tours
country for League, 50; suffers
cerebral hemorrhage, 50–1;
breaks with Lansing, 52;
mishandles patronage, 52–3; fails
to encourage postwar reform,
54; rigidity on League, 55–8; and
McAdoo, 60; desire for
renomination, 61 and *n.*; role in
1920 campaign, 68; death of, 111;
immigrant support, 233–43 *passim*
Wittke, Carl: quoted, 3
woman suffrage: *see* woman voting
woman voting: in 1920, 68–70; in
1928, 229–30
wool, 38
Woolley, Robert: quoted, 53; 145,
146

A NOTE ON THE TYPE

The text of this book was set on the Linotype in Janson, a recutting made direct from type cast from matrices long thought to have been made by the Dutchman Anton Janson, who was a practicing type founder in Leipzig during the years 1668–87. However, it has been conclusively demonstrated that these types are actually the work of Nicholas Kis (1650–1702), a Hungarian, who most probably learned his trade from the master Dutch type founder Kirk Voskens. The type is an excellent example of the influential and sturdy Dutch types that prevailed in England up to the time William Caslon developed his own incomparable designs from these Dutch faces.

The book was composed, printed and bound by The Book Press Incorporated, Brattleboro, Vermont. Typography and binding design by Betty Anderson.